MICHAEL J. SHANAHAN

WHENCE AND HOW
THE UNIVERSE ?

IN THE BEGINNING

Great Nebula, ORION.

WHENCE AND HOW THE UNIVERSE ?

(LES ORIGINES)

BY

J. GUIBERT

SUPERIOR OF THE "INSTITUT CATHOLIQUE" AND FORMERLY PROFESSOR
OF SCIENCES AT ISSY, FRANCE

AUTHORIZED TRANSLATION

BY VICTOR A. BAST, PH. D.

PROFESSOR OF SCIENCE AT ST. JOSEPH'S COLLEGE, MOUNTAIN VIEW, CALIF

FROM THE SEVENTH REVISED EDITION

BY L. CHINCHOLE

PROFESSOR OF SCIENCES AT THE "ÉCOLE SUPÉRIEURE DE THÉOLOGIE"
AT ISSY

ST. MARY'S SEMINARY PRESS
BALTIMORE, MD.

NIHIL OBSTAT :

JOANNES M. BYRNE,
Censor deputatus.

IMPRIMI LICET :

PATRICIUS L. RYAN,
Vicarius Generalis.

TO

HIS GRACE THE MOST REVEREND EDWARD J. HANNA

ARCHBISHOP OF SAN FRANCISCO

PRINTED BY LETOUZEY & ANÉ,

PARIS, FRANCE

1928

CONTENTS

CHAPTER II
ENERGY AND ITS TRANSFORMATIONS.

Principles of the conservation and of the dissipation of Energy.

CHAPTER III
ORIGIN OF LIFE.

CHAPTER V

ORIGIN OF MAN.

CHAPTER VI

UNITY OF THE HUMAN SPECIES.

CHAPTER VII

ANTIQUITY OF THE HUMAN SPECIES.

CHAPTER VIII

CONDITION OF PRIMITIVE MAN FROM PREHISTORIC
AND ETHNOLOGICAL DATA.

PREFACE

At no time, perhaps, since the days of Darwin, has the subject of Evolution so agitated the minds of men, as in the last half decade. It is no longer a topic confined to the discussion of scientific congresses and learned gatherings, but is on the tongue of everyone that is able to read a newspaper or textbook of history or of science. For many Evolution is assumed to be a fact beyond dispute and serves as a basis for the latest theories in physics, chemistry, biology, physiology, anthropology, psychology, ethics and religion. In some circles to deny or even to question the conclusions of the evolutionists is to proclaim oneself an ignoramus.

On the other hand, it would appear that the vast majority are opposed to the idea of Evolution as applied to man. It is even contended that not only has human Evolution a tendency to undermine religion and morality, but that there is apparently a determined effort on the part of certain materialistic and atheistic individuals to destroy the very foundations of Christian belief in the hearts of the young, by insidious attacks upon the Sacred Scriptures, and by formally teaching atheistic and materialistic notions concerning the origin of the universe in general and of man in particular.

That there is some ground for this opinion is evidenced by the numerous attempts that have been and are being made in various states by those who claim to have the interest of American youth at heart, to legislate Evolution out of the textbooks and out of the schools. Unfortunately, many of these anti-evolutionists, though perfectly sincere and in many instances justified in their opposition to certain aspects of Evolution, have a mistaken notion of the entire question, and thus give occasion to the anti-religious to raise the cry of a conflict between science and religion.

The watchman on Israel's towers must be alert, must be able to sense the danger threatening at the gates, and must be fully prepared to ward it off. The mission of the priest is to expound Christian doctrine and to defend the Faith against attacks from whatsoever source. To do so he must possess a general view of the intellectual conditions and the spiritual needs of the time. He must keep himself informed of scientific progress, that he may know what there is of fact or of theory, of truth or of falsehood. He must have a clear understanding of all the points at issue, particularly of those on which Liberalism apparently founded on modern science, pretends to find Christian Revelation at fault; and must possess, or at least aim to acquire an unquestioned competency in the secular sciences, that, when he speaks, he may deserve to be heard and may ever exercise such care to speak with accuracy and with authority, that the prestige that is incident to a knowledge of the sciences may not be entirely on the side of his opponents. Not only has he nothing to lose in the study of the secular sciences, but his apostolic ministry will benefit from every effort made in this direction.

Whence and How the Universe? The authorized translation of the seventh edition of Father Guibert's *Les Origines* as revised by Father Chinchole, Professor of Natural Sciences at the "École supérieure de Théologie" at Issy, France, is an attempt to assist the young student of theology to understand, and to cope with the difficulties intimately bound up with the above question. As professor of the natural sciences and of scientific apologetics, Father Guibert was in a position to appreciate the urgent need of a priesthood capable of withstanding the on-slaughts of the militant atheism and agnosticism of his day. *Les Origines* was the fruit of his desire to prepare his students to meet the difficulties that were rising thick and fast in the scientific world about them.

This work was not written to serve as a textbook of Exegesis, nor with the aim of explaining the dogmas of religion, but solely to furnish the data for clear and satisfactory answers to the questions that were occupying the minds of the men of his day. The author laid no claims to scientific pretentions; "To do justice to every point treated," says he "would have required a special volume for each question discussed and the competency of the specialist." His chief preoccupation was to remain fairly within the compass of the minds of the young men entrusted to his care; to steer them clear of the twofold danger of an illfounded complacence in the theories then current in the scientific world, and a blind attachment to some fundamentally ruinous conceptions which certain persons wrongly identify with the Faith.

Though writing primarily for theological students, the author had in mind a wider circle of readers for whom the scientific facts enumerated, discussed and interpreted would be a valuable aid in the formation of their judgment on many of the questions of the day. On this account he departed somewhat from the didactic method of the text-book and adopted a freer style and ampler form. His aim was to set forth in all honesty all systems, even those which he felt compelled to oppose; to declare with firmness what has been fully established; and to leave open any question that could not be solved. He fully realized that there are certain questions which are beyond the scope of the natural sciences. The latter can and do solve many problems, but require the aid of philosophy and of faith to reveal to us the ultimate causes of spiritual and material things and phenomena. Supplemented by these, science reveals to us a God creating the universe, a God establishing laws to govern this universe, a God creating life, a God creating man; it teaches the unity of the human species and the undeniably human status of primitive man. These facts Father Guibert has endeavored to emphasize, that his readers might be able to distinguish clearly the lines of demarcation between experimental science and philosophy, and between all science and faith.

Owing to the revival of interest in Evolution, Father Chinchole, at the earnest solicitation of his own pupils and

of numerous friends, has brought out this new edition of
Les Origines. He has preserved as far as possible the original text as it came from the pen of Father Guibert himself.
Thus the question of the Unity of the Human Species,
and in part that of the Origin of Man and of his Primitive
Condition remain practically unchanged. But science has
made progress since Father Guibert's day. So it was imperative to take cognizance of the new scientific data and
recent solutions of scientific difficulties. Many sections
had to be revised and numerous additions made. Further,
the question of Cosmogony viewed from a scientific standpoint had to be treated in greater detail, while the various
systems of interpretation of the Biblical Narrative have
been considerably abridged. So many problems in science
and philosophy are connected with the question of Energy
that the latter could not be overlooked. The chapter on
the Origin of Life has received some important additions, to
prove that life is not reducible to merely physico-chemical
forces. That treating of the Evolution of Species has been
retained but more fully developed, to bring into stronger
relief the difficulties of a scientific problem that is more
complex than one might at first suppose.

Prehistoric studies have made so remarkable advances
since 1910, that this work would be incomplete without
giving an account of the recent discoveries and their
interpretation. A few of the original illustrations have
been suppressed, but the addition of more than 80 new
ones drawn by the clever artist Riolet, and having special
reference to prehistoric documents, more than compensate
for the omission of the others.

The translator with the permission of Father Chinchole,
and in places at his suggestion, has made a few minor
alterations and additions to the text which he felt would
be of interest to his American readers. He has also added a
number of useful illustrations taken at the Mt. Wilson
Observatory.

Les Origines in its various editions, particularly the
seventh has been favorably received in Europe, and is
used as a text-book in many of the European seminaries.

It is hoped that this translation will extend the field of its usefulness.

The translator wishes to express his gratitude to those who have assisted him in bringing out this work. With Father Chinchole he heartily subscribes to these sentiments of Father Guibert : "In conclusion, I wish to say, that I am entirely dependent upon the revelations of science and the doctrines of faith. If through further progress science should clear up some doubtful points, or contradict some of the conclusions, which I now hold certain, I shall not hesitate to follow such indications, and if the Church, in whose infallibility I firmly believe, should decide some questions contrary to what I hold, I am at once ready to accept her teaching."

WHENCE AND HOW THE UNIVERSE?

INTRODUCTION

The problem of the origin of the world has at all times been the preoccupation of speculative minds, Every age, from remotest antiquity down to the present day has brought forward one or more cosmogonies as possible solutions. [1]

During the Ages of Faith, men sought ultimately for the First Cause, and found a sufficient answer in the belief that one God was the creator of all things, of heaven and of earth, of the plants and of the animals, of the body and of the soul of man. They seldom demanded more, since everything seemed fixed by a sort of primitive immutability. They saw but little change in the sun which gave them light, in the earth which supported them, in the beings that surrounded them, and so, the hypothesis of Perfect Stability alone presented itself to their minds. Even now, how many there are, who would be greatly surprised if told, that neither the sun nor the earth, nor any living being has that rigid fixity which an all too summary observation attributes to it.

It is a matter of no great surprise, therefore, to find that the problem of the origin of all things has not always had the prominence it holds today. Scientific investigations

---

[1] The term cosmogony is used in this work in its primary sense, as giving not merely the mythical accounts, but chiefly the scientific theories concerning the origin of the universe. To a great extent it includes also cosmology which aims at understanding the actual composition and governing laws of the universe as it now exists.

have given birth to new questions.   Men are not content
with the knowledge that God is the Creator of the world,
they wish to know under what conditions He created it
and what subsequent transformations it has undergone.

It was especially during the nineteenth century that
the natural sciences, particularly astronomy, geology,
paleontology physiology, and comparative anatomy,
physics and chemistry made rapid progress, and brought
to light a certain evolution of the world, and the role of
natural or secondary causes, the very existence of which
men in previous centuries never suspected.

This development is still continuing in the twentieth
century.   No Christian ever dreams of contesting the
fact, much less of grieving over it.   On the contrary, every
one can derive profit from it.   A more complete knowledge
of the works of creation will not diminish our admiration
for the divine Artisan, Who has wrought so perfectly and
Who has imparted to His handiwork the forces and the
necessary laws for its marvellous development towards
the end which He has proposed unto Himself—viz.   His
own glory and the good of man.

The Psalmist sang "The heavens show forth the glory
of God" (Ps. xviii, 1).   From Newton, the discoverer of
the wonderful law of universal gravitation, down to the
latest scholar that endeavors to penetrate still further into
the mysteries of Nature, to discover her most hidden laws,
each can, with equal right, repeat the same paean of
praise.

The role of natural causes will not make us discount the
necessity of a Creator any more than will the grandeurs of
the universe.   The one does not exclude the other.   He,
Who has created the world, has created its forces, has
established its laws and has willed that they fulfil their
assigned purpose.

Such is the doctrine of the Spiritual School.   Hence we
can not hold with the Materialistic School, that Science
can be atheistic.   Assertions of this sort, proceeding, not
from Science, but from a false Philosophy, cannot deserve
the name of modern.   They hark back to very ancient

times, having originated with Democritus and Epicurus.

The Materialistic School bas everywhere and at all times maintained that there exists a real conflict between Science and Spiritual Philosophy or the Christian dogma of God the Creator. In holding that the world is sufficient unto itself, Science can henceforth supplant all beliefs, all dogmas.

To gain the popular fancy, Materialism pretends to speak in the name of Experimental Science, the only one which exists for it, which has made any progress and which is so full of promise for the future. It even goes so far as to wish to monopolize unto itself all Science, all Truth, all Doctrine. The most pretentious of materialists has even gone so far as to say that "Science claims alike the material, the intellectual and moral direction of society". [1]

Contemporary literature, official teaching of all grades, scientific popularization under all its forms, have propagated the materialistic thesis, which maintains that "for the world there is neither beginning nor end; it is eternal; it evolves by its own inherent powers from the atom to the human conscience. Hence there is absolutely no need of a God to create."

To prove this thesis, materialists pretend to rely on scientific facts. They hold that these can be made to support the theories of the evolution of the mineral, the vegetable and the animal kingdom, including man. Taking what there is of truth or of probability, or even of pure hypothesis in these theories, they have wished to deduce them from materialistic, in opposition to spiritualistic, dogmas.

This procedure is not new. Caro [2] pointed it out about the middle of the nineteenth century. "The Materialistic School presents itself to the popular mind under the auspices of Positive Science. It is highly important that we deprive it of the advantage to be had from this usurped patronage, by showing that the true spirit of the experi-

---

[1] Quoted by Grasset in *Limites de la biologie*, p. xviii.
[2] Cf. *Le matérialisme et la science*, p. 150.

mental method is not to be found in these new doctrines.
To compel the Positive Sciences to take part in a series of
problems where neutrality is for them more than conven-
ience, I might say an absolute obligation and a
strict necessity, is to compromise them most injudi-
ciouslsy.

"A definitive critique would consist in running through
successively all the propositions which make up the materialistic doctrine, and in showing, by an exact analysis, the
equivocal admixture of observation and of hypothesis,
which forms the basis for each of them. One should examine rigorously the significance of the given facts, and
should deduce from them their true import, should question
them without preconceived opinions, and I hold with assurance that one would without much trouble, arrive at the
conviction that these facts interpreted as they ought to be,
do not justify the dogmatic conclusions forced upon them...
It would be the end of the scientific pretension of Materialism, which is its most potent spell, if it should become
manifest, that from beginning to end, the system, for it is
a system—originates only *a priori*, and is built solely
upon pure speculation. We should not be disavowed by
any scholar of the Experimental School were we to advance
the statement that, in the present state of the sciences, not
one positive fact warrants the conclusions of Materialism
on the problem of Origin or of Design." Too many persons
have been, and are still deluded by these audacious assertions. It is our desire to dissipate their uncertainties, their
doubts, and to resolve their difficulties by showing that the
conflict has no real foundation; neither in modern discoveries nor in the realm of reason.

To dispel the conflict, a knowledge of its causes is of
advantage. We cannot mention them all here, but there
are two which have played a most important role. They
are, on the one hand, the confusion of the well-defined
provinces of the Natural Sciences, of Philosophy and of
Theology, and on the other, the ignorance of one or other
of these sciences or even of all of them.

There can be no conflict between the Natural Sciences and

Philosophy or Theology, since each has its own particular province, its own methods, its own purpose, its own kind of certitude, and its own special mode of investigation.

The Natural Sciences, such as astronomy, paleontology, geology, physics, chemistry, biology, etc... study the Material World through observation and experimentation. They endeavor to classify facts, to deduce laws from them and to synthesize these latter into ever extending theories.

Philosophy, primarily, employs human reason to seek out the First Cause, to study the spiritual faculties of man, and his nature. Such is the province of natural theology, psychology, logic and metaphysics.

Theology makes use of the data of Revelation to ascend to God, to study His nature, His attributes, His providence, His concourse, to study man in his relations to God, his duties towards Him, his supernatural state to which God has raised him, his duties towards his fellowmen. It is evident that neither these questions nor those of Philosophy are in the domain of the Natural Sciences, nor can they be investigated by the latter's methods. Although the object of these three orders of knowledge is the same, the point of view is entirely different.

The Natural Sciences study man from the standpoint of anatomy, physiology, ethnology, paleontology, etc. Philosophy studies him from the psychological point of view, Theology, with respect to his relations to his Creator.

Prehistoric Science can investigate his antiquity, the traces of his industry, of his civilization, of his progress or of his decadence, etc. Philosophy will study his soul and its faculties, will ascend to the First Cause of the beginning of man, to God. Theology based upon Revelation will tell us in what condition man was created, to what end he is destined, what duties are incumbant upon him and what was his supernatural state. If paleontology or some other science purports to show the origin of animals and of man, Spiritual Philosophy will with right, show the essential difference between an intelligent and free spiritual soul and an animal devoid of reason. Theology defines the exact limits and completes the ideas of Philosophy, by teaching us that God in fact created man with his body and his soul and that he subsquently raised him to a supernatural state and destined him for a supernatural end.

As far as we may extend our investigations, we should not find any real conflict, as long as each remains within its own domain, and is content with the certitude which its own methods of investigation furnish. The false science of the materialist encroaches upon ground foreign to its own province, and there goes astray in wishing to solve problems not within its competency, and thus voluntarily gives rise to conflict. Draper, Büchner, Hæckel and Le Dantec have furnished us sad examples of this.

Confusion of domain is one of the principal causes of conflict. We find a second in the ignorance of Philosophy, of Theology, or of Religion manifested by certain popular writers, who are, sad to say, often in evident bad faith. This ignorance of Philosophy or of Religion on the part of some writers, is equalled only by their boldness of assertion. One of them, and by no means the least noted, boasted that he had never devoted two hours to a serious study of Philosophy and yet his works teem with erroneous assertions and denials in the metaphysical order. His ignorance of Religion is on a par. This makes him attribute to Catholic Dogma or to Spiritual Philosophy all the old worn out and long since discarded scientific hypotheses, or even the crochets of a writer desirous of throwing discredit upon such articles of belief which he does not share.

If ignorance of Religion or of Philosophy is one cause of conflict, lack of scientific knowledge, of which more later on, is another. An exaggerated and unilateral admiration for the facts of the experimental sciences or of observation alone, or for their method, may go as far as the denial of any other order of knowledge. But it would only be a strange stunting of the human intellect to interdict, as the Positivist School has done, all research outside of these limits. Even if it is true that to fathom one science it is necessary to devote oneself exclusively to it, it would be unsafe to ignore others entirely. We should be perverting our mind and should come almost to believe

that everything ends within the confines of this restricted
domain.   What errors and what conflicts arise from this
source alone! Have we not seen chemists and biologists
pretending to solve solely with the resources of their spe-
cialty, all the problems that confront the human mind?

Experience, if people would only heed it, shows that
these pretensions find favor with unsuspecting minds and
unfortunately with too many of our young folks.   Only
too often, for these, assertion takes the place of demon-
tration.   The authority of the writer, of the professor,
of the review, yea, even of a newspaper article, admits of
no discussion.   They accept as true, everything that is
stated in the name of Science.   A little more reflection, a
little more discernment, a little more of the philosophic
spirit in the reader, would be admissible, but even then
there are some gaps which cannot be filled up.   An earnest
study of Philosophy, a thorough course in Logic is not
the dominant characteristic of modern education.

It would be easy to discover other causes of conflict, as
for instance in the docility with which some have accepted
certain doctrines under the cloak of Science, or of Progress
or of Liberty. But "Cui bono?" Why multiply reasons?
The conflict is after all only apparent, not real.   Our
chief concern should be to dispel the notion of conflict.

Desirous of doing our modest share towards removing
the causes of a conflict that is equally harmful to Science
as to Faith we here outline our method of procedure.
Since the confusion of domains and ignorance of them,
are the principal causes, both must be dispelled. To do
this, it will be necessary, to state precisely and with care,
that which belongs respectively to the domain of Science,
of Philosophy or of Religion; to indicate the degree of
certitude proper to a fact, a theory or an hypothesis.   A
fact of observation or of experimentation is one thing, a
law another, a particular hypothesis another and a general
theory still another.   We distinguish, therefore, between
a fact, a law, an hypothesis, and a theory, for their degree
of certitude is far from being the same.   In fact the number
of certain facts is increasing from day to day; laws are

ever becoming more definite; hypotheses are being revised; and theories are either changing so as to adapt themselves to the new discoveries, or they are being abandoned altogether in favor of others that are more rational. We shall find numerous examples of this in the cosmogonic hypotheses and in the evolutionist theories. Let us say, once for all, that these variations are not always signs of weakness, but very often of vitality, of fruitful labor and of continuous progress. There is question here of truly scientific hypotheses, and not of theories which have no other foundation than the imagination of the writer, or the *a priori* assertions or denials of the materialist.

The human mind is confronted by more problems than it can solve. We shall therefore, try to avoid hasty conclusions and guard against asserting that there are no enigmas for man We believe it to be nearer the truth to declare that our ignorance is profound, whether we consider the questions in general or in detail. Who can flatter himself on having a knowledge of the exact nature of a single atom? of a single cell? of energy? Is it necessary to say that when we shall have occasion to expose the opinions of our adversaries, we shall do so with all fidelity, neither distorting their thoughts nor assigning to them an opinion which will not be their own. Our aim will be to combat error, not persons.

As the problem of the Origin of the Universe and its componant parts has given rise to so many difficulties and errors, we have determined to treat these questions to a great extent inseparable, as a whole. One question brings on another; one error dovetails into another; one truth implies another. The problem is exceedingly vast, complex and difficult.

We apologize for treating the subject too summarily within the narrow confines of a single volume, and too superficially, especially since the diversity of the questions raised would require all the competency of a specialist. Each question touched upon might well be the subject of a separate treatise.

Our aim is less pretentious. It is to resume and extend

a work which has stood the test and which appears to be
as necessary now as ever, if we may judge from the countless
publications treating these questions of Origins from the
materialistic point of view.

We shall treat successively :
1. The Origin of the Material World;
2. The Origin of Energy;
3. The Origin of Life;
4. The Origin of Species;
5. The Origin of Man.

Each of these questions raises up secondary problems,
which we shall examine in different articles, so as to
answer the principal difficulties of the present hour.

CHAPTER I

COSMOGONY OR THE ORIGIN OF THE UNIVERSE
THE PROBLEMS THAT ARISE

The cosmogony, or the origin and transformation of the universe is a problem which appertains at once, though from different points of view, to Science, Philosophy and Theology, hence also to Apologetics.

Science, starting from experience and observation, studies especially the role of secondary causes. It can and should ask itself: What was the primitive state of matter and of energy? What evolution or series of transformations have these undergone? Through what phases have the countless heavenly bodies, which we know, passed? The nebulæ? The fixed stars and our sun? The planets and their satellites? The terrestrial globe and the elements which compose all these bodies? What is the probable limit of this evolution? What are the laws that govern it, or rather that this evolution discloses to us? What cosmogonic theory is capable of summing up for us, in its entirety this evolution of the world, from its creation to its final destiny?

Philosophy ascends higher. By the light of reason it devotes itself to the quest for the First Cause, the Creator of matter, of energy, of life, of man, of the order of all the natural and secondary causes. It should refute the errors of the Materialistic School, which asserts that the world is eternal and sufficient unto itself.

Theology, in its turn, studies the facts of the Bible, appertaining to the creation of the world by God and gives them a correct interpretation. It goes further than Science or Philosophy.

The apologist will have to take the data of these three sciences into consideration. His scientific attainments will permit him to give an account of the solid grounds for some "bona fide" hypotheses, and of the minor importance of such others, as have for their principal object the overthrow of religious dogma. A very thorough knowledge of the universe and its successive transformations will have the effect of throwing into relief the value of certain proofs for the existence of God, for one who wishes to go beyond the simple facts of observation—beyond the natural causes and mount logically to the First Cause. In fine, it will be easy for him to show the non-existence of any contradiction between the facts from the different sources; rather that they complete one another to furnish us a very adequate idea of the work of creation and of the cosmogonic problem.

Every truly scientific cosmogony ought to be founded on exact data. Hence before setting forth hypotheses, we find it necessary to recall a few indispensable notions of astronomy, which will serve as a basis for them.

ARTICLE I

THE PRESENT UNIVERSE ACCORDING TO THE FACTS OF ASTRONOMY

§ I. — The Fixed Stars.

The Universe is the assemblage of worlds which people space. Our solar system with its central sun, its eight major planets, its myriads of minor ones with their satellites, and its comets, is but a small part of it.

Indeed, with the naked eye alone, we can count about five thousand stars, which are so many suns similar to our own. The 100 inch (2.54 m.) Hooker reflector on Mt. Wilson (fig. 1) reveals stars of the 18th magnitude. By long exposures with very sensitive plates, the camera discloses more than a billion such stars (fig. 2). A single one of the 80 000 plates which constitute the map of the heavens, contains from 10 000 to 20 000 stars. Astronomers, basing their calculations on the law of geometric progression, according to which the number of stars, in passing from one magnitude to the next, grows in the ratio of 3, 5, had long suspected this vast number. Did the law but hold true for the stars up to the 15th magnitude, the billion mark would already be passed. Certain clusters of stars (fig. 2) or certain nebulae resolvable into stars, show us that this number is the minimum. [1]

The heavenly bodies appear dispersed in space without any apparent order, but a very careful study does not fail to reveal special groups. The more important are the true stellar clusters as those of Centaur with its 6 000 stars, of Taucan with 10 000, of Hercules (fig. 2) with about 30 000, of Perseus, of Sagittarius, etc. These clusters present most varied forms; now regular, now irregular, some spherical, others lenticular or annular.

Should we consider the milky-way as such a cluster? Some have so held. [2] In such a case we would have to reckon with some hundred million stars in this group alone. Have the star-clusters been part of the milky-way or are they themselves other milky-ways? The problem does not appear solvable, although there are two solutions possible.

How far away are the stars? It has been relatively easy to determine the distance of the sun, by measuring its parallax, which is equal to 8"80 and placing it at 149 501 000 kilometers or 92 892 346 miles This has served as a basis for calculating the earth's radius. A like unit could not at all serve for computing the distance of the stars.

---

[1] *Revue des Questions scientifiques*, Oct. 1914, p. 571-583; *Science-Supplement*, New Series, vol. LXI, n. 1583, May 1, 1925, p. x.

[2] Dr. Huble, with the aid of the Hooker Reflector and sensitive photographic plates, has demonstrated that these seeming gaseous clouds are in part composed of stars, many of which are more gigantic than our sun. *Science-Supplement New Series*, vol. XLI, n. 1584, May 8, 1925, p. XII.

For this, the radius of the earth's orbit, say 150 000 000 kilometers or about 93 298 100 miles, was taken. The parallax of the nearest star, that of Alpha of Centaur, has a value of 0''.75, and places the star at a distance of 4 light-years and 4 light-months i. e. about 41 trillions of kilometers, or nearly 251 1/2 trillions of miles. We are at a distance of 8 minutes and 33 seconds from the sun. The nearest star is 4 light-years, or about 150 millions of trillions of kilometers, or 98 millions of trillions of miles away, Vega 25, the polar star 47 light-years. The latter's parallax is 0''.78.

The measurement of some stars whose parallax is less than one-tenth of a second becomes uncertain. It has been found necessary to employ another method for calculating the distance of the more remote stars. From a comparison of the true brilliancy of two stars, the distance of one of which is known, we can deduce the distance of the other, when both have the same apparent brilliancy. It is thus that the scientist has been able, by degrees, to determine the distance of a very great number of stars [1] situated from 400 to more than 50 000 light-years away.

The apparent brilliancy of stars is measured by photometry. It depends both upon their real brilliancy and their distance. It has served as a basis for the classification of the stars. The real brilliancy itself has been calculated indirectly by the aid of the spectroscope. It is known that the radiations of a heated body regularly pass from red to violet. All the gradations are found, from red and yellow to white stars, giving the spectrum of the electric arc, the most brilliant of any electric spark.

The temperature of the stars ought to be analogous with that of the sun, estimated as we shall see at 6 000° in the photosphere. [2]

---

[1] *Annuaire du Bureau des Longitudes*, 1921, p. 375 et sq. *Revue des Questions scientifiques*, July 20, 1922, p. 179; *Comptes rendus de l'Académie des Sciences*, March 14, 1910.

[2] New temperature determinations on the corona of the sun, based on observations made during the recent total eclipse, indicate that it is only about one half as hot as this. Calculations made by

That of the stars should be between 2 000° and 40 000°.
Let us ever bear in mind that it is a very difficult matter
to obtain a correct idea of a temperature above the dissociation point of chemical elements. Can a temperature
of 40 000° exist? Or are the thermic phenomena replaced
by others which absorb the energy emitted? It is difficult
to say, under the present impossibility of realizing these
temperatures in our laboratories. We hope this may be
obtained by means of the electric spark.

Are the stars immovable, as their appearance seems to
indicate and as is generally believed? On the contrary, they
are all endowed with incredible velocities. It is their
distance alone that gives us the impression of fixity. The
spectroscope has facilitated the discovery and the measurement of their radial and their real velocity. If the star
is approaching us, the lines of the spectrum are bent
towards violet; if it is receding, towards red. From the
amount of the displacement of the lines the velocity of the
heavenly bodies is deduced. [1]

Around what center do they move?   We do not know.
Is there only one center?   This does not seem probable.
Right here we encounter the whole question of relative
and of absolute motion, which has occupied the minds of
scientists and of philosophers at divers times.

The dimensions of the stars are of the greatest diversity;
ranging from those whose mass is scarcely larger than that
of our planets to that of Arcturus and of Betelgeuse, which
are more than a million times the mass of the sun.   Their
distances and angular diameters have been computed.
The radius of Arcturus is 154 times and that of Betelgeuse
275 times that of the sun.   The latter centered on the sun
would nearly cover the orbit of Mars [2] or a diameter of
400 million kilometers (248 million miles).   The radiant

Dr. W. W. Coblentz of the U. S. Bureau of Standards, show the
coronal temperature to be around 8 000° Absolute. *Science, New
Series*, vol. LXI, 1586, *Sup.*, p. x.

[1] Cf. *Annuaire du Bureau des Longitudes*, 1921, A. 20.

[2] Cf. *Revue des Questions scientifiques*, July 20, p. 181 and Oct. 20,
1022, p. 384 and vol. XLVII, p. 80, Oct. 1914, p. 442.

energy from a star depends upon its temperature. We shall have some idea of this when comparing it with the radiant energy of the sun. The latter supplies an equivalent of 100 000 horsepower per square meter (1.2. sq. yd) of surface. There are some stars that expend much more energy.

§ II. — The Nebulae.

The telescope and the camera have brought about the discovery, in the heavens, of bodies termed nebulae, because of their resemblance to terrestrial clouds (Cf. frontispiece). They appear under the greatest variety of forms, some irregular as those of Orion and of Cygnus; others regular (fig. 6). The latter may be spherical, annular (Lyra) (fig. 7), elliptical (Andromeda) (fig. 3) or spiral, as those of Triangle and Canes Venatici [1] (fig. 5). Of 500 000 visible nebulae the greater portion of them are spiral (fig. 6). The problems which the nebulae present are numerous and some very difficult to solve. What is their nature? their composition? their purpose? their evolution? Have they been part of the milkyway, or are they themselves other very distant milkyways? Are they fixed or endowed with certain motions? What is their velocity of translation? of rotation? At what distances are they situated? This last problem is the one that ought to be solved first, but is also this that still seems to offer some insurmountable difficulties.

The procedure followed for the stars cannot be used here with the assurance that the conditions are the same, consequently with the same guarantees. Likewise we should expect to find some of the answers quite divergent, according to the starting point of the investigator. [2] According to Kapteyn, the nebula of Orion is 600 light-years distant; that of Andromeda 650. For the latter, Messrs. Lindemann have given 1 000 000 light-years. This is evidently exaggerated. Mr. Curtiss believes them

[1] Faye, *Sur l'origine du monde*, p. 186 and 193; Arrhenius, *Worlds in the Making*, p. 174. *Revue des Questions scientifiques*, Oct. 1914, p. 420-443.

[2] Arrhenius, *Worlds in the Making*, p. 189.

to be, according to his measurements, not more than 300 000 light-years.

The dimensions of the nebulae will not be determined as long as we are ignorant of their distance from us. A minimum diameter for Andromeda (fig. 3) would be 40 light-years and a maximum 80 000. They seem distinct from our solar system. [1]

The number of new nebulae increases with improved methods of investigation. Herschell counted 2500; Keeler with the Crossley telescope estimated their number in the neighborhood of 120 000. The telescope on Mt. Wilson with its 2.54 m. reflector reveals more than a million, according to Jean Bosler. [2]

These nebulae are not stationary, but move with a velocity unsuspected of old. About 1890, Keeler believed their speed to be around 65 kilometers (40 miles) per second. Modern astronomers, as a result of new and repeated measurements claim velocities of 300, 500, 1000 and 1,200 kilometers (188, 313, 625, 778 miles) per second. There is always a possibility of error here, due to some other causes capable of producing displacement of rays upon which are based the calculations of velocity. The average velocity of rotation approaches 330 kilometers (204.5 miles) per second for the nebula of Virgo.

The early observers believed that all the nebulae were gaseous. It is now known that the number of these is very small, a hundred at the very most. They seem concentrated in the milky-way and closely associated with Novae and the stars with variable brilliancy (fig. 4), Wolf-Rayet. The direct measurement of their parallaxes confirms this opinion and places them at short distances: 150 to 300 light-years. They seem to be resolved into stars or into asteroids (fig. 8). They might be parts of real-star clusters with the greatest variety of forms and with dimensions equal to those of the milky-way. The form which appears most frequently is the spiral. It represents

---

[1] J. Bosler, *Revue générale des Sciences*, p. 530.
[2] Puiseux, *Revue générale des Sciences*, June 15, 1917, p. 345.

a stage through which the greater part of the nebulae are passing (Cf. figs. 5 and 6) since more than one-half present this aspect.

§ III. — THE SUN AND THE SOLAR SYSTEM.

The solar system is composed of one central body, around which gravitate in practically the same plane, eight major planets with their satellites and a myriad of minor ones, situated between Mars and Jupiter. They all move forward in the same direction (fig. 9).

The assemblage of planets represents only 1/700 of the system. The sun has monopolized almost the entire mass. The numerous comets belonging to the solar system move about the sun in very great ellipses, moving in all planes. The duration of their revolutions is as variable as their distances. Their mass is rather small, in spite of the fantastic dimensions of their nuclei and their tails. These latter may extend as far as 300 million kilometers (190 000 000 mis.) The meteors or shooting stars are asteroids of very small dimension, which from time to time pass through the earth's atmosphere. The resistance which they encounter brings them to incandescence, and some times occasions their descent upon the surface of the earth. Chemical analysis has disclosed all the elements already known on the earth with the exception of some fifteen. The sun, planets, satellites, are endowed with a rotary motion. This motion is direct for the sun and for the planets and their satellites situated on this side of Uranus. The satellites of Uranus and of Neptune have a retrograde revolution. It is the same for some of the satellites of Jupiter and of Saturn. The regular motion of the heavenly bodies has been known since very remote times. Thus the Egyptians determined almost with exactness, the length of the year, more than 4 000 years before Christ. But we must come down to the age of Kepler (1571-1630) to know the laws which govern their motions. This astronomer discovered three important laws which may be stated thus :

First Law : The orbits of planets are ellipses;

Second Law : or the law of areas. The radius vector of a planet describes equal areas in aqual times;

Third Law : The square of the period of any planet is

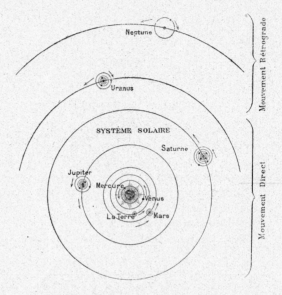

Fig. 9. — Distribution of the planetary orbits around the sun. Though apparently circular they approach the shape of an ellipse. The planets revolve from east to west. Likewise their satellites, except those of Uranus and of Neptune.

proportional to the cube of its mean distance from the sun $\dfrac{t^2}{(t')^2} = \dfrac{R^3}{(R')^3}$. From these laws Newton discovered universal gravitation and formulated its law, so admirable in its simplicity and clarity : "Bodies attract each other in direct ratio to their mass and in inverse ratio to the square of their distance. " $F = \dfrac{m.m'}{r^2}$ J. This law has enabled astronomers to calculate in advance and with mathematical precision astronomical phenomena, and has brought about remarkable discoveries, as that of Neptune by Le Verrier, in 1846. It has also permitted the determination of the mass of a heavenly body, and its density, when its volume is known.

Celestial mechanics is one of the most advanced sciences and the most precise of all. The mass of the sun has been determined as a function of that of the earth which is equal to $6\,063 \times 10^{18}$ tons, and was found to be 333 432 times this value. Its volume is about 1 300 000 times that of our globe. Its density, taking that of water as a unit, would be 1.4 while that of the earth is 5.5. This low density would imply a gaseous state. Observation of solar rotation confirms this. For the velocity of rotation is much greater at the sun's equator where it takes 24 days, than at the pole where it takes 29 days. The sun spots [1] themselves indicate a fluid condition, since they are due to real convective movements causing a continual interchange of the matter lying below the surface with that on top. This fluid state is confirmed by the existence of a superficial mean temperature of more than 6 000° which ought to maintain the matter in a gaseous condition. The density disposes the matter in zones of decreasing weight from the center to the periphery, if we do not take into account the convective movements which continually agitate the entire mass of the sun. The telescope readily discloses these phenomena.

Spectroscopy [2] plays an important part here in revealing to us the nature of the constitutive matter of the solar mass. By its aid we can analyze the photosphere or incandescent portion of the sun, and find there the greater part of the terrestrial elements : Ca, Fe, K, Na, S, O, C, Ni,

---

[1] Cf. Joung, *Le Soleil*, Paris, 1883, p. 78-142; Secchi, *Le Soleil*, chap. IV, Paris, 1875; Moreux, *Le problème solaire*, Paris, 1900, p. 177.

[2] Continuous spectrum = Incandescent solid;
Bright lines = Gas composed of simple incandescent bodies;
Bright bands = Gas composed of incandescent compounds;
Solar spectrum, or *Absorption spectrum* = Incandescent solid surrounded by a gas that acts as an *absorbant layer*.

H, N, He, etc.   The chromosphere which envelops the
photosphere, and the protuberances, or immense gaseous
jets, which rise to some hundreds of millions of miles, are
composed of gases of low density, such as hydrogen and
helium.   The spectroscope leads us to suspect the dissociation of the atomic elements at these high temperatures,
which we cannot realize in our laboratories.   At least
this is the opinion of Sir Norman Lockyer. [1]   Modern
notions on the constitution of matter are favorable to this
hypothesis.   The electric spark appears to break up the
atoms.

Thermodynamics give us some facts about solar heat
which are no less precise.   It has been able, to clear up
a number of problems connected with the temperature
of the sun, the intensity and constancy of solar radiation, the source of this formidable reserve of heat,
light, and electric energy, etc.   We hold today, that the
superficial temperature of the sun is from 6 000° to 8 000°.
Calculation shows that the heat increases with the approach
towards the center, where it attains an incredible intensity. [2]

Actual observation shows that the mean intensity of
solar radiation remains sensibly constant.   The data of
geology, combined with those of paleontology and paleo-
botany, tend to prove that for millions of years it has not
varied to any notable extent.   The temperature of the
Tertiary epoch must not have been much different from
that of the present day, if we may judge from the fauna

---

[1] *Inorganic Evolution*, McMillan.

[2] Wien's law : $\lambda T = 2940$ gives the absolute temperature when
we know the wave length (λ). $T = \dfrac{2940}{\lambda}$. λ is calculated in microns.
If the wave length is $0,5\mu$ for the sun, we find T to be $= 5880°$.
Stefen's law also enables us to compute this temperature.   By it
we obtain for T about 5600°.   The calorific energy radiated by a
body increases as the 4th power of its absolute temperature.   We
find therefore, by these two methods, that the sun has an absolute
temperature in the neighborhood of 5880°.   Cf. Tillieux, *Physique*,
p. 650.

Fig. 5. —- Canes Venatici, spiral Nebula, Exp. 3 hrs.

Sa NGC 4594   SBa NGC 2859

Sb NGC 2841   SBb NGC 5850

Sc NGC 5457(M101)   SBc NGC 7479

MOUNT WILSON OBSERVATORY

Fig. 6. — Types of normal and barred spirais

and flora of our climates. How explain this constancy of radiation? If the solar surface alone were to experience a sensible diminution it would quickly make itself felt, [1] but if the entire solar mass contributes to it, the constancy, is explained. The gaseous state of the sun gives free play to the phenomena of convection. The chemical reactions likewise contribute their share. At the surface, the elements combine at a constant temperature with a constant liberation of heat e. g.

$$Ca + O = CaO + 195 \text{ calories};$$
$$Si + 2O = Si\,O_2; 2\,Al + 3\,O = Al_3\,O_2, \text{etc.}$$

Their density causes them to descend again to a lower stratum, where they dissociate at a constant temperature, at the expense of the internal heat of the sun, absorbed in equally constant quantity. They rise again to the surface, where the recombination with liberation of calories brings them back to the same temperature again, and so on, as long as the energy furnished will be sufficient to dissociate the elements. The entire mass of the sun, contributing to maintain the radiation of the same temperature, the intensity of the radiation remains sensibly constant.

The intensity of the solar radiation is pretty well established. The sun, according to Faye, sends us 0.4 cal. (0.33 according to others), per second and per square meter, equivalent to 2.24 horse-power of steam. This would amount to nearly 300 000 000 000 000 horse power for the entire earth. But the earth receives only a small fraction of the radiation, 1/2 300 000 000. Around the sun, at about 215 solar radii distance, there is not only 0.4 cal. per square meter, but 215^2 or 46 000 times more, that is to say 18 500 calories per sec. The surface of the sun, being about 490 trillion square meters, we should thus have 114×10^{21} or 114 sextillions of calories emitted per second. For one year 3535×10^{21} calories. If we suppose, as we shall see, the sun capable of radiating a like energy during a minimum of 15 000 000 years, or a

---

[1] Cf. Faye, *Sur l'origine du monde*, p. 229.

maximum of 50 000 000 we can judge what a formidable
quantity of energy it must hold in reserve.

Whence does it obtain this energy? It is not due to
chemical reaction, for were the sun a block of carbon or
of silicon, the combustion would not suffice to feed it for
more than 2 000 years. Each kilogramme of matter in
fact, furnishes scarcely more than 7 000 calories. [1] Thermodynamics seems to offer a solution to the problem. We
know that a piece of work equal to 425 kgm. can supply
one calorie. The condensation of the nebula will itself
be a source of the calorific energy of the sun. Calculation
shows, in fact, that one kilogramme of matter coming from
the limits of the solar system would fall upon the surface
of the sun with a velocity of 615 kilometers per second.
The abrupt arrest of this projectile would then engender
45 000 000 calories. We thus have one source sufficient to
support the solar radiation for a minimum of 15 000 000
years at the actual rate of expenditure. Poincaré *by
slightly varying the conditions* finds 39 or even 52 millions.
A contraction of 1/1 000 of its diameter would furnish the
heat for a period of more than 20 000 years [2]. The sun
has a density of only 1.4. It could therefore contract
and develop some of the calorific energy from this source
also.

There may be other causes which might be added to
these two, and which might increase the power a hun-
dredfold. Radium if it existed in the sun—and everything
seems to point to this—(the presence of helium in its
atmosphere for instance) would of itself be another source
of energy. Each kilogramme of radium could disengage
100 times more energy than a kilogramme of matter coming
from the limits of the solar system and falling on the sun.
Hence, if the latter had only 1 100 of it, its life could be
prolonged 10 or 20 millions of years. It is evident from
this that the whole mass of the sun is not composed of

---

[1] Cf. Poincaré, *Leçons sur les hypothèses cosmogoniques*, p. 193.
Cf. Faye, *op. cit.*, p. 222.

[2] Poincaré, *op. cit.*, p. 199.

radium. In any case the duration of the solar radiation would not be indefinite.

We can now take up Cosmogony or the evolution of the worlds and in particular that of our solar system. An analogous study of the earth will permit us to give more precision to the cosmogonic theories.

ARTICLE II

COSMOGONIC HYPOTHESES

This simple, cursory glimpse of the Universe gives us a fair insight into the difficulty of the problem of its origin. The first creators of Cosmogonic Hypotheses had not even a suspicion of its complexity. In the measure that the science of astronomy progresses it becomes ever more intricate, ever challenging the investigator anew.

At the present time there is question, not merely of explaining the formation of our own solar system, but also that of the stars and of the nebulae; of supplying a reason for their morphological, physical and mechanical diversity; of determining the starting point of their evolution and of noting its phases; of explaining the differentiation following upon primitive chaos, the appearance of order out of confusion, etc.

A complete cosmogonic hypothesis should be able to tell from what source all the heavenly bodies derive their energy; under what primitive form they have received it; what successive transformations it has undergone; what it will come to in its final stage; if its quantity is conserved in the whole Universe; whether its quality is irretrievably degraded? With reference to matter, we have some similar questions to solve. What was there from the beginning? the molecule? the atom? the constitutive elements of the atom? one single substance? What is the possible duration of this universal evolution? We might easily extend this list of questions which clamor for solution without the least risk of error.

"We ought, parhaps," says H. Poincaré, (Preface, p. XLIX) "delay in our search for a solution until we have all the elements patiently gathered together; but if we had always been so reasonable, it is probable that we should never have created Science... Our mind then, imperiously demanded such solution long before it matured. It is on this account that the cosmogonic hypotheses are so numerous, so varied, that each day gives birth to new ones, all equally uncertain, but all as plausible as the older theories among which they take their places without causing the latter to be forgotten."

In spite of the difficulties, in spite of the gaps, which we ought to know how to recognize, the cosmogonic hypotheses are none the less precise. The work of astronomers, of physicists, of chemists has already produced some very interesting results, some certain and other probable solutions, and has given us a glimpse of new ones for the very near future. But it has also multiplied the interrogation points.

After briefly reviewing the older cosmogonic hypotheses, we shall give a rapid survey of the most important of those advanced during the XIXth and XXth centuries.

§ I. — Cosmogonic hypotheses anterior to the XIX century [1]

The notions commonly held by modern scholars, concerning the beginnings of the Universe are not altogether new. We find them in antiquity, though informally, in the poem of Lucretius. [2] With Descartes they begin to

---

[1] Consult Articles Cosmogony, and Cosmology in *The Catholic Encyclopedia*, Encyclopedia Press. For other works Cf. Bibliography.

[2] *De natura rerum*, book V, verse 432. "We no longer saw in the heavens the shining chariot of the sun, nor the torches of the world, nor the sea, nor the sky, nor the earth, nor the air, nor anything like the objects about us, but only a whirlwind of confused elements. Suddenly some particles separate from this mass. The homoge-

take on a more scientific aspect.[1]   Kant approximates
very closely the modern expression of them.[2]   We refer
the reader, desirous of going deeper into this subject to
the work of of H. Faye, who has made a very exhaustive
historical study of the hypotheses anterior to the xixth
century.   P. Duhem, in his *Système du Monde*,[3] gives

neous atoms come together. The world develops, its componant
parts take shape, and these immense parts were composed of atoms
of every kind." Without formulating a law, Lucretius admits of
a slow evolution in the formation of the physical world.

[1] We extract the following words of Decartes from H. Faye, p. 258.
"Let us for the moment permit our thoughts to rise from this world
to another entirely new world that I shall produce in the imaginary
spaces...

"Let us enter so far into these spaces that we may lose sight
of all the creatures that God created some five or six thousand
years ago, and after we have taken our stand in some determined
place, let us suppose that God created all about us so much matter
that whereever we turned, our imagination could no longer perceive
any place that was a void. Let us suppose that of these materials
some began to move to one side and some to another; some rapidly,
others more slowly... and that they continued thus following in
their motions the ordinary laws of nature; *for God has so marvelously
established these laws that even though we suppose He had created
nothing more than I have said, and even had not put into this any order
or proportion, but had made a chaos more confused and jumbled than
the poets could describe, they are sufficient to cause the parts of this
chaos to separate and to dispose themselves into such good order that
they would have the form of a most perfect world and in which one could
see not only light but also all the other objects, both particular and general that appear in this real world.*" This extract expresses very
nicely that which constitutes the basis of all modern hypotheses,·
the formation of the world through a law of evolution.

[2] Kant (1724-1804) was only twenty-four when he composed his
*Gedanken von der wahren Schaetzung der lebendigen Kraefte-Thoughts
on the true estimation of living things*. He embraced in one vast
synthesis, the formation of the entire universe. Because of his
inexperience in machanics and physics, his book must be revised
on many points. Wolf has published an excellent French translation of it in the *Hypothèses cosmogoniques*. In the beginning of his
work Wolf gives a very exact analysis and criticism of Kant's book.
Véronnet has reprinted this criticism in *Les hypothèses cosmogoniques
modernes*, Paris, 1914, and *Revue de Philosophie*, 1913, p. 52, 152,
238, 479.

[3] Paris, Hermann, 5 vols., 1913-1917.

the exact status of cosmogonic knowledge from **Plato**
down to the xvɪth century.   The work should be consulted
by those who wish to assure themselves that Science does
not begin with the xɪxth century.

§ II. — MODERN COSMOGONIC HYPOTHESES.

In France these are generally given under the name of
"The Cosmogonic Hypotheses of Laplace and of Faye."
We cannot enter into long technical details.   We shall give
only a summary statement of the cosmogonic theories in
favor at the present time.

1. LAPLACE (1749-1827).

This astronomer has set forth his cosmogonic hypothesis
in his *Exposition of the System of the World*.   A rapid
synthesis of all astronomical information had shown him :
    1. That all the planets sensibly move in the same plane;
    2. That they have a movement of revolution and of
direct rotation;
    3. That their satellites also move in the same direction;
    4. That the rings of Saturn move in the same direction
and seem to reproduce one of the stages of evolution;
    5. That there seem to exist heavenly bodies in all
degrees of condensation; from the gaseous nebulae to the
earth which we inhabit.
This assemblage of mechanical concordances ought to
have an immediate mechanical cause.   Laplace believed
he had found it in the common origin of movement and
of mass.   For him the sun and the planets had to be one
in the beginning and endowed with one and the same
movement of direct rotation.   The existence of nebulae
in the heavens seemed to indicate to Laplace the state
of primitive matter.   He supposed those of the sun and
of the planets dispersed in a space not less than ten times
greater than the orbit of Neptune.   Hence an exceedingly
low density (3 gr. per cubic myriameter) lower than
that of the X-ray tube, which would be 1 293 000 kilo-
grammes per cubic myriameter.   This density is therefore

400 million times greater than that of the primitive nebula. If the matter of the sun had been dispersed as far as the nearest star (4 light-years) we can see to what degree of rarefaction it would have been carried.

The solar nebula was endowed with a movement of direct rotation from west to east. Centrifugal force became sufficiently strong to detach, periodically, a series of rings in the equatorial region, because this force increases in inverse ratio to the cube of the radius $\dfrac{F}{F'} = \dfrac{(R')^3}{R^3}$, and the centripetal force in inverse ratio to the square of the radius $\dfrac{G}{G'} = \dfrac{(R')^2}{R^2}$. Diminution of the distance caused the centrifugal force to increase more rapidly than the centripetal. The rings formed, continued their direct movement of revolution. Their lack of homogeneity rendered them unstable and caused their disintegration. The mutual attraction of the molecules had the effect of grouping the fragments into spheroïds. These spheroïds or planets, in virtue of the law of areas should have had a retrograde rotational motion, but Laplace believed the retention of the direct motion could be explained by the action of friction. But, friction cannot occur in a medium with so low a density.

Critique.—Laplace's hypothesis needs to be modified on this point. This was done later on by Darwin. Laplace was ignorant of the existence of planets and satellites with a retrograde rotational motion. This was discovered after his time. [1] He considered the comets as being outside the solar system, whereas they really form a part of it. Solar heat he ascribed to the rotational motion, for here again he was ignorant of the laws of thermodynamics, the conclusions of which we shall see later on.

[1] Laplace, *Exposition du système du monde*, 1885, vol. vi., p. 498-509; Faye, *Sur l'origine du monde*, 1894; Wolf, *Hypothèses cosmogoniques*, Paris, 1886; Poincaré, *Hypothèses cosmogoniques*, 1913, p. 7 and 67.

His hypothesis does not lack importance or probability if we confine ourselves to the major points. The progress of astronomy demands a modification of details, a solution of new problems, a giving of other interpretations to all the questions of energy and to the explanation of the retrograde rotation of many of the satellites of Jupiter and of Saturn. It requires also, that we de not apply such a cosmogonic hypothesis to other stars, which, though they resemble the sun, are not identical with it. These, in fact, do not realize the conditions of the solar system, where the central body has absorbed 699/700 of the available matter. Some among them, more than one third, in fact, are double; others are grouped in immense masses. The greater part of the nebulae have been resolved by means of photography into masses of stars. Certain nebulae might even owe their origin to the collision of two heavenly bodies. They would thus be at the end, rather than at the beginning of their evolution.

[2. FAYE'S HYPOTHESIS.

After the discovery of the retrograde motion of four of the satellites of Uranus and of that of Neptune, Faye wished to complete Laplace's hypothesis. Since then two retrograde satellites of Jupiter and one of Saturn have been discovered.

To explain the origin of the heat without having recourse to a heated nebula, as Laplace had done, Faye had to take into account some of the facts of thermodynamics. His theory was brought out in his remarkable work *Sur l'origine du monde*, the fourth and last edition of which appeared in 1907 (p. 257-281).

Here is how he himself sums up the matter. Starting from the notion of a spiral nebula, he says: "In the beginning, the universe was reduced to a general, exceedingly tenuous chaos, composed of all the terrestrial chemical elements more or less combined. These material elements united with others by their natural affinity, were from the very start, endowed with diverse motions, which brought about separation into fragments or clouds. These latter have preserved a rapid translation and a more or less slow internal gyration. These myriads of chaotic fragments have given rise, through progressive condensation, to the various worlds of the universe."

"It will seem at first," adds Faye (p. 262), "very difficult to suppose that an hypothesis so simple as this can account for this multiplicity of forms, these nebulae, these clusters of stars, single, double and triple stars and over and above all, for our own very dull world with its central sun, its planets which are themselves miniature worlds and for its millions of comets. It will be admitted, at least, that being given the initial conditions and forces of a chaotic fragment, the laws of mechanics ought to make known the world which will result from it."

"A necessary remark here. Laplace and all those who have tried to explain the universe, start implicitly or explicitly, with the intervention of a Creative Power. For they take, as do we, the chaos, of which it is impossible to give an adequate account by the laws of nature, as their starting point. Among these laws, the principal, that of universal gravitation, is precisely the opposite of every tendency to diffusion of matter. Moreover, the chaos is not so simple a thing as we might at first suppose.

"It held in a state of potential energy all the various kinds of energy of the past and of the present under some form which they manifest today, such as motion, electricity, light, heat, or even that which governs the acts of living beings.

"In the life of the universe, and of our own solar world, a very small part of this primitive energy is indefinitely conserved and a certain stability is found realized; the rest under the form of heat is subjected to a frightful loss.—It is impossible to conceive how it could converge, in other regions, to form other material substances.

"It has been well said that the universe is an indefinite series of transformations, but we cannot see how an anterior state could have evolved from the great diffusion of matter, to the chaos from which the present state cer-

tainly has come.   It is necessary therefore to postulate a
God, as Descartes has done, for dipersed matter and for
the forces which govern it.''

Faye then, gives his own theory for the formation of
these heavenly bodies : single stars (p. 262), double
stars (p. 264), the solar system (p. 266), the formation
of circular rings (p. 267), the formation of planets
(p. 270), the formation of satellites (p. 273), the formation of comets (p. 275), the formation of the retrograde satellites of Uranus and of Neptune (p. 276).

Let us take up only his theory of the formation of the
solar system.   He supposes that the partial nebula from
which the sun ensued was, from the beginning, spherical
and homogeneous, and endowed with a slow whirling motion,
affecting one part of its substance.   He holds that the parts
which have the same velocity and a spiral gyration that
later changes into a circular gyration, reunite in the interior to form concentric rings.   The substances endued
with other velocities, or with other directions, gravitate
towards the center to form the solar mass.   The rupture
of the rings *which become unstable* gives rise to the formation of the planets.

To explain the direct motion of the lesser planets, Faye
relies on the nature of the attraction which varied from
the beginning down to the formation of Saturn.   As long
as the sun had not been formed, the attraction at the
interior of the nebula was proportional to the distance (R)
to the center, and could be represented by $F = AR$. (A)
designating a constant.   After the sun had been formed,
the attraction became inversely proportional to the square
of the distance to the center : $F = BR^2$.   (B) is a new
constant.   After the sun had been surrounded by a homogeneous nebula, the law had for its formula $F = AR + BR^2$.

The lesser planets, Mercury, Venus, the Earth, Mars,
Jupiter and Saturn were formed first, and had a direct
motion, because the rings from which they were derived
had this motion, and the elements, farthest from the center,
possessed a greater tangential velocity.

Under the influence of the second law, Uranus and

Neptune were formed with a retrograde motion, because at this moment the law of areas should have made its influence felt, and should have imparted a greater velocity to the internal elements of the ring which gave it birth. Their satellites also had to have this retrograde motion.

Faye believed he had thus solved a problem that was not even suspected by Laplace. His theory would less easily explain the retrograde motion of the satellites of Jupiter and of Saturn, whose own rotation is direct.

Critique.—H. Poincaré prefers to the opinion of Faye, that of Darwin which, (as we shall show later), *is based on the influence of the tides*. Faye, like Laplace, believed that the rotation of the planets depended upon the distribution of velocities in the particular ring which gave them birth, but being given the instability of the ring, its ephemeral duration, we may doubt that this difference of velocity had any influence upon the rotation. "We know" adds Poincaré, "that primitively the rotation of all the planets had to be retrograde, and that the influence of tides alone could make them direct." Faye, contrary to Laplace, postulates a cold nebula (fig. 10) which gradually becomes heated by absorbing solar radiation, at the *present rate* during 15 000 000 years. He is also right in considering the comets as belonging to the solar system. Their periodical motion around the sun proves this. They would be formed at the expense of matter which has escaped from solar and planetary attraction. Naturally, their orbits are quite varied in form, dimensions and planes.

3. Du Ligondès' hypothesis.

Colonel du Ligondès [1] wished to complete Faye's cosmogonic hypothesis by giving a mechanical explanation to the origin of the rotary motion of the nebula. He made it originate from motions more primordial than the nebula. The latter is a veritable chaos, formed from a

[1] Lt-col. du Ligondès, *Formation mécanique du système du monde*, Paris, 1897.

host of projectiles (molecules or meteors) which cross each other in all directions. The inevitable collisions will effect evolution and order in the nebula. The projectiles, not being perfectly elastic will transform their mechanical energy into heat energy at each collision, and thus they will bring about concentration and differentiation in this homogeneous mass. From this, will arise the sun and the planets with their respective motions. A slight preponderance of forward motion will be sufficient to cause the whole to assume a direct motion, for that which tends to go in an opposite direction will suffer from the collisions which will destroy the mechanical motion, and contribute to the development of heat energy and to concentration.

The manner in which the rings and the planets are formed is also peculiar. The rotation causes the nebula to assume the form of a disk. This breaks up into rings, which are transformed into planets in the following order : Jupiter, Neptune, Uranus, Saturn, the Earth, Mars, Venus and Mercury.

Critique.—Poincaré [1] raised the same objections against du Ligondès as against Faye, on the points that were common to both and added others that were special to the former (114.) ''If there were only semi-collisions, as they occur conformably to the laws of elastic bodies, the chaotic nebula subsequently would be altogether comparable to an isolated gaseous mass whose shape, when in final equilibrium would be a much flattened spheroïd without great central condensation. According to du Ligondès, in this flattening and condensation of the nebula, the real collisions play a very important role. Now these are indeed much less numerous than the semi-collisions. But are they, nevertheless, numerous enough to attribute to them the transformation of the nebula of our solar system, or is it not, rather, to be feared, that the effect of the semi-collisions prevails? This question has not been solved and so will bear further investigation.

''On the other hand, it seems to us rather premature to

---

[1] Poincaré, *Hypothèses cosmogoniques*, p. 114.

try to account by a prioristic methods, for the laws which hold the masses of planets to the great axes of their orbits, to the duration of their rotation and to the number of and to the subdivision into their satellites. If these considerations were justified, they should apply equally to the planetary systems that revolve about all the fixed stars, and all these systems should be identical—a fact which is scarcely probable." This critique applies to every similar tentative explanation given by other theorists.

4. — DARWIN.

Darwin seems to have offered a more satisfactory explanation of the direct and retrograde rotation of the planets. He had the phenomenon of tides intervene to modify the primitive retrograde rotation.

The law of areas obliges us to hold that in the beginning, all the motions of the planets were retrograde. They have remained so for the more distant planets, but have become direct for others under the influence of tides. Thus as long as the planet remained fluid, it was subject to the powerful action of the sun. Under this influence it assumed the appearance of an ellipsoid, whose great axis was turned in the central body, and was subjected to retardation. Gradually, the retrograde motion is suppressed and the planet then moves with relation to the sun, as the moon with respect to the earth. Its rotation has the same duration as its revolution and is, in fact, direct. The subsequent condensation of the planet, in virtue of the law of areas, acquires an accelerated velocity as its diameter diminishes. In this way was brought about the rotation of the earth which at present makes 365 turns on its own axis in the course of one revolution around the sun. It is the same for the other planets which have direct motion.

We may remark that the tides are still produced on the surface of the earth and probably also in the interior, and ought to have a tendency to increase the unit of time. Thus, according to Poincaré [1] would be explained "the

---

[1] Poincaré, *op. cit.*, p. 184.

apparent secular acceleration of the average motion of the moon." The planets in turn react on the sun and tend to modify its rotation.

5. NORMAN LOCKYER.

Norman Lockyer [1] (1920) has propounded his cosmogonic theories in his work : *Inorganic Evolution,* etc.   He wished to account for the difference of brilliancy and the spectral variations of the heavenly bodies.   His theory on the genesis of the great stars rests upon the simultaneous study of the chemical composition of the heavenly bodies, and the differences of temperature which they manifest among themselves.

A study of the spectrum of the stars permits a threefold classification according to the increase of temperature :

The spectrum of the flame composed of spectral bands;

The spectrum of the arc, made up of fine lines;

The spectrum of the spark, formed by new lines and certain lines of the strong arc.

These three spectra would appear successively in the formation of a star, only to disappear again in the reverse order.   Besides the different temperatures, these spectra would denote different atomic and intra-atomic stages.

Lockyer would explain the evolution of a star in this way :

1. A cold nebula is formed from a shower of meteors which collide with one another.   These collisions effect the liberation of the lightest gases such as helium and hydrogen, vhose spectra are well known — bright lines on a dark background;

2. The collisions increasing, the temperature rises and the matter is brought to incandescence.   A new spectrum appears—a bright spectrum with dark lines.   Some of the elements vaporize and play the role of an absorbing or inverting stratum, as in the sun;

3.   Finally we have an extremely hot gaseous star with

---

[1] Poincaré, *op. cit.,* p. 230 to 233; Lockyer, *Inorganic Evolution, as studied by Spectrum Analysis,* Paris, 1905.

the elements dissociated. The spectrum of such a star gives lines which would correspond to those of the proto-metals. The star cools down and passes again through conditions similar to those of the ascending series.

Lockyer thought he could always distinguish the latter condition from the former by a study of the spectrum. The ascending series would have the lower atomic weights; the descending the higher. The *Novae* or the new stars, would arise from the collisions of meteors. The spectra which the nebulæ present would be due to the liberation of helium and of hydrogen. We could thus suppose that a meteorite passing through a gaseous nebula becomes incandescent as do the shooting stars that pass through the earth's atmosphere.

The principal objection to this theory was based on the dissociation of simple bodies admitted by Lockyer. At the present time it appears probable. Still, some other hypothesis, as that of Schuster, could also explain the difference of stellar spectra.

6. SCHUSTER'S THEORY (1903).[1]

Schuster's theory is a modification of the preceding. He does not admit the dissociation of simple bodies, as did Lockyer. He saw in the difference of stellar spectra only the result of a different composition, on the surface of the heavenly bodies. The mean composition would remain the same. The convection currents would continue to stir up the elements in some, but not in the others where the lighter helium and hydrogen would show on the surface.

Schuster gave the following as the history of a star :

1. The collision of meteorites produces heat and causes the descent of the more dense elements towards the center. The He, and the H rise to the surface. Such would be the gaseous H stars of Lockyer's ascending series;

2. The star continues to increase; its greater attraction succeeds in capturing the He and the H. Its spectrum

---

[1] Cf. *The Evolution of Solars* in *Astrophysical Journal*, 1903, p. 165-200; Poincaré, *op. cit.*, p. 236.

becomes different and corresponds to Lockyer's very hot white stars;

3.   The absorption continues.   All the He and the H disappear and we have the metallic star of the descending series whose type is the sun.   It is convection that brings the metallic vapors to the surface of the heavenly body.

7. SEE'S THEORY (1911).

Mr. See [1] tries to explain the formation of the spiral and the annular nebulæ by the meeting of two cosmic clouds.   If the two clouds pass sufficiently near each other, their mutual attraction might cause their outer extremities to meet.   As they were moving in opposite directions, each of them would tend to preserve its own velocity and its own direction.   From this would result a rotatory motion around the point of contact, and the appearance of a spiral nebula with two arms resembling the two fans of a mill (fig. 6—7479).   Under the influence of attraction the matter condenses towards the center, while the fans, in obedience to the law of areas, gradually bend inward. In this way asteroids or even stars may be formed in the helices, whence will result clusters of spiraloid stars.

If the two cosmic clouds range themselves differently, by joining their extremities, an annular nebula could be formed.   Mr See holds that in the beginning the solar system was one vast spiral nebula; the elements of which grouped themselves into asteroids. [2] These, in turn, formed planets that, little by little, increased in volume. The sun has captured for itself the major part of the matter.

According to See the nebulæ would be formed from asteroids, which we wrongly take for gases.   They would

---

[1] J. See, *Researches on the Evolution of the Stellar Systems*, vol. II; *The Capture Theory of Cosmical Evolution*, chap. XIX, Paris, 1910.

[2] Dr. Edwin. P. Hubble with the aid of the Hooker Reflector has demonstrated that these seeming gaseous clouds are in part composed of stars, many of them more gigantic than our sun.   In the great nebula in the constellation of Andromeda, 23 new stars have blazed forth in the last two years. *Science-Supplement*; New series, vol. LXI, n. 1584, May 1925, p. XII (cf. figs. 3 and 8).

be less distant and in consequence smaller than we suppose. The nebula of Andromeda would have a parallax of 0".17. He holds that originally there existed around the sun a resistant atmosphere. A cosmic body, coming within the sphere of the sun's action would have to modify its trajectory. The latter, from parabolic or hyperbolic would have to become successively elliptic and circular. After the resistant atmosphere had been gradually absorbed by the sun, the planet continued to move around it in an orbit approaching that of a circle and always the same. The planets in their turn would have captured their satellites.

Critique.—The capture is possible, but it is difficult to explain by this hypothesis, why the greater part of the motions of the planets and of the satellites are direct and sensibly in the same plane. We should have to suppose that this solar atmosphere had a very much flattened lenticular form, and that only such bodies that passed throught it in the direction of its own plane had been captured. It would, perhaps, be necessary to add also, that it was endowed with a motion of direct rotation and that it communicated this to the captured bodies. [1]

Poincaré objects that the two arms of the nebula are habitually nearly symmetrical, which fact brings them well within the hypothesis of divergence, but not within that of convergence.

Curtiss, Bosler and other astronomers see, in the nebulæ, clusters of stars at the very great distance of 20 000 to 200 000 light-years from us.

8. BELOT'S HYPOTHESIS OR THE VORTEX HYPOTHESIS. [2]

According to Belot [3] collisions and vortices play an essential role in cosmogony and are the two principal factors in the formation of the worlds. The unexpected appear-

---

[1] Cf. Poincaré, *op. cit.*, p. 117-128.

[2] Cf. Poincaré, *op. cit.*, p. 271.

'Velot, *Compt. rend. Acad. Sciences*, 1910 to 1921 *passim*; 1920, p. 519, 658, 1563; *Revue générale des Sciences*, 1910, p. 642; *Science et Vie*, 1920, Sept.; *Essai de cosmogonie tourbillonnaire*, Paris, 1911.

ance of *Novæ* would prove to us the reality of such collisions, and the spiral nebulæ would be nothing else than
such vortices.

The solar system would be due to the collision of a
tube-vortex. In other words, a nebula, endowed with
a whirling motion, striking an amorphous nebula would be
expanded and transformed into our solar system. In fact,
the collision of two nebulæ gives rise to a central concentration, and produces a vibratory motion in the nebulæ.
At the equidistant centers of the vibration, will be formed
the planets, which will successively range themselves in
the plane of the ecliptic where they will be held by the
attraction of the central mass.

Belot makes his theory sufficiently extensive to explain
all the details of the solar system, of the multiple stars,
etc. It is undoubtedly a little premature, in the present
state of our knowledge, and a little arbitrary in the data
of the problem. Indeed, if we grant the requisite conditions, we shall find them in the mathematical solution.
Still H. Poincaré believes this hypothesis, though somewhat ambitious, merits attention (p. 277).

9. The abbé Moreux' hypothesis.

The Abbé Moreux [1] offers a new cosmic hypothesis,
which has the merit of neither neglecting recent advances
in the study of the universe, nor of having recourse to any
expedient invented to fill a need. Through direct observation he seeks for some evidence of the past. This
evidence consists principally in the clouds of dark matter
due to the vapors of calcium (fig. 10), which are interposed
between us and the nebulæ and form the long known black
patches; in the spiral nebulæ, with which all the theorists
have been occupied for the very reason that nearly all
of them have this more or less admitted form; and in
the new stars surrounded by a small spiraloid nebula.

Without wishing to go back to so obscure an origin for

[1] Cf. Abbé Th. Moreux, *Origine et formation des mondes*, Paris,
1922.

the whole stellar system, the Abbé Moreux believes that our planetary system might be the result of the evolution of a small spiral nebula that began with a collision of a partially condensed nebula with a current of black meteoric matter.

The two branches of the vortex would have first formed the great exterior planets, then the small ones, between Mars and Jupiter, and finally the inferior planets.

This hypothesis like the rest is very interesting, but we can not give a complete summary of it here.

10. Svante Arrhenius' theory (1907).

This theory more than all others has a decided materialistic tendency. We cannot ignore it therefore, since it pretends to show that the world suffices unto itself and can evolve indefinitely. S. Arrhenius himself gives us the reason for his theory in the preface of his *Worlds in the Making*. [1] There we read to this effect, p. III :

"I limit myself to the manner in which the nebulæ might be the result of suns and, inversely, how the suns might be formed by means of the nebulæ. I have held that, from all time this alternate evolution had to take place as it actually does take place.

"Cosmogonic problems have been rendered much more difficult by the discovery of the indestructibility of energy. A still greater difficulty seems to rise from the fact that the continual transformation of energy leads to this conclusion : that the universe tends ever more and more toward that state designated by Clausius by the name of calorific death.

"This would be a state in which all mundane energy would be uniformly dissipated in the universe under the form of movements of very small particles of matter.

"It is from this difficulty that I have essayed to free ourselves. It leads us, in fact, to an ultimate end of the evolution of the worlds that is entirely inadmissible and inconceivable.

[1] Svante Arrhenius, *Worlds in the Making*, Paris, 1910.

"The way out of the difficulty consists in admitting that the energy is dissipated or "degraded" in the bodies which are in the condition of suns, and, on the contrary, is restored, "ameliorated" in those that are in the nebula phase."

Critique [1].—If a termination of evolution seems to Arrhenius entirely inadmissible and inconceivable, it is certainly not in the name of Science that he is speaking since the latter according to his own admission leads to this conclusion. On the other hand, if he asks us to admit that the nebulæ "ameliorate" that is to say restore the available energy, it is likewise not in the name of true Science, as may easily be seen from an examination of the mechanism invented by him. It is therefore as an aprioristic materialistic philosopher, who wishes to do away with the Creator, that he speaks.

The theory of Arrhenius, in whatever form he presents it, has all the earmarks of a vicious circle. It is, moreover, in express opposition to the best demonstrated and most general principle of physics, that of the dissipation of energy. He admits this, but seeks to gainsay its value, by showing that the world is eternal, and therefore needed not be created. This position seems both unscientific and unreasonable. Arrhenius tries to escape this fact of observation, that the sun, and like it, all the heavenly bodies radiate their energy, and in consequence lose it as long as they are not isolated from the systems, and this other, that matter, originally dispersed, becomes more and more concentrated and so wastes its supply of available energy.

How will the reconcentration of radiant energy and the dispersion of concentrated matter be brought about?

1. In the first place, he supposes the world infinite so as to enable it to gather up all the radiation given out, from a center like the sun. This first hypothesis is gratuitous, unreasonnable, useless and in opposition to observation;

2. He calls upon the pressure of radiation from the luminous bodies to disperse the matter from the incandescent

[1] Poincaré, *Hypothèses cosmogoniques*, p. 56 and 254.

bodies in the direction of the cold nebulæ, where it will be collected and will again form suns. — Another gratuitous hypothesis, if we must give it the importance attached to it by Arrhenius. Indeed, only an extremely small fraction of matter will be projected into space. The extinct bodies like the earth and the moon (fig. 11), emit very little and preserve for themselves the greater part of their mass definitively condensed. The phenomenon of condensation is then not perfectly reversible.

Moreover, it is rather difficult to conceive the agglomeration of particles that keep on diverging with the solar rays, until they are gradually scattered and distributed around a center of emission in the form of extremely large spherical surfaces.

The hypothesis, that the particles encounter the nebulæ, is rather gratuitous, as the number of the latter is insufficient to collect them from all directions, and their distance is too great. As to those which do reach the nebulæ, are they going to combine with the molecules of these? Not necessarily, since they can pass through them or scatter about without colliding. Even if they should collide they would bring into play only an insignificant amount of energy and of matter. The particles that would be directed towards the other suns would become balanced, between two heavenly bodies which would repel them equally without causing their condensation.

If we suppose that these molecules condense to form asteroids, remote from the nebulæ and destined to fall again upon the sun, to restore the energy to it, we have another vicious circle. The sun has expended energy to hurl the particles into space, and it expends energy, in gathering them up again. Where is the gain in energy? Where is the perfect reversibility of energy which Arrhenius seeks?

His last expedient is to resort to explosives, whose mere contact will be sufficient to set them off. For him, a star, that has radiated heat and light and has become extinct, is not a dead star, but is simply a shell charged, not with T. N. T. but with radium. Under this form, we can give to our star much more energy than it has expended during its whole career. Now let us suppose two extinct stars colliding in the course of their perigrinations. They will explode and will create a new nebula, capable of evolving anew, and without doubt, becoming extinct and explosive bodies again; the series is complete. The eternal cycle is found.

But there is just one little difficulty. It is the recharging of the shell. There is nothing to prove that this supposed thing actually takes place. Everything seems to prove the contrary, since the shell would have exploded at the moment it became incandescent. But let us grant the charging. Shells habitually explode but once, dispersing their materials and their internal energy in every direction, making it impossible to collect either again. So would it be with the stars that collide with each other.

It is useless to pursue any further these puerile make-shifts, to demonstrate the eternal duration [1] of the universe

---

[1] Astronomy could go farther and measure the duration of the evolution of the worlds within certain definite limits. An attempt has been made to estimate the time necessary for the transformation of a nebula into a sun. Cf. Veronnet, in *Comptes rendus de l'Académie des Sciences*, Jan. 5, 1920. This duration is dependent upon the value of the primitive attracting mass which we may consider equal to that of the earth, equal to a gramme, to a molecule of hydrogen, or to an electron. Supposing that the phenomena took place on a scale obtained in our laboratories!... Calculation shows that an atom would have been enough to form a sun in less than 400 000 000 years. It might have formed a mass a million times greater (e. g. Arcturus) in 40 000 000 years more.

It is difficult to speak of hundreds of millions of years for the evolution of worlds.

In the midst of different densities, the time of formation is inversely proportional to the square root of the density.

Véronnet draws the following conclusion : "Summing up therefore, in the hypothesis of the formation in the center of an undefined nebula the period of formation of the sun could vary from 200 000 000 years to 640 000 years. The period of evolution, since its formation might vary from 0 to 850 000 years, and the temperature of formation would remain below 20 000°." *Comptes rendus des Sciences*, June 28, 1920. Idem., 1918, p. 328, 642, 812. Véronnet, *Revue générale des Sciences*, 1923, p. 168 to 171.

which would be in itself its own proper cause. We must seek elsewhere for its first cause. Spiritual Philosophy has still some days to live if materialists have no stronger arguments to oppose to the necessity of a God Creator.

Conclusion.

To sum up. In the beginning God created matter and energy under the most primitive form, with the capacity of evolving to their present condition. All the spiritualist authors, after Kant, Descartes, Faye, Wolf, Secchi and Th. Moreux, are unanimous on this point. It is impossible to state precisely the condition of primitive matter or energy. Many authors ascribe to the simple atoms, in the beginning, universal gravitation, in virtue of which each particle attracts every other particle with a force whose magnitude varies directly as the product of the masses, and inversely as the square of the distance between them. There is no doubt that it will soon be possible to go even beyond this, and suppose the creation of intra-atomic elements and intra-atomic forces. The work of creation will be none the less necessary, none the less admirable. On the contrary, the more wonderful the role of the secondary causes, the more sublime appears that of the First Cause who produces it.

The broadest cosmogonic hypothesis supposes a primitive nebula containing all the elements of the universe. The mutual attraction of the elements brought about concentration at several points. From this resulted the centers of the least extended nebulæ. These latter in their turn became other centers of attraction to form the nebulæ of lesser importance. These last in turn produced others. Thus we arrive at a nebula like that from which the sun originated.

It seems that, in their evolution, the nebulæ pass from an irregular amorphous form to more specialized forms : spherical, lenticular, spiroidal and spiral. They appear endowed with a motion of rotation and of revolution. The cause of this twofold motion might be mechanical i. e. the resultant of more primitive motions. It is, indeed, evident that the attraction of the elements of each nebula acting one upon the other, and the nebulæ in turn upon their neighbors, ought to give rise to every sort of curvilinear motion : hyperbolic, parabolic, elliptical and circular.   Each of them is the resultant of innumerable forces.   The problem of three bodies interacting upon one another, being still a real enigma for the human mind, we cannot dream of solving that of some millions of bodies acting one upon another.   So, generally speaking, the pretensions of real scientists are not so great.   They content themselves with following the evolution of the solar nebula, and then, apply the results obtained in this restricted field to the principal stars.   It is thus that Laplace and his successors have acted.'

Along with the motions of rotation and of translation, other forms of energy should be taken into account. Probably, under the influence of collisions, or semicollisions and consequently, of the resistance to the mechanical motion, heat, light, electricity, etc., would appear.   These forms of energy in their turn, would act upon the matter to modify its physical, chemical and, without doubt, its intra-atomical condition.   The radiation of heat, light and electricity disperses the energy and causes new transformations on other heavenly bodies. Thus they all seem to start from a state where the matter is at minimum density to result in a solid body like the crust of the earth. So from the point of view of energy, they pass from a state of unstable equilibrium with a maximum of free energy to a state of equilibrium with a minimum of free energy, in coming to final rest, the dissolution of the energy of the universe.

Is the world made to last forever?   Must this evolution be eternal as the Materialistic School pretends, and as popular writers assert in their search for arguments to eliminate God?   We have already given the answer in treating the theories of Arrhenius.   We shall go more into detail when taking up the subject of Dissipation of Energy. Let it suffice for the present to give the opinion of true scholars, astronomers and physicists.   The evolution of the world must have an end, as it has had a beginning, since its available energy tends to be dissipated... Such is the opinion of H. Poincaré. This is required, if the stability of the solar system was as real as Laplace, Poisson, Delaunay, Tisserand, Gylden believe it, and if there were not causes of instability overlooked by them. [1]

He finds at least three causes which suffice to invalidate their conclusions : 1. There are certain phenomena which cannot be explained except by admitting a slight resistance of the interplanetary medium. This resistance causes a diminution of the centrifugal force and should have the effect of drawing the planets towards the sun and some day precipitating them upon it;

2. The second force is the action of the tides exerted alike on the planets, their satellites and the sun, tending to diminish their velocity of rotation until it becomes equal to that of their revolution. This is already the case for the moon and probably for some of the lesser planets, Mercury and Venus. It is easy to foresee that the phenomenon will continue till the entire suppression of the rotation of all the heavenly bodies;

3. The earth being magnetic, we may suppose this holds good also for the other planets and for the sun. Hence, there is another resistance adding its action to that of the tides.

In his *Hypothèses cosmogoniques*, H. Poincaré has had frequent occasion to remark that "in any case we shall have to renounce the dream of the 'Eternal Round' and of the perpetual rebirth of worlds, and hold the solution given by Arrhenius, as still insufficient." (P. LXIX and CCLV.)

Faye in his *Origine du Monde* is not content with retracting the phases of evolution, but takes care to go back at once to the First Cause (p. 3-4). "The mysterious springs and works of this vast universe are of little consequence. The immediate impression and the intellectual reaction which follows it are the same for the learned as for the

[1] *Annuaire du Bureau des Longitudes*, 1898.

uninstructed, today as ten million years ago... We contem-
plate, we know, at least in its immediately comprehensible form, the world which of itself knows nothing.   Thus
there is something else besides terrestrial objects, besides
our own bodies, there is intelligence and thought, and as
our intelligence has not made itself, there must exist in
the world a Superior Intelligence from which ours is derived.   We are not exposing ourselves to deception in
holding it to be the Author of all things... in accordance
with the traditional formula : God, the Father Almighty,
Creator of heaven and of earth.''

To deny God is, as it were, to let oneself fall from these
heights heavily upon the ground.   These heavenly bodies,
these marvels of Nature be the result of chance...!   It is
false to hold that Science has ever ended in this negation.

ARTICLE III

EVOLUTION OF THE EARTH.

The cosmogonic hypothesis ceases to be a more or less
true hypothesis, when we come to an evolution more accessible to our investigations, to that of the earth.

The science which studies the earth is called geology.   It
examines the successive transformations of the earth's
crust.   It is enough merely to open our eyes to observe, to
stretch forth our hand to grasp, to analyze this crust, to
know it thoroughly.   Hence geology has already advanced
farther than the other sciences, since it is more accessible
to direct observation.   There still remain some enigmas it
is true [1] and this is fortunate.   But how many have
not already been solved!

Though we do not intend to write a treatise on geology,
we think it not amiss to give a brief summary of some of
the principal results already achieved.   The role of the
natural causes will thus become more intelligible to the

---

[1] Cf. Termier, *Revue des Questions scientifiques*, 1920, p. 68; Termier, *A la gloire de la Terre*, Paris, 1922. Nouvelle librairie nationale.

observer. The necessity for a Creator will appear more evident to every reflecting mind; for none of the natural causes is sufficient unto itself. Each is contingent, the effect of an antecedent cause, up to the point where the world cannot furnish any further explanation for its evolution, nor *a fortiori* for its existence.

In the history of the earth, we can distinguish a stellar phase, a planetary phase, a geological phase. The last still continues in our day. The deductive method appears to us the most appropriate for making known the ensemble of facts bearing on the evolution of the terrestrial globe.

1. The stellar phase began at the moment when the earth became detached from the solar nebula and ended when it ceased to be incandescent. Its duration could not have been considerable, because of the lightness of its mass. According to certain astronomers some tens of millions of years would have been sufficient for the solidification of all the matter and the disappearance of incandescence.

During this period the matter continued to condense, disposing itself in strata in the order of increasing density from the surface to the center. It is in the course of this first phase that the earth must have given birth to its only satellite, the moon. This soon became extinct and has long since cooled off. It is completely condensed, and has only a motion of revolution around the earth. Its rotation was impeded and finally suppressed by the phenomenon of tides.

2. The planetary phase began with the disappearance of incandescence and continued down to the moment when geological phenomena properly so called intervene. During this period the cooling continues. Around $1\,000^\circ$-800° a solid crust forms, particularly from scoriae : silicates, carbonates, metallic oxides, whose depth gradually increases in accordance with the law of cooling bodies. $R/R' = t/t'$. This crust undergoes numerous changes in consequence of the variation of density, and of the internal heat of the still molten materials, which fuses the elements of the crust.

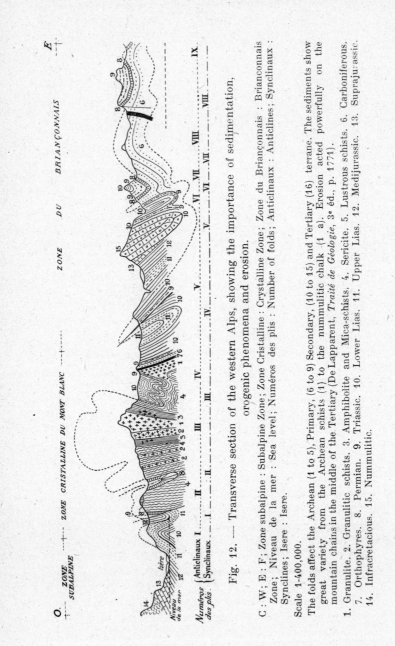

Fig. 12. — Transverse section of the western Alps, showing the importance of sedimentation, orogenic phenomena and erosion.

C : W ; E ; F ; Zone subalpine : Subalpine Zone ; Zone Cristalline : Crystalline Zone ; Zone du Briançonnais : Briançonnais Zone ; Niveau de la mer : Sea level ; Numéros des plis : Number of folds ; Anticlinaux : Anticlines ; Synclinaux : Synclines ; Isere : Isere.

Scale 1-400,000.

The folds affect the Archean (1 to 5), Primary, (6 to 9) Secondary, (10 to 15) and Tertiary (16) terrane. The sediments show great variety from the Archean schists (1) to the nummulitic chalk (1 a). Erosion acted powerfully on the mountain chains in the middle of the Tertiary (De Lapparent, *Traité de Géologie*, 3e éd., p. 1771).

1. Granulite. 2. Granulitic schists. 3. Amphibolite and Mica-schists. 4. Sericite. 5. Lustrous schists. 6. Carboniferous. 7. Orthophyres. 8. Permian. 9. Triassic. 10. Lower Lias. 11. Upper Lias. 12. Medijurassic. 13. Suprajurassic. 14. Infracretacious. 15. Nummulitic.

Under the action of continued cooling, the earth's shell, formed for the most part from metals, contracts. To add to the shell, the crust, already solidified, must split and be dislocated. This is the beginning of orogenic and volcanic phenomena.

3. The geological period could have begun with the action of external dynamic agents—with the condensation of water vapor, which later on is to play an important role in the shaping of the terrestrial surface. As long as the earth was at a temperature higher than 370º, the water would not condense, as this is the critical temperature for water. But after passing this point, the condensation proceeded with an intensity that it would be well to note.

If all the water in the oceans were spread over the entire surface of the terrestrial globe, it would have a depth of 3 000 meters (3 281 yds.) and a pressure of 300 kilos. (661.65 lbs). Now, water vapor at its critical temperature of 370º has a pressure of 200 kilos. (441.1 lbs.) When the temperature fell below 370º, a third of the aqueous vapor should have condensed, raising the pressure from 200 kilos. to the neighborhood of 300 kilos. which would represent a 1 000 meter head of water. This was a veritable deluge at high pressure and at high temperature. It has been styled the "critical deluge". The remaining two thirds of the aqueous vapor condensed between 369º and 100º, giving a 2 000 meter head of water. This was the "normal deluge". The water vapor which is still at a temperature of 100º would represent the equivalent of a column of water about 10 meters high. It would be only at this point that any one of these could begin the geologic phase.

It is difficult to know whether, in the diluvian period, the terrestrial relief was very accentuated. This would appear probable, since the terrestrial crust, even at this time would have had to split. In this case, it is easy to see what amount of hydration and of erosion these volumes of hot water, falling in veritable torrents upon the scarcely solidified and still seething crust, could produce. The solvent action of the water added to the mechanical action, should have altered the primitive terrestrial crust, from the stand point of physics in general and of crystallization in particular. Its chemical action on the material substances, capable of hydration, should have modified them profoundly. Something like the Archaean rocks should have been the result of forces so powerful, so varied, so inimitable.

Who knows but that a part of the Archaean rock owes its origin to these causes, and that it is necessary to abridge to a considerable extent the time of formation which the importance of these sediments would require, if we suppose them formed at the present rate of deposit. We should have here a means of putting the geological clock in agreement with the astronomical. It is sufficient merely to mention this. We do not deem it necessary to multiply the hundreds of millions of years for the duration of the geological periods. If we extend our investigations we arrive at the real geological data. Geography gives us an idea of the appearance of our globe the total area of which is 510 000 000 square kilometers. 3/4 of this or about 355 000 000 sq. kilometers is covered by the oceans and 1/4 or about 135 000 000 sq. kilometers, comprises the continents.

The oceanic depressions reach an average of 4 000 meters, with a maximum of 9 000 meters. The mean elevation of the continents is 700 meters, but certain ranges attain an altitude of nearly 9 000 meters (Mt. Everest is 8 950 meters). There are some depressions in the earth's crust reaching 18 000 meters. What could have been the cause? They are not equally great in all places nor were they formed by the same causes. Thus there are areas of elevation as for instance the Alps, the Carpathians, the Himalayas, etc., and areas of depression as the one in the present Atlantic ocean, that runs from north to south, and has two immense synclines of 6 000 meters separated by an anticline of 2 000 meters. The Pacific and the Atlantic oceans do not resemble each other in the least. What is the cause of their formation and of their difference?

The rocks which make up the crust of the earth present

a variety that, at first sight, is surprising. Anyone that imagines they were formed merely by cooling has no adequate knowledge of the facts. Certain rocks for example possess all the characteristics of marine deposits interspersed with an important and exceedingly varied fauna and flora. If we observe what happens under our very eyes, we perceive various forces constantly intervening to alter the appearance of the terrestrial crust. Now these same causes have been in operation ever since the beginning.

Geologists, like de Lapparent, have classed them as the agencies of *external* and *internal dynamics*. The former appear to have as their role the removal of the elevations, produced by the latter. We shall obtain a good idea of both when studying successively their effects, as manifested in what geologists have termed the phenomena of *orogenesis*, or the formation of folds in the crust of the earth, the phenomena of *glyptogenesis*, or erosion and removal of elevations, the phenomena of *lithogenesis*, or of sedimentation. [1]

Let us take up the principles of stratigraphy, which guide geologists in writing the history of the earth's crust. [2]

1. OROGENESIS.

How have terrestrial elevations, such as the Alpine range extending from the Pyrenees to the Himalayas, the ranges that stretch all along the western coast of the two Americas, the mountains of Alaska, the Rocky Mts., the Cordilleras of the Andes; or the continental chains of Europe, Asia, Africa and Australia, been formed? How did the oceans and the islands with which they are strewn, come into existence? We cannot help admitting that the earth's crust, originally a perfect sphere is now strangely furrowed. To what causes must we attribute this? What were the influences that brought it about?

From a careful examination of the rocks that compose the crust of the earth, geology can at least give a partial answer to this difficulty.

[1] Haug, *Traité de géologie*, vol. VIII, p. 9, Paris, Colin.
[2] Haug, *op. cit.*, p. 158.

On the very tops of the mountains, we meet with sedimentary strata of marine origin which were formed at the bottom of the ocean, thrown into folds and elevated to heights as great as 4810 meters in the Alps, and 8950 meters in the Himalayas (fig. 12), the Rockies and the Andes. These mountains show regular strata of immense thickness, that decrease from the center of the ridge to the seacoast.

The way in which they were formed is indicated by the sediments themselves. Having a thickness of thousands of meters, they should have been formed in oceanic depressions of equal depth. Having a length of some thousands of kilometers (the Alpine range, the Rocky Mts., the Cordillera of the Andes, etc.) they postulate an equal length of ocean.

The areas of excessive sedimentation should reappear as immense depressions, or geosynclines which could be extended around the earth. They owe their origin to the irregular elevations of the earth's crust. As the central part of the earth cools, it diminishes in volume. The crust, having already solidified, and being at an almost constant temperature cannot contract, so it bends and folds in the weakest places, in the geosynclines. [1] As these become deeper and deeper, sedimentation tends to fill them again with materials carried down from the emerged parts (fig. 13).

A moment arrives when the descent stops. As the central portion continues to diminish in volume, the contraction of the crust continues and gives rise to tangential forces which compress the sediments as in a vice. These, at first, fold over at the edges, then towards the center, and by and by, rise to the surface in the shape of more or less complex folds—vertical, inclined, horizontal, and shifting. The orogenic movements come in to complete the work of folding. A detailed history of a mountain chain,

----

[1] If we allow for the earth's crust a coefficient of expansion equal to that of glass 0.000 008, the contraction of the earth's crust, in the equatorial region, would amount to 256 kilometers for a drop of 800 degrees in temperature.

written in the sediments from which it is formed, would indeed be interesting. This is the field of stratigraphic geology, however, and we can give but a very general

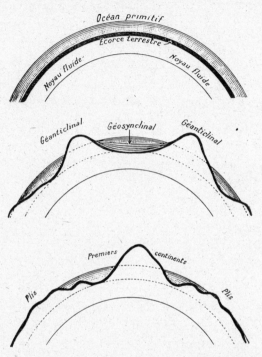

Fig. 13. — Diagrame showing the successive phases through which the Earth has passed from the first condensations of the oceanic waters to the formation of the first continents.

Océan primitif : Primitive Ocean; Écorce terrestre : Earth's Crust; Noyau fluide : Fluid zone; Géanticlinal : Géanticlinal; Geosynclinal : Geosynclinal. Premiers Continents : First Continents; Plis : Folds.

outline of the principal results that have been obtained by this very recent science.

Four successive upheavals of enormous proportions are known to have occurred in the various geological periods. They followed one another from the north to the equator, the direction of the folds at least in the beginning, having been from east to west. The oldest of these is the Huronian

(Algonkian, U. S. Geol. Survey) fold of the lower Precambrian age and affected the sedimentary formations in
the neighborhood of Lake Huron.   It delimited a circum-
polar continent which comprised the northern part of
America, Scotland and Scandinavia.   This ridge is in
non-conformity with the Archaean terrane against which
it leans.   Only strongly eroded fragments, that are reduced
to a state of peneplain, still remain.   Further south, and
noticeably in Caledonia (Scotland) and in Norway,
a second fold called the Caledonian, was formed during
the Silurian period.   The third or Post-Carboniferous
Hercyan fold, affects the carboniferous terrane in America
and in Europe.   The Alleghanys, the Armorican range, the
Central range, the Vosges, the Black Forest, the Bohemian
and the Ural ranges form part of this chain.   Erosion
has denuded these ridges to a considerable depth.   Though
once as mighty as the Alps, they are now only a few
hundred feet in height.

The most recent of these folds is that of the Alps, situated
to the south of the preceding.   It appears the most important for the reason that erosion has not leveled the ridge
to any extent.

The geosyncline from which it originates dates back
to the Secondary or Mesozoic period, and it was in the
middle of the Tertiary or Cainozoic that the uplift of the
Alpine ridge took place.   According to geologists, it encircled, or might have encircled the entire globe.   It began in
fact with the Pyrenees, and then continued successively
to the Alps, the Appenines, the Carpathians, the Balkans,
and the ranges in Asia Minor, the Iranian Arch, Persia,
the Himalayas, and the Malayan Arch.   In the Sunda
Islands, it is interrupted.   It is thought that it continues
across the Pacific, to join the Antilles and thence across
the Atlantic to the Pyrenees again.   Some very important
parts of it still remain.

The Alpine geosyncline rests slightly on the equator, thus
completing the circuit of the globe.

Dating from the same period, a second geosyncline almost
perpendicular to that of the Alps, called the Circumpacific,

bordered on the present Pacific and covered the territory
now occupied by the chains that extend through North
and South America. These constitute the most evident
traces of this geosyncline; the remainder did not give rise
to permanent chains, save under the form of debris as in
the Aleutian, the Japanese, the Philippine, and the Sunda
Islands (fig. 14). In the Secondary or Mesozoic period these
geosynclines delimited five continents :

The North Atlantic Continent;
The South-Atlantic, or Africo-Brazilian Continent;
The Sino-Siberian Continent;
The Australo-Indo-Madagascar Continent;
The (hypothetical) Pacific Continent.

On the site of these have arisen the Alpine and Circum-
Pacific chains in the middle of the Tertiary period.

This theory of Secondary period geosynclines, would give
us a partial key to the present aspect of the terrestrial
globe. In the Tertiary period, all these geosynclines were
transformed into mighty mountain ranges which became
united to the continents they had delimited. Thus the
American ranges in the West form part of the continent
today. As to the Pacific continent of the Secondary
period, it would have given way like a badly supported
key-stone. The Pacific ocean would occupy its place.
Of the Australo-Indo-Madagascar continent there remain
but three sections. The remainder has disappeared and
been replaced by the Indian ocean.

The Atlantic has a slightly different origin, if we may
judge from the appearance of this extensive terrestrial
depression. It seems to have been caused by a simple
flection of folds extending from America through Europe
into Africa. An immense flood area now covers one portion
of the North Atlantic and the South Atlantic continents.
Canada and the Finno-Scandinavian ranges would be the
northern, and South America and Africa the southern
portion of it. The Sino-Siberian continent has remained
unchanged, since the Secondary period, except for the
adjunction of the Tertiary chains of the Himalayas and
others of the same period.

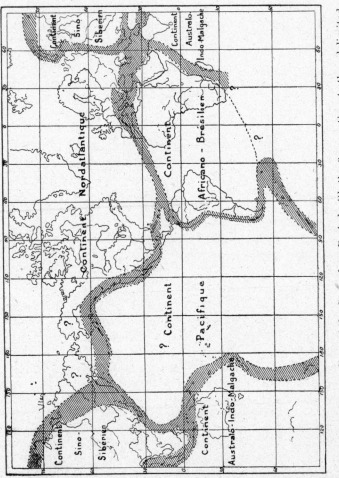

Fig. 14. — Geosynclines of the Secondary Period with the five continents they delimited.
(From E. Haug.)

This very cursory survey gives us at least some idea of the important series of transformations, that have taken place on the face of the earth in the course of the geological periods. Indeed, we see the highest mountains of the globe rising in the Primary (Paleozoic) and in the Tertiary (Cainozoic) periods in the place formerly occupied by the deepest oceans.

These movements were neither instantaneous nor continuous. They were for the most part oscillatory, and we may remark, that under one form or another, they continue down to our own day. Thus we have earth tremors, or slight oscillations of the earth's crust : violent oscillations as the recent earthquakes in Japan and periodically in California, Central and South America, Sicily, etc. : the subsidence of the earth's crust as the Rhine valley and the Valley of the Jordan extending as far as the great African lakes : volcanic phenomena often accompany these latter along the fault-lines of the Circum-pacific.

The transgressions and regressions of the oceans were the consequence of these movements, and Quarternary man was himself a witness of many of these oscillations, hence also of the transgressions and regressions of the seas. [1] These movements of the land had their effect upon both marine and continental fauna and flora. Stratigraphy can rewrite a detailed account of all these movements from the traces of them left in the sedimentary strata.

Another result of these orogenic movements was the bringing to the surface, through the cracks in the earth's crust, of materials of greater density, such as iron and other minerals, which, without such an upheaval, would never have seen the light of day. They appear either as veins or in the form of lavas. That the latter may become available as ores, they must be uncovered through the action of erosion and be recovered from below the surface of the water, where the minerals such as iron would be deposited.

[1] See : *Origin of glaciers*, p. 484.

2. Glyptogenesis, or erosion of continents.

The bold reliefs of the mountain ranges scarcely show how much the agencies of external dynamics such as rains, winds and ice, have intervened to cause their erosion and gradual disappearance. Geology makes a study of their action in detail. We shall merely note the results. [1]

The three original chains : the Huronian, the Caledonian and the Hercynian whose height must have almost equalled that of the Alps, are slowly being removed, transformed into peneplains of low altitude. The most recent, the Hercynian chain, represented in France by the Armorican massif, the Vosges Mts. and the Central massif, and in America by the Alleghany Mts., are not more than a few hundred feet (650 to 2 500 ft.,200-800 meters) high.

The Pyrenees, which are a little older than the Alps already show signs of old age : the peaks are less elevated (6 000 to 9 850 ft. 2 000 to 3 000 meters) and the contours are more rounded. The Alps rise to 15 750 ft. (4 800 meters) and the Himalayas to 29 000 ft. (8 840 meters).

De Lapparent has calculated the time necessary for the erosion and leveling of all the continents, and has found that, at the present rate of ablation, 15 cubic kilometers a year, 5 000 000 years would suffice. This fact would lead us to doubt the objectivity of certain figures relative to the age of the earth, or that of life, but this is of no importance.

3. Lithogenesis.

The materials washed away by the waters on the continents are carried to the oceans, where they sink of their own weight and form horizontal layers. As the nature of the sediments varies, we obtain strata of different composition and appearance : limestone, clay, marl, sandstone, etc. The location of the deposit also has an influence on the appearance of the sediment. [2] Near the shore, or within

[1] A. de Lapparent, *Traité de géologie*, vol. I, page 136 et sq. Paris, Masson.

[2] Id., p. 223 and 231.

the littoral zone there will be found gravel and sand, while in the neritic zone, farther out, we have very fine sand, clays and calcareous mud; still farther out, at depths varying from 200 to 1 000 meters (656 to 3 280 ft.) we have the bathylic zone, where there is only a deposit of lime-stone and red clay that had been held in colloidal suspension for a long period of time. These bathylic sediments are very extensive and form perfectly homogeneous strata, at times many thousands of yards in depth. The Alpine chain furnishes examples of this. Very little material is deposited in the abyssal zone, as it is for the most part far out from the coast, at a distance of more than 500 kilometers (311 miles).

These sediments supply man with the greatest variety of building materials, granites, limestones, marbles, slate, clay, gravel and sand. They yield the reserve energy which they contain, under the forms of coal and petroleum products; they supply the minerals from which man obtains the useful metals such as iron, copper, zinc, lead, etc., or the precious metals, silver, gold, platinum, etc ; elements indispensable for agriculture, the phosphates, nitrates and potassium salts; smaterials for the research student to reveal to him in part at least their secrets, as the mineral pitchblend, which contains infinitesimal traces of radium. Thus thele sediments form an almost inexhaustible mine for the mu tiple needs of human activity.

Interesting as the formation of coal, oil or fossils may be, we cannot enter into the conditions which brought them into existence. We shall merely say that coal has a vegetable origin. The luxuriant vegetation of the Carboniferous epoch had been carried down by the streams and deposited in layers of varying depth in the lakes and estuaries. A special fermentation transformed the cellulose into coals of different grades; pressure agglomerated them and the Hercynian uplifts buried them deep down in the earth, far from the action of erosion, until such time as man may avail himself of these precious reserves. [1]

---

[1] De Lapparent, *La Providence créatrice*, Paris, Bloud, and *Traité de géologie*, vol. II, p. 870; E. Haug, *Traité de géologie*, chap. x, p. 128 sq.

The petroleum products can result from the decomposition of organic substances, as also from the action of metallic carbides, by a series of reactions indicated by MM. Sabatier and Senderens. [1]

It is in these sediments that marine animals, on dying leave their remains, to be transformed into fossils. Paleontology needs merely excavate the most recently emerged strata, to have under its very eyes the most authentic evidence of life in these geological periods. There is here an inexhaustible mine of information of which we shall avail ourselves, for the solution of some of the problems that confront the human mind. We find in all treatises on geology the conditions under which fossils are produced. It is therefore useless to give them here at any length. Let it suffice to state, that the essential condition is the burial of the remains in a layer impervious to the agencies of destruction, water and air. The clays and limestone realize these conditions perfectly. Sandstone, being very porous does not, as a rule, preserve the traces of living things. Everyone knows that a fossil may be either a specimen found whole and entire (as the mammoths from the ice in Siberia) or its skeleton or its shell, or its imprint, or its internal or external outline, or its reproduction in petrified wood, or its residue : anthracite, bituminous coal, lignite or peat.

Paleontology has thus all the necessary documents for reconstructing the history of life on the surface of the globe. It is merely a question of finding, classifying and interpreting them. This is the work of specialists, at the present moment numbered by the hundreds and dividing the field among themselves.

4. STRATIGRAPHY.

We cannot terminate this rapid outline of geology without saying a word or two about the science of stratigraphy, which serves as a guide to scientists in drawing their conclusions.

The aim of stratigraphy is to determine the relative age of geological phenomena through the study of the strata

---

[1] *Revue des Questions scientifiques*, 1922, vol. II, p. 205.

and the order of their deposition, and thus, to write the history of the earth and that of life. It is based on the following principles :

1. Marine sediments are deposited in horizontal layers;

2. The lowest sediments are also the oldest, unless it be question of uplifted terranes or sediments;

3. In the terranes overturned by a violent uplift, the order of superposition of strata is the following, 1, 2, 3, 4 — 4, 3, 2, 1, etc.;

4. In the sedimentary terranes the order of superposition is 1, 2, 3, 4, — 1, 2, 3, 4, (fig. 16).

In other words, to meet with the series 1, 2, 3, 4—4, 3, 2, 1,

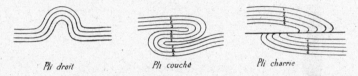

Pli droit   *Pli couché*   *Pli charrie*

Fig. 15. — Three principal kinds of Folds in the Earth's Crust. Pli droit = simple anticlinal flexure; pli couché = everturned fold ; pli charrie = displacement or fault.

would indicate a stratified fold, whereas the series 1, 2, 3, 4 —1, 2, 3, 4, would denote a sedimentary deposit. It may be remarked that whole ridges have been reduced to sediment distributed over areas more than 100 kilometers (62 miles) in width. Thus, for example, the sediment from the Central Alps extends over a distance of 450 kilometers (280 miles); [1]

5. The elevation of a ridge is posterior to the deposit of the last uplifted stratum, and anterior to the strata which rest upon that which is in uncomformity (fig. 12 and 17);

6. The fossils are contemporaneous with the stratum in which they are found, unless they have been, in some way or other, disturbed since their deposition;

7. A volcanic phenomenon is posterior to the deposition of strata permeated, covered or supported by lava;

[1] Cf. Termier; *A la gloire de la Terre*, Paris.

8. A volcanic rock is anterior to the sedimentary terrane in which it lies and posterior to the rocks which it encloses;

9. A valley is posterior to the strata which it intersects (fig. 16);

10. The order of elevation in river-terraces indicates the order of age. The oldest terrace is the highest (fig. 82). The channelling corresponds to a negative movement of the sea, or a positive movement of the continents;

11. The continuous strata are contemporaneous, no matter what may be the nature of the rocks which constitute the stratum;

12. All other conditions being equal, the same fossils

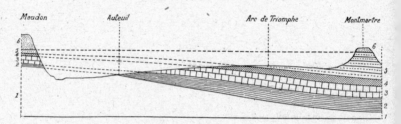

Fig. 16. — Transverse section of the Seine Valley.
(A. de Lapparent, fig. 692.)

characterize contemporaneous deposits. Thus, the trilobites characterize the Primary, the ammonites, the Secondary, the placental mammals, the Tertiary and man, the Quaternary   Each stage has its specially characteristic fossils;

13. The gaps in the series of sediments can be due to marine regressions, or to the action of erosion. The marine transgressions always cause abnormal superpositions (fig. 17). A section of terrane might be rather complex, so as to require the simultaneous application of two or more of these general principles, without taking into account others of minor importance (figs. 12 and 17).

Stratigraphy has succeeded in determining the order of formation of terranes in the well explored regions of the United States, France, England, Germany, Italy, Spain, etc.

The earth's crust has been divided into groups, systems, series, stages, substages and zones. We give on pages 86 and 87 a table of the divisions most generally adopted in France and in America. These divisions are altogether arbitrary, since the geological phenomena are continuous. We have

Fig. 17.

1. Archean Gheiss, greatly folded and vertically thrust. 2. Precambrians and
   conglomerates. 3. and 4. Cambrian. 5. Devonian. 6. Lower Carboniferous.
   7. Upper Carboniferous.

numbered these stages to facilitate their use. Their names are borrowed from the localities where the stages have been especially studied. These divisions have not all the same value. The depth of the sediments is quite variable. To obtain an idea of their absolute and relative importance, and of the duration of the sedimentation, as well, we need but consult the second table given below, prepared from data taken from de Lapparent's treatise on geology.

Table I.   GEOLOGICAL TIME TABLE. — AMERICAN AND EUROPEAN COMPARED

ERAS AMERICAN	MAJOR DIVIS. AMERICAN	GROUPS EUROPEAN	PERIODS AMERICAN	SYSTEMS EUROPEAN	EPOCHS AMERICAN	SERIES EUROPEAN	STAGES EUROPEAN
PSYCHOZOIC	Quaternary	Quaternary		Hedocene	Recent Alluvial Post Glacial		61 Recent
			Glacial	Pleistocene	Pleistocene	Upper	60 Reindeer Age
						Middle	59 Elephas primigenies Age
						Lower	58 Elephas Antiquus
			Late Tertiary (Neogene)	Neogene	Pliocene	Pliocene	57 Sicilian
							56 Astian
							55 Pleisancian
					Miocene	Miocene	54 Pontian
							53 Sarmatian
							52 Tortonian
							51 Helvetian
							50 Burdigalian
CENOZOIC	Tertiary	Tertiary	Early Tertiary Paleogene	Eogene	Oligocene	Oligocene	49 Aquitanian
							48 Tongrian
					Eocene	Eocene	47 Ludian
							46 Bartonian
							45 Lutetian
							44 Ypresian
							43 Sparmacian
							42 Thanetian
MESOZOIC	Late Mesozoic	Secondary	Epimesozoic Interval	Cretaceous	Lance	Upper	41 Danian
							40 Upper Senonian
							39 Lower Senonian
							38 Turonian
						Cretaceous	37 Cenomanian
			Comanchian		Montanian	Lower Cretaceo:s	36 Albian
							35 Aptian
					Coloradian		34 Barremian
							33 Neoconian
				Jurassic		Upper Jurassic	32 Portlandian
							31 Kimoneridgian
							30 Sequanian
							29 Oxfordian
	Early Mesozoic					Middle Jurassic	28 Callovian
							27 Bathonian
							26 Bagocian

PALEOZOIC	Late Paleozoic Carboniferous	Primary	Epipaleozoic Interval Permian	Permian		16 Saxonian 15 Autunian
			Pennsylvanian Mississipian	Carboniferous	Tennesian Waverlian	14 Stephanian 13 Moscovian 12 Dinantian
	Middle Paleozoic		Devonian	Devonian		11 Fammenian 10 Frasnian 9 Givetian 8 Eifelian 7 Coblentzian 6 Gadinian
	Early Paleozoic		Silurian	Silurian		5 Gothlandian 4 Ordovician
			Ordovician		Cincinnatian Champlanian Canadian	
			Cambrian	Cambrian	Ozarkian Croixian Acadian Wauroobian	3 Potsdamian 2 Acadian 1 Georgian
LATE PROTEROZOIC	Algonkian	Archean	Precambrian		Keweenauan Animikian Up.-Huronian Huronian	
EARLY PROTEROZOIC	Neo-Laurentian				Ep-Algonkian Interval Sudburian	
	Paleo-Laurentian				Ep-Archeozoic Interval	
	Keewatin Coutchiching					

SECOND TABLE

Archaean	lower,	10 000 meters (32 810 ft.) in Bavaria.
	upper,	6 000 meters (19 686 ft.) in the Central Plateau.
Precambrian	lower,	6 000 meters (19 686 ft.) in Finland and in the United States.
	upper,	13 000 to 14 000 meters (42 653 to 45 934 ft.) in the United States.
Cambrian		8 to 10 000 meters (26 to 32 910 ft) in Wales. 9 000 meters (29 529 ft.) in North America.
Silurian	:	5 000 meters (16 400 ft.) at least.
Devonian	:	10 000 meters (32 810 ft.) in Scotland.
Carboniferous		3 000 meters (9 843 ft.) at least, since the English Dinautian has this figure.
Permian	:	3 000 meters (9 843 ft.) or more.
Triassic	:	1 000 meters (3 281 ft.) or more.
Secondary	:	6 000 meters (19 686 ft.).
Tertiary	:	4 000 meters (13 124 ft.).
Quaternary	:	200 meters (656 ft.).

Counting in the known Archaean, the total sedimentation amounts to 75 kilometers (47 miles); from the Precambrian to the Triassic we should have about 50 kilometers (31 miles).

Is it possible to obtain an idea of the length of time necessary for the deposition of such a depth of sediment? It is. For by calculating the velocity of erosion, we can readily estimate the same.   These sediments came from previous mountain ranges, such as the Huronian, the Caledonian, the Hercynian and the Alpine.   De Lapparent has calculated that, at the actual rate of erosion, it would require some 5 000 000 years to level the continents.   Multiplying this figure by three, we shall have the time that was necessary to reduce the three earlier chains.   A maximum duration of sedimentation from the Primary period to our day should be 15 000 000 years.   Doubling this, for the Precambrian and the Archean periods, we obtain the respective lengths of the geological ages.   These figures are quite different from those uncontrolled values which are usually given.   It is not necessary to compute by the hundreds of millions of years for the duration of life upon the earth, for some tens of millions at the very most will suffice.   These questions pertaining to the duration of the geological ages are of little or no interest to theology, philosophy or apologetics. The natural sciences alone are interested in, and they alone would derive profit from the solution of these points.

We may conclude therefore : 1. That the main outlines of the earth's evolution are established. Those of paleontology are gradually being cleared up, but there still remains much that is puzzling even to the specialist. [1] The inorganic world is ever changing since it is subjected to the double action of external and internal forces. It tends toward a state of equilibrium which will be attained when all the available energy will be used up or dissipated, as we shall see when studying the question of energy. The world must eventually come to an end.

2. From the philosophical standpoint the conclusions appear both interesting and important. The world is not eternal; it is not sufficient unto itself; it has had a beginning. From this follows the absolute necessity for a First Cause, God, to give it existence and the necessary energy. In virtue of these points we see the natural or secondary causes at work. They have brought about the evolution of the various worlds from their primitive condition to their present state, and will continue their action until final equilibrium is reached and, with it, the dissolution of the universe.

Thus, the worlds which the materialistic school would have us believe eternal, would appear to have a beginning and an end; necessary, when everything shows their contingency, while they continually evolve; sufficient unto themselves, when at each moment they are dependent upon an anterior state. The universe was not created by natural forces, for the simple reason that there was a moment when they did not exist and that they are contingent, not necessary, nor eternal.

This study, far from estranging us from God, draws us ever closer to Him; far from demonstrating His action use-

---

[1] Cf. Termier, *Revue des Questions scientifiques*, 1920, p. 68 [sq., and Haug, *Traité de géologie*; Lemoine, *Traité pratique de géologie*, Paris, Hermann, 1922; De Margerie, *La Face de la Terre*, Paris, Colin.

less, shows it to be necessary. The contingent secondary causes call for a Necessary and Eternal First Cause. We may add that the admirable order manifested in the evolution of the myriads of worlds, supposes not chance but an infinitely intelligent Cause, capable of foreseeing everything, of regulating everything, of permitting, or rather of making the secondary causes act in such a way as to seem to suffice in themselves and to suffice for everything. *Melior est causa causæ quam causa causati.*

A more complete knowledge of the universe arouses in us a very legitimate admiration. For the more we strive to fathom it, the more we discover marvels hitherto unsuspected and evidences of perfect harmony —striking proof of the action of an Ordaining Providence. For there is here, not merely a question of combining the movements of three bodies under reciprocal influence, but of an infinity of bodies, of systems, of forms of energy, so as to make them pass from the primitive nebula to the present world, where everything is found to be marvelously regulated. The transcendency of this Ordaining Intelligence imposes itself with a certainty that no sophism can obscure. It is as evident to the most simple as to the most enlightened intelligences. To be an atheist; to pretend that the world suffices unto itself and has no need for a Creator is to shut ones eyes to the light, or to allow oneself to be blinded by materialistic prejudices, which are neither scientific nor philosophic, nor reasonable.

Caro was right when he said that Materialism is a preposterous dogmatism built up of negations without proofs, of ineradicable prejudices, of gratuitous assertions of indemonstrable hypotheses, covered over with a veneer of science to veil the weakness, the emptiness, the contradiction to reason which serves as its foundation. Whoever has read Büchner, Haeckel, Draper, Berthelot, Le Dantec, etc., must be convinced of the truth of this statement.[1]

3. From the theological or the scriptural point of view, does scientific cosmogony offer any difficulties? When

---

[1] Cf. *Dictionnaire d'apologétique*, art. Monde, vol. II, col. 876.

nterpreting the first chapter of Genesis, where some would
see contradiction to the sciences, we shall find that it
does not.   For, while theology treats only the role of the
First Cause: Creation, Providence, Concurrence, etc. [1],
without pretending to tell us how God operates through
the agency of secondary or natural causes, the natural
sciences investigate the role of the latter, and in doing so
they guard us against the danger of substituting them for
the action of the First Cause, and of making the former
play a part reserved to the latter and *vice versa*.

God appears to us all the more necessary, all the more
wise, all the more powerful, as we come to know His
works better.   More than ever, will it be true to say : " The
heavens show forth the glory of God." Such was, indeed,
the opinion of Newton, of Kant, of Faye, of Wolf, and even
of H. Poincaré.

ARTICLE IV

BIBLICAL COSMOGONY.

The first chapter of Genesis teaches us that God created
the world.   This religious document which Catholics hold
to be inspired has been the object of innumerable attacks
from the rationalistic school.   The partisans of this school
have tried to make out, that it is in contradiction with the
facts of Science, and, in consequence, have refused it all
credence, all authority.

It is the task of the apologist to show that the pretended
conflict between Science and the first chapter of Genesis
does not exist.   To prove this, we can invoke no better
testimony than the official teaching of the Church.   We
find it expressed in the Encyclical *Providentissimus* of
Pope Leo XIII, issued November, 18, 1893, and in a series
of answers of the Biblical Commission, establishing the

---

[1] Let us note, in passing, that we have not treated here the question of the Providence in the world, or of Divine Concourse.   For
these, see some work on theology or philosophy.

historicity of the first three chapters of Genesis (1909).
We shall first give the two texts, and then shall draw from
these the principle of solution. We shall then state the
main objections and, after having reviewed in a very
summary manner the various systems in vogue before the
Encyclical of Pope Leo XIII, shall give an interpretation
of the first chapter of Genesis.

§ I.—Extract from the Encyclical
PROVIDENTISSIMUS.

Congrediendum secundo loco cum iis, qui sua physicorum scientia
abusi, sacros Libros omnibus vestigiis indagant, unde auctoribus
inscitiam rerum talium opponant, scripta ipsa vituperent. Quæ
quidem insimulationes quum res attingant sensibus obiectas, eo
periculosiores, accidunt, manantes in vulgus, maxime in deditam
litteris iuventutem; quæ, semel reverentiam divinæ revelationis in
uno aliquo capite exuerit, facile in omnibus omnem eius fidem est
dimissura. Nimium sane constat, de natura doctrinam, quantum
ad percipiendam summi Artificis gloriam in procreatis rebus impres-
sam aptissima est, modo sit convenienter proposita, tantum posse
ad elementa sanæ philosophiæ evellendæ corrumpendosque mores
teneris animis perverse infusam. Quapropter Scripturæ sacræ
doctori cognitio naturalium rerum bono erit subsidio, quo huius
quoque modi captiones in divinos Libros instructas facilius detegat
et refellat. Nulla quidem theologum inter et physicum vera
dissensio intercesserit, dum suis uterque finibus se contineant, id
caventes, secundum S. Augustini monitum, "ne aliquid temere et
incognitum pro cognito asserant." [1]   Sin tamen dissenserint, quemad-
modum se gerat theologus, summatim est regula ab eodem oblata :
"Quidquid" inquit, "ipsi de natura rerum veracibus documentis
demonstrare potuerint, ostendamus nostris Litteris non esse contrarium; quidquid autem de quibuslibet suis voluminibus his nostris
Litteris, id est catholicæ fidei, contrarium protulerint, aut aliqua
etiam facultate ostendamus aut nulla dubitatione credamus esse
falsissimum." [2]   De cuius æquitate regulæ in consideratione sit
primum, scriptores sacros, seu verius "Spiritum Dei, qui per ipsos
loquebatur, noluisse ista (videlicet intiman adspectabilium rerum
constitutionem) docere homines, nulli saluti profutura" [3] quare
eos, potius quam explorationem naturæ recta persequantur, res
ipsas aliquando describere et tractare aut quodam translationis modo,
aut sicut communis sermo per ea ferebat tempora, hodieque de multis
fert rebus in quotidiana vita, ipsos inter homines scientissimos.
Vulgari autem sermone quum ea primo proprieque efferantur quæ
cadant sub sensus, non dissimiliter scriptor sacer (monuitque et

Doctor Angelicus) "ea secutus est, quæ sensibiliter apparent," [4] seu quæ Deus ipse, homines alloquens, ad eorum captum significavit humano more. Quod vero defensio Scripturæ sanctæ agenda strenue est, non ex eo omnes æque sententiæ tuendæ sunt, quas singuli Patres aut qui deinceps interpretes in eadem declaranda ediderint : qui, prout erant opiniones ætatis, in locis edisserendis ubi physica aguntur, fortasse non ita semper indicaverunt ex veritate, ut quædam posuerint, quæ nunc minus probentur. Quocirca studiose dignoscendum in illorum interpretationibus, quænam reapse tradant tamquam spectantia ad fidem aut cum ea maxime copulata, quænam unanimi tradant consensu; namque " in his quæ de necessitate fidei non sunt, licuitS anctis diverso modo opinari, sicut et nobis, " ut est S. Thomæ sententiæ [6]. Qui et alio loco prudentissime habet : " Mihi videtur tutius esse huiusmodi, quæ philosophi communiter senserunt, et nostræ fidei non repugnant, nec sic esse asserenda ut dogmata fidei, etsi aliquando sub nomine philosophorum introducantur, nec sic esse neganda tamquam fidei contraria, ne sapientibus huius mundi occasio contemnendi doctrinam fidei præbeatur. "[7] Sane, quamquam ea, quæ speculatores naturæ certis argumentis certa iam esse affirmarint, interpres ostendere debet nihil Scripturis recte explicatis obsistere, ipsum tamen ne fugiat, factum quandoque esse, ut certa quædam ab illis tradita, postea in dubitationem adducta sint et repudiata. Quod si physicorum scriptores terminos disciplinæ suæ transgressi, in provinciam philosophorum perversitate opinionum invadant, eas interpres theologus philosophis mittat refutandas.

In the second place the interpreter must take issue with those, who, misusing their knowledge of the physical sciences, scrutinize closely the Sacred Book, so as to take exception to the ignorance of the writers on such subjects, and thus disparage the text itself. As these attacks bear on sensible objects, they are the more dangerous, since they affect the masses, particularly the youthful student; for once these have lost their reverence for Divine Revelation on any one point, they will easily refuse credence to all.—It is quite evident, that just as the Natural Sciences, if rightly taught, from their very nature, are well adapted to show forth the glory of the Creator impressed in the works of creation, so are they capable of overthrowing the principles of sound philosophy and of corrupting morals, if perversely inculcated in youthful minds. Hence a knowledge of the Natural Sciences will be of great assistance to the professor of Sacred Scripture, as

by their aid he will the more easily detect attacks on the
Sacred Books, and refute them. No real conflict can
exist between the theologian and the scientist, if each
remains within his own province, bearing in mind the
admonition of St. Augustine, "to make no rash statements,
nor to give out as known what is unknown." [1]   If a disagreement should arise, let them conform to the rule laid
down for the theologian, by the same saint : "Whatever
they (the opponants) can demonstrate from true evidence
about Nature, let us show such to be not contrary to
Holy Writ and whatever they assert in their works,
contrary to these writings of ours, i. e. contrary to
Catholic Faith, let us prove as well as we can that it is
false, or unhesitatingly believe it to be." [2]   To comprehend
fully the justice of this rule, we must bear in mind that the
sacred writers or more correctly "the Spirit of God Who
spoke through them, did not intend to teach these things
(viz. the essential constitution of visible objects), matters
in no way conducive to salvation". [3]   Hence these writers
did not try to discover the true facts of nature, but rather
described them and treated them either as metaphors or
in terms conmonly used at the time, and which in many
instances are still in daily use even by the most eminent
men of science. In ordinary speech we deal primarily
and properly with objects that fall under the senses; the
sacred writer (as the Angelic Doctor reminds us) "concerned
himself with sensible appearances" [4] that is with what
God Himself, speaking to men, indicated in a manner common to men and intelligible to them.

A vigorous defense of Holy Writ does not exact that
we place on an equal basis the opinions which individual
Fathers or their commentators in turn, have maintained
while explaining it. For they, following the views of
their age, while commenting on passages where there is

[1] In Gen., *Op. imperf.*, IX, 30.
[2] De Gen., ad litt., I, XXI, 41.
[3] S. Aug., *ibid.*, II, IX, 20.
[4] *Summa theol.*, p. I, q. LXX, a. 1 ad 3um.

question of the physical sciences, may not have judged in
accordance with reality and so may have advanced opinions which are no longer acceptable.   We must, therefore,
carefully distinguish in their works what they hand down
in fact as of faith, or intimately related to it, what
they handed down in unanimous accord; for in the opinion
of St. Thomas, "in those matters which do not come under
the obligation of faith, the saints could hold divergent
opinions as may we". [1]   Elsewhere he makes this very
prudent remark : "In matters which philosophers hold in
common and which are not opposed to our faith, it is
safer, it seems to me, not to give them out as dogmas of
faith, even though, at times the philosophers so present
them, not to deny them absolutely as contrary to faith,
lest we give the wise ones of this world, occasion for con-
temning the faith". [2]   Although the interpreter should
show that none of the truths which those who study the
physical sciences give as certain and founded on strong
arguments contradict the Scriptures, when rightly explained, he ought not forget that at times a number of opinions advanced by them have later on been called in question and rejected.   And if writers on Physics, transgressing
their own proper limits, invade the province of philosophers,
by giving vent to erronious opinions, let the theologian
pass them on to the philosopher for refutation.

§ II.—Decisions of the biblical commission

On the historical character of the first three chapters of Genesis.

The Biblical Commission answers the following questions [3]:

Text—Commissio de re biblica de charactere historica trium
priorum capitum libri geneseos.

I. Utrum varia systemata exegetica, quæ ad excludendum sensum litteralem historicum trium priorum capitum libri Geneseos

---

[1] *In Sent.*, III, dist. III, q. 1, a. 3.
[2] *Opusc.*, x.
[3] Translation taken from "Rome and the Study of Scripture", by
Cyril Gaul, O. S. B.   The Abbey Press St.Meinrad, Indiana.

excogitata et scientiæ fuco propugnata sunt, solido fundamento fulciantur?

Resp. Negative.

II. Utrum non obstantibus indole et forma historica libri Geneseos, peculiari trium priorum capitum inter se et cum sequentibus capitibus nexu, multiplici testimonio Scripturarum tum veteris tum novi Testamenti, unanimi fere sanctorum Patrum sententia ac traditionali sensu, quem, ab israelitico etiam populo transmissum, semper tenuit Ecclesia, doceri possit, prædicta tria capita Geneseos continere non rerum vere gestarum narrationes, quæ scilicet obiectivæ realitati et historicæ respondeant; sed vel fabulosa ex veterum populorum mythologiis et cosmogiis deprompta et ab auctore sacro, expurgato quovis polytheismi errore, doctrinæ monotheisicae accommodata, sub historiæ specie ad religiosas et philosophicas veritates inculcandas proposita; vel tandem legendas ex parte historicas et ex parte fictitias ad animorum instructionem et ædificationem libere compositas?

Resp. Negative ad utramque partem.

III. Utrum speciatim sensus litteralis historicus vocari in dubium possit, ubi agitur de factis in eisdem capitibus enarratis, quæ christianæ religionis fundamenta attingunt; uti sunt, inter cætera, rerum universarum creatio a Deo facta in initio temporis; peculiaris creatio hominis; formatio primæ mulieris ex primo homine; generis humani unitas; originalis protoparentum felicitas in statu iustitiæ, integritatis et immortalitatis; præceptum a Deo homini datum ad eius obedientiam probandam; divini præcepti, diabolo sub serpentis specie suasore, transgressio; protoparentum deiectio ab illo primævo innocentiæ statue nec non Reparatoris futuri promissio?

Resp. Negative.

IV. Utrum in interpretandis illis horum capitum locis, quos Patres et Doctores diverso modo intellexerunt, quin certi quippiam definitive tradiderint, liceat salvo Ecclesiæ iudicio servataque fide analogia, eam quam quisque prudenter probaverit sequi tuerique sententiam?

Resp. Affirmative.

V. Utrum omnia et singula, verba videlicet, et phrases, quæ in prædictis capitibus occurrunt, semper et necessario accipienda sint sensu proprio, ita ut ab eo discedere numquam liceat, etiam cum locutiones ipsæ manifesto appareant improprie, seu metaphorice vel anthropomorphice usurpatæ, et sensum proprium vel ratio tenere prohibeat vel necessitas cogat dimittere?

Resp. Negative.

VI Utrum præsupposito litterali et historico sensu, nonnullorum locorum eorumdem capitum interpretatio allegorica et prophetica, præfulgente sanctorum Patrum et Ecclesiæ ipsius exemplo, adhiberi sapienter et utiliter possit?

Resp. Affirmative.

VII. Utrum, cum in conscribendo primo Geneseos capite non
fuerit sacri auctoris mens intimam adspectabilium rerum constitutionem ordinemque creationis completum scientifico more docere;
sed potius suæ genti tradere notitiam popularem, prout communis
sermo per ea ferebat tempora, sensibus et captui hominum accom-
modatam sit in horum interpretatione admussim semperque inves-
tiganda scientifici sermonis proprietas?

Resp. Negative.

VIII. Utrum in illa sex dierum denominatione atque distinctione,
de quibus in Geneseos capite primo, sumi possit vox Yom (dies),
sive sensu proprio pro die naturali, sive sensu improprio pro quodam
temporis spatio, deque huiusmodi questione libere inter exegetas
disceptare liceat?

Resp. Affirmative.

Die autem 30 Iunii anni 1909, in audienti ambobus Rmis.
Consultoribus ab actis benigne concessa, Sanctissimus prædicta
responsa rata habuit ac publici iuris fieri mandavit.

Romæ, die 30 Iunii 1909.

Fulcranus Vigouroux, P. S. S.
Laurentius Janssens, O. S. B.

1. *False Exegesis.*—Whether the various exegetical systems which have been elaborated and defended by the aid
of a science falsely so called, for the purpose of exluding
the literal historical sense from the first three chapters of
Genesis, are based upon solid arguments.

Answer : In the negative.

2. *Historical Character of the Three Chapters.*—Whether
we may, in spite of the character and historic mould of
the book of Genesis, of the close connection between the
first three chapters and those which follow, of the manifold
testimony of the Scriptures both of the Old and of the
New Testament, of the practically unanimous opinion of
the Fathers, and of the traditional view which—derived
from the Jewish people—has always been held by the
Church, teach that the three aforesaid chapters do not
contain the narrative of things which actually happened,
i. e. a narrative which corresponds to objective reality
and historic truth : and whether we may teach that these
chapters contain fables derived from mythologies and
cosmologies belonging to older nations, but purified of all
polytheistic error and accommodated to monotheistic
teaching, or that they contain allegories and symbols des-

titute of any foundation in objective reality but presented under the garb of history for the purpose of inculcating religions and philosophical truth : or, finally, that they contain legends partly historical and partly fictitious, freely handled for the instruction and edification of souls.

Answer : In the negative to each part.

3. *Historical Character of Certain Parts.*—Whether in particular, we may call in question the literal and historical meaning, where, in these chapters, there is question of the narration of facts which touch the fundamental teachings of the Christian religion, as for example, the creation of all things by God in the beginning of time, the special creation of man, the formation of the first woman from man, the unity of the human race, the original happiness of our first parents in a state of justice, integrity and immortality, the divine command laid upon man to prove his obedience, the transgression of that divine command at the instigation of the devil under the form of a serpent, the fall of our first parents from their primitive state of innocence, and the promise of a future Redeemer.

Answer : In the negative.

4. *Interpretation.*—Whether, in interpreting those passages of these chapters which the Fathers and Doctors have interpreted in divers ways without leaving us anything definite or certain, anyone may, subject to the decision of the Church and following the analogy of faith, follow and defend that opinion at which he has prudently arrived.

Answer : In the affirmative.

5. *Literal Sense.*—Whether all the constituent parts, namely the single words and phrases, in these chapters, must always and of necessity be interpreted in a literal sense, so that it is never lawful to deviate from it, even when expressions are manifestly not used in the strictly literal sense.

Answer : In the negative.

6. *Allegory and Prophecy.*—Whether, granting always the literal and historical sense, the allegorical and prophetical interpretation of certain passages of these chapters—an interpretation justified by the example of the

Fathers and the Church—may be prudently and usefully applied.

Answer : In the affirmative.

7. *Scientific Expressions.* — Whether, since it was not the intention of the sacred author, when writing the first chapter of Genesis, to teach us the innermost nature of visible things, nor to present the complete order of creation in a scientific manner; but rather to furnish his people with a popular account, such as the common parlance of that age allowed, one, namely, adapted to the senses and to man's intelligence, we are always bound, when interpreting these chapters to seek for scientific exactitude of expression.

Answer : In the negative.

8. *Yom.*—Whether the word *yom* (day), which is used in the first chapter of Genesis to describe and distinguish the six days, may be taken either in its strict sense as the natural day or in a less strict sense as signifying a certain space of time; whether free discussion of the question is permitted to interpreters.

Answer : In the affirmative.

In an audience graciously accorded to two consulting secretaries, June 30, 1909, the Holy Father ratified and decreed the publication of these answers.

§ III.—General principles for the solution of difficulties which may be raised in connection with scientific cosmogonies and the first chapters of genesis.

1. There can be no real contradiction between the Bible and Science for both have God for their author. In the one case He speaks through the book of Nature, and in the other through a book inspired by Him. The source of all difficulties lies either in a false interpretation of the Bible or of the data of Science.

2. The Bible and Science 1) do not pursue the same end; 2) have not the same object; 3) do not use the same methods.

1. The aim of the first chapter of Genesis is essentially

religious as is easily seen from the account itself, and as has been established by the exegetes of the Biblical Commission.   In fact, Moses wished to bring man to a recognition of God as his Creator, and so have him render the duties this title imposes.   Quite different is the aim of Science.   It investigates phenomena, inquires into laws and strives to formulate theories.   Every scientific cosmogony has for its end the writing of the history of the world.

2. Its object is likewise different.   The first chapter of Genesis shows us God, the First Cause, creating the world and everything that exists,   Science studies the nature and the role of secondary or natural causes operating in and transforming the universe.   The Bible does not concern itself specially with these natural causes, and Science has not God for the object of its researches.   These in reality are in the sensible order, that pertaining to God is of the suprasensible and intellectual order.

The first chapter of Genesis, then, is not a treatise on geology or scientific cosmogony, but what is of more importance, a popular narration of creation, a page of the most sublime theology.   Indeed we find there a very great number of dogmas, and among them some of the most important : the Existence of God, His Unity, His Omnipotence, His Wisdom,   His Providence, His Goodness : the creation by God of all existing things.   We find there, also, the unity of the human species : the fact of man's special creation by God, his supremacy over all creation, his duties towards God.   Incidentally we find here a condemnation of Atheism, Polytheism, Pantheism, Materialism under all its forms. [1]

---

[1] This is clearly the opinion of P. Hurter, S. J., *Compendium*, tract. VI, pars ɪɪ, sec. ɪ, n. 193.   We take the quotation from Vigouroux, who rightly attaches great importance to it. (*Mélanges bibliques*, 2ᵉ édit., Paris, 1889, p. 17.) *Advertendum est,* 1º *Moysis scopum non fuisse tradere doctas de astronomis, geologia, zoologia seu generatim de disciplinis naturalibus, sed institutionem tradere voluisse religionem* vulgi captui accomodatam;... 2º *De hisce loquitur non more physicorum et doctorum, sed concipiendi loquendique morem*

3. The scientific method differs from that employed by the sacred writer. Whereas the scholar endeavors to reproduce his thoughts in as precise a formula as possible, Moses has to adopt a popular language, adapted to the intelligence, the mentality, the needs of his contemporaries. This explains certain terms, certain classifications, certain remarks, a certain order followed, certain omissions, etc., to which the Biblical Commission makes allusion.

3. If, in spite of all, the contradiction seems to persist, it will be necessary to prefer certain scientific conclusions to doubtful exegesis. There is question here of matters in the scientific order, which do not lie within the field of biblical instruction. St. Thomas gives the reason for this "Lest the Scriptures be ridiculed by unbelievers." [1] Suarez lays down this general principle : "When the Scriptures are not compelling, opinions that are rather philosophical and more in conformity with reason should be followed." [2]

§ IV.—General resume of the principal objections advanced in the name of science against the first chapter of Genesis.

According to some there is contradiction between the biblical cosmogony and scientific cosmogony.

In effect the creation of the world could not be the work of six days, as the Bible seems to indicate, for Science shows

---

sequitur populi...   3º Inde sequitur longe paucura esse themata seu argumenta communia cosmoginiæ mosaicæ et disciplinis naturalibus ac plures contendere solent. Aliud tractat Moyses, circa aliud scientia naturalis suis observationibus innixa nihil certa statuere potest; hæc observat phenomena, inquirit in leges, secundum quas ordo præsens regitur, de quibus non est sollicitus Moyses; quare ipse, ut non nemo acute loquitur, prædationem veluti scripsit ad disciplinas naturales, exponens rerum exordia; quæ per insecuta sunt, relinquit indaganda physicis peritis, secundum illud Ecclesiastis : Mundum tradidit disputationi eorum.   (Eccles., III, 11.)

[1] St. Thomas, *Sum. theol.*, I, q. LXVIII, a. 1.

[2] Suarez, *De opere sex dierum*, lib. II, c. VII. Cf. Raingeard, *Notions de géologie*, 2ᵉ edition, p. 228.

that the geological periods were of immense duration and cosmogony postulates a much longer time for the formation of the heavenly bodies. The date of creation as arrived at from the Bible, would not show more than 8 000 years, while geology has good reason to demand some millions of years.

The order of creation would not be that given in the Bible, e. g., the creation of light before the sun.

The secondary or natural causes have had an important role in the evolution of the world, which fact is not taken into account by the Bible, since it shows God creating everything instantaneously and directly by the power of His will alone. Science reveals the world as evolving from its primitive state to the present day.

The Bible supposes that God created some things which do not actually exist, as the firmament, and which are but optical illusions : that it distinguishes things which have no objective reality, as light and darkness, the latter being but the absence of the former.

The classification of beings is not at all scientific and is altogether primitive. If the herbivora received the plants for their sustenance, the carnivora seem to have been strangely neglected.

There are objections also of a philosophical character which bear on the fact of the existence of God and of creation. These will be taken up in connection with the subjects of Energy, Life, Evolution of Species and the Origin of Man.

§ V.—Various systems of interpretation of the first chapter of Genesis anterior to the encyclical "providentissimus."

We shall find the solution of these difficulties, which are more apparent than real, in the interpretation of the individual verses of the first chapter of Genesis. We cannot treat *in extenso* the various interpretative systems employed to solve the difficulties which the first chapter of Genesis presents. They may be found fully expounded in the *Dictionnaire de la Bible*, and in the various manuals of Sacred Scripture and Biblical reviews. It will be sufficient to draw attention to the most important.

I. *Strict Literalism*, or *the creation in six days of twenty-four hours.* — This was the only system in vogue before the geological discoveries revealed the great antiquity of the earth and its long evolution. At the present time no one upholds it. It is, therefore, wrong for certain materialistic writers to say that it is universally held by Christians.

II. *Concordism*, or *the system of periodic days.* [1] — This system was brought into being in consequence of geological discoveries. In its multiple forms it strives at all times to find in the biblical text the equivalent of a page from scientific cosmogony, or from geology treating the phases through which the universe in general, and the terrestrial globe in particular have passed. In interpreting the word 'day' in the sense of a period, it has believed itself able to establish a true parallelism between the 'days' in Genesis and the geological periods. The biblical account would thus give us the chronological order of creation, as we find it in cosmogony and in geology.

Difficulties from the domain of Science. The weak point of this system is the desire to find in the first chapter of Genesis modern scientific facts, whereas it ought seek before all else the theological notions pertaining to God and to the works of His creation.

Such, indeed, is the mind of Leo XIII and of the Biblical Commission.

Concordists have not been slow to harmonize the difficulties that are constantly rising with the progress of astronomical and geological sciences. There was ever a new attempt to meet a difficulty which it had failed to foresee. It is easy to realize what an almost hopeless

---

[1] *Dictionnaire de la Bible*, art. Cosmogonie, vol. II, p. 1045, by Hamard; *Dictionnaire de Théologie catholique*, art. Hexaméron, by Mangenot, vol. VI, col. 2325. *Catholic Encyclopedia*, art. Hexameron, by A. J. Maas.

task it is to try to harmonize two things, one of which, Science, is constantly changing and the other, the Bible, ever immutable. The concordance of yester-year was not at all that of today. How useless were some of the true facts of Science which were not fully understood until the xixth and xxth centuries!

We might also add that concordance is lacking in the details where it would be necessary. The Concordists would have recourse to interpretations which are difficult to admit. It is enough to cite the case of the light being created before the sun. The Concordists place the source of the light in the primitive nebula : but if the light is anterior to the sun, it is also anterior to the earth and so could not illuminate the latter. When the earth was being formed, the sun had already been in existence, no matter what some scientists may have said, for, like the other planets, the earth is a fragment of the solar nebula, formed after the central body. The Concordists would also have recourse to electrical phenomena for the production of light on the first day. But all this is purely hypothetical.

Others have held that the sun, created on the first day at the same time as the light, could not appear on the earth until the fourth day, when the aqueous vapor would have been sufficiently condensed. Who does not see that the sacred writer is speaking of the creation of the sun and not merely of its manifestation?

According to others, geology shows us the continuity and the simultaneity of phenomena, without natural divisions : the geological periods are artificial. In fact, all the phenomena of nature are continuous. The oceans like the continents are formed slowly and only by degrees. It is the same for the greater part of geological phenomena. Hence, whatever was the order of the six days, the concordance, save for the creation of man, would have been realized.

Exegetical Difficulties.—Let us state that a real scientific revelation would have been necessary for Moses to write this page of cosmogony, and this would be contrary to

God's manner of acting. The word day, if it could be interpreted in the sense of indeterminate period, does not seem to have the meaning of a long period in the Bible. [1] All these reasons, strongly advanced and developed at great length in various articles and works, have gradually brought about the abandonment of this system of interpretation. Those who, like Vigouroux, were the upholders of it have come to recognize its weak points and have given it up.

III. *Idealism.*—This system of interpretation appears under a variety of forms. We might, perhaps, distinguish a Moderate Idealism and an Absolute Idealism.

Moderate Idealism holds that the sacred writer, in his account, follows an ideal plan which he has marked out for himself, instead of adhering to the chronological order of creation. He maintains that Moses does not speak of the duration, nor of the date of creation. This ideal plan is deduced from a study of the text and varies with the authors. However, they are all in accord in admitting the reality of the facts narrated, and their insertion in the compass of one week including the sabbatical rest. They are unanimous in admitting that Moses wished, above all else, to instruct his people on the most important points of dogma. God and His attributes; God and the works of His creation : God and Man. [2] They see, then, in the first chapter of Genesis, a page of Theology under the form of a popular recital, rather than a page from geology, as the Concordists would have it. In this they are in perfect accord with Leo XIII and the Biblical Commission. These two documents insist, in fact, on the dogmatic and not on the scientific aspect of the text; on the character of a popular narrative, conformed to the language and the science of the times and to appearances.

As to *Absolute Idealism*, let us simply note that certain

---

[1] Cf. P. Hummelauer, *In Genesim*, p. 60-65, for a detailed refutation of Concordism.

[2] Vigouroux, *Mélanges bibliques*, I, *La Cosmogonie d'après les Pères de l'Eglise*; Hummelauer, *In Genesim*, p. 49-55.

of its forms, denying all historical value to the biblical narrative, such as the Allegorism of Origen, are no longer accepted, nor, indeed, are the Hymnological or Liturgical System of Mgr. Clifford.

IV. The system which holds that the ideas in the first chapter of Genesis are borrowed from oriental cosmogonies is not susceptible of rigorous demonstration, for inspiration and arguments drawn from reason suffice to explain the contents of this chapter.

V. The system which sees only legends is neither Catholic nor Christian, nor in accordance with reason. A simple perusal of the first chapter suffices to convince every reader that is in good faith and is not misled, by the mirage of Babylonian legends, of the truth of this statement. These are not so much cosmogonies as ridiculous theogonies, and have nothing in common with the very pure monotheistic doctrine of this chapter. [1] We adhere to the Historico-theological system indicated by Leo XIII and the Biblical Commission as given below. It readily solves the difficulties, or rather forestalls difficulties.

§ VI.—THE HISTORICO-THEOLOGICAL SYSTEM.

The Bible explains the origin of the world in the first chapter of Genesis. Without concerning itself with the role of secondary causes, it goes directly to the First Cause, Which alone can be of any interest to it, because of the religious purpose it has in view. The sacred writer composed a work, not as a man of science, but as a theologian who wishes to make known to us, that there is a God and that we belong to Him.

He shows us God as the Creator of all that exists. From among His works, too numerous to mention, he chooses such as are, or appear to him to be the most important, the most wonderful, the most fitted to show forth the

---

[1] Cf. *Dictionnaire de la Bible*, art. Cosmogonie.—*Dictionnaire Apologétique*, art. Babylonie.— *Dictionnaire de Théologie*, art. Hexameron.—P. Dhorme, *Choix de textes Assyro-babyloniens*, Paris, Gabalda. — *Catholic Encyclopedia*, art. Hexameron.

omniscience, the wisdom and the infinite goodness of the Creator. He seems, also to choose the things which man is inclined to adore, those which man in his admiration had deified. The order adopted in the narrative of creation is one that is very rational for the sacred writer and his contemporaries. The expressions are accommodated to the language and to the knowledge of the time, in a way to be understood by all men at all times. It is on this account that he always speaks a language conformed to appearances, that is to say to the data of the senses, as has been noted by Pope Leo XIII, the Biblical Commission and all commentators. In the light of these principles, it seems we can give an explanation of the first chapter of Genesis which will solve all the difficulties that may be raised in the name of modern Science.

We shall take up the creation in six days as found in the text, and shall at once give the explanation which appears to us the most satisfactory.

The First Day.

1. In the beginning Elohim created heaven and earth. [1]

Moses here sums up, in a few words, the whole work of creation, and does it in a language accommodated to the intelligences of his contemporaries and of men of all times. In stating that God is the Creator of the world, he establishes the basis of all true religion, and refutes the legends and fables of paganism.

2. Now the earth was without form and void. There was darkness on the surface of the abyss. And the spirit of Elohim hovered over the waters.

The sacred writer had for his aim to show both the creative and the ordaining action of God. On the surface of the earth all is without form and void a *Tohu-Bohu*. The darkness came to increase the frightfulness of the disorder; but the Spirit of God hovers over the surface of the waters.

[1] Translated from the Hebrew text by Father Levesque, professor of S. Scripture at St. Sulpice.

He is about to establish an admirable order, and create the variety of beings described in the following verses.

3. Elohim said : "Let there be light", and there was light.

It is with the creation of light that the divine action begins.   For Moses the "Fiat lux" shows in an admirable manner the power of God.   An order from God, and light is created.   It would be impossible to sum up in fewer words a work so marvelous.   Here, no less than elsewhere Moses does not stop to describe the secondary causes brought into play.   This is not to his purpose.   He ascends to the Supreme Cause, and he shows us the work in a language that has always aroused the admiration of the learned as well as of the uninstructed.

The first difficulty arises here.   Why did Moses have God create the light before the sun?   Is it not in opposition to the facts?   Why has the creation of the sun been relegated to the fourth day?   The reason for this is very simple. Wishing to distribute the work of creation over six days, Moses had to begin with the creation of that which determines the days—the light.

But is it not unreasonable to create the light before the sun which produces it?   Not in the mind of Moses or of his contemporaries.   For, first, light appeared to them distinct from the sun.   Every morning the former appears before the latter rises, and in the evening the twilight is prolonged after the sun has set : for a time the light persists, even though the sun is hidden.   It was therefore rather natural to have the light created first since it appears first.

Then, again, for the ancients down to the xvith century of our era, the sun seemed to be fixed in the vault of heaven.   It would not appear reasonable, therefore, to create the sun before the creation of the firmament. This explains why Moses places the creation of the sun on the fourth day and that of the firmament on the third. The sacred writer has used the science of his own day, that of this contemporaries, not that of ours.   He would not have been understood had he spoken otherwise.

4. Elohim saw that the light was good. Elohim separated the light from the darkness.

The sacred author proceeds to show the goodness of the things created by an infinitely good God, desirous of lavishing His benefits upon men. This remark recurs after each act of creation. Might not this be to offset the errors of polytheists who affirm the existence of a good principle as the creator of the good, and an evil principle the creator of evil? For Moses it was otherwise. For him there was but One. All that It did was good.

Not less good was the separation of light from darkness, that is to say the distinction of days and nights. Then also we might suppose that, in the mind of the writer, darkness had as real an existence as light, thus we would have a simple reflection of the science of the period and, incidentally, in a popular language adapted to the intelligences of his contemporaries.

Though we clearly understand that darkness is only the absence of light, the first observers might have been ignorant of it, nay, not even have suspected it. Although they would see the one succeeding the other, the night spreading over the earth, they would see a simple succession where we see causality. We know from other instances how difficult it is at times to distinguish a cause from a simple antecedent. We should, therefore, not be surprised at this manner of expressing himself on the part of the sacred writer. Had not the Greeks and the Romans deified the dawn as well as the sun, and the night as well as the day? Finally might not Moses have wished to combat here also, some polytheistic error?

5. And Elohim called the light day, and the darkness night. It was evening, it was morning : the first day.

It is even thus that we continue to do, and we do not call night the absence of light. We would say: "It was morning and it was night." For the Hebrews the day began not at midnight as with us, but at the close of the day, around six o'clock in the evening. Here, again, it was necessary to conform to the received usage. We shall see, presently, why the work of creation is divided into six days.

The Second Day.

6. Elohim said : "Let there be a firmament between the waters, and let there be a separation between the waters and the waters." And it was so. [1]

7. Elohim made the firmament, and separated the waters which are below the firmament, from the waters that are above the firmament.

8. And Elohim called the firmament heaven.

Elohim saw that the firmament was good [2].

And it was evening, and it was morning : the second day.

We find here again the language of appearances. [3] The firmament by an optical illusion always appears to us as an immense vaulted dome upon which the heavenly bodies seem fixed. The illusion has been so strong, that it has endured unto the present day and is inevitable for one who has no definite scientific knowledge. The ancients have always held the existence of one or more concentric celestial spheres. Upon one was fixed the sun, upon a second, the moon, upon a third, fourth, fifth, sixth and seventh the various planets, and upon the eighth, the last, the stars. Why then be astonished if Moses speaks to us of the firmament? If he had done otherwise, he would not have been understood by his contemporaries. Here, again, he wished merely to say that God was the Creator of this marvellous spectacle which spreads out before us. He left to the scientist to discover the reality of the same

[1] "And it was so." In the Hebrew text and in the Vulgate this phrase is at the end of v. 7. Following the parallelism of the succeding days and the Septuagint and Itala.

[2] This phrase is not in the Hebrew. It is replaced by "And it was so" at the end of v. 7. Following the parallelism and the Septuagint and Itala it ought to be placed here.

[3] Cf. Ps., ciii, 2-3 "Who strechest out the heavens like a pavilion; who coverest the higher rooms thereof with water."

and to distinguish it from mere appearances. Supposing the reality of the firmament, it was quite natural to admit that it separated the upper waters from the lower. We often find traces of this theory in the Bible, especially with reference to the deluge. The fact of seeing the rain fall spontaneously suggested the idea of upper reservoirs. With our knowledge of the aero-telluric circulation of the water vapor, the role of heat and of gravity in this movement, we have no need for such an hypothesis. But the Science of the xxth century is not that of the xvth century before Christ. And, let us note, once for all, inspiration is not revelation. It adds nothing to the scientific knowledge of the sacred writer.

The Third Day.

9. Elohim said : "Let the waters that are under the heavens be gathered in the same place and let the dry land appear." And it was so. And the waters which are under the heavens gathered together in one mass and the dry land appeared. [1]

10. Elohim called the dry land, earth, and called the gathering of waters, the sea.

And Elohim saw that this was good.

We have here the creation of the oceans and of the continents. This is the result of putting the confused elements in order. This separation of continents and of oceans is necessary for the development of the fulness of life. It was necessary to act in good time, even before the creation of life itself. It was the logical result of the preceding separations : day from night, upper waters from the lower. Moreover, the oceans and the continents form two very important elements for the sacred writer in describing their special creation. The earth and the oceans had already been deified by Paganism. [2] It served

---

[1] Following the Septuagint and the parallelism of the preceding strophes.

[2] Cf. Dhorme, *La Religion assyro-babylonienne*, Paris, 1910, p. 65 sq.

his purpose, therefore, to affirm that they were not divinities, but the handiwork of God.

Creation of the Vegetable Kingdom.

11. Elohim said : "Let the earth produce grass the seed bearing herbs according to their kind, and the fruit-bearing trees according to their kind, having in themselves their seed, upon the earth." And it was so.

12. And the earth brought forth grass the seed bearing herb according to its kind and the fruit-bearing trees having in themselves their seed according to their kind. And Elohim saw that this was good.

13. It was evening and it was morning : the third day.

Moses comes to the creation of life. He begins, as is but natural, with the creation of plants which must serve as food for the animals. He divides them into two or three categories, after the then received usage; the grass the seed-bearing herbs and the fruit-bearing trees, just as we say : herbs, cereals, fruit-trees, etc., without concerning ourselves about the scientific classification.

It was not merely a question of creating plants. It was necessary to give them that mysterious power of reproduction. This also is the work of God. Wasn't it by this means that Moses wished to destroy the polytheistic error so widely diffused, which had deified this reproductive power? If life exists, it has God for its author. If it perpetuates itself, God has so wished it. This, then is the teaching of the Bible.

The Fourth Day.   The Creation of the Heavenly Bodies.

14. Elohim said : "Let there be lights in the firmament of heaven to distinguish the day from the night; let them serve as signs and for the seasons and for the days and for the years.

15. " And let them serve as lights in the firmament of the heavens to illumine the earth."

And it was so.

16. Elohim then made the two great lights; the greater

light to preside over the day, and the lesser to preside over the night, and also the stars.

17. And Elohim placed them in the firmament of heaven to light the earth, and to preside over the day and over the night.

18. And to distinguish the light from the darkness. And Elohim saw that this was good.

19. And it was evening and it was morning: the fourth day.

The creation of the heavenly bodies on the fourth day has thus its proper place. They could not be created before the firmament, because this was destined to sustain them. They could have been created after the light, since this was considered distinct from and, in a way, independent of the sun. The relative importance of the heavenly bodies, the sun, the moon and the stars, is indeed one of appearances and not of reality. Their role and incidentally their utility is manifold. Beyond that which we would ascribe to them and which we scarcely need mention. Moses sees one body for the day and one for the night. The stars that scintillate like thousands of little fires in the firmament, are considered from man's standpoint, as entities of minor importance. The sun and the moon have for their principal function the regulation of the seasons and the years. In time man as a husbandman had need of an accurate calendar, to know the time for the performance of various kinds of occupations. He had to consult his chronometer in the sky, as do we. The heavenly bodies supplied this for him. The Egyptian calendar appears to go back more than 4 000 years before Christ. There was a year of 365 days. Moses certainly knew this, and could not let the role of the heavenly bodies pass by unnoticed, and without reference to the First Cause of so regular a succession. When we, ourselves, wish to speak of the admirable order which reigns in the world and which presupposes an Ordainer, we draw attention to this mathematical regularity in the movements of the heavenly bodies, to this constant revolution and rotation; and even set our watches by them.

The Fifth Day.   Creation of Marine Animals and Birds.

20. Elohim said : "Let the waters swarm with a multitude of living things, and let the birds fly over the earth and at the surface of the firmament of heavens". And it was so. [1]

21. Elohim then created the great monsters of the sea, and all sorts of animate creeping things with which the waters swarmed, and according to their kind, and all sorts of birds according to their species. And Elohim saw that this was good.

22. Elohim blessed them while saying : "Be ye fertile, multiply and fill the waters of the seas, and may those that fly multiply upon the earth."

23. And it was evening and it was morning : the fifth day.

After having peopled the heavens with the celestial bodies, God wished to populate the oceans and the air. A very simple classification, but very intelligible, since in conformity with current usage. Again we have the popular language and the narrative adapted to the intelligences of his time and of all times. In the oceans God created a multitude of living beings which the sacred writer does not even attempt to classify, so great was their variety in his eyes. It was the same for the birds of the air. It is sufficient to note that the latter like the former are the work of God's hand, a work that is good. To them, also, God gave the power to reproduce themselves, and to multiply so as to continue in some way the work of creation. He thus draws attention to a fact for which philosophers would invoke the role of secondary causes, and notes that these themselves have been created by God, and are active in the measure that they are in accord with the injunction "Be ye fertile, and multiply."

---

[1] This phrase is neither in the Hebrew nor in the Vulgate.   Following the parallelism of the other creations and the Septuagint, Symmachus Theodotian and Itala versions.

The Sixth Day.   Creation of the Land Animals.

24 Elohim said: "Let the earth bring forth living
things according to their kind : cattle, creeping things and
beasts of the earth, according to their kinds."
And it was so.

25. Elohim then made the beasts of the earth according
to their kind, and all the things that creep on the ground
according to their kind.
And Elohim saw that this was good.

The logical order calls for the creation of the animals.
Their classification is very simple and popular : the domestic animals, great and small cattle, the most interesting
and the most important for man; creeping things, a rather
negligible number, and the beasts of the earth, designating no doubt, the wild animals not domesticated.
And Elohim saw that this was good.

It is always the same refrain to throw into relief the
goodness of every creature that is the work of Infinite
Goodness. Moses wished to convince man of this, and
to do so he repeats the idea after each new act of creation.
The zoolatry of the Egyptians of which the Hebrews had
been witnesses is thus condemned by this declaration of
Moses, that all the animals are the work of God. This
dogma was of special interest to an agricultural people
who found in the domestic animals all the resources necessary for their subsistence and their raiment, and was
necessary to induce them to give thanks to the Creator of
all these gifts.

The Creation of Man.

26. Elohim said : "Let us fashion man after our own
image and conformable to our likeness, and let him be
lord over the fishes in the sea, over the birds of the air,
over the cattle, and over every (beast of) [1] the earth and

---

[1] Word omitted from text.   Cf. verse 24 and the Syriac.

over every creeping thing that creeps on the earth."

27. Elohim created man after his own image;

Male and female He created them.

28. Elohim blessed them and Elohim said to them : "Be fertile, multiply and fill the earth and subjugate it.   Have dominion over the fishes of the sea, over the birds of the heavens and over every beast [1] that creeps on the earth."

29. And Elohim said : "Behold I give you every seed-bearing herb which is on the surface of the whole earth, and every fruit-bearing tree giving seed. Such shall be your nourishment."

30. "And to every animal of earth, and to every bird in the heavens and to every thing creeping on the earth which has the breath of life (I give) every green herb for food."

And it was so.

31. And Elohim saw that everything that He had done was very good.

It was evening and it was morning : the sixth day.

Man was to be the master-piece, the king, the high-priest of creation, the only one who could and had to know and love his Creator.   The sacred writer lets us understand in the first words what will be the greatness of this last creature of God.   "Let us fashion man to our own image and conformable to our likeness."   God, intelligent and free, will give to man intelligence and free-will; God Who knows Himself will make man know Him; God Who loves Himself, will make man love Him as the Sovereign Good, as his First Principle and as his Last End.   These words alone are an entire Theology in themselves, and sum up the loftiest conclusions of any Philosophy worthy the name. Science cannot elevate man to an equal plane.   Thus how puerile appear the objections which a certain so-called

---

[1] According to the Septuagint and verse 26 it must be read : "And over all cattle, and over every beast of the earth, and over every creeping thing that creeps on the earth."   Moreover the *hâyâh* beast of the earth, as it is understood in this chapter, does not creep.

science has tried to raise against this first chapter of Genesis, and especially against the creation of man.

But to continue the thought of the sacred writer. Created to the image of God, man has a role to play on earth. He will be the master of creation. "Let him have dominion over the fishes of the sea, over the birds of the heavens, over the cattle, over every (beast of) the earth, and over every creeping thing." Indeed, however great, however marvellous the other beings might be, man must rule them by his intelligence, and make them serve his needs. God created the first human couple, blessed them and said to them : " Be ye fertile, multiply, fill the earth." If man had never lost sight of this divine mission, that of giving birth to beings like himself, of thus continuing the work we call the master-piece of creation, what might not have been his greatness and the glory which he would have procured for God!

Moses knew man had become so perverse as to forget his true role, to profane the gift of God, to deify the vice of impurity. It was necessary to recall the divine doctrine; it was necessary, here, more than any where else to tell man : "God alone is the author of life, your mission is to continue His work as He wishes and to the extent that He wishes."

Before taking up in particular the question of the origin of man from the standpoint of his prehistoric condition and of his evolution, it would be useless to treat at this place the various problems which these subjects raise.

Divine Providence has given to the other creatures possessing life and the power of reproducing and multiplying themselves, the food necessary to sustain them. For some, the plants, for others, the fruits. The carnivora seem to have been overlooked, no doubt, by design, since they would appear more harmful than useful to man. But the 31st verse properly concludes : "And Elohim saw that all that He had done was very good. "It was evening and it was morning: the sixth day."

The psalmist will one day sing of the same work in a magnificent hymn of praise addressed to the Creator :

"Bless the Lord all His works; in every place of His dominion, o my soul, bless thou the Lord." Ps. cii, 22.

"How great are Thy works, O Lord! Thou hast made all things in wisdom; the earth is filled with Thy riches. May the glory of the Lord endure forever. The Lord shall rejoice in His works." Ps. ciii, 24, 31.

The Seventh Day.   The Sabbatical Rest.

Ch. ii, 1. So then were made the heavens and the earth, and all their order.

2. Elohim finished on the sixth day the work He had wished to do. And on the seventh day, He rested from every work which He had wished to do.

3. Elohim blessed the seventh day and consecrated it, because on this day He had ceased from the entire work of creation.

4. Such are the beginnings of the heavens and of the earth.

The sabbatical rest was imposed upon man to enable him to render to God the worship that is His due, and to refresh him after fatigue.

The weekly rest thus goes back to the origin of the world. To bring out its importance, Moses could not do better than show God working six days and resting on the seventh. There was here an evident anthropomorphism. This explains to us the division of the creation into six days. Moses did not at all intend to say that God required six days of twenty-four hours to create the world, but merely that He created everything, that He is the First Cause.

If he divided the work into six days, it was merely to impress this doctrine more readily upon the minds of his contemporaries.

Regarding the knowledge of how the secondary causes function in this work he says almost nothing, but leaves to us the task of investigating them with the data derived from reason.

Thus, comes to naught what has been considered the

great scientific objection—that the duration of and the recent date assigned to creation by the Bible, runs counter to Science which reveals its great antiquity. The Bible had an altogether different purpose than that of fixing the duration of the world's evolution since its creation. It leaves to Science the task of determining that.

To sum up. The first chapter of Genesis is limited to a popular historical narrative of creation, a page from a divinely inspired book of Theology to make known to us God, His attributes, His relations with the world which He created, with man, the king and high-priest of creation, and the duties of man towards God. The whole is presented under a form intelligible to the men of all times, in a language conformed to appearances, specially accommodated to the intelligences and to the knowledge of the period, in a sequence of six days in view of the sabbatical rest destined for divine worship.

We may add that nothing can equal the sublime majesty of these first pages of the Inspired Book. Nothing shows us better the divine omnipotence in action : *Fiat lux et facta est lux*; "Let there be light. And light was made;" or the infinite goodness of the Creator Who pours out His benefits over all His works; Who prepares a home for man with everything necessary for the complete development of all his faculties and for inspiring him with sentiments of veneration, of respect, of gratitude towards his Creator, and with a love that will render him worthy of divine love and the possession of God. Scientific discoveries can only confirm this idea of beauty, of goodness, of providence, of order, of finality which exists every where in the world. [1]

[1] Cf. *Dictionnaire d'apologétique,* art. Monde, vol. II, col. 87.

CHAPTER II

ENERGY AND ITS TRANSFORMATIONS
PRINCIPLES OF THE CONSERVATION AND OF THE
DISSIPATION OF ENERGY

§ I.—THE PROBLEM STATED.

The problem of Energy forms part of the question of origins, for reasons that it will suffice merely to mention at this place, before giving the demonstration of it in the course of this chapter.

These reasons are :

This question is the necessary complement to cosmogony, since Energy is the immediate cause of all the material phenomena in the evolution of the world.

From the study of Energy and its transformations we shall obtain a more complete knowledge of the exact role of the secondary causes, and of the necessity for a First Cause.

The principle of the Conservation of Energy is too often, either badly stated or insufficiently understood as, for example, in the following propositions : Energy (taken in the sense of capacity for work) is conserved. Energy is indestructible. Nothing is lost, nothing is created. The transformations of Energy are eternally possible. These statements are, as we shall see, either inexact or entirely false.

The principle of Carnot, or that of the Dissipation of Energy, is either passed over in silence, forgotten, ignored, presented as the negation of conservation, or its importance minimized or denied in the name of the evolutionistic theories, or of the monistic principles which it contradicts, because it supposes a First Cause which some do not wish to admit. [1]

A number of philosophical errors result from the false interpretation of these principles, or from the negation of the principle of the Dissipation of Energy. "The world is eternal since nothing is created and nothing is lost, be it matter or energy. There are but transformations of energy, ever reversible. The world suffices for itself and explains itself. It is useless to look for a First Cause outside of the world. Life and Evolution of Species are only transformations of energy. The physico-chemical forces are the only forces operating in living beings, including man—they suffice to explain the origin of vegetative, sensitive and intellectual life."

The objections based on this question of energy are at the pressent time very numerous, very popular, the best understood, but too often the worst refuted.

They form the basis of modern Scientific Materialism.

§ II.—Definition of energy.

The word Energy comes from the Greek ἐνεργεια meaning "work". According to its etymological definition, therefore, it is synonymous with work. From mechanics we learn that work itself is the product of a force by the displacement (s). $W = F. s$. If I raise a weight of one kilogramme to a height of one meter, I have expended an amount of energy equal to one kilogramme, and I have accumulated this energy in the potential state in the body raised. I can restore it by letting the body fall to the ground. It is because of this, equality that the word energy has practically the meaning of a force capable of

---

[1] Cf. Brunhes, *La dégradation de l'énergie*. Paris, Flammarion, p. 380-385. We can recommend this work to the reader, as it is from the pen of an eminent physicist who knew how to visualize the problem of energy under its most interesting aspects, and to raise a good number of questions. Cf. *Dictionnaire d'Apologétique*, art. *Énergie*, by the same author. Also *Catholic Encyclopedia*, art. Energy, by Michael Maher.

performing work or that of the work produced by a force.

Before giving the real definition of energy, let us distinguish the available or useful energy, from the total energy of a body, or of a system of bodies, for, from the point of view of present interest, they are quite different. The *available* energy of a body or system of bodies is its capacity for doing work, such as the energy of a waterfalls, of an explosive, of illuminating gas, of coal, etc. Man can harness this energy, can use it. The *total* energy of a body or system of bodies is entirely different. In calculating it, we are not preoccupied about the use to which it may be put. We may define it thus : The *total* or *internal* energy of a body is the numerical value of the whole effect which it could produce, if it were brought from absolute rest or from potential zero, or from an initial state; and reciprocally, that amount of energy it would be necessary to supply to bring it to its actual state. The internal energy of a kilogramme of water at 100° C. comprises the total number of calories from 100° to -273°, in addition to all the other forms of energy, mechanical, electrical, molecular, atomic, intra-atomic, etc., which it could possess.

We do not know the total energy of a body, because we do not know all the forms of energy, nor the potential zero of all. It would be difficult to say what the total energy of the sun is, for this twofold reason. We know only the variations of energy between two determined conditions, for example between two temperatures, two pressures, two electric potentials, two chemical states.

§ III.—A TENTATIVE CLASSIFICATION OF THE FORMS OF ENERGY.

Energy appears under forms so numerous and so varied that it is very difficult to classify them, in such a way as to bring out the relations which can exist among them. Nothing appears so dissimilar as gravity, heat, sound, light, electricity and mechanical energy, all of which are readily recognized and based especially on our sensations.

From the fact that all energy is due to motion, we could, it seems, have a classification, not indeed, ideal, yet very complete. The nature of motion characterized by its extent, or its period or by the object in motion, might serve as a starting point for the following classification : 1. Kinetic energy; 2 Molecular energy; 3. Atomic energy; 4. Intra-atomic energy; 5. Electric energy; 6. Radiant energy. Each of these includes many other forms, often bearing names so different as to mask their resemblances. Let us take them up successively to note their individual characteristics and their mutual relations. We shall thus get an insight into the unity of energy manifestations in the world and a better understanding of the two great laws of the Conservation and the Dissipation of Energy.

1. KINETIC ENERGY.

Kinetic energy appears under the forms of Gravitation, Gravity and Mechanical Energy.

Gravitation manifests itself under the form of the revolution and the rotation of the heavenly bodies, which include the nebulæ, the star clusters, the planets, the satellites, the comets and the asteroids, or under the form of external or internal tides on the surface or in the interior of the heavenly bodies, etc.

Newton discovered its law, and states it thus : Bodies attract each other directly as the product of their masses and inversely as the square of the distance between them [1]. It is the most general form of energy. In fact, we find it in gravity which operates on the surface of the earth and on all the heavenly bodies. In all probability it is to be found in molecular attraction under its different manifestations, in gases, in liquids, in solids, in mixtures, in solutions, in sols and in gels. We find it in chemical compounds and probably also in intra-atomic attractions and in electro-magnetic phenomena. Universal gravitation

---

[1] $A = \dfrac{mm}{d^2} K$; $K = 6. 7. 10^{-8}$ expressed in dynes for two masses of one gramme each placed at a distance of one centimeter.

is first in order of time.   Physicists hold that the existence of attraction in the primitive nebulæ was sufficient to give rise to all the other forms of energy, already mentioned.

Gravitation is the most unfathomable and the most mysterious form of energy.   Why do bodies attract one another?   Among the various explanatory hypotheses not one answers the question.   The pulsating spheres of Bjercknes offers indeed some insight, but does not explain either the vibrations of matter, attraction in cases of concordance, or repulsion in cases of discordance.   Gravitation thus appears the most intangible of all the forms of energy.   However, in 1919 and 1921 (Sept. 12) the *Comptes rendus de l'Académie des Sciences* described an experiment made by M. L. Majorana which would permit of a variation of attraction by its partial absorption.   Two spheres placed in equilibrium on a very sensitive balance are no longer so, if one of them is surrounded by, but without being in contact with a double-walled flask filled with mercury, or with a mass of lead equal to 10 tons in weight.   The weight of the enclosed sphere seems to be diminished by one billionth.   Slight as this variation may be, this experiment will without doubt compel a considerrable modification of physical, mechanical and astronomical facts.   Gravity acts with a velocity 50 000 000 times greater than that of light.   According to Majorana, it would be due to an energy flux continually emitted by ponderable matter.   We have here a very simple hypothesis for a very obscure problem.

Gravity manifests itself on the earth under the form of vertical displacements, and with an intensity that is different for all the celestial bodies.   It is only a particular instance of universal attraction.   On the earth, the value ' g ' or the intensity of gravity is 978.10 at the equator : 980.94 at Paris; 980.15 at New York; and 983.11 at the poles.   It varies in inverse ration to the square of the distance like universal gravitation.   At the surface of the celestial bodies, it is proportional to their mass, hence greater on the sun, less on the moon, very slight on the asteroids.

The centrifugal force developed by the rotation of the earth could nullify it, if its velocity were to reach 11 kilometers (6. 8 mis.) sec. Those who would be on the surface would not be able to verify the existence of gravity, though real. If they could check the rotation they would see the force of gravity appear, and gradually increase to a maximum. This proves how difficult it is for us to know all the existing forms of energy, their nature or their cause. Mechanical friction in fact invariably develops heat (or mechanical motion) or even light. Magnetic resistance develops electricity and *vice versa*. Why? Is it for an analogous reason? That is to say, by suppression of one form of energy which masks another and produces apparent equilibrium? Or is it by transformation of energy, one form becoming another, or one succeeding another? Often we shall not be able to say.

Mechanical Energy manifests itself under the form of displacement of bodies on the surface of the earth. Such is the natural energy produced by winds, streams of water, waves of the sea, marine currents, tides, change of position by living beings and their physical activity. Also the artificial energy of motors used by man for transportation, navigation and industry of whatever sort or origin : atmospheric, hydraulic, thermic or electric.

These natural forms of energy have been partially brought under control, utilized, transformed by man and adapted to his multiple needs, so that material activity and progress is measured by the amount of mechanical energy brought into play. This activity, one might say conditions the economic life of peoples and of nations. Only civilized peoples know how to put these natural forms of energy to profitable use. From time immemorial, men have known how to transform mechanical work into heat, but it is but two centuries since the reverse process became known, and less than a century since chemical and electric energy have been transformed into mechanical work and *vice versa*.

Mechanical energy can be represented as a potential state, where the body which possesses it is provisionally fixed, but capable of giving way to an exterior medium. Such is the case of a reservoir of water at the head of a fall, before use. Its formula is $W = F. s.$ The energy becomes actual when the body which possesses it is given a certain velocity. [1] Such is the case of a projectile on issuing from a cannon. Its formula becomes

$$W = \frac{mV^2}{2} \text{ or } \frac{PV^2}{19,6}.$$

2. Molecular energy.

Molecular energy resides in the molecules, and manifests itself under the form of molecular attraction or repulsion. We can verify its existence in a number of phenomena, which it will suffice to enumerate.

The change of volume in solids, liquids and gases, called expansion, tension or pressure, contraction and condensation.

Changes of state, or the passage from the solid to the liquid phase, then to the gaseous and *vice versa*, from the gaseous state to the liquid, solid or crystalline condition. These changes are called fusion, vaporization, ebullition, condensation, liquifaction, solidification and crystallization. Some take place with absorption and others with disengagement of energy. The heat of fusion and of vaporization is restored by the reverse phenomena.

Mixtures of gases, of liquids and of solids, are called diffusion (mixture of gases), dispersion (a solid in a liquid),

---

Mechanical energy being a function of velocity, it might be interresting to give a certain number of the greatest known velocities: aeroplane 85 meters a second or 306 kilometers an hour; sound, 340 meters a second or 306 kilometers an hour; shell, 1 500 meters a second or 306 kilometers an hour; Explosion wave of dynamite nº 1, 2000 meters a second; Detonation wave of dynamite nº 1, 7 000 meters a second; Shock produced by dynamite nº 1 in steel, 5 000 meters a second; Earth, at the equator, 465 meters a second; Earth's revolution, 30 kilometers; Mercury revolution, 100 kilometers; Solar system from 25 to 100 kilometers; Comet of 1848 at perihelion, 550 kilometers; Cathode rays 25 000 kilometers; α rays 10 000 to 20 000 kilometers; β rays 160 000 (acc. to Becquerel), 236 000 to 280 000 (Acc. to Kaufmann); Light, heat, electric waves 300 000 kilometers.

occlusion (a gas in a solid) solution (two liquids), absorption (liquid by a solid).

The elasticity of solids, of liquids and of gases, gives rise to the phenomena of tension, and of distension utilized by industry.

Sound, or the vibratory motion perceptible to the ear, manifests itself under different influences in gases, liquids and solids, in living beings by the voice when speaking; shouting or singing.

The circulation of the sap in plants, where the phenomena of osmosis, capillarity, diffusion, evaporation, surface tension, etc., come into play.

The Brownian movement, or the continual agitation of microscopic particles held in suspension in a liquid, seems to show the existence of molecular vibrations.

All these phenomena occasion an interchange of molecular energy, where attraction appears to play the dominant role, as if the molecules were ever in search of a position of perfectly stable equilibrium apparently realized in solids, and especially in crystals.

Molecular attraction would be an instance of universal gravitation applied to molecules. Heat, in acting on bodies, becomes an energy, antagonistic to attraction, restores the molecules to their former position of stable equilibrium. This molecular attraction seems rather closely related to atomic attraction. The cases of unstable equilibrium are comparable to the cases of unstable physical equilibrium of saturated vapors. [1]

3. Atomic energy.

Atomic or chemical energy is due to the atomic attraction, designated under the name of chemical affinity. It manifests itself in all the reactions that take place, be they of combination or of decomposition. These two classes of reactions are + or — exothermic or endothermic, that is to say they absorb or disengage heat.

If one of them, as $H_2 + O = H_2O$ is exothermic, the reverse

---

[1] Cf. Duhem, *Revue de Philosophie*, vol. I, p. 457.

reaction $H_2O = 2H + O$ will be endothermic. It is the same for all explosives, as C_2H_2, with the difference that the combination is endothermic, and the decomposition is exothermic.

This atomic energy can be measured by the number of calories disengaged, so will permit one to anticipate the amount of energy to be withdrawn, or to be supplied to a given chemical reaction.

The chemical energy stored up in coal and fuels is utilized in industry for motive power, heating, lighting, etc. Again, it is the chemical energy accumulated in explosives that is used for national defense. All industries are more or less dependent upon chemical energy.

It is in virtue of these atomic phenomena that the plants, under the influence of the actinism of the sun accumulate the necessary chemical energy for their growth. It is these phenomena of the chemical order that furnish the animals, through their food, with the necessary energy for their activity.

4. INTRA-ATOMIC ENERGY [1].

The atom is now looked upon as a very complex structure or sort of solar system with a central positive nucleus, around which corpuscles or negative electrons revolve, realizing a true mobile equilibrium. But the atom at times gives rise to very important manifestations of energy when disintegrating as for instance in radium.

The discovery, by Becquerel, in 1896, of the activity of the salts of uranium (uranium nitrate), furnished the first instance of this. It was found that this compound continually disengages energy capable of making an impression on a photographic plate, renders the air conductive, and hurls cathodic rays into space. In 1898, the element thorium, which possesses analogous properties, was discovered.

---

[1] *Revue des Questions scientifiques*, Oct. 1920, p. 379, 1921, p. 158; 1923, p. 475 et sq.; Perrin, *L'atome*, Paris, Colin; Berthaud, *Les nouvelles conceptions de la matière*, Paris, 1923.

Madame Curie succeeded in isolating the salts of polonium, and later those of radium whose activity is a million times more powerful than that of metallic uranium. It is obtained in the form of the bromide or of the chloride.

The intra-atomic energy in radium shows itself in very many ways. Radium ionizes the air, that is, renders it electrically conductive. It emits α particles or atoms of helium, at a rate of 136 000 000 a second and negatively charged β particles identified with the cathodic rays. It throws off γ rays which are identical with the very penetrating X rays. The α particles have a velocity of 18 000 to 20 000 kilometers a second (11 160 to 12 400 miles). The β rays, or rather the β particles have an initial velocity of 100 000 to 290 000 kilometers (62 000 to 180 000 miles) a second. The calorific energy disengaged by radium permits it to maintain a temperature 1.5° C. higher than the surrounding temperature. A gramme of radium disengages 132 little calories an hour. One kilogramme disengages 132 large calories an hour. It has been estimated that radium would lose the greater part of its weight and of its energy in 1760 years. One kilogramme of radium could furnish a total of 4 500 000 000 calories, whereas one kilograme of coal only furnishes 8 000. It is generally admitted that radium itself might be the product of the disintegration of other radioactive substances, and in disintegrating it gives rise to a whole series of elements as shown in the following table : [1]

	Atomic Weight	Period
Uranium	238.5	4.4×10^9 yrs.
Uranium X	234.5?	24 days
Ionium	230.5	30.089 yrs.
Radium	226.5	1730 yrs.
Niton	222.5	3.85 days
Radium A	218.5	3 minutes
— B	214.5	26.7 minutes
— C	214.5	19 minutes
— D	210.5	16.5 yrs
— E	210.5	5 days
— F	210.5	136 days
Lead	206.5	

[1] Cf. Tillieux, *Physique*, p. 442.

Radium seems to offer an example of disintegration of matter. We cannot produce these phenomena. For a greater reason we cannot bring about integration. [1] It is not at all impossible that all substances may be radioactive, but for the great majority the phenomena cannot be verified. The cause of this enormous energy proceeds, it would seem, exclusively from the destruction of the atom. In modern theories it is supposed that the atom has in itself, as a necessary condition for its existence, a special form of kinetic energy analogous to that of the solar system. It is the slow transformation of this energy which gives rise to all radio-active manifestations. Like a gyroscope set going at full speed, it appears inert and immobile, and offers a resistance proportionate to its energy. When its velocity abates it loses its equilibrium, rolls on its support or falls, and gives rise to new and very important manifestations of energy. Or like a top, which set going at full speed, remains stationary in a position of true equilibrium. After it has lost the greater part of its velocity, it rolls on the ground seeming to wake up from its inertia.

5. ELECTRO-MAGNETIC ENERGY.

Electro-magnetic energy seems to reside in the ether. It is difficult to say whether it is a conveyance of ether, or of electrons along a conducting medium, a vibration, or a tension. Perhaps it is all these at the same time, perhaps something entirely different. If we do not know its intimate nature, we do know, however, under what forms

---

[1] Much progress has been made within the last few years in the disintegration of atoms. So far nearly ten percent of the elements have been transmuted. Sir Ernest Rutherford in England has produced energy by transmuting six elements, boron, nitrogen, fluorine, sodium, aluminium and phosphorus. Miethe a German scientist and Nagaoki a Japanese experimenter claim to have changed mercury into gold. The Dutch chemists, Arthur Smits and Dr. A. Karssen, have obtained mercury from lead. While two Americans, Drs. Wendt and Irion, have changed tungsten into helium, through the intense heat of the electric current. Cf. Sharpshooting at the Atom. G. B. Seybold. *Popular Science Monthly*, vol. CIX, 2, p. 34. Also *International Critical Tables*, vol. I, p. 365, 1926, art. Artificial Disintegration of the Elements, G. Rudolf.

it appears. We know its effects, we can reproduce them, transform them, and put them to use.

Electricity and magnetism are the two principal but inseparable forms. *Electricity* can manifest itself under a static condition in an insulated conductor, and under a dynamic condition in a circuit, for it will operate under the form of direct or continuous current, or of a monophase or polyphase alternating current : under a difference of potential of a few millivolts or of thousands of volts, with an intensity of a few milliamperes, or of thousands of amperes, thus producing work of extremely small values, as well as of very great proportions estimated by the thousands of kilo-watts.

In our day, electricity has become the most extensively used form of energy, because it is so easy to produce, transform, manipulate, and transfer to great distances, through the agency of dynamos, alternators, transformers and motors.

Magnetism is as mysterious as electricity from which it is inseparable. It appears in the static condition in magnets, in the dynamic condition in electro-magnets, and in all circuits where an electric current is passing. No electric phenomena can originate without also giving rise to magnetic phenomena and *vice versa*.

But there is no reason why the two should be confused as is sometimes the case, for their effects are quite different, indicating two forms of energy, even though the ether conveys them both.

Ionization is a new form of electric manifestation which may profoundly change our notions of the nature of electricity.

A vacuum tube with three electrodes made use of in radio constantly hurls negative electrons from the cathode against the opposite wall of the tube. These electrons produce a real electric current, and have found innumerable applications in wireless and radio. They seem to be due to the constitutive elements of the negatively charged atom and are liberated at the cathode. All incandescent bodies emit them, and *a fortiori* the sun. They play an important part in the phenomena of the Aurora Borealis (polar auroras), of vapor condensation, of atmospheric electricity, and especially in the constitution of matter and the origin of energy. [1]

6. RADIANT ENERGY.

This energy seems to be due to the vibrations of ether, excited under special conditions by other forms of energy. The kinds of radiant energy are theoretically without number for there should be as many kinds as there are different wave-lenghts, $\lambda = \dfrac{\varrho}{n}$. Practically, however, they have been grouped into a very small number of categories, according to the effects which thay produce. Thus we have electric, calorific, luminous, ultraviolet oscillations and X rays, or ultra rapid oscillations.

Sound waves propagated in gases, liquids or solids, give us an idea or an image of these waves, propagated in the imponderable medium called the ether. The human ear can perceive a series of sounds ranging between 16 and 40.000 vibrations per second, representing 11 octaves. The formula $\lambda = \dfrac{\upsilon}{n}$ permits as to calculate the number of vibrations when we know λ and υ.

This same formula is used to compute the number of vibrations of every form of radiant energy. All one needs know is υ the velocity generally 300 000 kilometers (186 000 miles) a second and λ obtained by means of the phenomenon of interference. At present we know of electric oscillations exceeding 20 000 a second, the λ being equal to 15 kilometers (8.3 miles), and at the other extremity of the scale 60 000 000 000 electric vibrations a second with λ equal to 6 millimeters (0.2362 inch). The scale of electric

---

[1] Cf. Perrin, *Les idées modernes sur la constitution de la matière*, 10 conférences, Paris. Gauthier-Villars, 1913. Cf. Tillieux, *Essai d'un traité élémentaire de Physique selon les théories modernes*, Paris, Béranger, 1921.

vibrations is composed of more than 35 octaves. The series will be extended at either extremity.

If we take as a starting point, the twofold oscillation which would be produced once every second in an alternator, its octave will produce two oscillations, the second octave will give four, and so on. Beginning with the thirteenth octave, we have electric oscillations perceptible by the aid of detectors. The thirty-fifth gives 34 to 68 billions of vibrations a second. These are among the most rapid electric vibrations known. Wave detectors disclose those of 60 billion vibrations having a wave length of 6 milli-meters. Beyond the 35th are found four unknown octaves, at the 39th begin the infra-red or calorific radiations and go to the 47th. The 48th and 49th octaves comprise the red to violet light radiations, with from 400 to 750 trillion vibrations a second. From the 50th, 51st and beyond, we have the ultraviolet rays which can affect a sensitized plate. From the 52nd to the 64th, there is still an unexplored region. The new radiations found by the physicists Holweck and Millikan unite the shortest ultra-violet rays with the longest X rays. [1]

Around the 65th octave with 37 quintillion or 37×10^{18} vibrations, we have the different kinds of X rays ranging downwards to join the ultraviolet rays and upwards to other possible though still unknown vibrations. [2] These 65 octaves of electro-magnetic phenomena, discovered within less than a century, permit us to foretell others without mentioning the innumerable applications that will result therefrom.

---

[1] *Revue des Deux Mondes*, p. 936, June 1922; *Revue des Questions scientifiques*, 1923, p. 485.

[2] Dr. Millikan claims to have discovered a new ray with high frequency and short wave length. The most penetrating of the rays is calculated to be about 1-10 of the shortest gamma rays and one-ten-millionth that of ordinary light. This is a region as far above the X rays as the X rays are above ordinary light. (*Science*, 62, 445-8, 1925.)

§ IV.—QUALITY OF ENERGY.

A question comes up here which must be solved before we shall be able to understand anything pertaining to transformation of energy. It is : Have all the forms of energy which we have so rapidly reviewed the same value? Are thay equally available, equally capable of spontaneously giving rise to new forms of energy? The question has a practical as well as a metaphysical aspect, and so the physicist can and ought to take it into account as well as the metaphysician. The answer leaves no room for doubt. Whether we have water at a high or a low temperature, is not an indifferent matter. With all the calories in the ocean we might not be able to boil an egg. Similarly, we cannot arbitrarily substitute one form of energy for another. Although one large calorie equals 425 kilogramme-meters and *vice versa*, the engineer will prefer mechanical energy to heat, because it suits his needs better. It will be the same for electric or the readily available chemical energy. We must therefore distinguish the forms of energy from the point of view of their intrinsic quality.

For one and the *same form* the energy becomes more available as the potential is raised. We call potential, the difference of height, of pressure, of temperature, of voltage. The reason for this is simple. With an elevated potential we can obtain all the lower potentials. But the reverse is not true. There are then higher and lower forms of the same kind of energy.

The same distinction may be made between the various kinds of energy. Thus of the higher form we have mechanical, electrical, and chemical energy and of the lower, the different kinds of radiant energy—X ray, light, heat, electric oscillations, sound, etc.

Any form of mechanical, electrical or chemical energy can be changed into heat, but the reverse operation gives very poor results, about 10 or 15% in the steam engine. Mechanical energy may be transformed into electricity with good results and reciprocally up to 90 to 98%. For many cases of chemical energy we may say the same.

We may therefore consider mechanical, electrical and chemical energy as belonging to the higher forms of energy, since it is possible to pass from one kind to another with good results. A body at high temperature can give up heat to a body at a lower temperature and perform in this way mechanical or chemical work, so heat may, in this instance, be considered as a higher form of energy, though in a much more restricted sense.

§ V.—Quantity of energy.

We can evaluate the variations of the energy of a body or a system of bodies by the use of special units for each form.   These units are derived from the manner in which one from of energy is compared or interchanged with another.

The practical unit of work is the kilogramme-meter; the work naecssary to raise a kilogramme of matter to the height of one meter.   The unit of heat is the large Calorie or quantity of heat necessary to raise a kilogramme of water 1° C in temperature. The unit of electrical energy is the joule equal to 102 grammes-meter.

Knowing that one Calorie can produce 425 kilogram-meters and *vice versa*, it is easy to compare the different common forms of energy.   Mechanical energy is computed in kilogrammeters, molecular in calories or in kilogramme-ters, atomic in calories, intra-atomic in calories, electro-magnetic in joules or kilowatt hours, etc.   Along with the units of work, we have the units of power as the watt, the hectowatt, the kilowatt for electrical power, horse-power and the dyne for mechanical power. [1]

§ VI.—The sources of energy.

A source is a reservoir from which nature or man can draw for a considerable length of time without lowering the level, the temperature, the potential, the pressure, or

[1] *Text book of Physics*, or *Annuaire du Bureau des Longitudes*, 1921, p. 384.

the luminous intensity, etc. Such are water-falls, gases under pressure, the electric current, solar light and heat, etc. The source is continually being replenished, thus permitting it to maintain its potential and its constant supply. Rain and snow replenish the falls, the springs, the rivers, etc.

Among the sources of energy some are natural and some artificial.

Natural Sources.—At the head of the list we must place universal gravitation, since it seems to have been the cause and source of all others. Thus we have the *Sun* whose activity sustains the gravitation of the planets, the mechanical energy of the tides, of winds, of water courses, the molecular energy in the circulation of the sap, etc., the atomic energy in virtue of which plants grow and coal was formed, the intra-atomic energy, the electro-magnetic energy of the atmosphere and of the soil, the radiant energy of electricity, heat, light, ultra-violet rays, amounting to more than 38×10^{30} large calories per year, the energy even of living beings, while giving off heat, light and radiations indispensable to life.

Then again, as said above, we have the *water-falls* and the various kinds of *fuels* which sustain all human industry. These two sources derive their activity from the sun and supply man with immense reserves of energy for use in his manifold activities and to satisfy his needs relative to heating, lighting, mechanical work, transportation, intercommunication, national defense, etc.

Artificial Sources.—Man harnesses and transforms the energy derived from the natural sources, and thus makes it an artificial source to supply his various needs. Statistics published in 1915 show that man uses 120 000 000 horse-power annually. This will give us some idea of the important place that energy holds in the life of man. It is the basis of all manufactories. Lighting and electric railways alone absorb 75 000 000, steam railroads, 21 000 000 and navigation, 24 000 000.

The 75 millions were divided thus : the British Isles, 13 millions; Continental Europe, 24 millions; the United

States, 29 millions; the British Colonies, 6 millions; Asia and South America 3 millions. It is easy to see from this where material progress is making most headway. There is still a great future for hydraulic energy, since Europe and the United States use only 1/20th of the hundreds of millions of horse-power available.

Before man knew how to use energy, Divine Providence [1] had placed it at his disposal under the forms of heat, light, and ultra-violet rays. It had brought into being the plants which have been sustained ever since the beginning by solar radiation and whose remains placed in reserve in the bowels of the earth have formed the coal, that marvelous store-house of energy destined to serve the needs of humanity a long time to come. To realize the full importance of the sources of energy, it will be useful to examine the following statistics relating to oil and coal.

From 1857, the date of the beginning of oil production down to the end of 1913, the world production was 692 million metric tons (2 204 622 lbs.) From 1913 to 1921, between 500 and 600 millions were produced making a total of 1250 million tons. The total quantity of petroleum, at all places where it is known to exist, is estimated at from 5 to 6 billion tons.

The output of coal for the one year 1913 alone was 1 500 million metric tons. From 1880 to 1921, the total from all the mines in operation was 30 000.000 000 tons. The world's known reserves surpass the 7 trillion mark. [2]

In concluding this subject, let us state that the few million horsepower which man uses is an insignificant amount in comparison with the 114 sextillion which the earth receives annually from the sun. The day when this source fails, life will no longer be possible. We shall see later what is to be thought of such an eventuality.

---

[1] Cf. De Lapparent, *Providence créatrice*, Paris, Bloud.
[2] Cf. *Revue des Questions scientifiques*, July 20, 1922, p. 208.

§ VII.—Transformations of energy.

We may consider the nature, possibility and reversibility of energy transformations.

Nature of Energy Transformations. — Some transformations are homogeneous, others heterogeneous. The *homogeneous* transformations are such as produce new energy but of the same kind. They are due to the *difference of electrical, mechanical, chemical and thermal potential.* The latter is raised or lowered according to the exigencies of the case.

The *heterogeneous* transformations are such as produce energy of a different kind, for example, all forms of energy produce heat. Each of the forms of energy can, theoretically, produce the other forms. Mechanical energy should give all the others and *vice versa.* Likewise, electric, magnetic and chemical energy. Let us see whether it can be done practically.

Possibility of Energy Transformation.—The transformations are *natural*, if they are produced without the aid of external energy. This is the case of the *fall of potential* under its various forms, of the change of the various kinds of energy into heat, of the transformations of higher into lower forms, and of certain transformations of higher forms into other likewise higher forms.

They are *artificial* whenever they are not produced by themselves but require the application of some external form of energy, for example, the raising of the potential again, the passage of a lower form to a higher, the passage of heat from a cold to a hot body, transformation of heat into mechanical, electrical or chemical energy. They cannot take place except at the expense of at least an equivalent amount of external energy.

Reversibility of Energy Transformations.—The *reversible* transformations are such as can be produced alternately in the opposite directions; in general all oscillations as for example those of a pendulum. This pertains only to homogeneous transformations. In the case of heterogeneous transformations one form of energy produces

another of a different kind and *vice versa*. A dynamo
charges a storage battery, and the latter in its turn operating the dynamo would realize for a time this theoretical case of reversibility. Very few of these transformations are reversible. None of them are perfectly so
because there is always some heat or other available form
of energy produced. To have complete reversibility, it
would be necessary that the output both ways should
always equal unity. This, as we shall see, is never the
case.

The *irreversible* tranformations are such as cannot of
themselves restore their original energy. Such is the case
of all artificial transformations which cannot act of themselves, whether they be homogeneous or heterogeneous.
Thus water cannot return to its source; the difference of
potential cannot raise itself spontaneously : the difference
of temperature is not reestablished spontaneously; heat
does not restore spontaneously the form of energy which
produced it.

§ VIII.—Principle of the conservation of energy.

The *Principle of the conservation of energy* is stated thus :
In an isolated system the *quantity of energy* remains constant. We are here concerned only with the quantity
and not with the quality as is often supposed : with an
isolated system, that is a system which gives out nothing
and receives nothing from without. An isolated system
does not exist naturally unless we take the entire universe.
In fact every system gives out some energy. It receives
a smaller quantity. We can isolate a body or a system
of bodies, artificially, or suppose it isolated to verify the
principle in a given case. We are going to show the reality
of this principle for the different forms of energy, be they
homogeneous or heterogeneous transformations.

Kinetic energy. The *uniform* duration of the motion of
rotation, or of revolution of the celestial bodies is the best
proof of conservation of kinetic energy. The conservation
of mechanical energy, in the case of the lever is also evi-

dent. In fact the positive work is always equal to the negative work, $F \times D = F' \times D'$.

It is the same for a mechanical accumulator and for an oscillating pendulum. The potential energy becomes kinetic and *vice versa*. At each instant their sum is the same, for the one increases at the expense of the other. If the pendulum is stopped, a part of its mechanical energy is gradually transformed into heat energy, but at each instant the sum of the mechanical and of the heat energy is equal to the initial sum.

Even available energy is conserved whether in the potential state or in the kinetic state, when there is no transformation, e. g. the rotation and revolution of the heavenly bodies, an unharnessed water-fall, etc.

The conservation of *molecular* energy might be verified in the melting of ice and in the freezing of water. In the one case, 79 large calories are supplied to melt one kilogramme of ice, in the second case the kilogramme of water gives out the same number when freezing. The vaporization of a liter of water at $100°$ C. requires 537 calories. The condensation of the vapor should liberate the same amount.

The conservation of *atomic* energy is easily demonstrated. The energy given out by a chemical reaction is absorbed by the reverse reaction. For example :

$$H_2 + O = H_2O + 58 \text{ Cal.} ; \quad H^2O = H_2 + O - 58 \text{ Cals.}$$
$$C + 2O = CO_2 + 94 \text{ Cal.} ; \quad CO_2 = C + 2O - 94 \text{ Cals.}$$

For *intra-atomic* energy, we cannot perform the reverse reaction, that is to say the integration of matter, but we can state that the principle ought to be verified here unless we admit perpetual motion, that is to say a contradiction, or if you prefer, the production of an effect without a cause.

Instances of *electro-magnetic* energy. The transformation of the potential (F) and of the Intensity (I) can be brought about in every transformer and takes place according to the equation $E \times I = E' \times I'$, e. g.

$$5\,000 \text{ E} \times 10 \text{ I} = 50\,000 \text{ W} = 50 \text{ klw.}$$
$$500 \text{ E} \times 100 \text{ I} = 50\,000 \text{ W} = 50 \text{ klw.}$$

if we disregard the heat produced.

The transformation of electricity into work, and of work into electricity verifies the principle as shown by the formula $W = E \times I$.

It would be the same for the transformation of electricity into chemical work. To electrify one molecule requires 96 000 coulombs, and reciprocally the formation of one molecule produces 96 000 coulombs.

In conclusion, let us mention the transformation of heat into work and that of work into heat. A piece of work of 425 kgm. produces one large calorie, and one large calorie produces 425 kgm. The experiments performed by Joule and Hirn were the first important verifications of the principle of the conservation of energy. It goes without saying that we must take into account all the forms of energy appearing at the moment of transformation.

The principle of the conservation of energy, according to the experiments of Atwater, applies even to living beings themselves as we shall show later. Its extent is therefore general. But it is important to recall that there is question here of the *quantity* and not of the *quality* of energy, and that the principle applies perfectly only in an isolated system for the universe taken as a whole, since there is nowhere a naturally isolated system. Our solar system does not conserve the same quantity of energy since it radiates energy into space. It is the same for every star. Hence the principle loses the interest and the value which the materialistic school attributes to it, in attempting to rely upon it, as a demonstration that the world is sufficient unto itself. This is a scientific and philosophic error.

§ IX.—PRINCIPLE OF THE DISSIPATION OF ENERGY.

We see that the quantity of energy remains constant only in an isolated system. Does the quality, of which we have already spoken, remain constant? Is it conserved? Is it at all times equally transformable? available? To answer any of these questions, we must state and demonstrate a second law or second principle of energy. It is that formulated by Carnot or as it is called today, the principle of the dissipation of energy. [1]   It is stated thus : *Energy is constantly being dissipated,* that is being transformed into lower forms of energy with decreasing reversibility and *tending to a state of thermic equilibrium,* where every new form of energy would be impossible.   It could also be stated in this way : *the available energy is being dissipated.*   It is this kind of energy which interests us here, which has caused the evolution of the celestial bodies including our own solar system, which comprises all mineral, vegetable, animal and human activity.   The others are already unavailable.

To remove all misunderstanding we repeat : This principle applies only to the *quality* of energy, and that of conservation to the *quantity.*   The one should not contradict the other.   They are mutually complementary.   If the first law has been more frequently taught, more extensively popularized it is not because it is more certain, but rather because it seems to respond to a secret desire to see the world endure forever.   The principle of the dissipation of energy has attracted less attention, has been neglected, has even been denied, because it reveals a fact of minor interest to certain minds that have dreamed of an eternal world, a world without beginning or end, and sufficient unto itself.   Some have gone too far in their efforts to convince the benevolent reader that true Science cannot demonstrate the legitimacy of this principle, in contradiction to the idea of indefinite progress.   For some years past, however, we find the principle stated in the textbooks of Physics.   The work of M. B. Brunhes (*The Dissipation of Energy*) has contributed not a little to make it better known, and to dispel some of the obscurities that may have surrounded it.   We can give here only the main outlines of the problem, with a pertinent solution.   We shall first give the evidence upon which the principle is based, and then give the solution of some

---

[1] Cf. Brunhes, *op. cit.,* chap. *Le principe de la Dégradation de l'énergie.*

of the more common objections. We believe it is easier
to demonstrate this principle than that of the conservation of energy, since there is no need for an isolated system,
and since it is enough to note what takes place in nature
without any experimentation, to establish the fact that
everywhere and at all times energy is being dissipated. There
is only the embarrassment of making a proper choice, from
the multiplicity of arguments which confront the observer.

Indeed whether we examine the natural or the artificial sources of energy, we see them all being more or less
rapidly, but none the less inevitably dissipated. Let us
take a few instances so as to bring out more clearly this
fact of universal dissipation. The principle source of
energy for us is the sun. What becomes of its energy,
accumulated within itself by the mechanical work of
condensation? It manifests itself primarily under the
forms of light and heat energy. But what is of greater
importance is that it disperses its light and heat and
other forms of energy into space, at a velocity of 300 000 kilometers a second. It disperses it in such quantity, that
but a few millions of years will suffice to cool it off, as is
already the case with the earth.

Furthermore, the heat radiations have a temperature
that becomes lower in proportion as the distance from the
sun increases, and for this reason become less and less
available. If we take into consideration our solar system
alone, we might say that not only is its energy being degraded, but it is being lost since the radiations extend indefinitely into space. Even if it were isolated, the dissipation would be just as real. The heat emitted by the sun
would tend to warm up the whole system uniformly, so
that in time it would arrive at a state of thermal equilibrium. At that time no further transformation would be
possible. This would be like a steam-engine whose condenser would have the same temperature as the boiler.
No movement would any longer be possible. Thermal
equilibrium once established, no difference of temperature, nor any transformation of energy can be spontaneously produced.

We know only too well that certain physicists have tried to escape this conclusion and avoid this difficulty. But they have not succeeded, as we shall see when examining the objections of Boltzman, Spencer, Le Bon and others.

We may add that the sun, in dispersing its energy far out into space and receiving scarcely any from other systems, is destined to cool down more and more until it arrives at absolute zero -273 C. The extinction of this source of energy will bring about successively and rapidly that of others which are dependent upon it, as the circulation of air and water, the existence of plant and animal life, etc., on the earth. We have seen above how Arrhenius tried to get around this difficulty by having recourse to various hypotheses; one as weak as the other. We shall not repeat them here.

If we consider the character of these *transformations*, we notice that those only take place spontaneously and naturally which tend to degrade their energy, that is, only the lower forms and among them the very lowest, heat. This is true for all homogeneous transformations, since they take place spontaneously in the sense of a lowering of potential without being able naturally to reverse the process. It is also true for the heterogeneous transformations, in which we always note the appearance of heat as the last and only state. It is true for all forms of energy, from the kinetic to the radiant forms.

The spontaneous homogeneous transformations dissipate their energy solely by the lowering of potential. The raising of it is not and cannot be spontaneous. A bar of iron heated at one extremity will spontaneously distribute its heat along its whole length, but once equilibrium is realized, it will no longer reheat itself from one end, but its temperature will remain uniform throughout. Similarly, two bodies with different electric potentials, when put into communication, will acquire the same potential, without the possibility of spontaneously reestablishing the difference of pressure. Water never returns to its source by its own inherent power. To effect this it would

be necessary to expend a quantity of energy at least equal
to that furnished by the water-fall.

The principle of the dissipation of energy will be fully
demonstrated, if we recall that *all forms of energy give rise
to calorific phenomena*, that is to the production of the
lowest form of energy, and that *this radiates into space
and tends to thermal equilibrium* from which all reverse
transformation is impossible. In fact, if we review the
different forms of energy, from kinetic to radiant, we shall
see them all being transformed and ultimately resulting
in radiant heat.

Let us take first a case of kinetic energy. The principle of the dissipation of energy finds its exemplification
in phenomena of the highest importance from the standpoint of numbers, value, extension, and duration. Thus
in the condensation of the primitive nebula, we find that
the energy of gravitation has given rise to all the other
forms of energy, and ultimately to the heat which the
celestial bodies radiate and incessantly dissipate. It is
the condensation of the sun which explains the appearance
of the prodigious quantity of heat radiated during millions
of years. The same explanation holds for all the heavenly
bodies whose energy is being constantly dissipated.

At first sight, it would seem that there is no dissipation
of energy in the *rotation* of the celestial spheres, since the
motion seems to keep the same velocity and the same duration. Yet there is. The perfect stability of such a
system could be realized only, if the elements were unchangeable and move in a medium devoid of all resistance.
Now, these bodies are not unchangeable, for in a gaseous
or a liquid condition there exist the phenomena of tides.
These absorb mechanical energy, transforming it into heat
by the inevitable friction between the fluid and the solid
particles. In the case of the earth, between the water of
the oceans and the solid crust of land. This friction has
already suppressed the *rotation* of the moon, and tends
to do the same for all the celestial bodies. If it is imperceptible to us, it is because of the very slight action of the
tides compared with the sum total of the energy of our

system, and because of the short duration of our observation.

Is the *revolution* of the heavenly bodies in their orbits subject to dissipation? Yes, unless the interplanetary or intersiderial medium is absolutely devoid of resistance, for-in this case also, the energy exerted to overcome the resistance is transformed into heat, and the centrifugal force, for the same reason, ought to be diminished. Little by little, the planet should approach its center and end by being precipitated upon it. This is pretty well admitted. Cf. Poincaré, Faye, Wolf, etc. This is borne out by the phenomena displayed by the meteors, shooting-stars and the *Novae*. It is supposed that the medium, in which the heavenly bodies move, offers a certain amount of resistance, from the fact that it contains uncondensed elements, and since it is difficult to conceive how this medium which is capable of vibrating, can be devoid of all rigidity. Still even if we suppose this medium offers no resistance, and in consequence the heavenly bodies are capable of continuing to revolve indefinitely, the principle of the dissipation of energy would not be affected. In fact, it applies to the instances of *transformation of energy*, and not to those where the energy remains in the potential condition. In this latter case, we should have no transformation, since it is always the same mechanical energy under the form of active force. It does not produce any other form of energy, but is more like water in a reservoir. There is no transformation and consequently no dissipation.

We must not confuse this instance of continual motion, which is perfectly conceivable, with that of perpetual motion, where there would be creation of a new quantity of energy. Such would be the case if this revolution were continued indefinitely, in spite of resistance or the production of other forms of energy. Perpetual motion sought by the advocates of eternal evolution is inconceivable.

We must also consider the application of this principle to *mechanical energy*. It will suffice to consider instances on our own globe. All motion must overcome some resistance, is subjected to friction, is accompanied by loss of mechanical energy and the appearance of heat. The locomotive which pulls the train can only overcome friction if the rails are horizontal, the action of gravity if it ascends. In the descent, the breaks absorb the mechanical energy and are heated. The flowing stream and the rolling waves transform their mechanical energy through friction into heat.

In the case of *molecular energy*, the phenomena of condensation, solidification, crystallization and contraction, take place spontaneously with disengagement of heat. For the reverse operation an equal amount of heat must be supplied. Thus we have the dissipation of another form of energy.

Atomic energy offers even a better example. All the reactions which take place spontaneously change the higher form of chemical energy into the lowest form, heat. Such are the exothermic compounds as fuels and other combustibles. $C + 2O = CO_2 + 94$ large calories. The energy contained in the millions of tons of coal consumed by modern industry, is changed into radiant heat. Such also are the instances of exothermic decomposition like NI_3 (Nitrogen triiodide) $= N + 3I$ produced by slight friction.

Intra-atomic energy becomes evident by the disengagement of rather intense heat, to maintain the radio-active body at a temperature 1.5^0 C. higher than the surrounding medium. Radium therefore does not escape the law of dissipation either, in spite of what may have been said about it. It is not a creator of energy.

Electro-magnetic phenomena accompany all disengagement of heat at a rate of 1%, 10%, 50%, 100%, according to the kind of transformation. Joule's law shows the relation between the heat disengaged, and the intensity of the current used with a known resistance :

$$H = \frac{C^2\ Rt}{4.16}$$

Objections stated and refuted.

Let us now consider some of the objections. Very few authors have bothered about the demonstration of this principle, which, with that of the conservation of energy, governs the universe. While the latter has been brought into prominence, been popularized and exploited in all the materialistic theories, that of the dissipation of energy has been passed over in silence, ignored misconstrued, dissembled, even attacked and denied by certain popular writers. It did not fall in with their theories of the eternal duration of the world, of infinite progress of a Materialism determined at all costs to do away with the First Cause, God, and to attempt to explain the world by itself. So we should not be astonished if we meet with many objections to this principle. We cannot consider them all, but shall take up the most important, the most specious, and the most wide-spread. As an aid to a better understanding and refutation of them, and to avoid repetition, we shall put them into two categories — scientific and philosophic.

A.—Scientific objections.

The first scientific objection to the principle of the dissipation of energy is drawn from the stability of the solar system. It holds that there is no dissipation in the solar system. We have seen that there must be. The rotation ought to decrease under the action of tides, and the revolution terminate in all probability by a descent of the planets upon the sun. A like result seems to attend all the other stellar systems. If there is no friction, the principle of conservation alone must hold.

Another objection. If the solar system is not stable, if the planets are fated to fall upon the sun, this would not be the end of a world, but the beginning of a new evolution. In fact, the collision of two stars, yes the mere grazing each other would result in such a disengagement of heat, that they would be volatilized, reduced to a state of nebula, and the series of phenomena would begin all over again.

Such was the opinion of Kant, Arrhenius, Haeckel, etc.

The objection, though widely held has very little scientific value. At the moment of collision the two celestial bodies would have already radiated light, heat and other forms of energy. There would remain only their mechanical energy, already reduced by friction which has brought about the diminution of their centrifugal velocity. Thenceforth the transformation of this residue of gravitational or kinetic energy will nicely result in heat. It will represent a very small part of the energy of the original solar nebula. If it had been sufficient to produce the volatilization of two heavenly bodies, it would not be sufficient to restore to the system, the energy it has lost in the course of its previous revolution. In evolution and in action it would be reduced to the class of *Novæ*. Its energy would in turn be radiated in to space until extinction reoccurs. This is not all. Calculation proves that the new volume of the two bodies would not be more than the fourth part of the original. A new collision would produce less heat and so on, until it would be insufficient to volatilize the substances. Just like a rubber ball that rebounds two or three times and falls to the ground, inert.

Arrhenius, evidently recognizing the all too manifest insufficiency of the collision theory, has attempted to give a more complex but equally insufficient solution. For him the light of the sun, acting on its molecules, repels them far from the sun. At a certain distance, their mutual attraction being stronger than the repelling force of the light, they coalesce to form a new nebula. Would not this merely have to evolve to form another sun?

We have already expressed our opinion of this more imaginative than scientific hypothesis. We may say the same for all those ill-intentioned popularizers who would have us believe in the birth of new worlds.

Could we not as some one has said, suppose that the radiated energy, on arriving at the limits of the universe, is reflected as from a concave mirror, and then is concentrated at different points where it will be able to

re-enkindle extinct celestial bodies that might happe
to pass through these imaginary foci? This would indee
be a perfect solution if only the most elementary laws o
physics were not opposed to the desired result. As a matte
of fact such a focus can never supply as high a temp
erature as the source. We might also ask, how we ar
to imagine this immense reflector and these foci? Hov
to conceive the possibility of an extinct heavenly body
passing very rapidly through these hypothetical foci
being instantaneously supplied with the energy necessary
to reenkindle it and render it capable of again radiating
energy for thousands, if not millions of years more?

Perhaps radium may come to the aid of Materialism.
It was at first supposed that this substance was infinitely active, a little eternity in itself, but this notion has
since been considerably modified. Whatever be its power,
it gradually decreases, and in 1775 years it loses most of
its activity. So on to the end.

Some venture another explanation. Thus G. le Bon,
in his *Evolution of Forces*, tries to show how radioactivity
can explain the eternity of the world. We give but a
summary of his idea. Radio-activity is for him the dematerialization of matter. The latter returns to a state of
energy or ether. Energy or ether in its turn becomes
matter again in being transformed into radium. Thus
the circle is complete. Very simple. The world is eternal. [1]

This seems to be a revival of Lavoisier's principle of the
conservation of matter. We shall it is true see radium
being transformed into other substances, among which
is helium. We shall see it desengaging electricity, heat,
X rays and other forms of energy, but we shall not witness
the annihilation or the dematerialization of matter.
Radium presents one of the most interesting cases of transformation of matter, and of energy, but there is no transformation of matter into energy.

[1] For further details, see Le Bon, *Evolution of Forces*, Appleton;
Perrin, *Atomes*, p. 278.

However ignorant we may be about the intimate nature of either, we must not confound them. A vibration supposes a vibrating body, but the one is not the other, so energy is not matter. [1] But might it not be true, or ought we not accept the theory that matter and energy are but two states of the same thing, say the ether? Here again we should have the task of explaining this new perpetual motion which unceasingly creates energy, without being exhausted. Indeed radium radiates its energy into space. It leaves its residue inert. By what mechanism can these same rays and this same material residue be reunited to reform radium? Whence will they obtain their energy? G. Le Bon has not yet solved this little problem.

Radium, no more than any other substance, can create energy. It is simply an accumulator, a transformer of energy. It must also draw its energy from other sources, perhaps under the influence of the high temperatures and great pressure at the center of the celestial bodies. When it has once dispensed its energy it cannot recover it.

One might suppose that the xxth century had seen the entire disappearance of searchers after "Perpetual Motion". It does not exist. But Spencer believed he had found a solution, not merely for one particular instance, but for all cases. In his *First Principles*, p. 429 and 519, he states his law of the instability of a homogeneous substance. For Spencer homogeneity is a condition of unstable equilibrium. All physicists hold that the opposite is true for matter and energy. And they have good reason for supposing so. Is not a crystal a homogeneous substance and does it not present the maximum of stability? Is a gas at a homogeneous temperature going to become spontaneoulsy heated and cooled? Does a liquid or a solid behave differently?

It is surprising what proofs Spencer adduces in support of his law. "Heat a bullet" says he, "and then leave it

---

[1] Cf. L. Poincaré, *New Physics and its Evolution*, Appleton; Verronet, *Revue générale des Sciences*, 1923, p. 165 et sq.

to itself.   Soon the exterior will be less hot than the interior. '' We add : '' Wait a moment, and the temperature will become uniform and homogeneous to vary no more. '' He also cites the case of a balance oscillating in vacuo. But this is an index of its stability.   It tends towards equilibrium and arrives at it. [1]

Spencer also mentions the case of a homogeneous nebula (matter) becoming spontaneously heterogeneous (energy). He concludes from it the possibility, of passing from a homogeneous to a heterogeneous substance, from stable equilibrium to unstable.   There is here an evident defect of reasoning based on the confusion of the terms homogeneous and stable, or homogeneity of matter and the homogeneity of energy. *Material homogeneity* is not synonymous with *stability or instability of energy*.   These are two distinct questions.   Stability of energy is the absence of a difference of potential.   Hence spontaneous transformation is impossible.   Instability of energy is the difference of potential.   Hence natural spontaneous transformation is possible.   Material homogeneity is the identity of the elements and the identity of distribution. An available energy acting on a homogeneous mass can render it heterogeneous and *vice versa*.   Such is the case of a nebula subjected to the action of molecular attraction, that will group the molecules, will make them collide and will also produce other forms of energy.   *The nebula then is not in stable equilibrium, although materially homogeneous.* It is in unstable equilibrium and this suffices to explain its evolution.

The pendulum at rest is in stable equilibrium, it will not depart from it.   The nebula completely evolved, with its energy transformed into uniform heat, will not depart from this conditions of stable equilibrium, although it might be materially heterogeneous.   The famous law of Spencer, therefore, is based upon a confusion of terms.

Another scientific error is made when we say that potential energy becomes actual, and *vice versa indefini-*

[1] Cf. Brunhes, *op. cit.*, p. 348.

tely.[1] Or under another form the present world is in a descendant phase; it will one day, like the pendulum, pass through the ascendant phase. [2]

The pendulum and the rubber ball, taken as examples, prove exactly the contrary, since their energy is gradually being dissipated and they finally come to complete rest. Their mechanical energy is transformed into heat energy, which is then radiated into space and lost for ever to the pendulum and to the ball, which of themselves cannot recover it, so as to set themselves in motion again. We may even say, these are cases of perfect irreversibility. We do not represent a pendulum in equilibrium spontaneously causing itself to oscillate after finally coming to rest. We do not represent streams flowing upwards to their source, nor decomposing fruit reascending the tree and evolving in the opposite direction. And yet if reversibility were possible, these facts ought to take place. It would be easy to extend the list of improbabilities and of impossibilities which the reversibility of the phenomena in the universe supposes.

Gustave Le Bon would attach much importance to the idea that there may have existed, at different periods of the universe, laws radically different from those which we know. But then, what becomes of the constancy of the laws of nature so often adduced? This is not metaphysical mockery. We speak in the name of Science.

Do the numerous physical and chemical phenomena such as fusion and freezing, vaporisation and condensation, composition and decomposition, charging and discharging storage batteries, prove, as some contend, the possibility and the reality of a cycle or perpetual motion? Not at all. All these phenomena are accompanied by a disengagement of heat and as a result by dissipation of energy. Furthermore, these partially reversible transformations rapidly come to an end. If the battery can, while discharging, operate a motor, and the latter operate

[1] Cf. Hæckel, *Riddle of the Universe*.
[2] L. Poincaré, *op. cit.*

as a dynamo to recharge the battery, it is evident that the action would not last for a very long time. (The usual efficiency of a storage battery is only 75 %.) This holds good for any and all cases that may be cited. There is always dissipation of energy under the form of heat, and as a result the system must come to a stop.

The Brownian movement has also been put forward as supporting perpetual motion. Can it be continual? Perhaps. Perpetual? No. It is always possible to suppress or augment the viscosity of the liquid in which it is produced. It is undoubtedly the result of various molecular influences of the liquid on the microscopic particles which are held in suspension. It would be necessary to know the theory of molecular movements to be able to explain the Brownian movement. If we admit the kinetic theory of gases, we can have two hypotheses. Either the medium offers no resistance to the movement, and then the latter continues without transformations and in consequence uselessly, or the medium is resistant, and then the energy is dissipated.

Let us note that the principle of dissipation of energy might encounter one limited case, as that of the ideal pendulum where the friction being nil, no heat would be produced. We may say, in this case, the principle of conservation of energy alone would apply, but the system could not do any useful work.

Might there not be living beings at least, capable of restoring their lost energy and thus prevent all dissipation? Living beings partially restore a certain amount of energy, only to let it be dissipated later on. Hence they merely retard dissipation, but do not prevent it. The instance of plants utilizing the solar radiations to form combustible products is a better example. The nitrogen and carbon cycles in the vegetable and the animal kingdoms can only continue, on condition that solar energy is constantly supplied. The day the sun ceases to radiate energy, all vital movement will be arrested upon the earth. This will constitute the most important and the most irreparable instance of energy dissipation.

All the objections from the realm of Science which, it was imagined, would show that the principle of dissipation of energy was defective and untenable, are vain, have no scientific basis and are in opposition to the data of observation, of experience and of reason.

B. — PHILOSOPHIC OBJECTIONS.

The objections of the philosophical order have no more value than those from Science. To be convinced of this it will be enough to sum up those that seem most important.

The agnostic holds, we are ignorant of all forces, all forms of energy, all possible transformations and all the laws of these transformations; we do not know the quality or the quantity of the energy which our solar system possesses, *a fortiori* that of the other celestial bodies; hence we cannot apply the principle to our solar system nor to the universe in general.

Let us frankly admit there is still a great amount of ignorance and uncertainty about these points, some of it real, some fanciful. It might be advisable to separate the one class from the other. But even if we are quite ignorant of some things, it would not be wrong to try to give a scientific explanation. It should not be necessary to be inconsistent, to give a little weight to these assertions. There is no need to be cognizant of all the forms of energy to assert that the principle is true. According to what we have already said, though our ignorance on this subject may be profound, still we know quite a number of the forms of energy, their laws, their transformations, their qualities and their quantity. Now, it is of these forms of energy that we speak, in announcing the principle of the dissipation of energy. We verified the principle in all the cases of energy transformation. This was more than necessary to establish its reality. Then even if new forms of energy, new transformations should be shown to exist, they would in no way change the actual fact of dissipation. If the new forms of energy would not be dissipated (a thing that is hardly possible) it would still remain true that a part of the energy of the universe is being

dissipated, and as a consequence very slowly, but just a
surely tending to a limit. As the stars are only othe
suns, it is evident that the principle applies to them also.

There are some who contend that this law is only *prob
able* and not certain, and therefore there still exists
possibility that the energy is spontaneously restored
Boltzman upheld this thesis and tried to prove it.   Maxwel
brought in his "celebrated demon". Arrhenius hi
constantly cooling nebula.

Here is the way the advocates of this theory argue
The final thermal equilibrium can be prevented, if the
molecular equilibrium of two intimately mixed gases car
be produced, that is, if the two gases can separate spontaneously or if a difference of temperature can be spontaneously produced.

Now the kinetic theory of gases together with an estimate of probabilities will show that some mixtures of
gases can separate automatically. Let us take a liter
mixture of O and H. Let us suppose the container divided
into two compartments. The molecules of O and of H being
in continual motion will arrive at a point where all the
O is on one side, and all the H on the other. The law of
probabilities would give the chances of separation. If
there were ten molecules the probability would be
1/3 628 000. Now one gramme of H contains 10^{22} atoms.
On calculation we find not merely one chance in a billion
years, but one chance in unity followed by a billion
ciphers. We may say that the advocates of the hypothesis will find the probability of the chances being equal
very slight. Even were it realized it would not last a
fraction of a second, and we should have a homogeneous
mixture again. It seems that the principle of the dissipation of energy has the value of a mathematical certitude.
A fortiori, if instead of a cubic decimeter of gas, we took
all the gas and all the forms of energy in the universe.
Yes, more than this, the causes which influence diffusion
exist and the mixture remains forever homogeneous.

For certain writers, like Haeckel, Arrhenius and al., the
world is *infinite*, matter is infinite, energy is infinite and

the possible transformations infinite.   From this it would follow that the principle of dissipation of energy would have no importance, or would not apply to the universe. Assertions of this kind need not be discussed, although they are very wide-spread, and are accepted with all confidence because made in the name of Science.

Let us distinguish the question of fact from that of possibility.   As a fact the world is not infinite.   The proof for it is that the stars and the nebulæ which compose the world are finite in number, that there is a possibility of increasing their number in space, of conceiving the number as being double, triple or tenfold, etc.   It is merely time wasted to insist on this.

Furthermore for *infinity to be actually realized*, when there is question of number or dimensions, is a contradiction. Where there is number there is a limit; when there is length, breadth or thickness, there is a limit.   It is impossible to conceive an infinite straight line actually realized. for it always has two ends.   *Infinity actually realized* should not be confounded with *indefinite*, that is undetermined, nor with *mathematical infinity*, which expresses an entirely different idea.   Thus an infinitely small angle is an angle that tends towards 0.   A line prolonged to infinity is a line of indeterminate, indefinite length, that is as long as we may wish but ever finite.

Time no more than quantity can be infinite.   There are two limits as for a straight-line, a beginning and an end.   Time can be extended, hence it is not infinite. To say that the world is infinite, that it is eternal, that force is infinite, as have Bückner, Haeckel, etc., is to utter a series of contradictions.   Creation *ab aeterno*, in the sense of St. Thomas, cannot mean that the world was infinite in duration, since the duration of the world can be measured, and because Divine Eternity is a continual present.   Time began with the world; before creation, there was God, but time did not exist.

It is surprising to see how these notions are too often lost sight of; more surprising still the concessions that are made to materialism, under the pretext that there are other means of demonstrating that the world is not sufficient unto itself, that it is not necessary, that it is eternal. We have too often experienced the value of this argument for men of intelligence, to believe it good or capable of producing strong convictions on the necessity of a Creator of the world and of energy.

The last objection of a philosophical character gives the raison d'être of all the others. We find it in different authors, with various shades of meaning, but all dependent upon that of G. Le Bon (*Evolution of Forces*, p. 97).

"If we reject hypotheses similar to ours (that of a new cycle of growth and of evolution, i. e. of eternal recommencements) given in opposition to the principle of the dissipation of energy, we must go back to that of a God Creator producing all the worlds by his will, i. e. from nothing, which is very much more mysterious than the substratum from which we have endeavored to make them originate. The gods having been eliminated from nature where ignorance has introduced them, we must endeavor to explain all things while dispensing with them."

It is difficult to find a more illogical reasoning, more errors in one proposition. They are evident to the reader and we need not dwell upon them. If the principle of the dissipation of energy applies to the universe, let us hold to the view of the necessity of a God Creator. As all the transformations of energy are accompanied by dissipation and as perfect reversibility does not exist, we believe the principle absolutely certain, and we accept the consequences; a God Creator is necessary for the creation of matter and of energy. Science has never eliminated Him. Science is concerned solely with secondary causes, but reason goes back to a First Cause in this as in every other instance.

§ X. — SCIENTIFIC CONSEQUENCES
OF THE PRINCIPLE OF THE DISSIPATION OF ENERGY.

This principle dominates all physics, all chemistry, the entire organic and inorganic world, the entire globe, the whole universe. Its experimental evidence leaves no room for doubt, so numerous, so clear, so decisive are the proofs. *Its logical* demonstration imposes itself upon every open minded person as a necessity in the transformations of energy. That which brings about its transformation is the same as that which renders it irreversible. As the water-fall is due to gravity, so the tendency toward thermal, electrical, mechanical and chemical equilibrium renders these conditions irreversible. We may conclude, therefore, that, as the world evolves, it proceeds towards a state of stable, irreversible thermal equilibrium.

This state, more or less remote, according to the bodies, or the species of body, and according to the available energy, will inevitably and successively be attained by all the elements, animate and inanimate creatures, liquids and gases, planets, star groups and nebulæ. We might consider one by one the consequences of the disappearance of some particuler form of energy and of its total transformation into unused and unavailable radiant heat. First, we shall see the disappearance of all life on the face of the earth, when the solar radiations (chemical, calorific and luminous) will no longer be sufficient to support it. Already at 0° C. plant life is considerably reduced, and with the disappearance of plants that of animals will inevitably follow. Then some degrees below zero all vegetation disappears and with it all life. In vain will man then try to replace the solar energy by that of coal, petroleum or hydro-electric power. The latter no longer exists at 0° and the other wo are by no means inexhaustible, supposing that man has not already squandered it long before. All circulation of water will cease below 0° C. and at —3° or —4° C., the oceans will be frozen over. From this time forward, the frozen earth will be but an inert, uninhabitable body.

Hence it is false to say that the earth evolves towards indefinite progress. A state of quiescence, inertness, death, such is the inevitable result of natural evolution. From the fact that the world evolves towards this end, and that its available energy is not infinite, reason must conclude that this evolution has had a beginning in time, a beginning whose date is indeed uncertain, but not proximately indeterminable.   The sun has not existed for more than 300 000 000 years if it has always radiated the same quantity of energy, or even if it began by radiating a much smaller quantity.

§ XI. — Philosophical conclusions.

In consequence of the scientific truth that the world is not infinite and its various forms of energy with their transformations not indefinitely possible, we are logically brought to these conclusions.   The world has had a beginning.   It ought to have an end.   If, in fact, it were to exist for all eternity, it would be for an eternity in which the series of possible transformations would have spent itself, and in which all its energy would have been dissipated, so that it would itself be reduced to an inert mass.   It cannot, by any means last forever, since its energy has been dissipated and the end of its evolution easily foreseen.   Many planets are already cold, having long since passed through the incandescent phase.   This is what is happening to the sun and to all the stars which are themselves real suns.

Logic in its most elementary form permits us to go even beyond these first two conclusions.   Since the world has had a beginning and ought to have an end, it is not a necessary entity; it has not in itself the reason for its existence; it does not suffice unto itself; it is not its own cause.   The various forms of energy which are manifested simply play the part of secondary causes.   No more than the world itself, have they the reason for their existence in themselves.   They require a First Cause which gives them existence, just as for matter from which they are inseparable and upon which they are contingent.

The First Cause, whose necessity is imperative to explain the world, must not be contingent but necessary, not temporary but eternal, not material but spiritual, not dependent but independent and sufficient unto Itself, not a slave to necessity but free, not finite but infinite.   It must be God, God such as we know Him through the sound philosophy of the Spiritual School, and not an anthropomorphized God such as the Materialistic School, including Le Dantec, Haeckel and others, have conceived in order to ridicule the idea itself. This God we shall consider the Creator of matter, the Creator of energy, the Creator of the order which is found in the world, and the Creator of the laws which govern this world. And we recognize Him as an infinitely intelligent and infinitely perfect being.

This argument for the existence of God which we are pleased to employ as an answer to the modern objections of the Materialistic School is intimately bound up with the classic arguments drawn from the *contingency* of the world and its laws. Dissipation of energy, in fact, is a palpable proof of this contingency. — From the *order* in the world : The natural sciences, physics, chemistry, biology and astronomy discover this order everywhere and bring it into evidence.— From *causality :* The study of the transformations of energy shows us the relation between cause and effect; it forces us to ascend logically from the innumerable secondary causes back to a necessary First Cause. — From the *principle of sufficient reason :* Every form of energy, every transformation has in itself this sufficient reason for its existence. This proof for the existence of God has, if we may rely upon personal observation, the double advantage of adequately explaining the role of secondary causes which it would be wrong for us to ignore, and of showing their insufficiency to account for the origin of all things together with their energy and thus of bringing into prominence, for the benefit of the men of today, the absolute necessity of God.

For a fuller development of these arguments for the existence of God and His attributes, we must refer our readers to some treatise on Natural Theology. We must content ourselves with clearing away encumbering objections having a scientific appearance, of unmasking the sophisms of the Materialistic School, and of indicating the solutions which should interest every intelligent person desirous of going beyond the transient contingencies, which strike the imagination without satisfying reason. It suffices to have given with fidelity the facts and the laws for the overthrow of the theory of the eternity of the world, of its independence, of its necessity as held by materialists. The truth is just the opposite. The secondary causes indeed, play an important role in the world, but are not sufficient to explain its origin. A First Cause Which is independent of all other causes and Which we call God the Creator, is necessary.

CHAPTER III

ORIGIN OF LIFE

§ I.—THE PROBLEM

The object of this chapter is to investigate how life began on the earth. If it is true, as scientists hold, that at a remote period no living thing inhabited the face of the globe, how, and by what force were the originally inert molecules subsequently endowed with vital power? We shall not, however, concern ourselves here with the problem of determining whether all living forms have been derived from only one primitive form, or are descended from many forms. The only question under consideration here is stated as follows : In what manner did the first living protoplasm originate?

The Bible gives us one solution. It is that God created life. Though this answer is clear, it does not appear precise enough for all interpreters. Being the First Cause, is not God the author of life? In creating all the elements of the universe hasn't He rendered them capable of combining into a living form when the conditions are favorable? Has not God often intervened as immediate cause of life, in personally synthesizing the first animate substance, and establishing the laws for the transmission of life and the evolution of its forms? In every hypothesis the sacred text requires that we go back to God the Creator.

And what does Science say about the origin of living beings? Let us carefully distinguish between experimental science, which registers facts, and philosophy, which sets out from the facts to ascend to causes. The scientist must make a strong effort to stay within the bounds of experience.   This follows from the very nature of his mind in the higher region of causality.

Experience is evidently powerless to resolve the question at issue.   We undoubtedly are dealing with a fact, but with a fact for which there remains no evidence.   Even if we should discover with certainty a trace of the first living thing, this trace can tell us its nature and its relative age, but nothing at all about the manner of its origin. The facts which fall under our experience at present, are but a basis for philosophical induction to arrive at an idea of the beginning.   The closer the agreement on the nature and the truth of the experimental data, the more accentuated is the disagreement, in the conclusions drawn from inductive reason.

The entire Materialistic School tells us that life began spontaneously without outside intervention, solely under the action of physico-chemical forces. This is apparently a "necessary postulatum" a "philosophical necessity".   The facts undoubtedly tend to prove the contrary.   But Science ought to explain the universe solely by the forces inherent in the universe.

The Spiritual School, proceeding from the same data and by a strong chain of deductions, arrives at a recognition of the necessity of an intervention outside the world, for the creation of life.   It believes that Science does honor to itself in bowing before the Supreme Cause, each time Philosophy invokes Him.

Is there any need to insist upon the great importance of the question before us? That which interests some, importunes others, and we have here a palpable proof for the existence of a personal, active God.   In this way, God becomes the object of human Science.   The path is clearly marked out.   Let us interrogate the facts, and then apply reason.   Let us examine into the actual origin, then into the primitive origin of living beings.

§ II.—What experience teaches.

In the present state of Science, we can announce as incontestable the following fact. Not only has the spontaneous transition from inert matter to an organized condition never been observed, but it has been established that all known living substances, even the very lowest, came by way of generation from similar substances already endowed with life. It is only after long delays and patient investigation, that Science has established so important a fact. [1] We hope our readers will take kindly to the following survey of the works which have helped to overthrow the old hypothesis of Spontaneous Generation.

1.—Before the experiments of Pasteur.

All antiquity believed, with Aristotle, that a considerable number of beings, whose origin was unknown, were formed without the agency of parents, by the sole forces inherent in inorganic matter. The ooze of streams or all putrefying matter seemed susceptible of becoming spontaneously organized and of developing reptiles, fish, insects, worms and other small animals. From this originated the celebrated formula : *Corruptio unius generatio alterius.* *"The corruption of one thing is the generation of another."* [2]

---

[1] "The ideas that might appear in the sciences present two aspects that are opposite in their development. The true ideas, most often starting from a very small number of simple well observed facts grow in proportion as knowledge increases and extend themselves more and more; the erroneous ideas, ordinarily comprising a great number of obscure and poorly understood facts, on the contrary, decrease and disappear in direct ratio to the progress of science. The question of spontaneous generation is found to be in shis second class in the sense that it becomes ever more circumscribed in the light of experience. Applied, at first to the mollusks, the articulates and even to vertebrates the instances of spontaneous generation have long since been relagated to the most obscure part of natural history, that is to the infusorial animalcules." Claude. Bernard (Report on the Alembert award attributed to Pasteur *Comptes rendus de l'Académie des sciences,* 1862, vol. LV, p. 977).

[2] This formula, very true in the general sense that a substance is never destroyed without giving birth to another, signifies here

The Middle Ages accepted as an established fact the spontaneous generation of certain beings. But Christian philosophy interpreted the fact in a sense quite opposed to the materialistic conception of life. St. Thomas, by no means, denied spontaneous generation, bu the strongly reproved Avecinna for attributing it to the power of matter alone. In the eyes of the Angelic Doctor, if matter produces life, it is in virtue of a special power given it by God, and this power comes into action under celestial influences. [1]

In the xvith century, van Helmont (1644) still gave formulæ for the production of adult mice and scorpions without the agency of parents [2]. The spirit of observation was however developing and in the xviith century the experiments of Redi [3] and of Swammerdam [4] dissipated many of the fables. Redi (1698) proved that the worms generated in putrefying meat were the larvæ developed from the eggs of flies. To preserve the food intact it was only necessary to wrap it in fine gauze. This is what Redi did. The flies having been kept away, neither larvæ nor worms developed. In consequence of these experiments the idea of spontaneous generation was for the time abandoned. But soon, the microscope revealed a new world of extremely minute animalculæ. Igno-

that the putrefaction of a living being engenders another. We may laugh at this to day, and yet modern scientists, like Trecul, teach that before abandoning an organized body, life recovers its forces to produce another of different nature. *Comptes rendus*, 1872, vol. LXXV, p. 1161.

[1] S. Thomas, *Sum. theol.*, I^a. q. LXXI, art. 1, ad 1um. *Non quod aqua aut terra habeat in se virtutem producendi omnia animalia, ut Avicenna posuit; sed quia hoc ipsum, quod ex materia elementari virtute seminis vel stellarum possunt animalia produci, est ex virtute primitus elementaris data.*

[2] "Make a hole in a brick, place in it some crushed sweet basil, cover with a second brick—... expose the two bricks to the sun and after some days, the odor of the basil will change the herb into real scorpions", Van Helmont, Belgian physician.

[3] Redi, physician to the grand-dukes of Tuscany.

[4] Swammerdam (1637-1680), physician in Amsterdam.

rance of the manner of their propagation revived the old
ideas of generation without parents.

The priest Spallanzani (1729-1799) attacked the idea
and triumphantly put it to rout [1]. One particular fact
showed him what errors the advocates of spontaneous
generation had to guard against. The eels that cause
black wheat rust, when dry seem to be only inert dust.
But a single drop of water placed on this dust is sufficient,
even after many years, to bring back life. This life, then,
had merely been suspended, and not extinct. "What at
times," said he "we take for spontaneous organization
is only the sleep of latent life." [2] Encouraged by his
success, Spallanzani attempted to prove that the corpuscles developing in infusions exposed to the air were due
to atmospheric germs. To this end he enclosed in sealed
vessels some infusions sterilized by boiling. These experiments doubtless would not be very convincing today,
because the precautions sufficient to remove all possibility
of error were lacking. Nevertheless, he demonstrated that
the anticipated result was much oftener obtained when
the given conditions were better realized. Other naturalists, in France and in Germany, repeated the investigations
of Spallanzani and followed them up so successfully, that
in the middle of the xixth century the hypothesis of spontaneous generation had been pretty well regarded as an
obsolete opinion.

In 1858, Pouchet, Professor of Zoology at Rouen, suddenly revived the whole discussion. He asserted having
seen some infusoria spontaneously developing in a fermentable liquid, previously sterilized and exposed to air
freed from germs. Many members of the Academy of
Sciences, among them Claude Bernard, de Quatrefages,
Payen, etc., revealed to Pouchet some sources of error,
against which he had not protected himself. But he

---

[1] At the same time, the hypothesis of spontaneous generation
was held by the English clergyman Needham (1713-1781). He was
the founder of the Academy of Sciences at Brussels.

[2] Cf. D. Cochin, *L'évolution de la vie*, Paris, Masson.

still insisting, the Academy of Sciences, desirous of throwing light upon so important a question, proposed its examination as a subject matter for one of its prizes (1860). It is now that Pasteur (1822-1895) enters upon the scene. [1]

2.—Pasteur's versus Pouchet, Musset and Joly (1859-1865).

Pouchet stated the question thus. It is a fact that everywhere and at all times a fermentable liquid, exposed to the air becomes covered with a mould and filled with infusoria. Now the few germs disseminated in the air can not explain so prodigious a fecundity of life. Moreover, we may pass air, entirely purified from every germ, into a putrescible bouillon previously sterilized by boiling, and life will manifest itself. He performed numerous and varied experiments in support of his thesis. [2] Hence, he concluded life can appear without germs, and spontaneous generation is experimentally demonstrated. He used a hay infusion in which the *bacillus subtilis* (fig. 18) developed.

Pasteur undertook to prove that the germs of the air are the true cause of all putrefaction. In two series of experiments, he established irrefutably the two following facts. First, pure air really deprived of all germs can never

---

[1] "One can visualise only with difficulty the fiercenes of these contests as a result of which, the ancient hypothesis, the chimerical illusion of spontaneous generation, vanquished by the evidence, overwhelmed by the weight of experimental proofs, beat a retreat before the triumphant doctrine of germs, that has rejuvenated science and has entered into indisputable possession of the future." Discourse of Dupuy, Minister of Public Instruction, on the 70th anniversary of Pasteur, celebrated at the Sorbonne, Dec. 27, 1892.—Cf. *Life of Pasteur*, by Vallery-Radot; Descour, *Pasteur and his Work*, Stokes; Bisot, *La carrière et les travaux de Pasteur*, dans *Correspondant* of Dec. 10, 1922; *Revue des Questions scientifiques*, Oct. 1922, p. 315-342; *Études, Louis Pasteur*, Jan. 20, 1923. *Revue des Deux Mondes*, Dec. 15, 1922. *L'œuvre scientifique de Pasteur* Duclaux, *Pasteur. The History of a Mind*, tr. and ed. by Erwin F. Smith and Florence Hudges. Saunders.

[2] *Comptes rendus de l'Acad. des Sciences*, 1860, vol. L., p. 532.

bring about putrefaction in a truly sterilized fermentable liquid. Secondly, pure air, not deprived of its germs does not of necessity bring about putrefaction in a sterilized fermentable liquid, since these germs are not always sufficiently abundant and, especially, not always active

Considering the first case. *Pure air, entirely freed from germs does not bring about fermentation in a putrescible liquid, previously sterilized.* Pasteur first used a solution of sugar and albumen, later on he worked with various

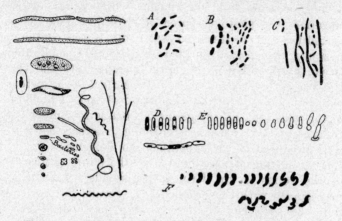

Fig. 18. — Different kinds of Microbes and Ferments.

Left. Different shapes assumed by microbes. Right. A, B, C, D, E, different states of the *bacillus mesentericus vulgatus* ; F. Virgulate bacillus of cholera.

infusions and also with blood, milk, urine, yeast, etc. These, he rendered, sterile or deprived them of their germs by boiling. [1] As he thus followed the same method as Pouchet, he could not be accused of destroying the generative power of the infusoria by the use of heat, nor of changing the question at issue.

In these preliminary experiments, he had occasion to

---

[1] The greater number of times boiling for five minutes sufficed to sterilize the mixture... for milk, it was noticed, that it was necessary to heat to 112° under a pressure of 1 1/2 atmosphere. *Comptes rendus*, vol. I. p. 303.

note the principal causes of error which Pouchet had not known how to remove. Thus germs are not equally resistant to the destructive power of high temperatures. Some are often supposed killed, when their vitality is only suspended or latent. Certain spores are enclosed in a coagulable substance which protects them from the heat. They are often met with on hay and on other substances, which Pouchet and his supporters preferred to employ in the preparation of their infusions. The germ-covered mercury used by Pouchet without previous sterilization was another source of error. In fact, he inverted the vials of sterilized water into vessels containing mercury, then passed purified oxygen and a small quantity of sterilized hay through the mercury into the vials. But Pasteur clearly showed that the surface of the mercury was contaminated with atmospheric dust, so that the liquid of the vials took up the germs on coming in contact with the mercury. It was not astonishing therefore that germs were produced in the experiments of Pouchet. [1]

After having assured himself of the entire destruction of the germs in the fermentable liquids, [2] Pasteur was preoccupied with the production of normal but perfectly pure air. He had to destroy or remove those germs

[1] Cf. *Histoire d'un savant par un ignorant*, Paris, Hetzel, 1883, p. 116.

[2] It was necessary to note that the germs are unequally resistant to the destructive power of the heat. M. Doyère proved that the rotifers, the tardigrades, can endure for a long time a temperature of a 100° or more to pass to a condition of inert dust, without losing in the meantime the power of reviving. L. Gavarret verified the same phenomenon among the infusoria, which, after having been submitted to a temperature at which every animal ordinarily perishes, could still revive. Certain organisms cause a coaguable substance to ooze from their bodies, which serves as a protective covering against the destructive agents. M. Coste discovered that these organisms are to be met with chiefly on hay and in certain substances very frequently chosen for their infusions by the partisans of spontaneous generation. These cysts are not always held back by filtration; they are so tenuous that they pass even through paper, mercury, cotton filters, etc... Cf. Milne-Edwards, *Rapports sur la zoologie*, Paris, 1867, p. 33.

which are always floating in the atmosphere. To do this, he passed the air through a tube containing platinum heated to redness. The germs were destroyed without the composition of the air being altered. No signs of life appeared in the balloon flasks thus prepared. That no one might accuse him of depriving the air of its plastic force by heating it, Pasteur resolved to remove the germs by simple filtration. To filter the air he at times placed wadding, previously sterilized in an oven, at other times previously calcined asbestos, in straight tubes. The filtered air coming in contact with the fermentable liquids did not produce putrefaction.

In some very rare cases, there was manifestation of life. But these exceptions did not upset Pasteur's thesis. For, if Pouchet had been right, life should have manifested itself in all the experiments, as it was always normal air that came in contact with the fermentable liquids. On the contrary, considering the difficulty of destroying or removing the germs, we can readily understand how fermentation might be produced. We know nowadays, that certain spores of hay can survive.

At 100° C.	more than 16 hours.
At 105°-110°	from 2 to 4 hours.
At 115°	from 30 to 60 mins.
At 125°-130°	from 4 to 5 mins.
At 135°	from 1 to 5 mins.
At 140°	from 1 to 2 mins.

To give a clear demonstration that fermentation had failed to take place solely because the germs of the air had been removed, Pasteur took some threads of the wadding and the asbestos on which the germs were, and placed them in a sterile liquid. As soon as the spores were introduced, the formation of germs began. He made this fact more apparent, by drawing out the neck of the flasks into long twisted tubes, so that the air had to pass through many windings before coming in contact with the liquids. In a first series of flasks, he permitted the air to enter suddenly. Several were soon covered with mould. The air had been introduced rapidly, so as to distribute

the germs on the walls of the tubes.   In a second series,
he caused the air to enter very slowly.   All these flasks
remained unaltered, since the germs remained behind adhering to the sides of the tubes.   That such was the real
reason why the flasks remained sterile, was well shown
when Pasteur brought some of the germs in contact with

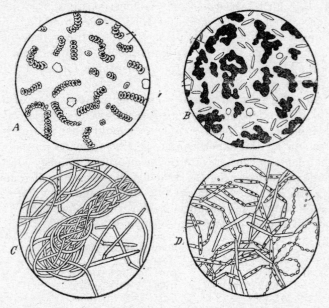

Fig. 19. — The bacillus of anthrax (*bacillus antracis*).

A. Drop of blood with normal globules before innoculation with bacilli.
B. Drop of blood of an animal killed by anthrax. — C. Anthrax bacillus
in bouillon culture. — D. Bacilli and spores.

a drop of water, that had remained unaffected on the
side of one of the tubes, and caused germs to develop.
In this way he had brought fermentable matter into contact with the germs of the air.

   In virtue of these facts, we have a right to conclude
with Tyndall: "Just as, when we see beans growing in a
garden, we say without hesitation that a seed had been
sown in this place, so when a liquid is putrefying we must

say with the same assurance that germs had been sown in the air" (fig. 19).

Pasteur rendered his conclusions more convincing still by showing that in spite of a small number of germs in the air, ordinary air does not necessarily bring about putrefaction.

The principles of Pouchet led logically to the following conclusion. Whenever we bring air into contact with sterilized fermentable bouillon, we should have the production of life. Pasteur, on the contrary, clearly states "that it is always possible to take, in a specified place, a considerable quantity of ordinary air, previously subjected to no physical or chemical alteration and show that it is nevertheless entirely incapable of producing any change in a highly putrescible liquid." Pouchet, Joly and Musset wrote to the Academy of Sciences that this assertion was erroneous, as being contrary to their own experiments. When Pasteur defied them to give an experimental proof for their claim, they accepted the challenge. " If a single one of our balloon flasks remains unchanged", said Joly and Musset, "we shall honestly admit our defeat." "I affirm" said Pouchet, "that at any place on the globe I may take a cubic decimeter of air, and as soon as I bring it in contact with a putrescible liquid confined in hermetically sealed balloon flasks, these will *immediately* swarm with living organisms."

The Academy appointed a commission to have the alleged experiments of both parties repeated in its presence. After a number of conferences which Balard reports at length in his memoirs of February 25, 1865, Messrs. Pouchet, Joly and Musset refused to accept the evidence and withdrew, leaving Pasteur alone before his judges. [1] He began by establishing the truth of the experiments already performed. He presented a number of balloon flasks in which some fermentable liquid had been exposed

[1] See the interresting report of Balard, in *Comptes rendus*, 1865, vol. LX, p. 384.—The members of the commission were: Dumas, Brongniard, Milne-Edwards, Balard, reporter.

to the air, some on the Jura Mts. at Soleure, and others at
Montanvert on Mount Blanc.   Several had remained unaltered for three or four years.   The sealed ends of these were
broken, and the air of the laboratory caused floculi of
mould to appear in about three days.

Then, 56 flasks, prepared for the purpose, were opened
at different places where it was presumed the composition
of the air might be entirely different.   Air from the large
amphitheatre of the Museum was introduced into 19.
Other 19 were opened on the highest point of the dome;
18 others were shipped to Bellevue and opened under
some large poplar trees, in the center of a grassy lawn.
In the first series, 14 flasks remained sterile, in the
second, 13, in the third, only 2 remained unaltered so full
of germs was the atmosphere at Bellevue.   Thus, the proposition of Pasteur, that ordinary air does not necessarily
produce life in a medium suitable for the production
of germs, was proven.

From all these experiments he drew a conclusion very
clearly contrary to generation of life without the agency
of germs.   The old adage, *Omne vivum ex vivo* "*Every
living thing comes from a living thing*", is found to be
verified for the world of infinitely small beings, as well as
for those visible to the naked eye.   The controversy
might have been considered ended, at least in the field
whither Pouchet had carried it, had it not been revived
in a memoir of Dr. Bastian dean of the Faculty of Medicine
at London.   This doctor claimed he had found the *physico-
chemical conditions* suited for the production of life without
germs.   "My observations" said he "were made on
urine brought to ebullition.   To induce the production of
bacteria I brought in potash and oxygen as chemical influences, and a temperature of 50° C. as a physical influence."
Pasteur accepted the new challenge.   Previous to his
appearance before the commission named by the Academy, he made known to Dr. Bastian three sources of
error against which he had not taken proper precautions.
The water used for washing the vessels was contaminated; the potash solution contained germs; the flasks were

not properly disinfected. The English doctor was floored and took the train bound for London (1877). [1]

3.—Pasteur's discussions with Fremy and Trecul in 1871.

Pasteur refuted the idea of spontaneous generation in an excellent series of researches into the subject of fermentation. He had discovered that fermentation is a function of life, that the phenomenon is produced in fermentable liquids by the living yeast cells. For example, the must of grapes ferments, because of a microscopic organism which lives in the mass and which, while protected from the air, decomposes the sugar into alcohol and carbonic acid. But whence this organism? According to Pasteur,

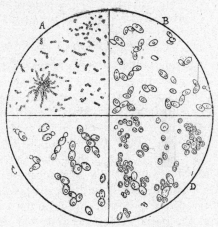

Fig. 20. — Ferments.

A. Vinegar: — B. Sour wine; — C. Mycoderm of reconditioned wine; — D. Aged wine.

the germs floating in the air are deposited on the grapes during the summer, then when in autumn the grapes are crushed, the germs mixed in the juice bring about fermentation (fig. 20).

This theory, so beautiful in its simplicity was set forth before the Academy of Sciences in 1872, and was

[1] "The German Butschli thought he had produced protoplasm from a mixture of oil and a soapy material. Butschli's protoplasm might resemble living protoplasm, exteriorly, but differs essentially first in its chemical composition, and then is incapable of multiplying and differentiating. In brief it is lacking in all vital properties. Butschli therefore has succeeded in making but a protoplasmic statue." L. Picard, *Chrétien ou agnostique*, p. 19, note. Cf. Maumus, *La cellule*, vol. I, p. 286.

vigorously opposed by Frémy. The learned professor
reasoned like Pouchet : "Fermentation produced at all
times and in all places cannot be the result of chance
atmospheric dust. The ferments like the immediate principles of plants, are created by the organism itself."
"Certainly", he added, "a living organism cannot be
begotten from inorganic matter, but it can be produced
by organic matter. The ferment of wine, for example,
is created by the parenchyma cells which constitute the
juice of the grape."

This was but a revival of the old theory of spontaneous
generation under a new form. This system of Frémy[1],
supported by Trecul[2], has been styled *hemiorganism*,
since it holds that a living being spontaneoulsy begotten
in a substance was already half organized. To refute
this theory, Pasteur undertook a series of experiments that
were even more delicate than any of the preceding. [3]

He had to prove that the alcoholic fermentation of
wine was due entirely to atmospheric yeast-spores. Into
40 flasks prepared for this purpose, he introduced some
filtered and perfectly limpid must of grapes. After boiling, the liquid remained unaltered, although communicat-
ting directly with the outside air through the twisted
necks of the bottles. He then washed a few grapes in a
few cubic centimeters of water. Under the microscope
he could discern a number of organized corpuscles which
resembled yeast cells. But this was not enough. He
divided the flasks into four series. To the first, he added

---

[1] Frémy, Professor of Chemistry, was the successor of Gay-Lussac
at the Museum.

[2] Trécul was Professor of Botany at the Museum. Trécul thought
he had demonstrated the generation of organic ferments " in the
nterior of sealed thick-walled cells, still occupying their natural
position in the piece of branch to which they belonged ". He gave
the following definition for spontaneous generation : " A natural
process by which life, on the point of leaving an organized body,
concentrates its activity on certain particles of this body, and forms
beings altogether different from that from which the substance had
been taken. " *Comptes rendus,* 1872, vol. LXXV, p. 1161,

[3] *Comptes rendus,* 1872, vol. LXXV, p. 781, 973, 1171, 1219.

nothing, and the grape must remained unaltered. Into the second series of flasks, he placed a few drops of the water in which the grapes had been washed. In about 48 hours, all were in complete alcoholic fermentation. They had received the spores and germination was the result. Into the third series, Pasteur introduced some drops of the same washings which had been previously boiled. Not one flask showed signs of fermentation, all ten remained sterile. Finally into the remaining ten flasks, Pasteur placed some juice of grapes that had not been crushed. In this last series only one flask fermented. The sources of error however are so difficult to remove, that we can readily understand the fermentation of one out of ten.

The conclusion was evident. The must of the grapes is incapable of fermentation by itself. The organic yeast which produces the fermentation of the must in the wine-vat comes from the outside, and not from the inside of the grapes. To this communication Frémy and Trécul were strongly opposed. They offered various objections which Pasteur hastened to solve likewise, by interpretation of his own experiments. To render his answer more telling, to prevent the destruction of the supposed generative force of the grape must by boiling, to have a sufficient quantity of the life producing substance in an unaltered condition, in fine to preserve the parenchyma cells from change, he resorted to the following procedure.

In his vineyard at Arbois, he constructed a hot house enclosing some grape vines. Having noticed that the yeast-cells were deposited on the grapes only in July, during the month of June, he wrapped the growing grapes in wadding. The grapes ripened as usual, but the cotton had filtered the air and had kept the organic corpuscles out, thus preventing them from reaching the hulls of the grapes. Autumn came, the grapes were crushed with all the precautions necessary to keep out the exterior germs. No fermentation manifested itself in the tubes, and yet all the conditions exacted by Frémy had been realized. The liquid was in sufficient quantity, the parenchyma cells were in the same condition as in an ordinary vat, no boiling had altered the inherent power of the organized matter. The conclusion was imperative, that the living fruit itself was incapable of engendering organic ferments without exterior germs. In a control experiment made with ordinary grapes, fermentation took place. Thus, thanks to the patient researches of Pasteur, hemiorganism was overthrown. We must refer the reader to the *Life of Pasteur* by Vallery-Radot, translated, into English by Mrs. R. L. Devonshire for his other remarkable discoveries, all of which confirm his theories and to the article of de Briot in *Le Correspondant*, Nov. 12, 1922, on infectuous diseases, pasteurization, food-preservation, surgery, vaccination, etc., etc.

4. Tyndall's experiments.

The noted English physicist Tyndall attempted to verify personally the results obtained by Pasteur. By a very ingenious arrangement he was able to bring into evidence the germs of the air and their action upon fermentable infusions.

" Build a little chamber and provide it with a door, windows and window-shutters. Let an aperture be made in one of the shutters through which a sunbeam can pass. Close the door and windows, so that no light shall enter, save through the hole in the shutter. The track of the sunbeam is at first perfectly plain and vivid in the air of the room. If all disturbance of the air of the chamber be avoided, the luminous track will become fainter and fainter, until at last it disappears absolutely, and no trace of the beam is to be seen. What rendered the beam visible at first? The floating dust of the air, which, thus illuminated and observed, is as palpable to sense as dust or powder placed on the palm of the hand. In the still air, the dust gradually sinks to the floor or sticks to the walls and ceiling, until finally, by this self-cleansing process, the air is entirely freed from mechanically suspended matter.

" Chop up a beefsteak and allow it to remain for two or three hours covered with warm water : you thus extract the juice of the beef in a concentrated form. By properly boiling the liquid and filtering it, you can obtain from it a perfectly transparent beef-tea. Expose a number of vessels containing this tea to the moteless air of your chamber, and expose a number of vessels containing precisely the same liquid to the dust-laden air. In three days every one of the latter is found swarming with the bacteria of putrefaction. After three months, or three years, the beef-tea within the chamber is found in every case as sweet and clear and as free from bacteria as it was at the moment when it was first put in. There is absolutely no difference between the air within and that without, save that the one is dustless and the other dust-laden.

"Clinch the experiment thus : Open the door of your chamber and allow the dust to enter it. In three days afterward you have every vessel within the chamber swarming with bacteria, and in a state of active putrefaction... Multiply your proofs by building fifty chambers instead of one, and by employing every imaginable infusion of wild animals and of tame : of flesh, fish, fowl, and viscera; of vegetables of the most various kinds. If in all these cases, you find the dust infallibly producing its crop of bacteria, while neither the dustless air nor the nutritive infusion, nor both together are able to produce this crop, your conclusion is simply irresistible that the dust of the air contains the germs of the crop which has appeared in your infusions." [1]

In connection with these experiments, Tyndall very satisfactorily explains why the brewer places yeast in the barley extract when making beer. What would happen if he should leave the malt to all the hazards of atmospheric dust? It would indeed ferment, but there is every chance in the world that it would not give the desired product. For with the yeast germs are mixed very many other ferments capable of modifying the result.

For more than a year Tyndall gave himself up to the

---

[1] Extract from a discourse made in Glasgow in 1876. Cf. Vallery-Radot, *Life of Pasteur*, p. 663. Fyndall, *Fragments of Science*, p. 544-545.

minutest researches[1] into the action and the vital resistance
of putrefying organisms and infectants.   He suffered many
disappointements, but the failures as well as the successes
led him to the same general conclusion, that all fermentation
or putrefaction is the effect of preexisting germs.   After
so many efforts, he had good right to make this statement :
"There is no inference of experimental science more certain than this one.   In the presence of such facts... it
would be simply monstrous to affirm that these swarming
crops of bacteria are spontaneously generated."

Virchow, the dean of German Science adds : "We do not
know a single positive fact which establishes that spontaneous generation has ever taken place.   Those who say
the contrary are contradicted by scientists and not by
theologians."

Haeckel the spirited Jena professor made the same
statement, although he holds to spontaneous generation,
since he considers it an indispensable postulatum for his
monism. "To do away with spontaneous generation"
says he, "is to proclaim a miracle."[2]

5. Experiments of Pasteur's disciples.

The foregoing statements and facts made in opposition
to the theory of spontaneous generation, have received
brilliant confirmation in the realm of experience.   Phy-
sicians, surgeons, specialists in micro-biology, in adopting
these theories and Pasteur's methods of asepsis have there-
by unqualifiedly demonstrated their value.   Surgeons
have succeeded in performing the most delicate operations
formerly so formidable and so obscure, without the least
contamination.   The physician has recognized in the
micro-organism the immediate causes of contagion.
The micro-biologist has cultivated, isolated and studied
at leisure these infinitely small organisms, discovered by
Pasteur, and whose rôle, is so considerable in nature.
Vaccination and serotherapy have as a result made marvel-

[1] Cf. Tyndall, *Fragments of Science.*
[2] *Riddle of the Universe,* p. 258.

lous advances. Many branches of industry, such as the preservation and preparation of articles of food, alcoholic, lactic, acetic and other fermentations have ben completely revolutionized by these discoveries. These are, therefore, so many proofs of the argument of Pasteur that life comes from life, and there is no such thing as spontaneous generation. It does not take place, nor can it take place in a perfectly sterilized medium. If a thesis has ever been demonstrated experimentally this is certainly an instance of it. If the laws of nature are constant, as is asserted, then it must always have been as it is now and always will be so. There is no spontaneous generation, there was none and there never will be any. This is indeed the mind of Pasteur.[1]

6. New investigations.

In spite of all this, the advocates of spontaneous generation have not given up the contest. They have devoted themselves to further research. A history of the same would be too long. We shall, however, analyse those which have stirred up most comment.

The Experiments of Bastian (1908). Bastian, Pasteur's old opponant, after thirty years of silence, reappeared on the scene with his book *Evolution and the Origin of Life.* In the preface, he declares that if he has kept silent it was not for the reason that he had abandoned his cause. Persevering in his ideas, he has on the contrary multiplied his experiments in view of their confirmation. At first he worked with organic liquids. He heated an alkaline solution of urine to 110°, for thirty minutes, so as to kill all living germs. Of fifty flasks so treated fourteen fermented. He proceeded in the same way with infusions of hay, potatoes and cucumbers, with yeast water and with milk. After having heated these liquids to 110-115°, or even to 120°, he noticed very different results. Fermentation took place in a certain number of flasks.

He then employed saline solutions previously heated to 115° in hermetically sealed tubes. Sometimes he

---

[1] *The Life of Pasteur*, Vallery-Radot, p. 256.

poured a few drops of a solution of sodium silicate and
ammonium phosphate, and some dilute phosphoric acid
into thirty cubic centimeters of distilled water. Sometimes into the same amount of distilled water, he poured
a few drops of the sodium silicate solution and some ferric
nitrate. At the end of a considerable period of time, often
after three months, there formed at the bottom of the
tubes a deposit of elements which Bastian dignified with
the name of organisms.

The experiments of Bastian call for a number of observations. In the first place, he supposes that he had previously killed all the germs in the organic liquids, as well
as in the saline solutions used in the experiments, and he
cites the regulations formulated by specialists for obtaining
a microbicidic temperature. But does he not know that
there are new surprises in this matter every day? True
the microbicidic temperatures ordinarily kill the germs,
but frequently, for various known and unknown reasons,
spores have resisted an extremely high temperature.
Even the results obtained by Bastian confirm this supposition. He worked with fifty flasks, for instance, and only
fourteen fermented. We readily understand why all the
flasks did not show signs of fermentation, if the fermentation is due to the germs; for it may be said that the germs
had not been killed in the fourteen flasks. But, if all
the germs are rendered inactive, we do not understand
why all the flasks did not ferment, since the vital power
is evidently of the same nature in all.

Again if fermentation takes place without germ life,
it is incomprehensible why it produces precisely the bacilli
of "known forms" which would have been generated
from preexisting germs, had they not been killed. That
these bacilli should be produced and no others, it is necessary that their germs should have been preserved despite
the efforts of the experimenter.

As to the bacilli being produced in living cells without
previous germs, we have already seen how Pasteur has
demonstrated, against Frémy and Trécul, that it cannot
take place.

Finally, it would, indeed, be strange if so many experimenters had miserably failed in their attempts to find life engendered without germs when Bastian sees it, as he says, multiplied in nature.   Dr. Maumus of the Pasteur Institute was asked what should be thought of Bastian's experiments; whether they had been conducted with all scientific exactness, or whether the conclusions which he draws are legitimate, or are merely the ideas of a mind transgressing too much the restricted limits of his own field of observation.   Having studied and solved as many of the questions as he was able, the Doctor made known the results in his work : *La cellule*, p. 345-383.   After remarking that Bastian did not always realize the microbicidic temperatures, that the supposeed microbes remain inert, do not multiply and cannot be stained, and are in many instances but simple chemical precipitates, he said he thought it best to repeat the experiments of Bastian and by thus controlling his results, give a more equitable judgment and one more conformable to the reality of the facts.

He followed the minutest details, taking for his experiments the same chemical substances, the same apparatus, the same solutions.   Bastian had used four mixtures, he employed the same in his own experiments.   The composition of these mixtures was [1] :

1	Distilled water	3 tubes sterilized at	120°	for 15 mins.
	Ferric nitrate	3	id.	130°	15 mins.
	Sodium silicate	3	id.	120°	30 mins.
2	Distilled water				
	Ammonium phosphate	id.			
	Sodium silicate				
3	Distilled water				
	Ferric nitrate	id.			
	Colloidal silica				
4	Distilled water				
	Ammonium phosphate				
	Phosphoric acid	id.			
	Colloidal silica				

[1] Cf. Maumus, *La cellule*, p. 345-383, Paris, Bonne Presse.

Under the miscroscope Bastian had discovered bacteria, torules, moulds, other organisms and crystals. Dr. Maumus observed only crystals giving as proof for his statement their form, the impossibility of staining them, or of making cultures with them, (except in rare cases of contamination) although he had kept them in an oven at 37º for 10 months.

He used three excellent culture media : Martin's bouillon; ordinary agar-agar, and a jelly made from Maze pulse. Of 120 tubes prepared with mixtures 1, 2, 3 and 4, four had been contaminated with the *bacillus subtilis* whose presence in the laboratory was known, and which is avoided only with great difficulty (380). Two others showed *cocci* which also came from the outside.

Dr. Maumus sums up his opinion (p. 382) thus : "Our experiments, inspired by the labors of Bastian, have permitted us to draw conclusions entirely opposed to his and there, where he sees life, we have found only pseudo-micro-organisms, which as yet have never been transformed into living germs. We may, therefore, conclude that the phenomenon of life is not the result of chemical affinities, always possible to realize in a laboratory, in a flask or test-tube, and that the researches of Bastian, far from bringing forward a new argument in favor of the theory of spontaneous generation, have only confirmed the philosopher and the biologist in the truth that, as the basis of all vital manifestation, we must always place a creative act. "

Burke's radiobes. — Mr. Burke director of Cavendish-Laboratory at Cambridge made researches into the action of radium, and obtained results which were, apparently in spite of himself, interpreted by some as spontaneous appearances of life. He introduced beef-bouillon along with peptonized gelatine, and sodium chloride into three flasks marked A. B. C. This culture-bouillon was carefully sterilized as for developing microbes. By cooling the mixture he obtained a semi-solid mass. The surface of this gelatinous mass was then sprinkled with radium bromide in flasks A, with radium chloride in flasks B, while flask C was left intact. After a few days, while the flask C remained unaltered, the flasks A and B underwent changes which to an experienced eye resembled those of microbic cultures. Examined under the microscope the gelatine was found strewn with little spherical bodies, smaller than $3/10^{\mu}$. These globules increased in size, developed and divided, producing daughter-cells. Mr. Burke even believed he had noticed a nucleus in the interior. Ever maintaining a great reserve, he saw in these results thus obtained " a manifest indication of a continual adaptation of internal condition sto external conditions, which we have held to be vitality." To these seemingly living beings, created by radium, he gave the name of *radiobes*.

This was not the first time that bodies having the appearance of living cells had been produced under the influence of various salts in sterilized bouillon cultures. [1] This is the reason why scientists received these discoveries of Burke with little enthusiasm. Besides it was easy to show that these radiobes did not act like living microbes. If we heat a tube containing microbes, the microbes do not disappear, but remain without again reviving, whereas the radiobes disappear without trace, only to reappear later on. Treated with hot water, the microbes die, but they are insoluble; the radiobes dissolve. In the light the radiobes disappear only to reappear in the dark after some days; it is quite otherwise with microbes. These move about in a culture-bouillon, propagate and multiply; the radiobes move in sterilized gelatine, but give little or no evidence of multiplying or propagating themselves.

But then, how explalin Burke's radiobes, if they have no life but only physico-chemical action? The scientist Ramsey formulated a theory. Whenever we sprinkle salts of radium on gelatine, the water of the gelatine is decomposed, and there is formed around each particle of salt a small bead whose envelope is gradually coagulated. From this

---

[1] See Maumus, *La cellule*, p. 305; *La plasmogenèse de Herrera*, p. 327 : *Les cellules de Harting*, p. 332 : *La cellule de Benedikt*.

we have the appearance of a cell. This pseudo-cell grows by the action of the radium on the remaining gelatine which is there imprisoned. The growth can be such, that in time it may produce division into sections. But the process stops when the elements of the reaction are all used up. When heat is applied the gelatine melts, and the bubbles of gas disappear, and the pseudo-cells also disappear without trace. The radium, however, does not disappear and this is why the process can begin again, and why the radiobes seem to be regenerated. The old adage : *Omne vivum ex vivo* paraphrased *All life from life* so strongly supported by Pasteur's experiments, has not been affected in the least by the radiobes of Burke.

The arborescence of Stephane Leduc. — One of the latest attempts to revive spontaneous generation, and not the least sensationnal, was made by Stephane Leduc, professor at l'École de médecine at Nantes. [1]   Having devoted himself for some time to the study of physical phenomena, in connection with living beings in general and those which produce osmosis in particular, he believed he had learned the mechanism of life, and had discovered the means of producing it without previous germs. This was the subject matter of a communication to the Academy of Sciences, November 26, 1906.

Leduc sowed a seed formed from equal parts of sugar and copper sulphate in an artificial plasma formed from water, gelatine, potassiumferrocyanide (5 %) and a little salt (2 %). This seed swelled up, budded and grew, put forth roots and rootlets, then some vertical stalks, some of which attained a height of 30 centimeters. There were lateral leaves, terminal organs in the shape of spines, balls, ears, and tendrils, just as in plants (fig. 21). Leduc believed he had come upon the physical force in a fair way on towards the creation of living beings. The experiments were heralded as a revolution in Science, removing the line of demarcation between mineral and living substances.

[1] Cf. *Le Cosmos*, Nov. 4, 1905, and *Revue pratique d'apologétique,* vol. I, p. 471 and vol. III, p. 478.

But the triumph was of short duration.   For it was soon
shown that all the phenomena observed by him, recall a
well known chapter on osmosis in physics.   D'Arsonval
characterized this discovery very well, when he styled it
"the parody on life".   Bonnier said that arborization
thus obtained "might make a good add for a pharmacists
show-window."

The little grain of copper sulphate coming in contact

Fig. 21. — Arborescence obtained by Leduc.

with the potassium ferrocyanide forms with it copper ferrocyanide which envelops it, and serves as a separating but
semipermiable membrane.   The sugar enclosed within
this membrane calls for water.   This latter penetrates by
osmosis and dilates the membrane which finally bursts,
but reforms immediately and indefinitely as long as the
interior osmotic pressure is greater than that of the exterior
liquid.   These ruptures can take place in any direction,
and the plant-like growth can thus assume the greatest
variety of forms.

This experiment recalls the classic series of Traube who
produced arborescence in a solution of sodium silicate, using

a small crystal of copper or iron sulphate at the bottom of the vessel (fig. 22, 23, 24, 25).

These experiments of Leduc do not lack interest, for they draw attention to one of the physical processes which the living organism utilizes in its growth and development, in the exchanges taking place between the interior and

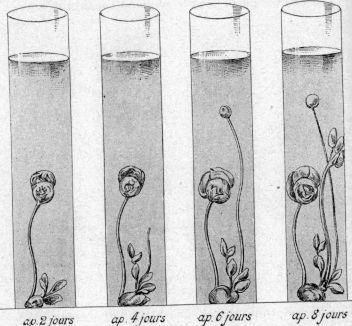

ap. 2 jours   *ap. 4 jours*   *ap. 6 jours*   *ap. 8 jours*

Fig. 22.   Fig. 23.   Fig. 24.   Fig. 25.

Traube's experiments

Fig. 22. After 2 days; fig. 23. After 4 days; fig. 24. After 6 days; fig. 25. After 8 days.

exterior media, and in the formation of organic arborescence. For all these phenomena suppose the action of physical forces. But life supposes something beyond mere physico-chemical forces. It exhibits, in particular, the phenomena of assimilation and of reproduction, which are not found in any way, in the experiments of Leduc. [1]

Yves Delage's sea-urchins. — The experiments of Yves Delage, professor at the Sorbonne, on the artificial fertilization of sea-urchin eggs, have been wrongly adduced as an argument in favor of spontaneous generation. Delage, himself, made no pretence of having created life; he worked solely with eggs already living. He took some sea-urchin eggs, preserved them carefully from the action of male elements, submitted them under certain conditions to the influence of saline solutions [2] and noticed the production of the phenomena of segmentation, and of growth, which regularly follow natural fecundation, but never beyond the morula or the blastula stage, nor the dimensions of one millimeter. Now, this development of a living oganism from a previously unfertilized egg, though indeed extraordinary for sea-urchins is not an anamoly in nature. The phenomenon of parthenogenesis is met with among the lower forms of life, and even in forms as high up in the scale as the bees.

Dr. Carrel's experiments. — The experiments of Carrel on the survival of tissues *in vitro* have also been interpreted in a materialistic sense against his own wishes and intentions. We give Dr. Maumus' summary of these experiments. [3] Carrel was chiefly preoccupied with the search for new methods of prolonging the life of tissues cultivated *in vitro.* He succeeded in this by renewing the culture medium composed of three parts of normal plasma and two parts of distilled water. In a second attempt, he obtained for his cultures a state of alternate life; in a third, the

[1] See outline and criticims of Leduc's e periments in *Revue pratique d'apologétique*, vol. III, p. 477-483, Maumus, *op. cit.*, vol. I, p. 298-305. See the illustrations, in *Nature*, vol. LXIX, p. 33. Cf. *Cosmos*, vol. LVI, p. 32-33.

[2] Maumus, *op. cit.*, vol. I, p. 938-413.

[3] Maumus, *op. cit.*, vol. II, p. 238 et sq. Dr. Alexis Carrel (Rockefeller Institute for Mod. Research.) started the artificial cultivation of a minute bit of cartilage from the heart of an unhatched chick over 12 years ago, and it is growing yet, long after the fowl would have died if it had hatched. Dr. Edwin Slosson, in *The Progress of Science. The Scientific Monthly*, vol. XXI, p. 2, p. 217, Aug. 1925.

tissues were maintained in a manifestly continuous living condition. In these different states, the cells multiplied and really lived for several months. Carrel succeeded in doing even better than this. After the usual preliminaries, he removed in one single mass, the thoracic and the abdominal viscera of a cat, and then united the blood vessels and placed the whole in Ringer's solution at a temperature of 38°. At this moment the blood pressure was low, but the heart still beat slowly, but regularly. Carrel then transfused into the visceral organism a certain amount of blood from another cat. The lungs became red, the blood pressure was raised and the heart beat regularly at a rate of 120 to 150 per minute. Carrel extended his experiments still farther. He injected food into the stomach of this organism and it was digested normally.

These results are indeed remarkable, "and it is curious to see this visceral organism living isolated after having been separated from the central nervous system and from the rest of the body, though it is also true that there can exist a certain independence between the vegetative life and the other vital relations." However there is no creation of life here, but merely its momentary preservation under special conditions.

It was, it seems, the introduction of oxygenated blood that activated the heart by a sort of reflex taking place in the vegetative life. The conditions of temperature and the special medium supply the rest. [1]

Despairing in their efforts to produce life in the laboratory, some have supposed nature to be more powerful in this respect. Some have affirmed again and again that life is produced spontaneously at the bottom of the ocean. It will be enough to recall the adventures of Haeckel's *Bathybius* now recognized as a mere precipitate of calcium sulphate. As to Haeckel's *moners*, they exist only in his imagination.

The reader will pardon us for having insisted at such length on these experimental facts. Too often, however,

---

[1] Cf. *Études*, April, 1913.

books content themselves with a mere allusion. Besides the interest attached to them, we find here a necessary foundation for the support of our arguments. It seems to us pretty solidly established that all known living substances, even the very lowest, come by way of generation from like substances already endowed with life. Experiments cannot go beyond this general formula.[1]

[1] It will not be useless to add here a few testimonies.

Littré : "Life, as it appears to our eyes, propagates itself only by way of parents; we have no experimental right to make figure at the beginning, a vital property with an action that it no longer has today. " *Génération spontanée et Transformisme.*

Flourens qualifies the hypothesis of spontaneous generation as "very convenient and very absurd." *Longévité.*

W. Thompson (Lord Kelvin) : "Science furnishes a multitude of invincible proofs against the hypothesis of spontaneous generation, as you have heard from the mouth of my predecessor in this chair, Mr. Huxley. A minute examination has not, up to this day, discovered any principle of life other than life itself". Discourse at the opening of the assembly at Edinburgh, in 1871. *Popular Lectures and Addresses.*

Tyndall (1871) : "And if you ask me whether there exists the least evidence to prove that any form of life can be developed out of matter, without demonstrable antecedent life, my reply is... men of science frankly admit their inability to point to any satisfactory experimental proof, that life can be developed save from demonstrable antecedent life." Four years later : "I affirm that no shred of trustworthy experimental testimony exists to prove that life in our day has ever appeared independently of antecedent life." Quoted by Scharpe in *The principles of Christianity,* 1906, p. 56.

Virchow : "Never has a living being or even a living element—let us say a living cell—been found of which it could be predicated that it was the first of its species. Nor have any fossil remains ever been found of which it could be likely that it belonged to a being the first of its kind, produced by spontaneous generation." Address at Wiesbaden, 1887. From Hertwig, *Allgemeine Biologie,* 2, Aufl., p. 263.

B. Moore, F. R. S. : "In the existing condition of science, there is little hope that any worker will be able to produce the simplest manifestation of life in any artificial way from non-living matter. He has certainly no more chance of success in his endeavors than Wagner in Goethe's Faust had of brewing a Homunculus in his retort". Quoted by Windle, in *Facts and Theories.*

§ III. — SPONTANEOUS GENERATION
IN THE LIGHT OF REASON.

Experiments prove that there is no such thing as spontaneous generation. How does it happen then, that at the present time, certain popular writers affirm its possibility, its necessity, its reality, though admitting the data of experience in other things?

It is not through the science of observation that the contrary is proved. This can be done only in virtue of aprioristic philosophy which is generally materialistic. Indeed, some contend, if there never had been any spontaneous generation, the intervention of God must have been necessary to produce life; but this hypothesis we reject, since it appears to us inadmissible.

The mechanistic school does not admit a specifically irreducible difference between the mineral and the living organism. The materialists, to give to their thesis a scientific appearance, try to justify it by the intrinsic study of life and its constituent elements. Each of them views the subject from a special angle. Some hold, that it is impossible to assign a line of demarcation between the mineral and the living kingdoms; others try to convince us that the crystal has the same characteristisc as a living organism; a third group uphold the role of physico-chemical forces in life; a fourth hold that the mineral serves as food for the living being and recall the synthesis of organic substances by the chemist, and maintain that as a fact, life or something that strangely resembles it, has been created in the laboratory. A last group considers the problem solved by affirming that nature, more powerful than the chemist, realizes the synthesis of life in its laboratories, but under forms so low, simple and primitive, that we cannot even discover it.

To these vague insinuations we might well answer, with an inductive argument which leads to a solution radically opposed to this hypothesis. The laws of nature are universal and constant. Now life proceeds from life. This then, was always so and will always continue to be so.

Never has life developed from mere physico-chemical forces, nor will it ever originate from this source. If a law is susceptible of being demonstrated by experimentation, it must be recognized that that of a living being coming from a living being, has all the facts in its favor. A scientist would not deny this.

To this reason, which is very general in character, we wish to add others that are more special, drawn from the nature of life itself. Since we do not admit of the physico-chemical explanation of life, we shall first point out the role of these physico-chemical forces in life, then we shall bring out the differences which distinguish the living organism from the mineral, by giving the characteristics of life and we shall conclude by showing that, although the physico-chemical forces are necessary as a condition for life, they are not life, they do not explain life and they do not of themselves produce life.

1. CHARACTERISTICS WHICH LIVING AND NON-LIVING BEINGS HAVE IN COMMON.

We may consider this subject from the point of view of chemistry and from that of energy. From the *chemical* aspect, living beings are, like non-living, composed of atoms and of molecules. We find in them simple elements as oxygen, nitrogen, hydrogen, carbon, sulphur and phosphorus, even certain metals as iron, calcium, etc. These elements are differently combined just as in the mineral kingdom, to form the greatest variety of substances of greater complexity. It is therefore, to chemistry that we must look for the constitution of living beings. The chemist has been working for some time along these lines and with a certain degree of success, since he has partially determined the nature of organic compounds, necessary, or useful for life, or produced by life, thyroxin, insulin, vitamines, etc., and has even realized the synthesis of certain organic substances such as hydrocarbons, sugars, alcohols, urea, adrenalin. If chemistry has not realized the synthesis of all substances it hopes to do so. "We find that chemistry aims to analyze every material that comes under its ken in the most minute fashion. It separates and isolates the pure principles, scores of which may compose a mixture such as our blood. It studies the properties of these pure principles minutely, and then it: proceeds even to a far finer analysis; it takes these pure principles apart to their very atoms—indeed it is now engaged in dissecting and analyzing the very atoms themselves... This ultimate or molecular analysis, as we call it, can satisfy only in part the chemist's unconquerable determination to know *all* about the thousands of principles he is able to isolate in this world of ours; for having taken the molecules apart and studied how atom is united to atom, often dozens of them in a single molecule, he does not rest until he has succeeded in reconstructing (synthesizing) perfectly his principles... Having thus acquired complete knowledge of the ground plan of important principles which we find in nature, the chemist in many instances has found it possible to improve on nature and construct more perfect principles... It is this insistence on complete ultimate analysis which gives to chemistry one of its most powerful resources, for with complete knowledge comes *control*, in the form of wise use of what nature offers and also in the opportunity for improving on what nature... has furnished to man." [1] We hesitate to say this hope is unrealizable. Still the synthesis of the residuum of life, and that of the necessary products of life is not, nor should it be confounded with the synthesis of life itself. We shall indicate later the role of matter in life. It is evident that it is indispensable.

From the standpoint of *energy*, we know that life utilizes the physico-chemical forces, and that these are even necessary for its existence. We know that the two great laws of energy are verified in living beings, as in the mineral kingdom. It will be well to give the proof for this, so as to remove all misapprehension about the special function of these forces or forms of energy, utilized by the living organism.

[1] *The future Independence and Progress of American Medicine*, in *the Age of Chemistry*, p. 21-23.

Let us take up first, the principle of the conservation of energy. It has been shown that a living being does not create energy; it merely receives it, transforms it, uses it, but does not destroy it. With it, as with the mineral, the quantity of energy given out is equal to that which it received. We shall examine separately the case of plants and of animals.

Plants, other than fungi, draw the energy that they need for their existence from solar radiations. In fact, it is due entirely to the action of the chlorophyl that plants assimilate the material necessary for growth. The green plants, as we know, fix the CO_2 and H_2O to produce the carbohydrates. It is supposed that the synthesis begins with that of formaldehyde CH_2O to be followed by more complex products $(CH_2O)_n$ which form the sugars and the starches, etc.

This primary synthesis is undoubtedly chemical. It begins with absorption of the energy furnished by the sun. The products formed hold this energy in reserve. The plant will utilize it for other and more complex syntheses. It is thus that the sugar accumulated in the roots is changed at the moment the plant blooms, rises into the stalk, and is used there to produce the flowers and seeds, that is for the conservation of the species. The plant closes this cycle of chemical phenomena within itself, in view of its own development and that of the species. The chemical substances used by the plant are not properly speaking, foods, for they do not constitute an available form of energy. Neither CO_2 nor H_2O possess any. The plant does not draw its energy from these, but from the solar rays, that is under inorganic conditions.

From the chemical point of view, the plant is a veritable laboratory where the most varied and the most complex syntheses and analyses are made. We shall see later on, whether there isn't something else beyond this. Let us merely note that the plant may serve as food for animals and also for some plants.

In *animals* also, we note the transformation of matter and of energy. Animals draw their sustenance from the vegetable kingdom (herbivora) or even from the animal kingdom (carnivora). Unlike the plants, they find their food already prepared, capable of furnishing the energy necessary for vital functioning. They assimilate nutritive substances that is they transform other more complex substances identical with their own protoplasm. In this process of assimilation, numerous chemical analyses and syntheses of alimentary substances take place within the organism. As proof of this it is but sufficient to cite the case of the herbivora, which build up their own *animal* tissues from the *plants* on which they feed.

Do the animals obey the laws of energy? Are they not themselves creators of energy, as one might at first suppose? We may lay it down as a principle that the animals draw all their energy from their food. They transform it, use it and restore it under various forms and ultimately under that of radiant heat. This proposition has been of late clearly demonstrated by numerous experiments. Notably those of Atwater which we shall summarize here.

This American scientist proposed to determine whether the human organism drew all its energy from its food. By controlling the intake and expenditure of energy he verified the equality $E = I$.

The intake (I) was calculated from the calorific value of the foods supplied to the subject during a period of 24 hours. The expenditure (E) was determined from the energy given out under the form of heat, work and waste. Atwater, after many and long observations, found $E = I$ to one or two thousandth part. It is unnecessary to say that the experiments were carried out under exceptionally precise conditions considering the apparatus used, and the competency of the investigator. We may find these experiments described in the *Experiment Station bulletins*, published by Atwater and others[1].

---

[1] Atwater, *Experiments on Metabolism of Matter and Energy in the Human Body. Exp. Sta. Bul. 69, 109, 136 Supt. of Documents.* Digest of metabolism experiments in which the balance of income and outgo was determined. *Rev. Ed.*

We give merely the results obtained with a subject in complete repose and those obtained with one at work.

First experiment :   The subject in complete repose.

Duration of observation	Intake in 24 hours.	Expenditure in 24 hours.
1 day	2 304 cals.	2 279 cals.
9 days	2 118 —	2 136 —
33 —	2 288 —	2 270 —
155 —	450 000 —	449 950 —

The agreement between E and I is remarkable, especially for the last and most important figures

Second experiment : The subject enclosed in a calorimetric chamber operates a dynamo whose energy is absorbed by a calorimeter.

Energy supplied	Energy restored	Difference
3 669	3 656	0.004 %

The difference is insignificant and quite within the limits of experimental error.

These experiments permit us to assert that the principle of conservation of energy applies also to living beings. The living being does not create energy but merely transforms it.

The principle of dissipation applies also, since the living being restores the energy under the form of heat.   To live, an adult man requires about 1,800 large calories a day, or one calorie an hour for each kilogramme of weight. Additional calories are required for all physical or mechanical work performed, or to resist cold, etc.   This supplementary outlay may triple or quadruple that which is necessary for the mere maintainance of life.   The output of the human motor has been measured.   It is quite high and may reach 35 %, or fall below 10 % under adverse conditions.

As the organism works without appreciable difference of temperature, we cannot say that it is a thermal motor. Under these conditions its output would be around 0; e. g. 1/300, if the difference were 1°.   It appears evident that the organism utilizes the chemical energy without it passing through the form of heat. This is only waste, a residue.

From all this we may conclude that the living organism has need of energy to live and to work; that it does not create it, nor does it destroy it. But we may add and we are going to show, that energy does not suffice to produce life. It is *the condition* for, not the *cause* of life : *Requiritur non sufficit.*

2. CHARACTERISTICS OF THE LIVING ORGANISM.

The living world is distinguished from the non-living by an assemblage of characteristics which we shall group as logically as possible, so as to bring out their value more fully. We shall consider them from the point of view of chemistry, physics, anatomy, energy, physiology and philosophy. Though one of these taken alone might leave room for doubt, the whole assemblage presents an argument so compelling that it seems impossible to escape the conclusion, that life differs essentially from physico-chemical forces, and that it is something more than its mere resultant.

Chemical characteristics :

Nature of the simple elements utilized by the living being. These elements are oxygen, hydrogen, carbon and nitrogen, along with sulphur, phosphorus, calcium, potassium, sodium, chlorine, iodine, fluorine and iron. This limitation of elements indispensable to life to so small a number is in itself a very special note of a living organism, and therefore characteristic of life. The presence of foreign elements is not tolerated in the living organism.

Nature of complex substances. Some are essential, others special. Among the essential, we must reckon the albumins. We find them in all living beings, without exception, and never any where else. Nitrogen plays a fundamental part in life. The vitamines, though infinitesimal in quantity, hold an important place. Among the substances peculiar to living organisms, are the carbohydrates and the fats. The former are especially found in plants, the latter, both in plants and animals.

High molecular weight. Organic substances are distinguished from inorganic by the complexity of their molecules.
These are formed from thousands of atoms, and in
consequence their molecular weight is very high. We shall
give only two examples taken from A. Gauthier. Egg-
albumin whose formula is C_{250} H_{400} N_{67} O_{81} S_3 has an atomic
weight of 5,739, and that of hemoglobin of a horse the
composition of which corresponds very well with the
formula C_{680} H_{4098} N_{210} O_{241} S_2, is 16,218. In this molecule
there are 5 238 atoms.

The molecule of the inorganic compounds is rather simple
H_2O, $Ca\ CO_3$, $H_2\ SO_4$; the number of atoms in these, runs
from two up into the tens, while the molecular weight
rarely runs into the hundreds. The complexity of the
organic molecule renders its analysis rather difficult, and
at present we have not yet realized the synthesis of albumin. Attempts are being made to obtain its exact analysis by successive destruction of its chemical structure. [1]

Instability of organic substances. The organic compounds, especially the highly organized and most essential,
such as the albumins, fats and carbohydrates have a very
unstable structure. They are in fact all exothermic,
that is give out at the moment of their decomposition, the
energy which they have absorbed at the moment of
their formation. Their synthesis is therefore endothermic.
The peculiarity of inorganic substances, formed spontaneously and naturally under the action of only physico-
chemical forces, is that they have no available energy, but
are in a state of stable or even of the most stable equilibrium. Such is the case of water (H_2O) carbon dioxide,
(CO_2), most oxides, sulphides, salts, $Ca\ CO_3$, $CaSO_4$, etc.
For all organic substances it is the reverse. The proof of
it is, that they supply energy to the living organism,
are combustible, are decomposed after death to pass
spontaneously to the condition of degraded, inert substances. Sugar breaks down into water and carbon dioxide,

---

[1] Lambling, *Précis de biochimie*, p. 3 et sq., Paris, Masson; Molliard,
Nutrition de la plante, Paris.

the nitrogen compounds are transformed into these same products, and into others just as inert, such as the ammonia compounds.

The living organism restores chemical energy. Whereas in the mineral kingdom, the chemical reactions of their own accord tend to break up the molecular structure and so to dissipate the artificially acquired energy, the living organisms, on the contrary, are restorers of chemical energy. They synthesize increasingly complex substances beginning with the simplest, as for instance the production of the carbohydrates, starches and sugars from carbon dioxide and water. The same cause cannot produce effects so different, so contrary. The living organism, it is true, utilizes the physico-chemical forces, but directs them and is far from being like the mineral under their entire sway.

Variety of chemical compounds. We find variety both in the individual itself and in the different species. Everyone knows the chemical complexity of a single cell. It is very different from the chemical uniformity of the crystal, typical of the mineral. In the latter, the physico-chemical forces tend to group together all the identical elements, while in the former life has need of very different elements, and these only in very minute quantities, for the exercise of all its functions. The one cannot be identical with the other. The living organism is distinct from the crystal. In the one and the same organism the cells, considered chemically, are specifically different from each other. Thus we have nerve-cells, and cells that form the muscular, cartilaginous and osseous tissue, etc. There is no such differentiation of the same substance in the mineral kingdom. If some different crystals are grouped together, it is by accident and not of necessity. We can separate them. It is not the same with the diverse elements of the organism, where each plays its own determined role indispensable to life. In the organisms of different species the chemical diversity is still greater. The impossibility of transfusing the blood of one species into another is the best proof.

Nature of the chemical reactions taking place in the laboratory of the living cell. Two opposite reactions are constantly going on, one of synthesis and one of analysis, of assimilation and of elimination, of anabolism and of katabolism, of restoration and of dissipation. The two operations are simultaneous. They imply a number of reactions. We see all these operations, so various, so numerous, so opposed, so complex and so important, taking place in a single laboratory, the microscopic cell. These reactions are not transitory, but continuous. If they should stop, life would be extinguished as a lamp deprived of oil. These reactions are more important than we might be led to suppose. An adult destroys in one day 500 grammes of organic matter which would necessitate very powerful chemicals, if done artificially in our laboratories. There is nothing similar to this in the mineral kingdom, not even in our best equipped laboratories.

The cell in functioning utilizes physico-chemical energy but directs it, tranforms it and makes it serve its purposes. Some have believed they could solve these enigmas by saying that the living organism uses diastases. The action of these is marvellous, it is true, but it is the living organism that produces its own diastases, its own colloids, as well as the compounds of which it has need.

To sum up. These reactions, these analyses and syntheses are very powerful, of variable intensity, according to need, very numerous and continual; they are directed, not merely sustained by the living organism and are mutually interrelated.

In the final analysis the chemical reactions in the living organism differ entirely from all others. The chemical reactions may be represented by a general formula: $A+B = C+D$., for example $H_2SO_4+Zn = ZnSO_4+2H$. All the elements of the two terms of the reaction are different. The vital reaction, however, is altogether unlike this, being $A+B = B+C$. The more food the living being consumes, the more it grows, the more it multiplies and the more it eliminates. The living organism forms a part of the two terms of the reaction, since it assimilates the food and renders it like itself. There is no parallel in the inorganic world. Life directs the reaction, makes it serve its own purposes in view of its growth, and propagation, and prepares reserves which it may draw upon when needed. The living organism promotes or retards the chemical reactions, according to the needs of the moment. Inorganic reactions depend only on the elements and the forms of energy brought into play. Here everything is in obedience to the laws relating to the dissipation of all possible forms of energy; to the laws of Berthollet and Berthelot's principle of maximum work or rather of maximum heat. As a result of inorganic reaction, the mineral is reduced to an altogether different condition, to the perfect equilibrium realized in the crystal.

In the living organism, the transformations are in the opposite direction, toward a maximum of unstable equilibrium, toward the greatest reserve of energy. Unless we shut our eyes to the evidence, we must admit an important difference here, between vital phenomena and physicochemical phenomena. This difference is shown under a special form by J. Friedel. [1]

"Life is not a special kind of chemistry, it is something other than chemistry. The chemical reactions which it manifests to our eyes take place in accordance with an order, a plan and an organization which do not exist in inanimate substances. Life is at once a state of transformation and of permanence; of transformation through the flow of material which is constantly renewed in the living mill of the body, and of permanence through this mill which develops in accordance with its own law, conformably to a mysterious plan, even when the matter which it converts is completely renewed.

"If we leave this examination of different organisms to pass to the chemical study of the transformations of organized nature, we again receive an impression of finality under another form; the cycle of carbon and of nitrogen in the living organism. The living organisms, the most

[1] *Le matérialisme contemporain*, p. 76 and 83, Paris, 1922.

capable chemists, without being conscious of it, continually, manufacture the most complex products, necessary for their own and others lives, working thus in a perfect agreement which in no way resembles a universal contest but rather a perfect and general harmony."

R. de la Vaux [1] adds: "Living nature is not merely a very complex chemical substance, but a stupendous sum of hereditary traits. The reaction of protoplasm with a certain relatively simple inorganic substance, immutable, in the course of ages, has evidently nothing in common with an ordinary chemical reaction." So eminent a physiologist as Haldane of Oxford, in spite of his own brilliant work, carried out with the aid of physics and chemistry, on the fine adjustment of respiration to environment despairs of the complete success of the fundamental sciences, in explaining the automatic adaptation of the body to its life, needs and to its own reproduction, and falls back on metaphysical conceptions. [2]

Physical characteristics of the living organism.

The colloidal state. [3]—The living organism is not a solid, nor a liquid, nor a gas, but a fourth form of matter called a colloid realized naturally only in the living organism, and never outside of it. This condition is necessary for life, it is a condition for life, but it does not create life as some would hold. It is on the contrary created by life which has need of its multiple functions. What then is a colloid? Formerly the colloid was opposed to the crystalloid, since in dialysis the crystalline substances alone passed through the diaphragm, and the non-crystalline substances such as starch, albumin, etc. did not dialyse. The col-

---

[1] *Revue gén. des Sciences*, 1922, p. 358.

[2] Haldane, *Mechanism, Life and Personality*, 1914 : *Organism and Environment*, 1916, *The future independence and progress of American Medicine*, in *The Age of Chemistry*, p. 49.

[3] Cf. *Rev. des questions, scientifiques*, Oct. 1920, p. 682; July, 1921, p. 133. Lambling, *Biochimie*, Senderens, *Les colloides et la vie*, dans *Rev. gén. des sciences*, June 30, 1922, p. 358, Houllevigne, *La Matière*, p. 61-68. Paris, Colin, *Revue des ques. scien.*, vol. xxvii, p. 519; vol. xxix, p. 31. Articles by Marechals, S. J.

loidal state is that of a dissolved substance, which does not realize the consecutive phenomena of the true solution.   In a true solution, the soluble substance is readily dissolved in the solvent.   In the colloidal state it remains in suspension, not as in a mixture, but under special conditions which make the colloid an intermediate phase between the true solution and the mixture.   Milk is an example of this.

That the colloid is held in suspension in the solvent is deduced from a number of facts.   The clouded appearance and lack of transparency shows that the molecules are in suspension.   The particles may be seen with the ultramicroscope.   Ultra-filtration permits their separation.   The action of heat causes coagulation and precipitation.   A positive or negative electric charge produces the same result, even more readily.   The positively charged acids and negatively charged bases also produce coagulation apparently, because the colloidal particles are either negatively or positively charged.

Unlike true solutions the colloids do not sensibly lower the melting point or raise the boiling point.   They do not follow the laws of definite proportions.   They are not identified with mixtures which likewise lack these characteristics.

The colloidal state is not reversible under reverse influences.   The colloids, milk, albumin, coagulated blood, etc., do not dissolve by a contrary operation.   The living organism, however, can dissolve a coagulated substance, so as to digest it, but this is done by other physical or chemical processes as yet quite difficult to understand.   The living organism is colloidal in character, is a sol or gel, since all the characteristics of the colloids are found in the protoplasm of the cell in the blood, in the ova, in all the different fluids, in all the tissues, even in the bones themselves.   It is the same for wood.

Some would diminish the importance of this characteristic of life by saying that the chemist makes colloids, and indeed makes them from the metals gold, silver, platinum, iron, etc.   All that is necessary to produce a metallic colloid is to pass a spark between two metal electrodes immersed in water. In industry colloids are used for the promotion of certain synthetic reactions, notably in the manufacture of sulfuric acid and of ammonia, where they play the role of catalysts, as do the colloidal diastases in the organism. But let us repeat again that life creates its own colloids, its diastases for its own use. Life, therefore, is not created by them, but is anterior and superior to them.

A special environment is necessary for life. We may consider the environment as partially interior and partially exterior to the organism. As regards the interior, we shall note merely the very special conditions of heat and of osmotic pressure.

Animals require a certain temperature within the very restricted limits of five or six degrees for warm-blooded, and a little more for cold-blooded animals. There is for both an optimum temperature, most favorable for life, a maximum temperature, which it cannot pass without fatal consequences, and a minimum temperature, also indispensable for the preservation of life. These temperatures vary with the species, but quite within the limits of 36° to 45° C. for warm-blooded animals.

If the exterior environment in which it lives does not offer a favorable temperature, the living organism reacts in different ways. Rather it adapts itself to the conditions like the cold-blooded and hibernating animals, preserving only a diminished form of vitality, a sort of sleep, as the marmot, the bears, the reptiles and the larvæ; or it succombs if the temperature is too low or the low temperature lasts too long. Habitually, the animal goes in search of the most favorable temperature and adapts itself to it Its organism increases the process of combustion if the temperature decreases, or decreases its activity when the temperature rises, or provokes perspiration to lower the internal temperature by evaporation. It is not necessary to say that there is no parallel to this in the mineral world, where the inorganic substance remains altogether passive and takes the temperature of its surroundings.

Osmotic tension [1] exhibits phenomena strikingly analogous to these. The living organism has its own very
limited osmotic tension. The environment in which it
lives has another. The two tend to equilibrium, a condition not always favorable to life. The living organism
tries to maintain its osmotic tension constant in spite of
the causes of variation. It changes its procedure according
to the circumstances and according to its aptitudes. It
succombs when the limit of its possibilities is passed. Let
us give a few instances, where the necessity of a favorable environment is brought out. The osmotic tension
of the living cells of a salt-water fish transferred to fresh
water, will cause an absorption of water and a rupture of
the cells; in the reverse procedure, the cells of fresh
water fish placed in salt water will be emptied of their
normal water. In either case death habitually follows.
There are however some fish which can pass from one environment to the other. A modification of their osmotic
tension is imperative. The same necessity imposes itself
at the moment of absorption of food. The organism reacts
automatically by processes which Science has not yet
discovered. We shall speak of this in connection with the
forms of energy which the living organism directs.

We could mention other media special to life, such as the
material medium or food, the respiratory medium air or
water, the energy medium light, chemical rays, heat and
perhaps electricity, etc.

Anatomical characteristics of the living organism. We
find in the living organism a group of anatomical characteristics, which we shall seek for in vain in the mineral. We
can never speak of anatomy, when dealing with the latter.
Let us be satisfied with a mere mention of the cells, the
tissues, the organs, the systems, the forms all of which
are variable with the species.

The cell is the first characteristic of every living organism and of everything which pertains to life. We find
it even in the fossils. Structurally the cell is very com-

---

[1] Lambling, *Précis de Biochimie*, p. 19.

plex; in spite of its small size, in spite of its microscopic dimensions ranging from a few microns to some milli-meters. The most powerful microscope reveals only a small part of it. The ultramicroscope, while extending the range of visibility much farther, falls far short of revealing all. In the cell we find as a basis, the atoms—

so numerous, so varied, so diverse in their ope-rations—forming the molecule or organic micella. These latter must group themselves in great numbers to form tissues that are barely visible. These latter in turn form the differentiated divisions of the cell, and these combined constitute the cell, the primal unit indispensable to life. All treatises on histo-logy, all the classic handbooks of biology give us descriptions of the cell and cuts to illustrate the principle features. We can give

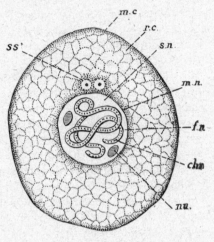

Fig. 26. — The Cell.

S. s., directive spheres; *m. c.*, cellular mem-brane;—*r. c.*, spongioplasm;—*s. n.*, nu-cleoplasm;—*m. n.*, nuclear membrane;—*f. n.*, chromatic filaments;—*ch. chr.*, chro-matine granules;— *nu.*, nucleolis.

only a very general idea. A complete cell, when examined un-der the microscope, exhibits from the exterior to the interior, the following parts : a transparent cellular membrane ; proto-plasm which constitutes the major portion of the mass, forming a network of meshes filled with a liquid ; two small directive spheres visible at the moment of cellular divi-sion ; a nucleus, a spherical globule, more refractive than the rest, and situated near the center of the nuclear mem-brane ; a chromatic filament twisted into a knot, in which are found the chromatic elements ; the nuclear fluid which fills the nucleus and lastly the nucleoli. All these elements have a special function in the life of the cell and its multiplication (fig. 26).

This anatomical structure of the cell is so complex, that no one would seriously attribute its formation solely to mechanical forces. The impress of life is there. This is why some have tried to find a less complex element as a basis of life. Haeckel called it the *moner*. This would be a cell without a nucleus, without a vestige of organization. It has never existed, except in his fertile imagination and in the drawings made by the inventor. No one has ever been able to find it, and yet it is little short of marvellous with what docility the entire monistic school has reproduced it and spoken of it, as though it had actually been seen, studied and controlled... There must be a transition stage between the mineral and the living organism. The master has said so. We must not examine into the matter too closely. The *moner* has gone the way of the *Bathybius* Haeckeli, and certain fraudulent plates.

The cell is too often considered a very simple element. The above is sufficient to prove the contrary. From a study of the cell itself and the diversity of its products, we marvel at the great variety of its forms, even in the same subject and with much greater reason in those that are specifically different. They have been classified under such general headings as bone-cells, cartilage-cells, muscle-cells, nerve-cells, fat-cells, epithelial-cells, connective-tissue-cells and blood-cells, or, according to shape, into spherical, spindle-form, polyhedral, starshaped, branching ameboid, etc.

The cell is so complex that we may look upon it as an organism in itself. In fact the protozoa are unicellular. Here, as in the thousands of other unicellular creatures of different species, we find one cell performing all the necessary functions of vegetable or animal life. Thus far the molecular and the atomic structure of the cell has not been realized outside of the living organism. The physico-chemical forces, even when guided by able investigators have not succeeded. Only crude imitations of it have been produced. To quote from a report of a committee, appointed by the American Chemical Society in June 1919, to prepare a statement of plans and policies for the facilitation of research in Medical-Chemistry [1] "Now, while multitudes of definite chemical substances have been isolated from animal and vegetable tissues, the identification of which is a contribution to our knowledge of the chemistry of the cell, no comprehensive and exhaustive study of the contents of even a single type of cell has ever been attempted. In fact, it is only when we begin to consider the cell from a strictly chemical point of view that we are led to recognize how scanty indeed is our knowledge of the chemistry of this vital biological unit. Thus, we do not even know, in exact terms of physics and chemistry, what the factors are that distinguish living from lifeless material. What are indeed the chemical and physical forces that lead to cell subdivision, the wonderful step in life development? What are the forces that lead to perpetuation of life? To instinctive self-protection? What are the conditions for the equilibrium in the colloidal system we call protoplasm, which make an obvious difference between life and death? What is the chemical structure of proteins? Of the components of brain tissue, underlying the most wonderful of all life processes, consciousness, memory, thought, and feeling? What is the chemistry or physics of the inheritance of body form from generation to generation, even of the finer traits of mind and temperament carried from parent to child, through the minute cells of procreation? Are some of the millions of chemical molecules present even in these minute cells in some way the carriers of this wonderfully accurate transmission of qualities? These are but a few of the extraordinarily important problems of chemistry and physics in the ultimate field of cell life." The committee however seems hopeful of final success. "They are tremendous problems, but many believe they are not beyond the power of the human mind in control of the scientific tools of chemistry and physics.

---

[1] *The future independence and progress of American Medicine*, in *The Age of Chemistry*, p. 55, 56.

Indeed, until these exact sciences do shed more light on these problems, there will be speculation, theory, philosophizing but not knowledge. It will take many generations of many workers to attain this knowledge, but who can question for a moment that complete success in these problems would spell for mankind health of the body, health of the mind and the happiness of untold millions of sensitive beings?" We must confess that we are not so sanguine of the ultimate success of chemistry and physics, in solving these problems. The physico-chemical forces can demolish the cell as a gust of wind destroys a building, but they cannot build it up again. In uniformity they realize the stable equilibrium found in the crystal. But life requires variety and mobility for all of its infinitely varied functions. In a word, the cell presupposes life, is produced by life, is necessary for life. We find nothing like it in the mineral world, not even in the crystal.

The tissues.—In the metazoa, cells of the same kind unite to form tissues, having specific and well defined functions. Such are the innumerable varieties of epithelial, nerve, muscular, lymphatic, blood, cartilagenous, bone and connective tissues. Such a complex and varied organization, in view of a well defined purpose, presupposes something more than the sole action of physico-chemical forces, which invariably tend to uniformity, to equilibrium, to rest. The structure and operation of the tissues is in view of the activity of the living organism. The tissues prepare the elements; the nerves transmit the sensations; the muscles execute the movements; the lymph and blood distribute the food and energy throughout the whole organism; the bones secure the necessary form and rigidity, etc. Each is made for a determined purpose and admirably adapted to realize it. There is in all this an evident finality, for which physical and chemical forces alone cannot account. As we have said for the cells, these forces can demolish this structure, but they of themselves cannot reconstruct it anew.

The organs.—The tissues by themselves, are powerless. They must combine and divide the functions among themselves. They thus constitute the various organs of the body, such as the eyes, the ears, the various glands, the bloodvessels, the lymphatics, the heart, the lungs, etc. These are indispensable for the conservation of the individual and of the animal species. In the plant, we find also organs developed along parallel lines, but in an inferior degree. Thus, there are the roots, the stalk, the leaves, the flowers, fruits, seeds of every variety.

The systems.—The organs cannot be independent of one another, they too must unite among themselves for the execution of a common function. Thus, they constitute complicated apparatus for vision, hearing, locomotion, circulation, respiration, etc., so intimately connected that the loss of one set is sufficient to interfere with the proper functioning of the others.

These combinations in view of the attainment of one and the same end are constant in the same species, but indefinitely varied in the different species. Let us take but one example, that of the apparatus for locomotion as found in the various stages of life, from the protozoa to the vertebrates. The end to be attained is always the same - change of position, but the means to this end are exceedingly varied. We must say that physico-chemical forces, operating haphazard, do not suffice to explain these marvels that are realized in all living creatures, but never in the mineral. There is something more, something of a different order in the one that is not in the other. In this we have the reason why, from the standpoint of anatomy, the living organism differs essentially from the mineral. Hence, we may conclude that the spontaneous and automatic transition from the one kindgom to the other is impossible.

To explain life, we do not begin by denying the evidence of its wonderful organization. If, in spite of our researches, it remains mysterious, presents problems scientifically insoluble, some inscrutable enigmas, let us admit it and not have the naivete to believe on the word of some popularizers, that nature has no secrets, that everything is explained by the action of mechanical or chemical forces. If the study of life discloses evidences of a Superior

Intelligence that has fashioned, organized, multiplied and diversified it without limit, let us not hesitate to acknowledge the fact. Science and Truth must eventually arrive at this. Men of Science will then no longer waste their time, seeking for impossible and contradictory solutions.

Energy characteristics of the living organism.—In the living organism we find all the manifestations of energy, from those classed as chemical to those that are optical. Hence it is, that, certain popularizers have been led to consider life a mere question of energy transformation. Haeckel has even had the naivete to write : "From the motion of the celestial bodies and the fall of a stone... to the growth of the plant and the conscience of man,... everything is reducible to the mechanism of the atoms." [1] The same idea is found in his other works. We meet with similar notions in certain treatises on biochemistry. Loeb [2] tells us : "Nothing prevents us from supposing that these experimental sciences will one day succeed in producing these living machines artificially." But it is our opinion that a closer examination of the energy manifestations of the living organism will show them to be widely different from those in the mineral.

Chemical energy is among those forms which the living organism brings into play. It is, by far, the most important of all, the most indispensable—the condition for life without constituting life itself. It manifests itself, as we have already said, under the form of syntheses and analyses, of assimilation and secretion, without showing that these phenomena restore the chemical energy in its entirety. The living organism utilizes the energy, stores it up and dispenses it according to its needs and its personal activity; it is the master and not the slave, nor is it the product of energy. The living organism is the restorer of energy, whereas inorganic substances incessantly dissipate it.

We must unquestionably connect with this subject the

---

[1] Haeckel, *Les preuves du transformisme.*
[2] Loeb. *Dynamics of living matter'* .06, Lemoke.

very important, yet still very mysterious, action of the diastases [1] whose agency has been invoked to explain the riddles connected with life. These are living substances secretions from the cells, which have the power of transforming unlimited quantities of matter without themselves undergoing any considerable change. Thus rennet coagulates 400 000 times its volume of milk. The action of the diastases is quite varied and explains in part the functions of living organisms, particularly that of digestion or the destruction of the organic molecule, destined for food and perhaps also the building up of another organic molecule.

The action of the diastases can bring about the formation of carbo-hydrates. Thus amylase transforms starch into maltose $2 C_6H_{10}O_5 + H_2O = C_{12}H_{22}O_{11}$, and the maltose in turn is transformed into glucose. $C_{12}H_{22}O_{11} + H_2O = 2 C_6H_{12}O_6$. Other diastases produce dehydration. While still others bring about oxidation, reduction, hydrogenation and dehydrogenation. The diastases have as their counterpart in the inorganic world the various catalysts that are at present so extensively studied and utilized. The diastases and the catalysts are colloids whose action is beginning to be looked upon as universal. They are however only the condition for life, but are not life; they are the product of life and are far from being its efficient cause.

Energy reserves are built up by the living organism under the form of chemical substances in anticipation of its future needs. Such reserves are starch, sugar, fats and albumin, etc. To prepare these, the living organism must perform some very complex syntheses, which never occur spontaneously in the mineral kingdom, solely under the action of physical or chemical forces. These can indeep destroy the energy reserves, but cannot restore them again. A blast of wind, an explosion can destroy an edifice but they cannot build one.

Mechanical energy manifests itself in the living being

[1] Cf. Lambling, *Précis de biochimie;* Duclaux, *La chimie organique;* Dalbis, *Anatomie et physiologie animales,* p. 382.

under the forms of circulatory, vibratory, ameboid and locomotor movements, such as creeping, swimming, walking, flying, carrying, digging, building, etc., and under the form of static effects and muscular tension. Each of these is characteristic of life, in the degree that it manifests itself, since each of them goes counter to other mechanical actions, especially contrary to the action of gravity and of friction which the living organism overcomes. Moreover, these mechanical movements are produced in view of the conserving of the individual and of the species, and assume a character of immanence and of spontaneity, or at times even of freedom that the simple mechanical actions of organic matter cannot claim, not even as manifested in elastic bodies, where all is passive, in spite of appearances to the contrary.

To grasp the full meaning of this spontaneity we must consider these movements, these actions in the highest organisms, where we can study, control, experiment with and modify them, and not in the lowest where all real control is well nigh impossible. The true scientific and philosophic method requires that we go from the known to the less known, and that we avoid the reverse method under penalty of going astray. There is no reason to fear anthropomorphism if we wish to see only what the lower beings really show us. Let us then conclude that mechanical energy is necessary for life, is the manifestation of life, but is not life.

The forms of *molecular energy*, and among them *osmosis*, play an important role in the living organism. Osmosis permits the penetration of foods into the cells and the elimination of waste. This twofold operation still remains mysterious and inimitable. We can make semipermiable membranes which permit the exchange in one determined direction, but outside of the living organism we cannot realize the simultaneous reverse operation. It has been considered possible to explain the absorption of food, and the elimination of waste by the simple phenomenon of osmosis, but neither the one nor the other is totally explained by it.

According to Lapique it is inexact to say, that all the exchanges going on in the cell can be explained by the laws of osmosis. We are obliged to recognize, in the cell, the existence of a vital function expending energy to overcome the physical equilibrium as a pump overcomes hydrostatic equilibrium. He proposes to call this function epictesis (acquisition while wearing out.) [1] The living cellular membranes are not passive like those of an inorganic dialyzer, but are active, with a vital activity. Indeed circulation takes place in two directions, the cell absorbing what is useful and rejecting what has become useless and harmful. Absorption does not cease, when the tension is equal on both sides, as is the case with inorganic membranes and as the law of equilibrium demands. The cell maintains its own tension, often very different from that of the environment. It can even absorb a liquid like itself, having the same osmotic tension. Thus it is that the serum of an animal is absorbed by the intestinal epithelium.

Certain poisons, as the venum of the rattle-snake, if introduced directly into the blood, cause death, but when introduced through the intestinal membrane, are neutralized and become harmless. Thus, the membranes take an active part in the phenomenon. In the intestines, we find fatty acids and oleates, whereas in the lymphatics, we find neutral fats; the intestinal mucous has therefore made the synthesis. In the intestines, we find albuminoids; in the vena porta, albumins. Here again a synthesis has been performed during absorption. It would be useless to insist further on the facts which prove the fundamental difference, between vital phenomena and physical phenomena. They may be found, if desired, in the textbooks of biochemistry, where they are fully and often unwittingly set forth by the author.

Heat energy in the living being. We frequently find the living organism compared to a thermal machine, and we are led to suppose that it is nothing more than this. In this machine, we are told, the heat is transformed into

[1] *Comptes rendus, Académie des Sciences,* 1922, p. 1491.

work thus affording a simple explanation. The truth and
the reality are, however, somewhat different. Heat is
necessary for the living organism, but is not sufficient to
explain its vital functioning. Heat is a product, a residuum of life, but it does not create life. Heat is a condition for life, but it is the living being that produces its
temperature, uses on its own account a certain number of
calories for its own preservation, and lets the others radiate into space. If there is excess, it finds means to
accelerate the disappearance; if there is a deficiency, it
increases combustion to maintain normal temperature.
Thus, the human organism can supply during a cold bath,
an additional 200 calories per hour, and a rabbit when
plunged into liquid air at -196° C. can maintain its own
temperature for some minutes. The mineral takes the
temperature of its environment, the living organism creates
and maintains its own temperature. On the one hand,
we have the passivity of matter, on the other, vital
activity.

Electric energy in the living organism. The mineral
receives an electric charge, the living organism produces
it, but by methods entirely different from those of
industry and of inanimate nature. The electric shocks
produced by the electric eel and the electric ray are as
painful as those from a powerful Leyden jar, and can destroy a very large animal. The ray produces its discharge
at will for its own defense, to kill its prey, or to protect
its young from attack. What the mechanism is that the
fish employs, we are far from knowing, in spite of the progress made in electricity. In the nervous system cir-
culates a current whose nature origin and function deserves
to be studied, but which is just as inadequate to explain
life. It is produced by life, but it is not life. The more
our knowledge of energy in the living organism progresses,
the more complicated become the vital problems, the more
we see them differing from the mineral kingdom to which
some have too hastily tried to ascribe them.

Light energy in the living organism.—Let us close this
brief resume with a mere mention of this peculiar form of

energy in the living organism. It is very common in marine organisms. Many classes of animals, from the protozoa to the vertebrates, possess the curious property of being phosphorescent or luminous. This energy is also liberated by the animal and in a number of cases spontaneously, when it has need for it. Here and nowhere else is found realized the ideal light, with almost 100 % efficiency. Life, or rather the Author of life, has here, in marine and other animals, solved a problem that has been the despair of the scientist—the production of cold light. We say nothing of the optical marvels realized in certain luminous fish. They are real masterpieces of optics.[1] It would be useless to look for their production by physico-chemical forces alone.

Physiological characteristics of the living organism.

These characteristics of the activity in the living organism are more significant, more important and more specific than the preceding. They are sufficient in themselves to constitute an essential difference between the living organism and the mineral. They are such as one might call vital energy, if the term were not ambiguous and might lead to the belief that life supplies characteristic forms of energy, and in consequence, is capable of having their equivalent in other forms. In employing the term vital energy, we intend merely to say, that the living organism receives a direction, a specialization which is not a simple result of the physico-chemical forces brought into play. We shall run through the various physiological manifestations of life, merely to see that we are in a domain different from the mineral kingdom, and that there is something superadded.

Generation—Omne vivum ex vivo—All life from life. Such is the adage that is confirmed by all the scientific observations on life, since the celebrated experiments of Pasteur. Not a single exception has been found. It is therefore a law as general as one could possibly wish; as

---

[1] Cf. Richard, *L'océanographie*, p. 360; Vuibert et Nony, *Rev. gén. d. Sciences*, 1922, p. 677.

clearly demonstrated as one could exact, by the most competent of men Pasteur, and after him all biologists. No one has ever created life in his laboratory, or has ever created one living cell.

On the other hand, all living beings transmit life, and life identical with that which they possess. It is indeed the most conclusive counter experience which one can imagine, since it has been realized for millions of years and is being realized millions of times each day, in all stages of life, from the protozoa to the most highly organized of creatures. Everywhere, life begins with the unicellular stage, to develop subsequently into the multicellular adult.

Nutrition of the living organism.—This term synonymous with assimilation and elimination, is a very complex phenomenon. To live, the organism needs continual nourishment—*assimilation* of food, whence it draws the energy necessary for its activity, and *elimination* of the products consumed, digested and not assimilated, to avoid obstruction, intoxication and death. This twofold phenomenon characterizes the living organism alone. It presupposes absorption, digestion and respiration. There is nothing analogous as has been said, in the crystal. [1] The crystal does not assimilate. It attracts the dissolved elements, but they are like itself. The living organism transforms the food, assimilates it, as the word itself well indicates, makes it like itself.

$$A+B = nB+D.$$

In the living organism assimilation takes place, by intussusception; in the crystal the growth is by accretion, i. e. by superposition and juxtaposition, $C+C = nC$. In the living organism there is creation of cells, tissues and organs of diverse kinds. There is nothing similar to this in the crystal. The living organism cannot live without assimilating; the crystal exists indefinitely without new accretions.

Development of the living organism is the habitual conse-

---

[1] Dastré, *Life and Death*, tr. by W. J. Greenstreet, '11, Scribner.

ιuence of assimilation. It can be considered quantita-
ιively, qualitatively and specifically. From this threefold
ιtandpoint, it is characteristic of life and differs essentially
΄rom the development of the crystal with which some have
ried to identify it.

Quantitative development viewed externally represents
he passage from the unicellular stage to the stage, where
ιre grouped together either a few cells or some millions

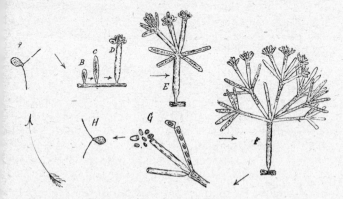

Fig. 27. — Evolution of an Alga. (Sciadiu n arbuscula.)
A. Spore;—B, E, F. Development;—G. Spore formation;—H. New spore.

ιf cells (fig. 27). This collossal edifice is constructed in fact,
ιy one single cell from the material which it has been able
ιo gather and to assimilate. It, therefore, differs in this
ιespect from the development of the crystal, which does
ιnot assimilate nor diversify its materials.

The development is qualitative, since the cell constructs
ιor creates an organism whose component parts are not
identical, nor homogeneous but very heterogeneous, and
yet so intimately bound together, so united as to form one
whole, admirably adapted to its purposes. There is
nothing similar to this in the crystal where uniformity
reigns.

The development is specific in the sense that the
offspring reproduce the specific characteristics of the
parents, and that life presents us with some hundreds of

thousands of different species, both in the vegetable and
in the animal kingdom. In the species, we find race and
individual variety to such an extent that it is impossible
to find two leaves exactly alike. Life, indeed, has its
laws, but also a certain spontaneity which permits of
rather extensive variations. There is nothing like this
in the crystal.

Reproduction.—The living organism can perpetuate
itself only by reproduction, since there is no spontaneous
generation. This faculty, special to all living beings, adds
a new note very characteristic of life. If all do not reproduce themselves, all have the power to do so. Its operation is most wonderful, most inexplicable, most mysterious. Ever since the scientist attacked the problem, he
has been able merely to verify the fact without explaining
it. How can one cell potentially contain in itself an organism so complicated as that of a plant like the oak, the
beech or the redwood, etc; or as that of an animal like the
horse, the ox or the elephant? It matters little, whether
the mode of reproduction be that of kariokynesis or by
spore, asexual or sexual, they are all equally marvellous.
Physico-chemical forces alone will never suffice to explain
this essentially vital phenomenon.

Take merely the reproduction of a unicellular organism.
Pass in review the various phases of its multiplication, as
numerous as they are varied. It undoubtedly rests upon
cellular division, but a division where everything is prepared, organized, classified in view of attaining the strictest
similarity. There is here a plethora of precautions (fig. 28).
What is to be said of more complex organisms? How explain
the fact of heredity which transmits all the ancestral characteristics down to the minutest chemical, anatomical and
physiological details? The attempts made by biologists
to give simple explanations drawn from the domain of
the physical sciences, have always failed and will always
fail in the presence of the numberless marvels of reproduction and of heredity. We smile at an explanation like the
following : "Multiplication of living beings is a simple
consequence of assimilation." It is probably based on

certain experiments which show a direct connection between the vitamine content of foods and reproduction. The experimental evidence is too meagre to give us assurance in the matter. But apart from this, it would be necessary to first explain assimilation which is something quite different from an ordinary chemical reaction.

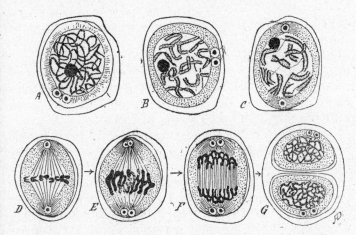

Fig. 28. — Cellular division of a mother cell of pollen.

A. Mother cell;—B. Filament dividing into V shaped segments;—C. Directive spheres arranging themselves at the two poles of the cell;—D. The protoplasm;—E. Division of directive spheres;—F. Nuclear fragments moving toward the poles;—G. The two daughter cells with their own envelope.

The chemist has never realized it, and never will realize it. Besides, it would also be necessary to prove that there is no distinction between reproduction and assimilation. Who does not know that they are two functions parallel perhaps, but essentially distinct since the one can take place without the other.

Reparation of lesions.—Some accidents can arise to mar and disarrange this masterpiece, the living organism. A lesion can injure the entire organism; a vein or an artery may burst, causing a loss of the blood which maintains life. A muscle may be bruised, or severed, rendering it inactive; a nerve may undergo the same fate, and thence-

forth transmission of sensations will become impossible.
A shell may fracture the skeletal frame, and life will be
extinguished. But note! The living organism can repair
certain lesions, even those that are very serious and extended. We shall adduce no other proofs than the marvels
of restoration effected by surgery during the late war.
What machine repairs its own injuries? The living
organism is therefore something more than a mere machine.
It has been said that the crystal repairs its lesions. Yes,
as the wave fills up the holes on the sea-shore. Restoration
in the living organism, presupposes assimilation, differentiation, cellular reproduction and multiplication at once
qualitative and quantitative. Life alone has the power
to do this.

Substitutions.—The living organism can sustain permanent injuries. Organs and members may be amputated.
But the wonderful thing about all this is, that the organism adapts itself to the condition, uses that which still
remains and goes on as before. The war has brought to
light many instances of substitution. To cite only one,
which is by no means the least demonstrative. Men had
for years attempted to localize the various functions to a
particular lobe or section of lobe of the brain. Now
the serious cerebral injuries sustained by some of the men
during the war necessitated the severance, or the destruction of notable parts, or even of an entire hemisphere.
In spite of this, it soon became apparent that substitution
had been made with such perfection, that all the functions
were very speedily reestablished. The *Revue des Sciences*
of August 1920 concluded that the previous theories had
to be revised and this marvellous fact of substitution
recognized.

The function therefore does not depend exlusively upon
the organ; the latter is but an instrument employed by
the soul. There is here as in the previous phenomena
something more than the mere physico-chemical processus
that certain authors would insist upon. [1] There must

[1]. Cf. Cuénot, *La genèse des espèces animales*, p. 291, Paris.

be a principle of life, a directive cause, and what is more, a Creative Cause of this wonderful vital process.

Antixeny.—This term has been invented to denote the struggle of the organism with the causes of destruction that originate outside the organism; the struggle with the mechanical, chemical and physical forces of heat, light, osmotic tension, microbes and toxins. It would require volumes to describe the means of defense which the organism can employ against the numberless causes of destruction. To know how to bring them into operation is not the least condition for success in hygiene and therapy. The procedure of the living organism in this struggle for life is quite varied. Either it flees from the danger or it surmounts the obstacle, or it steels itself against the injury, or it is liberated from it, or it eliminates the obstacle, or absorbs it, or kills it, or raises insurmountable barriers against it. We note merely phagocytosis, serotherapy, vaccination, the various secretions and excretion, regulation of temperature, osmotic tension, arterial tension, etc. These are some of the means of defense of the organism employed by the organism itself. Does the mineral kingdom offer anything similar to this?

According to Cuénot, p. 291, "Life would be almost inconceivable, if living beings had not possessed from the very beginning, these useful reactions which supply for them the work of the mechanic whose office is to regulate precisely, now more now less, the movement of industrial machinery. When these wear out, when the metazoa grow old, regulation becomes ever more difficult."

Let us cite a typical instance of osmotic regulation. We know that for fresh water fish, the interior medium has a much higher osmotic pressure than the water, which surrounds the fish. The blood of the carp freezes at —0.49°, the freezing point of fresh water is 0.02°. To obtain the osmotic pressure in absolute value we multiply the respective freezing points by the factor 124. The osmotic pressure of fresh water then in absolute value is in the neighborhood of 2.48 meters of distilled water, whereas

that of the interior medium of the fish is 60.76 meters.
"It is remarkable" say Paul Portier and Marcel Duval, [1]
"that the delicate tissue of the gills which permit the
gaseous exchange between the surrounding water and the
blood, should maintain constant, all during life, this important inequality of the osmotic pressure with the fish's
exterior medium." More remarkable still. Investigators
have kept carp in solutions which were gradually concentrated from 3.5 to 17 grammes of salt to the liter of water
for from 3 to 5 hours, and found, that the osmotic pressure
of the carps' blood increased in proportion to the increase
of salt in the surrounding water; but it increased less rapidly than that of the exterior medium. The result of this
is that the pressure, at the beginning much higher than
that of the water, becomes lower for the strong concentra-
tions. The fish is incapable of maintaining its osmotic
pressure at a constant level, as do the mammal and the
bird, yet it possesses a *tendency to regulation*. They
noticed also that the weight of the fish diminishes in the
measure that the salt content of the exterior medium
increases. With a salt concentration of 15 grammes to
the liter, the diminution of weight becomes noticeable,
and it seems that at this point the gills are strained, for
the fish gives evident signs of distress foreshadowing death.
Yet there is here a rapid attempt at adaptation to the new
environment very characteristic of life. A slow transition
from fresh water into water made saline by degrees,
might perhaps permit the carp to adapt itself completely
to the new environment as do the eel, the salmon-trout,
the shad and other organisms of our rivers. The algae,
like animals, react to the concentration of the medium, to
maintain their turgescence by an augmentation of their
own concentration.

Senescence. [2]—In life everything wears out, everything
grows old. It is a sort of necessity resulting from vital

[1] *Comptes rendus. Acad. des Sciences*, May 22, 1922, p. 1366 and
1493-1495.

[2] Cf. Dr. Maumus, *La cellule*, vol. ii, p. 256 et sq.

activity. When assimilation is below elimination, the intake less than the loss, the organism wears itself out, dwindles away, and becomes incapable of continuing its essential functions. The process may be sudden or slow, cellular or organic, but it matters little; it is inevitable. Again we must repeat there is nothing similar to this in the crystal which can last indefinitely : witness the crystalline rocks of the Archean period which have come down to our own day.

Death of the organism.—This is the last characteristic or rather, the disappearance of all true characteristics, assimilation and excretion and of all vital activity. The living organism arrives at an absolutely irreversible limit, and in this it is also distinguishable from the crystal which can repass through all the previous conditions, provided the necessary energy is supplied. The corpse, however, cannot recover life spontaneoulsy. It is not in the power of man, nor even of a cell to restore life. He alone Who created life can restore it, reestablish it. The causes of death are as nnmerous as the causes which arrest one single, necessary function of life; asphyxia, a more rapid elimination than assimilation, cessation of the action of the heart, of the brain, of the kidneys, a serious injury, etc.

We cannot speak of the death of a crystal, of the mineral, except by metaphor. Hence we are surprised to see this expression taken in a literal sense in some scientific works. Why this confusion? Do some hope, by a play on words, to fill up the abyss which separates the living being from the mineral, life from death? After death, the substance of the plant or of the animal, falls under the entire sway of the physico-chemical forces. Henceforth it belongs to the mineral kingdom. The organic substances as the proteins, the fats, the carbohydrates, take increasingly simpler forms, until reduced to the condition of carbonic acid, water, urea, ammonia, CO_2, H_2O, $CO(NH_2)_2$, NH_3. They remain in this condition indefinitely unless absorbed again by another living organism to take part anew in the vital cycle, but in this case it will again be life, that will give life and not the physico-chemical forces.

Characteristics of the philosophical order.

If now we cast a glance at the whole living organism in the full activity of its life, we shall discover some new characteristics which are like a synthesis, the coordination of all the others, and give us an insight into their nature. We do not wish to compose a philosophical treatise on life. It will serve our purpose to give briefly the most characteristic traits of the organism as a whole; its *unity* in material, morphological and physiological multiplicity; its *finality*, or the disposition of the means to the end to be attained; its *activity* proper to a living being intimately united with matter; *the nature* of a living organism endowed with a vegetative soul as in the plant, a sensitive soul as in the animal, and an intellectual soul as in man.

The threefold *unity*, chemical, anatomical and physiological, is manifest to anyone who takes the pains to study the living organism. There is question here of a substantial unity in the philosophical sense, and not of an accidental unity as might be a chance grouping of atoms, of cells, of organs or of functions. Suppress but one chemical element in the living organism, such as nitrogen, carbon, hydrogen, oxygen, iron and even some others in infinitesimal quantities as in the vitamines and we suppress life itself.

So, anatomically each cell, each tissue, each organ, each system is in continuous relation with all the others. They are not thrown together pell mell, but are regularly and harmonically blended into one whole of which all are but parts.

Physiologically, the multiplicity of functions is the basis of the conservation of the individual and of the species; all converge towards the same end. This is indeed, a division of labor, but of labor coordinated in view of a single purpose. It is this which leads us to conclude a unity of action, a unity of purpose and a unity of nature. [1]

In the living organism, we find an intrinsic *finality*,

---

[1] Cf. Cardinal Mercier, *Origin of contemporary Psychology*, Kenedy.

that is to say, a marvellous adaptation of means to the end to be realized, viz. the conservation of the individual and of the species. Everyone ought to be able to recognize this finality. But the materialist ever preoccupied with consequences which might be drawn from this in favor of a Creating Intelligence, prefers to pass over it in silence, when he cannot make it the object of his ridicule or formal denial. We cannot discuss with those who would not see.

Considering the living organism from the chemical, anatomical and physiological point of view, we see the means admirably adapted to the end. From the lowest cell to the most complete, the most complex organ, every-thing, concurs, to the realization of its own particular purpose. The cell assimilates and rejects for the whole organism, or rather each cell exercises this indispensable function provided for by special cells, and by special functions of the different organs. The latter in turn directs their activity toward a common end, thus there are organs of locomotion, of vision, of hearing, of circulation, of respiration, etc.

Again finality is evident from the fact that the living organism is a differentiated and organized being, which possesses a certain hierarchy of functions. Again we repeat we find nothing like this in the mineral, not even in the crystalline state.

We say that it is *differentiated*, that is, fitted for its varied activities by its great variety of chemical elements, and by its extremely varied anatomical structure. The organism is individually and specifically differentiated. The crystal homogeneous, designed for immutability and fixity.

The living being is *organized*, that is supplied with special organs designed for special functions such as vision, hearing nutrition, locomotion, elimination and reproduction. These organs, the living being itself builds up from the unicellular stage to their complete development. It sustains them, it repairs them, and replaces them, unlike anything in the inorganic world where no organs nor even a sign of assi-milation can be discerned. This is so true, that the living organism, even in the fossil state, may always be distinguished from the mineral, since it always retains traces of its organism.

Tne living organism possesses a certain hierarchy of functions in which each element from the systems, organs and tissues down to the cells, plays its individual role in complete dependence upon the whole, in view of one and the same end.   Assimilation follows digestion, absorption, seizure of and search for food.   Thus the nerves command the members and these the organs, etc.   Admirable order reigns among the thirty trillions of cells which make up a single human body and all execute their functions punctually, for the best interests of the individual and of the species. The unity of which St. Paul speaks when he says "the body is one and hath many members : and all the members of the body, whereas they are many, yet are one body"I Rom., xii, 12, continues down to the minutest cell. It is of very minor importance, whether the obedience is a conscious one or not it is a real ∿bedience.   The instances of the organism's automatic defense against an enemy, the cold, the heat, the microbes, etc., bring into prominence this dependence and mutual solidarity.

The activity proper to the living being is a new and important factor.   This activity is distinguished from that of the mineral kingdom in this, that superadded to that of matter, it is continuous, autonomous, spontaneous, immanent, irreversable, specific.   It has neither degree nor mechanical equivalent.   Life is an activity superadded to matter.   In fact the living organism vitalizes matter by assimilating it.   At death, matter loses its life, and yet the corpse has all the elements of the living organism. The elementary life of the cell, which can be noticed in the corpse for some time after death, is only a momentary and partial continuation of the life of the elements in the organism. [1]   It disappears very quickly.

The fact that Dr. Carrel has been able to maintain this "elementary life" and even the life of some of the organs, proves merely that he has realized, not indeed life itself,

---

[1] Cf. Dr. Maumus, *La cellule*, vol. ii, p. 201.

but merely the conditions for the continuation of preexisting life. [1] The fact that he has been able to graft apparently dead tissues, proves that he has supplied these tissues with the conditions necessary for life, and not that he has actually created life. The tissues alone could not recover their life. Partial assimilation *in vitro* of certain tissues is very limited, and very much out of its natural element, since the cells do not differentiate, do not create any organ.

The activity of the living organism is a continuous activity in its most essential manifestations. The living being must continually assimilate and reject to escape death, that is the complete cessation of all vital activity, dissolution and reversion to the inorganic state of CO_2, H_2O, NH_3, $CO(NH_2)_2$. The instability of protoplasm is not sufficient to explain the continuity of the phenomenon. Nocturnal sleep and hibernation are only the slowing down of this activity. In the seed, or in the spores, the living organism attains a minimum of activity. This condition cannot be too greatly prolonged without bringing on death. Indeed, after a certain time, seeds will no longer germinate. There is nothing in the crystal or in our chemical substances that can compare with this.

The activity of the living organism is *autonomous* and *spontaneous*, that is, is dependent upon the living organism itself. [2] The latter is indeed capable of augmenting, retarding or suppressing entirely any particular activity. It is therefore, the conscious or unconscious master of this activity. Matter on the contrary, is in itself, inert and passive. The projectile has only the velocity imparted to it from without. It cannot augment nor diminish the same. Among animals this spontaneous activity becomes more manifest, the higher they rise in the organized scale. In man it becomes free for certain acts.

The activity of the living organism is furthermore *immanent*, i. e. begins and ends in the subject itself. [3] The

[1] Cf. Cardinal Mercier, *op. cit.*
[2] Dr. Maumus, *op. cit.*, p. 227-242.
[3] Cardinal Mercier, *Origin of contemporary Psychology*.

living organism acts for itself, for its own profit or for that of the species. It is the beginning and end of its own activity. The mineral has only a transitive activity. It receives all its activity from without and transmits it outside itself. E. g. the projectile has its velocity imparted to it, and at the moment that it explodes, it produces heat or the destruction of the object intended. Such is the case with all mechanically impelled objects. The type of immanent activity is that of assimilation, of growth and of cellular reproduction. $A+V = nV+D$. This, however, does not prevent the living organism from being the seat of transitive and passive activities, since it is material, but there is something more than this.

Life is *irreversible*. It begins with birth and terminates with death. This series of activities is irreversible at all stages. The dead are not naturally restored to life. It is otherwise with inorganic activities or forms of energy. The crystal may form, dissolve, reform and melt again, etc. Water may volatilize, condense, and revolatilize under the influence of physical energy.

Life is a *specific* activity characterizing living beings in general and the species in particular. The vegetative life of the plant is a different activity from that of the sensitive life of the animal, and this again is different from the intellectual life of man. But even considering vegetative life alone, it is different in the plant, in the animal, in the amoeba, in the sponge, in the sea-urchin, in the moth, in the mollusk, in the insect, in the fish, in bacteria, in the reptile, in the bird and in the mammal. The one is not the other, nor transmutable into the other. Each has its characteristic notes; or rather its characteristic notes are the more specific the more divergent is the living type. The transfusion of blood, impossible between different species, is a striking proof of this.

Life has no *mechanical equivalent*, although all its various forms of energy have.

Life *has no degrees*. There is life or there is not.

Life, therefore cannot be the result of physico-chemical forces. It cannot be produced by them alone. These are the condition for life, not the efficient cause of life.

Life supposes the existence of a vegetative soul [1] in the plant, a sensitive soul in the animal, and a spiritual soul in man. It is the soul which uses, directs, organizes energy and matter. It is the soul which builds up the living organism with the material and the energy drawn from the exterior medium. It is the soul which unconsciously regulates the vegetative and the sensitive activities, and consciously the intellectual activities. As to the nature of the soul, philosophy teaches us that it is simple in the plant and in the animal, spiritual in man, vegetative in the plant and sensitive in the animal. In man the soul, at one and the same time, functions as a vegetative, a sensitive and an intellectual soul. That which can do more can do less, but the reverse is not true.

Intelligence and liberty constitute the most important and the least reducible differences, between the living organism and the mineral. But this is not the place to discuss these questions. We shall treat them later in chapter v.

Let us sum up the conclusions which we have drawn from this array of characteristics of the living organism. We could give only a very summary account of them, but we think we have established the fact that scientific progress accentuates rather than diminishes these differences. They have not appeared and do not appear reducible to physico-chemical forces. They permit us to suppose in the living organism the existence of a principle of action, which philosophers have called by a very significant name — the vital principle, the soul of the living organism.

We leave to philosophy the task of determining more precisely the nature of this principle, which is considered as simple in the plant and in the animal, and spiritual in man. That of the animal is distinguished from that of the plant by being sensitive, and from that of man by a nature essentially different and of a higher order.

[1] Cf. Cardinal Mercier, *op. cit.*

Mineral activity, vegetative activity, sensitive activity and intellectual activity, such are the characteristics of the four kingdoms we have considered.

In this study of life we have considered it exclusively in its lower state and believe we have proved that it differs fundamentally from physico-chemical forces, and is not reducible to them. Experience and reason agree in demonstrating that there is no spontaneous generation, nor ever can be, and that inorganic matter can never pass to the condition of living matter, except under the influence of preexisting life.

§ IV. — PRIMITIVE ORIGIN OF LIFE.

In the preceding paragraphs we have merely mentioned some of the elements in the solution of the question of the origin of life. We shall now show : 1. that life actually had a beginning on earth; 2. that it did not begin by spontaneous generation; 3. that it began by a divine act of creation.

Now it is certain that life had a beginning on earth. — To prove this we need not have recourse to metaphysics, nor say that an eternal series of vital phenomena would form a *concrete* infinite number which the mind could not conceive. Geology is sufficiently advanced to show that life had a beginning and even at what epoch it began.

There was a time when the earth's crust was entirely in a state of igneous fusion at a temperature of more than 3 000⁰. In fact the substrata in every country on the globe are formed of identical rocks, whose structure attests the primitive state of fusion at a temperature undoubtedly higher than that of the lava from our present day volcanoes. Now on this glowing earth, in this furnace atmosphere, no life was possible; no germ could exist. We cannot imagine an adaptation which would have enabled primitive organisms to live in so hot a medium, for there is a limit to adaptation. Above 1 000⁰ water dissociates into its elements, while at this same temperature the molecules of organized substances could not remain united. How then shall we conceive a living being whose elements could not be held together?

Furthermore, if we admit that the earth came into existence by way of evolution from the solar nebula, according to the plausible hypothesis of Laplace and Faye, would not life have been incompatible with this original state of dispersed atoms?

Certain authors have held that the earth might have been sown with germs adhering to the cosmic dust, dispersed into space on the trajectory of comets and shooting stars. Admitting that it is probable that the earth, while travelling through space, gathers some cosmic dust too minute to affect our senses; admitting even, what is scarcely probable, that some living germs are found in this dust as they are found in the dust of our own atmosphere, what may we conclude from this? The question would merely be pushed back a little farther. How did life begin on the heavenly bodies? Whence have come these seeds of life? For these bodies have passed through the same phases as the earth itself. In connection with this we may quote a few lines from an article on "The Problem of the Origin of Life" written by Paul Becquerel in *Les Nouvelles littéraires artistiques et scientifiques* (Paris) and quoted in the *Literary Digest*, July 11, 1925. "If we wish to explain the origin of life on the earth's surface, without recourse either to spontaneous generation or to supernatural creation, there is only one likely solution. It is that the earth, like an ordinary bouillon of cultures has been sowed with germs from another inhabited planet. Have meteors, cosmic dust, the propulsive force of stellar radiation, or universal attraction brought such germs hither? My conclusion is very clear. Terrestrial life did not come from another world. As my experiments on the microbicidal action of ultraviolet rays at low temperatures have shown, no germ can traverse the interstellar void without being killed by the sun's ultraviolet radiation.

"But there are forces yet more dangerous in the high atmosphere! They are the cathodic rays, which, striking upon the fine crystallized dust of frozen nitrogen, produce the magnificent boreal auroras! Not only are these rays fatal to germs, but after absorption they produce the X-rays, whose redoubtable powers we know only too well.

"These X-rays would reach the interstellar germs adhering to the nitrogen crystals, and even those lurking in the interior of cosmic dust particles, where they might have penetrated if these were porous : and there the germs would be inevitably annihilated.

"As for transportation by meteorites, Pasteur himself demonstrated that these are sterile. In the present state of science, we must then be content to concentrate our researches upon the earth. To regard the origin of life as having taken place elsewhere, is to elude the problem". Becquerel then goes on to formulate a new hypothesis which we shall take up later. This much is certain, whether it was on the earth, or on some unknown star, it is certain that life had a beginning. In what way did it begin?

Life did not begin by spontaneous generation.—The materialistic school sustains the opposite opinion with a desperation that is quite comprehensible. We shall give their arguments as drawn from Haeckel, and then in opposition those which prove our own proposition. The reader will readily perceive towards which conclusion real science and solid reasons incline.

Haeckel clearly puts before us the following alternative : "Natural evolution or supernatural creation—we must choose between these two possibilities... Reject monism and nothing remains but the irrational hypothesis of a miracle of supernatural creation." It all reduces to this : Life began either through spontaneous generation, or by divine creation...

Now this second hypothesis he rejects as irrational and anti-scientific. Hence life began through spontaneous generation. Haeckel regards as anti-scientific every system in which nature, atoms or motion is not entirely explained by itself, and by itself alone, be it for primitive creation or for order and organization. Such a purely gratuitous *postulatum* supposes solved, all the problems which philosophy is precisely trying to solve.

Having reasoned thus, Haeckel goes on to show how the spontaneous formation of the first protoplasm took place. "Living bodies had to be formed chemically at the expense of inorganic compounds. Thus had to appear this very complex substance containing both carbon and nitrogen which we have called protoplasm, and which is the constant material seat of all vital activity. The first moners arose through spontaneous generation at the beginning of the Laurentian period. They were produced from inorganic compounds, simple combinations of carbon, carbonic acid, hydrogen and nitrogen."[1] Facts so vague and reasons so devoid of solidity prove only too clearly that Haeckel admits spontaneous generation, because it is a philosophical necessity to avoid God.

Using as a basis for his arguments the recent synthesis of sugars from water and carbon dioxide by means of ultra-violet rays, Becquerel (*loc. cit.*) formulates a new hypothesis on the origin of life on this earth. "Cosmic forces" he writes, "were formerly quite sufficient to form on our planet organic substances and bring about, under conditions of which we still are ignorant, the synthesis of living protoplasm.

"The beautiful experiments of Daniel Berthelot and of Hoxlasa on the synthesis of sugars and starchy substances are most hopeful. They make possible a theory of "radio-biogenesis."

"According to this conception which I have been the first to develop, it is possible that, at an extremely remote era, possibly ten million centuries ago—for the evolution of terrestrial life has taken much longer than is generally supposed—the sun gave out much more ultra-violet radiation than now. Besides, sedimentary strata being rare, the crystalline rocks forming the greater part of the ocean bottom must have been much more radio-active than at present. Under the action of these physical forces on the

[1] Cited by Vigouroux, *Les Livres saints*, 3d. edit., vol. III, p. 179. The same idea is expressed in *The riddle of the Universe*, in *History of Creation*, and the other works of Haeckel.

waters charged with mineral substances and carbonic acid,
in conditions yet unknown, there is nothing improbable
in supposing that there may have been formed colloidal
organic substances, complex systems of albuminoids and
from these, protoplasm, living germs.

"Carried to other regions covered with protective
sediments, these germs then developed apart from the
influence of these dangerous radiations.   It was thus that
probably began, in the Archean seas, the reign of the
microscopic protozoophytes — those strange cellular mixtures that were neither animals nor plants, whence issued, by
way of differentiation, the animal and vegetable kingdoms.

"Let us hope that science with the astonishing means
now at its disposal, may in the not far distant future corroborate this hypothesis experimentally."

Apart from the fact that what has been produced by
chemists is not life, not a living organism, but merely
certain life products, we may say that since Becquerel
hopes that "science... may in the not far distant future
corroborate this hypothesis experimentally" he admits
the possibility of the reactions going on at the present
time—that is he admits the possibility of spontaneous generation under the influence of ultra-violet rays, for which
there is no experimental evidence.   All that we can do
is hope—and hope in vain.

Other partisans of spontaneous generation bring forward
no stronger arguments, and seem to have no other object
than the destruction of all idea of a Creator God.   It is
very regretable that certain scientists should spend their
whole lives in trying to do away with creation.   Far from
promoting the science of life, they retard the proper understanding of it.   Their role is to study the character of
secondary or natural causes.   Numerous and important
though they may be, they cannot in the least diminish
the necessity of a First Cause Which has produced them,
in creating life.

For us the following propositions seem unassailable.   The
laws of nature are constant in time, as well as in extent.
Now in our day, it is a certain law that life is not produced

spontaneously. Hence, in the beginning, life could not have developed from matter through the sole influence of physical or chemical forces. The constancy of the natural laws throughout the centuries is the foundation of all scientific induction. If the forces can change their nature, it becomes impossible to pass from the science of past facts to a knowledge of present facts. The physical laws being unchangeable, that which takes place today must have taken place at other times. Without doubt, as de Lapparent has justly remarked, there have been differences of intensity in the action of these forces, but there has never been any difference of nature. This principle is the indispensable basis of all science, particularly that of geology.

Is the spontaneous production of life or its nonproduction merely a simple difference of degree in the action of a force? If inorganic matter could have created life by itself at other times and is incapable of doing so today, has there not been a change of nature? We cannot object that the physical conditions are no longer realized in our day, for the atomic elements, humidity, heat, organic matter, light, the ultra-violet rays, the colloidal state, everything is operative. If matter does not produce life any longer it has then changed its nature.

These considerations pin down the partisans of spontaneous generation [1] so tightly, that to safeguard their hypothesis they assert that life ought to be produced in the same manner even at the present time. But, we have shown and we believe conclusively, that no life is actually produced through spontaneous generation, nor can it be produced. This, then is why we reject the spontaneity of the first beginning of life.

Life began by a divine act of creation. — We must perforce admit that such is the logical consequence of our study. We must have recourse to a Power higher than mere matter and physical forces; to a Power possessing life in an eminent degree, Who determined its inception by an act of His will.

[1] Cf. Le Dantec, Loeb, Guilleminot, Arrhénius.

Haeckel was altogether wrong in holding that it would be against reason to recognize in nature the intervention of God. [1] True science is not atheistic by definition. It starts from well established facts and evident principles and then proceeds to the conquest of all the consequences that may logically be drawn therefrom. Now starting from concrete facts, as life and its origin, and safe principles, as that of causality, our reason comes logically to a Sovereign Being, a personal Creator of the world, Who has not abandoned His work after having created it.

Science is not a jumble of observations and experiences. It consists in going back to secondary causes, while philosophy ascends to the First Cause. For Haeckel the supreme cause is mechanical motion. But for us, mechanical motion does not merely fail to explain the world or life, but must itself be explained by a prime mover. This Prime Mover, Who suffices unto Himself, Who communicates all motion, we find logically at the end of all our reasoning. Let us remark that our concern in this matter is not so great as the materialist's. For, even if life did begin spontaneously, for us, God would still remain the necessary First and Supreme Cause. While all that is necessary, to overthrow the monistic religion of Haeckel and his school, is to be confronted by a dilemma which can he solved solely by the admission of a God.

The ancients believed they could see God face to face. Even among the Hebrews, there was the saying : "I have seen God and therefore I shall die." Even so, the modern spirit, estranged from God by the secularization of all the sciences, is dismayed and troubled when it sees His image looming up at the end of their reasoning. Just as a traveler is perplexed and uncertain which way to turn, when his path leads to the edge of a precipice, so

---

[1] "Since it is accepted that the starting point of every living being is a germ, it follows that the origin of life on the terrestrial globe implies the existence of a *First Cause.*" E. Ferrière, *La vie et l'âme*, Paris, p. 361.

the mistaken minds of today begin to doubt when their logic leads to God. We, however, adore the majesty of Him Who reveals Himself to our reason, as well as to our faith. We take courage, when we feel that the legitimate deductions of modern science cannot even disturb the surface of our age-long belief.

CHAPTER IV

ORIGIN OF SPECIES

ARTICLE I

GENERAL NOTION.

In the study of the laws of life and the conditions under which it is produced, we have been led to this conclusion : In the beginning, when the earth had cooled down and was covered by the first oceans, and was in a condition to receive and sustain living beings, God created life by an act of His omnipotence. Since nature alone is incapable of imparting vital motion to inorganic matter, it was altogether necessary that a Superior Power intervene.

Though life is one, the living organism assumes thousands of different forms, which are divided into two great classes termed the vegetable and the animal kingdoms. Among the plants, we find various types exhibiting fundamental differences, ranging from the unicellular algae to the mighty oaks and red-woods, with every degree of complexity. There is the same variety, the same gradation among the animals. There is nothing more simple in appearance than the infusoria, and yet no machine so complicated or operated so intelligently as the organism of a mammal. In both kingdoms, there is a gradation of the numerous species. What has effected this? Has God directly fashioned each of these forms successively or simultaneously, or has He endowed matter with the power of evolving from lower organisms to higher? If the latter, to what extent can we demonstrate it by actual facts? Or, would the physico-chemical forms of energy suffice to explain this development, this evolution of living beings? There are here two different questions, one scientific and the other philosophic in character. Two main systems that pretend to give a true solution of the scientific problem. One holds to the theory of the Constancy, and the other to that of the Evolution of species.

The theory of constancy regards species as nontransmutable types, and teaches that God has directly fashioned each and every one, by as many distinct creative acts.

The theory of evolution or the theory of a common descent, starting from the organic plasticity of species, denies them absolute constancy, and regards them as so many distinct branches issuing from a common trunk.

The evolutionists are divided on this philosophical problem into two opposing camps. The one holds that the formation of species has been the result of a special law imparted by the Creator for the development of life. Under this aspect, their theory is a form of Creationism. For the others, living species do not at all manifest a biological plan conceived by the Creator. They are but the inevitable result of purely mechanical laws to which life must conform itself.

No question, during the last half of the nineteenth century has created so much commotion in scientific and learned circles. The reason for this is found in the fact that some of the gravest interests of religion and morality, are intimately bound up with this question. Agnostics and freethinkers have exploited Evolution in opposition to Faith and Spiritual Philosophy. In attributing to nature alone the creation of all its wonderful works, in proclaiming the brute origin of man, they arrive at the negation of God and of the human soul. Catholics and other devout Christians, justly alarmed at such consequences, have bitterly combatted the theories that seem to lead logically in this direction. Thus, there was a time when the materialists and evolutionists on one side, and Catholics and creationists on the other, were lined up almost to a man in opposition to each other. Later, however, there arose a tendency towards moderation. Instead of adopting extreme solu-

tions, men tried to take a more just account of the facts
of experience and of philosophical principles. They were
careful to distinguish the philosophical problem from the
scientific. The latter has reference to the role of secondary
causes, the former to that of the First Cause. The result
of this is that antipathies were removed, ideas became more
definite and precise, and an approach was made towards a
reconciliation on this much disputed question. We must
however add, that latterly, owing to an overinsistence on
the materialistic aspect of evolution in our educational
institutions from the university down to the primary
grades, and in our magazines and newspapers, there seems
to be a recrudescence of the bitterness of the days of
Darwin.

Considering the order which reigns in nature and of
which chance cannot be the author, we regard it as certain
that God has presided over the formation of species.
But, what appears an open question, is the method He
employed in creating them. Were there as many direct
interventions, as naturalists reckon specific forms; or has
there been only one initial act by which the First Cause
implanted in them a law of evolution or formation by
common descent? Such is, in our opinion, the field of
discussion.

We shall conscientiously set forth all the necessary
data, and then shall leave to the reader the task of choosing which side to follow. Let us merely remark, that,
on this point as in every controversy, it is imprudent to
form a judgment without previous investigation. Further,
the admitted solution can be considered only an opinion,
for while evolutionists do not lack plausible arguments,
the modern advocates of constancy cannot in justice to
them be taxed with ignorance.

Following a rapid review of the history of this question,
we shall take up one after another the *facts* brought forward by evolutionists : the *reasons* which have caused
some Catholics to be favorably disposed towards modified
evolution; the *arguments* of the advocates of constancy
against evolution; the facts and the reasons which have

demolished *Darwinism*, and the principal other mitigated forms of evolution; finally the refutation of *materialistic and atheistic evolution* or *monism*. We leave man out of this discussion, reserving him for a special chapter.

ARTICLE II

HISTORICAL REVIEW.

There are some questions that are as old as the world itself and which will last as long as the world lasts. Such are the problems relating to the world's destiny: the existence of God, creation, the origin and end of man, the spirituality and immortality of his soul. Then there are questions of lesser importance that have in a sense a date of birth, and often also a date of demise. The question of the origin of living species certainly belongs to this class. It was first clearly stated only at the beginning of the last century, in 1809, by the French naturalist Lamarck. [1]

Some have, however, seen traces of it even among the ancients. Thus Plato and Aristotle with their prototype ideas, have been advocates of the constancy and autonomy of species. Aristotle, especially, struck by the order that reigns among the species, could not see it the result of blind forces. It is wrong therefore for Darwin to invoke him as one of his predecessors. On the other hand, Thales of Milet, Anaximander and later on the atomists Leucippus and Democritus, believing that living organisms were spontaneously formed from slime under the action of the sun, inclined towards the extreme variability of forms. The poet Lucretius followed them, and he seems to have been the first to note the struggle for life and the theory of natural selection. [2]

---

[1] For the history of the ideas bearing on the Origin of Species, see bibliography. Also *Études*, June, 1921, p. 524 et sq.

[2] "In the first centuries, many of the races of animals necessarily had to disappear without being able to reproduce or propagate them-

During the Middle Ages, the problem made no advance
whatever. At this period, particularly during the xııth
and xıııth centuries it was not experimental science but
rational philosophy that made progress. In the xvıth
century however, we find Bacon convinced of the variability of types, since he proposes to found an institution
where an attempt might be made to tranform the organs,
and where the problem of the manner in which species
become diversified and multiply, might be investigated.
The naturalists of the xvıııth century were much preoccupied with the question of the origin of species.—Many,
among them, Tournefort, Bonnet, de Maillet, Robinet,
believed in the real relationship of species and supposed
them descended from common ancestors, but to account
for this, they have recourse to the most bizarre and fantastic hypotheses.—Linneaus, after having declared that
"there are as many species as God created in the beginning" later on supposes that God created only genera o
which the species were simple varieties.—Buffon [1] at firs

---

selves. For all those that we see living about us are safeguarded from
destruction only by the cunning, strength or agility they have received
at birth. Many that recommend themselves to us by their utility
survive by reason of the protection we afford them. The crue
race of lions and other kinds of ferocious beasts are protected by
their strength, the fox by its cunning, the stag by the swiftness o
its running. The faithful and vigilant race of dogs, the whole pro
geny of beasts of burden the herds of wool producers and horne
animals have been confided to the protection of man... But why
should we have protected the useless animals, that nature has no
endowed with the necessary qualities to lead an independent exis
tence? Bound by the fetters of fatality, these creatures have served
as prey for their rivals until nature has entirely destroyed thei
species." Lucretius, *De natura rerum*, Bk. V, vs. 800.

[1] Here is a passage in which Buffon visibly inclines to a commo
descent : "When we consider, as Daubeton remarks, that the foo
of a horse in appearance so different from the hand of man is never
theless composed of the same bones, and when we consider thi
hidden resemblance no more marvellous than the apparent differ
ences, and this constant conformity and this design followed from
men to the quadrupeds and from the quadrupeds to the cetacians
etc... in which the essential parts, as the heart, the intestines
the spinal column, the senses, etc..., are always found, does it no

upheld the common origin of species, but in the end recognizing fully the struggle for existence and natural selection, he became undecided, and professed that the species is neither constant nor transmutable.—Kant, Diderot, [1] Maupertuis, [2] Okan and Goethe are supposed to have had some idea of evolution. But it was Erasmus Darwin, the grandfather of Charles Darwin, that gave the most methodical explanation of the formation of species. It was his belief that species were modified under the influence of internal needs, rather than under that of external conditions. In this, he approached more closely the ideas of Lamarck than those of his grandson.

Lamarck (1744-1829) was a colleague of Cuvier at the Paris Museum of Natural History. His ideas are contained in his three principal works : *Philosophie zoologique* (1809); *Histoire des animaux sans vertèbres* (1815-1822) and *Système des connaissances positives* (1821).

He was led to adopt evolutionism by the embarassment in which he found himself, when classifying species and trying to distinguish their natural limits. This confusion

seem to indicate that *in creating the animals the Supreme Being wished to employ one single idea, and at the same time vary it in all possible ways,* that man might admire both the grandeur of the execution and the simplicity of the design ?" Cited by Perrier, in *Philosophie zoologique,* Paris, 1896, p. 60. In the course of the same passage, Buffon arrives at the idea... *even that all the animals had come from only one animal, which, in the course of the ages, produced, by perfecting or deteriorating, all the other races of animals. Ibid.,* p. 61.

[1] "Just as, in the animal and vegetable kingdoms, an individual begins, so to say, to increase, continue, decline and die, might it not be the same with the entire species?" Diderot, cited by E. Perrier, p. 55.

[2] "Could we not explain how from two individuals the multiplicity of dissimilar species might have come into existence? Might they not have had their beginning in certain fortuitous productions, in which the elementary parts might not have retained the order that thay had in the father and mother animals Each degree of error would have made a new species : and so through repeated dispersions would have come the infinite diversity of animals that we see today, the diversity that grows with time, but in which perhaps the course of ages only brings about imperceptible increase." Maupertuis, cited by E. Perrier, p. 53.

of neighboring types induced the belief that he had under his eyes so many varieties derived from common ancestral forms.   The first animals, placed in different environments experienced new needs.   To satisfy these needs, the organs already existing were modified and new organs appeared, while the unused organs became atrophied and disappeared entirely.   Heredity, then, fixed these variations acquired through necessity, in the descendants of the transformed animals.   Lamarck showed how his principles applied to the long neck of the giraffe, to the horns of the ruminants, to the hoofs of the pachyderms, to the feet of the palmipeds, to the neck of the wading birds, etc.

The two fundamental laws as announced by Lamarck are:

1. In every animal which has not passed the limit of its development, the frequent and sustained use of any organ gradually strengthens that organ, develops it, enlarges it and imparts to it a power proportioned to the duration of such use: while the constant neglect to use such organ insensibly weakens, deteriorates and progressively diminishes its faculties until it finally disappears;

2. All that nature has caused the individual to acquire or to lose, under the influence of circumstances to which the race had been exposed, and in consequence, under the influence of the predominant use of such organ or constant disuse of such part, is preserved through generation in the new individuals that are produced, provided that the acquired modifications were common to both sexes, or to those which have produced these new individuals. Cf. Perrier, p. 76.

In Lamarck's eyes, animals and plants constitute a scale which represents "the order which holds in nature and which, along with the objects that this order has caused to exist, results from the means that it has received from the Supreme Author of all things.   It is but the one general and immutable law that this Supreme Author has created in all things, and the assemblage of the general and particular laws to which this order is subjected.   By these means, which it continues to use without alteration, it has given existence, and that perpetually, to its productions. It varies them, it renews them incessantly and thus everywhere preserves the complete order which is its effect." *Philosophie zoologique*, vol. I, p. 113.

Étienne Geoffroy-Saint-Hilaire (1772-1884), leaned very much towards the ideas of Lamarck. But it is to environment, especially to the respiratory medium, that he attributed the greatest influence on species. Whereas Lamarck maintained the transformation of adults, Geoffroy Saint-Hilaire believed that the embryos alone were subjected to modification. In his opinion, the species represented so many monstrosities suddenly produced and transmitted by heredity. Otherwise he saw in evolution the excution of a plan, so that "each thing comes at a moment predetermined" and willed by God. [1]

The ideas of Lamarck and of Geoffroy-Saint-Hilaire find only a feeble echo in the naturalists of their day. They succombed momentarily to the influence of Cuvier and his school. From 1798 on, C. Cuvier brought out a series of memoirs which he published in 1812, under the title *Recherches sur les ossements fossiles*, a work of the highest value in which are found, exposed with remarkable exactness, the fundamental notions of two sciences; comparative anatomy and the paleontology of vertebrates.

[1]"Nature has formed all the living beings only on one single plan, essentially the same in its principle, but which it has varied in a thousand different ways in all the accesory parts." Geoffroy-Saint-Hilaire, *Mémoires sur les rapports naturels des Malkis.* "The world about us is alpowerful in altering organic bodies... The insensible modifications of one century end by joining together and forming one complete sum; whence it comes that respiration becomes a difficult and finally an impossible operation. So to for certain systems of organs. This necessitates then that it create for itself another arrangement, by perfecting or altering the pulmonary cells through which it operates, favorable or unfavorable modifications, which reproduce themselves or which have an influence on all the rest of the animal organization. For if these modifications increase the harmful effects, the animals which experience them cease to exist, to be replaced by others with forms that are a little altered, but altered to conform to the new circumstances." *Influence du monde ambiant sur les formes animales.*

He demonstrated that the Tertiary rocks abounded with genera and species of extinct animals, such as the paleotherium, the apoplotherium, the xiphodon, the dichobune, the chaeropotamus and the adapis. In the Lower Quaternary lived the now extinct mastodons, the hippopotami, the elephants, the large carnivora such as the different species of lion, tiger and hyena. Much lower than the Tertiary, in the cretacious rocks we meet with no mammals, but we find oviparous quadrupeds, tortoises and crocodiles, e. g. the mosasaurs of Maestricht. In the Upper Jurassic are found large reptiles, like the carnivorous megalosaurs, the herbivorous iguanodon. In the Jurassic schists, the ichthyosaurs, the plesiosaurs, the pterodactyls, e. g. the flying lizard and still farther down fish of a species unknown today.

Cuvier has had the merit of discovering these *distinct* fauna and of drawing attention to the cause. He has found it in that which is today called marine transgressions and regressions, which occasioned the invasion and disappearance of fauna. He does not by any means admit, as has been said, the hypothesis of multiple and successive creation as did his disciple d'Orbigny in his *Prodrome de Paléontologie* (1850). In this work are described 18000 species of fossil invertebrates, classified according to the chronological order of their appearance in the twenty-seven stages of the earth's crust. He admits as many as twenty-seven successive creations. The disappearance of living organisms according to him, would be due to powerful disturbances on the face of the globe. Cuvier, d'Orbigny Agassiz, all believed in the constancy of species and upheld it in opposition to Lamarck.

In the period of forty years, between Lamarck and Darwin, we find only a few scientists who have expressed opinions more or less transformistic[1] in character. Thus, Herbert, Rafinesque, Naudin and Hooker in botany;

[1] French writers seem to prefer the term transformism to evolution. In truth the term is more expressive of the underlying doctrine.

Grant, Haldelman, Schaffausen, Isidore Geoffroy-Saint-Hilaire and Wallace in zoology; Omalius d'Halloy and Keyserling in geology.

In 1859, appeared the work of Charles Darwin (1807-1882). He had been preparing it for twenty-five years. A voyage around the world between 1831 and 1836 was the inspiration of his researches. At the age of twenty-two, he embarked on the *Beagle*, commissioned by the English Government to explore the southern part of South America. The voyage lasted five years and on his return, the theory of evolution had already taken shape in Darwin's mind. In South America he had verified a variation of species from north to south, the near relationship between the continental species and those of the neighboring islands, the close affinity, which the toothless mammals and the present rodents bore to the extinct species of the same families. Variability of all living creatures appeared to him the general rule. On his return to England, he made an extended study of domestic animals, and cultivated plants and the manner in which man obtained the races and varieties by intelligent selection.

He believed that natural selection was capable of perfecting the species, if we admit the constant intervention of the struggle for life, and later on of sexual selection. We shall discuss these different ideas later on. Darwin had, at first, ignored the question of the origin of man, but the conclusion which he did not wish to draw himself, others, like Huxley in England and Haeckel in Germany, drew for him. In 1871 however, Darwin published his *Descent of man and Selection in relation to sex*, in which he demonstrated the animal origin of man's body and soul.

The materialistic school loudly welcomed the idea. The whole group of young scientists acclaimed Darwin their master. Wallace, Huxley, Spencer, Haeckel, Büchner, Vogt, Draper, Romanes, Weismann, etc., recognized him as such. But with them, as with the other popular writers of the time, the question changed from one of science to one of philosophy. There was no longer a question of the evolution of species, but of the spontaneous formation of life, the animal origin of the entire man, of a universal monism, comprehending in one vast synthesis the whole universe, bringing up the question whether the world is sufficient unto itself and entirely explains itself without the intervention of a Creative Cause. The errors that have been written on this theme alone are incalculable.

Hence it is not astonishing that with the appearance of scientists of the first rank, such as de Quatrefages, Blanchard, Faivre, Hébert, Fabre, Barrande, d'Archiac, Agassiz, Woodward, etc., the doctrine of Darwin and his disciples began to be opposed. At the present time the doctrine of evolution and of monism has been universally spread through the official teaching in our educational institutions and by our popular writers. The great majority of naturalists are evolutionists but often from motives other than scientific reasons. True scientists who have studied the problem coolly and without prejudice, see in evolution an interesting hypothesis, but one that is far from being demonstrated. Many of them reject the philosophical monism of Haeckel, which is altogether unscientific. [1]

The importance of the various arguments must be strengthened by a closer study of the facts. But the deeper we go into this question, the more we perceive the truly deceptive weakness of the proofs adduced by Darwin and his school, and the manifest insufficiency of the theories brought forward, by materialists to explain evolution. We shall on occasion cite some of their too little known but significant avowals. [2]

Albert Gaudry was one of the first French paleontologists to adopt transformism. In 1867, he published his first work on *Les vertébrés miocènes de l'Attique*. He thought he had found in the fauna of Pikermi some real intermediates, between the genera and the families that today are clearly distinct. He has, through his works, contributed

---

[1] Cf. de Sinéty, *Un demi-siècle de Darwinisme,* dans *Rev. des ques. scientifiques,* Jan. 1910.

[2] Depéret, *Transformations of the animal world,* Appleton.

much to the diffusion of transformism. The unity of plan in creation and the constant progress of the animate world, such are the ideas which he tried to throw into relief.

If there was a real progress in the whole, it is impossible to recognize it in the details, since the organisms are complete from the very beginning. Further, recent discoveries prove that all the groups are much older than was at first admitted, and a great number of series established by Gaudry do not correspond to reality. [1]

Among the works of Gaudry we draw attention to the following : *Les animaux fossiles au Mont Luberon* (1875); *Les enchaînements du monde animal* (1878 to 1890); *Essai de Paléontologie philosophique* (1896); *Les ancêtres de nos animaux.*

The theory of evolution has found an ardent supporter in the American anatomist and paleontologist Edward Cope, a bold mind, who is allied with Haeckel in his attempt to confuse the scientific with the philosophic domain. In his explanatory theories, he approaches the school of Lamarck and is considered the head of Neo-Lamarckism. He has made a special study of American fossil vertebrates. He recognizes a progressive and a retrogressive evolution, and does not believe that selection is capable of producing new forms, and devotes himself to the observation of phylogenetic series, rather than of embryonic series. For him the over specialized types are incapable of producing new species and end by becoming extinct. He admits that all the groups of carnivora, ungulata and quadrumana have originated from types of small size. In 1868, at the age of twenty-eight, he published his first work *On the Origin of genera.* Cf. Bibliography for other works.

Zittel published his *Handbuch der Paleontologie*, [2] between 1876 and 1893, in which he attempts a severe critical revision of all the data of paleontology. He has put evolutionists on their guard against hasty and uncer-

---

[1] Cf. Depéret, *Transformations of the animal world*, p. 12-110.
[2] Zittel, *Textbook of Paleontology*, tr. and ed. by C. R. Eastman, McMillan.

tain solutions, and has drawn attention to the uncertainties and miscalculations of paleontological evolution.

Ch. Depéret has written a similar work. In his *Transformations of the animal World*, [1] he brings out the insufficiency of the theories and proofs, and the errors of method of which some evolutionists are guilty. We shall have numerous occasions to cite him.

The works on evolution are so numerous at the present time, that we should never dream of enumerating all the authors or their works. We prefer to take up at once the problem of evolution.

ARTICLE III

FACTS INVOKED IN SUPPORT OF EVOLUTION.

The problem of evolution is not solved as some have so glibly asserted. We become convinced of this in making a rapid survey of some of the stronger arguments adduced in its favor. To recognize their value and their scientific and philosophic import, it is necessary to recall, once for all, that evolution depends :

On the certitude of the facts of alleged variability. Are they real or imaginary, demonstrated or merely supposed?

On their number, or their extension. Are they accidental in a single subject, or do they affect a race, a species, a family or a class?

On their nature. Is it physical, chemical, anatomical, physiological or psychical variation? These are far from having the same value for all.

On the degree of variation : whether it is little or great, extending to the race, the species, the genus or the class. In accordance with this, evolution will be superficial or fundamental.

On the mode of variation which might be continuous or discontinuous, natural or artificial, phylogenetic or

---

[1] Cf. Depéret, *op. cit.*, 11 sq., p. 45 sq.

ontogenic, progressive or recessive. Whereas the first are important, interesting but rare, the second are of no consequence, uninteresting and of frequent occurrence.

Every effect has a cause. Our reason is rightly desirous of knowing it. It is important that we do not deceive ourselves, that we do not take the condition of the variation for the cause; that we do not confound the natural secondary causes with the First Cause. Both exist and play their special role, but we must be able to distinguish the one from the other, if we do not wish to commit very serious blunders in science and in philosophy. It is because they have not had regard for these elementary principles, that so many popular writers have fallen into scientific and philosophic error. They seem to be guided by the opposite principles in which it is easy to discover the defect of their reasoning. Thus from even superficial resemblance, they conclude the relationship of organisms; from quantitative variation, a qualitative; from a racial variation, a specific variation or even more; from isolated, individual variation, a continuous, universal variation; from a recessive variation, a progressive variation; from an artificial variation, a natural variation; from an ontogenic variation, a phylogenetic variation: from an oscillating, restricted variation to a continuous, unlimited variation. We note similar errors when they treat of the causes of these variations. They confuse real causes with necessary conditions; extrinsic finality, at times hypothetical, with intrinsic finality which the materialists will not admit; external causes with the internal causes, arising from the living organism; secondary causes with the First Cause.

As a result of all this they have tried to produce being from non-being, the perfect from the imperfect, the greater from the less, order from disorder, life from death, sensibility from insensibility, intelligence from instinct, the infinite from the finite, the necessary from the contingent. But let us conclude these remarks which might indeed recall others, but which suffice to serve as a warning against certain hasty assertions, and let us proceed to the arguments adduced by evolutionists.

§ I.—Continuous variability of all organisms, or resemblances of all the living types, in accordance with the attempts at classification and the data of comparative anatomy and physiology.

Lamarck derived his idea of evolution from the difficulty which he encountered while attempting to classify species. He thought he saw a continuous series of beings passing laterally from one species to another... Classification, even today, offers real difficulties and biologists are far from agreeing on all the details, or even far from knowing how many types to admit. It is based on resemblances and differences, the resemblances, being more or less accentuated according to their position in the classification.

The kingdoms, branches, orders, families, genera, species, races and varieties have common characteristics increasing in number and precision. Every one is agreed on this point. There is no need to give lengthy proofs for it. Cf. table on page 258.

It is an easy matter to follow the different degrees of complexity of the bonds, uniting the simple animals with the most highly developed types. In the protozoa, the cells whether isolated or in colonies, are all alike. The cellular colonies begin to differentiate in the coelentera. With the echinodermata, internal organs distinctly appear between the ectoderm and the entoderm. From this stage on, the parts either group themselves radially around a common center, or they dispose themselves in a straight line. In the latter case, the parts either remain quite distinct, as in the worm, or they become more or less fused together and condensed into a very close unity, as in the higher types. In his work *Animal Colonies*, Perrier brings out very well, the simplicity of the plan according to which the different classes are formed. [1]

---

[1] It was ever this unity of plan that struck Geoffroy-Saint-Hilaire : "The diverse forms under which (nature) was pleased to create each species, are all derived from each other; it was sufficient

Neighboring species differ only slightly from each other. In their continuous series it is difficult to find the lines of demarcation. Even in species that seem very widely separated, whether in the same class or in the same branch, the homologous parts are constructed in the same manner. Thus in the horse, the mole, the mouse, the porpoise, and the whale, the fore-limb has the same number of bones functioning in the same manner, fig. 29. The paws of the

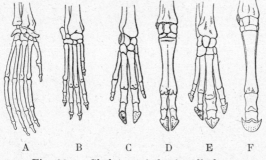

Fig. 29. — Skeleton of the fore-limb.

A. Ourang-outang; B. Dog's paw; C. Pig's foot; D. Ox's hoof; E. Tapir's hoof; F. Horse's hoof.

mammal, the wings of the bird and the limbs of the reptile are composed of essentially the same parts. [1]

With evolutionists, we may admit the resemblances

for her to change in some, the proportions of the organs, to render them fit for their new functions, to extend or restrict their use... All the most essential differences that affect each family belonging to the one same class, come solely from another arrangement, another complication, another modification in fine, of these same organs." Cf. Perrier, *La Philosophie zoologique*, p. 93.

[1] "Isn't it very remarkable, that the hand of man, made for grasping, the foot of the mole destined for burrowing in the ground, the leg of a horse, the fin of a porpoise, and the wing of a bat, are all constructed on the same model and possess similar bones, situated in the same relative positions? Isn't it extremely curious that the hind feet of kangaroos, so well adapted to the enormous leaps that this animal takes in the open plains; those of the koala, climber and leafeater, and equally well fitted for grasping the branches; those

existing among the species, and thus find common traits even as high up as the vegetable and animal kingdoms. But fidelity to purpose demands that we draw attention to an increase of divergence, between living beings, in the measure that we depart from the species, the genus, the family, the order or the class. These differences are, indeed, such as to easily mask the resemblances in the eyes of the uninitiated, and to necessitate a great deal of convention to find any similarity, between organs so distinct as a wing, an arm, a feather or a scale.

Finally, let us add. If the resemblances can easily be explained by a common origin, it is quite otherwise with the differences, which at all times seem to exclude it, and when pushed far enough actually do exclude it. No one at the present time would hold the descent of the vertebrates from the mollusks, nor the mammals from the fish, nor the herbivora from the carnivora, and yet the resemblances are at times so real as to make it quite difficult to distinguish, in the fossil state, a very great number of really different species, without known bond. Let us remember that resemblance does not signify descent.

In two species, the differences are already so marked that we cannot make the one descend from the other in our search for a bond, or a more or less remote common ancestor. Have the links between the kingdoms, the classes, the orders, the families, the genera, and the species been found? Some have so held, and the fact has been repeated over and over again in all the effusions of popular writers and in our standard textbooks. But we may express the truth somewhat differently, and say, some have believed in the existence of these intermediate forms, and there are some good reasons for this belief, but in the opinion of Depéret they are not to be found, either among the spe-

of the perameles which live in subterranian galleries, and which feed on insects and roots, and those of some other Australian marsupials, are all constructed on the same extraordinary type, that is to say, the bones of the second and third digits are very slender, and enveloped in a single skin in such a way as to resemble a single digit, provided with two claws. '' Darwin, *Origin of Species*, p. 512.

cies actually existing or in the geological periods. They have been found between one variety and another, between one race and another without a gap, but when there is question of the species, all are clearly distinct. Their varieties group themselves around a central type, yet ever excluding the possibility of confusing them with the neighboring type. [1]

What would be the result if, instead of the species, we were to take the genera or the families... or the branches? Darwin himself has recognized the necessity of these links and their too manifest absence. He ascribed this absence to their disappearance in the course of the geological ages, and to our too imperfect knowledge of fossils, or to the inevitable gaps which must occur on account of the difficulty of fossilization. In spite of all his efforts, he could not render this argument conclusive. In vain do we peruse his works to find one decisive proof of this continuous variation without a single gap. It does not exist. The examples adduced by Darwin and his disciples do not go beyond the limits of the species, as we shall see when treating of actual variations.

Everyone, whether evolutionist or advocate of constancy, is in accord in admitting continuous variation within the species, but this in itself cannot prove the existence of variation beyond the limits of the species and with greater reason beyond that of the genus. Besides, the classifications are too subjective, too *a priori*, too foreign to the real geneology of species to indicate their origin. The new classifications, attempted to this end, do not appear any happier, for they cannot gain the adherance of all evolutionists.

We may always recognize a real order in the series of living beings, that permits various and to our mind very satisfactory classifications, but an order that is ever variable according to the starting point. To give some idea of these relations, we insert below a brief classification of all animals in general and of the vertebrates in particular.

[1] Cf. Depéret, *The transformations of the animal world*, p. 129-.190.

CLASSIFICATION OF THE ANIMAL KINGDOM

EMBRANCHMENT	CLASS	ORDER	SUB-ORDER	FAMILY	GENUS	SPECIES
VERTEBRATA	Mammalia	Primates	Bimana	Hominidae	Homo	H. Sapiens
			Quadrumana or Simidae	Catarrhinae	Anthropoid	Anthropopitheeus (Chimpanzee)
		Lemuria or Prosimiae		Lemuridae	Maki	Mongous
		Carnivora	Aelurcidea	Felidae	Uncia	Tiger
		Pinnipedia		Trichechidae	Trichecus	T. Rosmarus (Walrus)
		Insectivora		Erinaceidae	Erinaceus	E. Europeus
		Chiroptera	Megachiroptera	Vespertilionidae	Vespertilio	V. Serotinus (Bat)
		Rodentia		Muridae	Mus	M Rattus (Rat)
		Proboscidia		Elephantidae	Elephas	E. Indicus (Elephant)
		Ungulata	Artiodactylia	Suidae	Sus	S. Scrofa domestica (Hog)
		Ruminantia		Bovidae	Bos	B. Taurus (Bull)
		Solidungulata	Perissodactylia	Equidae	Equus	E. Cabalus (Horse)
		Edentata	Vermilinguiae	Myrmecophagidae	Myrmecophagus	M. Jubata (Anteater)
		Sirenia		Manatidae	Manatus	Manatee (Sea-cow)
		Cetacea		Balaenidae	Balaena	B. Australis (Whale)
		Marsupialia		Didelphydae	Didelphys	D. Virginiana (Opossum)
		Monotremata	Platypoda	Ornithophinchid	Ornithorhincus	O. Paradoxus (Duck-bill)
	Aves	Carinatae	Columbae	Columbidae	Columba	C. Livia (Rock-pigeon)
		Ratitae	Struthiones	Struthionidae	Struthio	S. Camelus (Ostrich)
		Saurae			Archeopteryx	
	Reptilia	Chelonia		Chelonidae	Chelone	Ch. Midas (Green Turtle)
		Crocodilia		Crocodilidae	Crocodilus	C. Americanus (Alligator)
		Sauria	Lacertilia	Lacertidae	Lacerta	L. Viridis (Green Lizard)
		Ophidia		Pythonidae	Python	P. Malurus (Rock snakes)

	Batrachia	Anoura (Amphibia)		Ranidae	Rana	R. Esculenta (Bull-frog)
		Urodela		Salamandridae	Salamandra	Salamander
		Apoda		Caecillidae	Caecilla	C. Lumbriecides (Blind-worm)
	Pisces (Fishes)	Pippei	Dipneunona	Lepidosironidae	Lepidosire	L. Annectens (Lung-fish)
		Telestoi	Acanthopteri	Percidae	Perca	P. Fluviatilis (Perch)
		Ganoidei	Chondrostei	Acipenseridae	Acipenser	A. Sturis (Sturgeon)
		Plagiostomi	Squali	Carchariidae	Carcharis	C. Rondeleti (Shark)
		Cyclostomi	Radiesta	Crisiidae	Crisia	C. Eburnia
ARTHROPODA	Insecta	Diptera	Brachyura	Muscidae	Musca	M. Domestica (House Fly)
	Arachnida	Scorpiones		Scorpionidae	Scorpio	S. Paudinus (Scorpio)
	Myriapoda	Chilopoda		Scolopendridae	Scolopendra	S. Bourbonica (Centiped)
	Crustacia	Decapoda	Brachyura	Portunidae	Carcinus	C. Maenas (Green Crab)
MOLLUSCA	Brachiopoda	Arthropomata		Terebratulidae	Terebratula	T. Vitria
	Cephalopoda	Dibranchiata	Octopoda	Octopodidae	Octopus	Octopus
	Gasteropoda	Pulmonata		Helicidae	Helix	H. Hortensis (Garden Snail)
	Lamellibranch	Monomvaria		Ostridae	Ostrea	O. Virginica (Oyster)
VERMES (WORMS)	Annelida	Oligochaeta		Lumbricidae	Lumbricus	L.Terrestris (Earth worm)
	Turbellaria	Planarida		Planariidae	Planaria	P. Torys (Flat worm)
ECHINODERMATA	Echinoidea	Echinoidea		Mellitidae	Echinarachnius	E. Parma (Sea Urchin, Sand Dollar)
	Asteroides	Asteroidea		Solastridae	Echinaster	E. Sentus (Star-fish)
	Crinoidea	Crinoidea	Articulata	Encrinidae	Encrinus	Encrinus (Stone-lily)
	Holothurioidea	Holothurioidea	Apoda	Pentactidae	Pentacta	P. Frondosa (Sea-cucumber)
COELENTERA	Cnidaria	Hydroidea		Hydridae	Hydra	H. Viridis
		Discophora		Medusidae	Aurelia	A. Flavidula,Jelly-fish)
	Spongiae	Calcispongia		Syconidae	Sycon	S. Carteri
		Silicispongia		Euplectellidae	Euplectella	E. Aspergillus (Venus'Flower Basket)
		Horny		Spongidae	Euspongia	E. Officinalis (Common Sponge)
PROTOZOA	Sporozoa	Hematosoa		Sarcocystidiae	Sarcocystie	S. Micopheri
	Infusoria	Ciliata		Paramecidae	Paramecium	P. Bursarium
		Flagellata		Euglenidae	Phacus	P. Longicauda
	Rhizopoda	Radiolaria	Acantharia	Acanthometridae	Acanthometra	A. Litholophus
		Feraminifera		Rotaliidae	Rotalia	R. Valvulata
		Amoeba		Amoebidae	Amoeba	A. Diffluens

This table will help to bring out more prominently the import of certain arguments of evolutionists and the advocates of constancy. These facts clearly show a direct morphological relation, between the species of the same genus, less pronounced between the genera of the same class, and still less between the extreme species of the animal kingdom. [1]

Is this bond which unites the living organisms purely ideal or imaginary, or is it indeed the result of a common descent? For evolutionists the relationship is real. All living organisms descend from the one same trunk from which have sprung the various branches with their ramifications. They find that this affiliation is a scientific explanation of the formation of species, and that the contrary hypothesis of the advocates of constancy appears less scientific, and even less worthy of the Creator. We shall return to this idea later.

§ II.—Artificial variability of animals and of plants.

Darwin developed the idea of the artificial variability of animals and of plants in his two works : *Origin of Species by means of natural Selection* and *Variation of animals and plants under domestication*, comprising more than 1 500 pages. He reviewed all the variations of domestic races and of the majority of cultivated plants. He made a deep and protracted study of 150 races of pigeons with their various forms and instincts.

De Quatrefages has given an admirable resume of the same and has, at the same time, noted its importance and its limitations. [2] "The pigeon is one of the oldest of domesticated animals, since it is found in the Fourth Egyptian Dynasty. It was selected and hybridized with such care, that it has produced the great number of races, more than 150, noted by Darwin. The variations are quite fundamental, but the individuals still remain inter-

---

[1] Cf. *Revue des questions scient.*, 1922, vol. II, p. 69.
[2] Cf. De Quatrefages, *Darwin et ses précurseurs*, p. 91, 92.

prolific. Indeed among the different races of pigeons, the arrangement of the long wing and tail feathers changes. Of the latter, the variations range from 12 to 42. The bill lengthens, curves and narrows down, or becomes from one to nearly three times shorter and broader. It is either naked or covered with an enormous membrane as if puffed up. The feet are either large and clumsy, or small and delicate. The entire skull in its general contours, in its proportions and its reciprocal relations, presents variations from one race to another that at once strike the eye. These relations are so well modified that, in standing and walking, the body is at times nearly horizontal and at other times not far from vertical. The ribs in certain races are two or three times larger than in others. The number of vertebrae also varies.

"To sum up. The importance of these differences is such that, if the majority of the races of pigeons had been found living wild, ornithologists would certainly not hesitate to consider them as so many separate species if not so many distinct genera."

Buffon and Cuvier considered the rock pigeon, *columba livia*, the chief stock of our modern pigeons, but both of them thought the multiplicity and diversity of the races could not be explained, except by the introduction of one or more species. Darwin derived them all from the rock pigeon and proved his point. [1] The same mus tbe said of the different races of dogs, among which Darwin discovered characteristics that are still more differentiated, bearing on size, shape, instincts and other organic details. Every one can see for himself the profound difference between the greyhound, the bulldog, the New Foundland, the terrior, the eskimo dog, the shepherd dog, the pointer, the poodle, the Saint Bernard, and the mastiff, etc.

Darwin found his greatest delight in studying the fowls, which are remarkable for their morphological and organic variations. Thus, for instance, the head of the cock pre-

[1] Cf. Darwin, *Variation of animals and plants under domestication*, Appleton.

sents every possible variety. He also drew attention to instances of profound variation in cows and sheep.

To all these instances the remark of de Quatrefages could apply, if we based it solely on morphology. But physiology proves that there is unity of species, since these different races are indefinitely interprolific, both directly and indirectly.

Still we can readily conceive the process by which nature or rather the Creator might have developed species. The races in becoming accentuated and in diverging, might have reached a point where the physiological separation of species was produced. It is easier to imagine than to verify, when we come to control it whith exact data. We do not know any instance of the creation of a new domestic species. The rabbits of Porto Rico cross with those of Europe, contrary to what has been asserted. [1]

Darwin and evolutionists take pleasure in citing the variability of plants cultivated by man, whether for food, for pleasure or to verify the possibility of evolving them at will. Plants are indeed profoundly modified by cultivation, at least morphologically. To mention a few of the more striking instances. The wild cabbage with its insignificant, slender stem is one of the plants that presents the greatest variety in each of its various elements, roots, stalk, leaves and flower, whether in shape, size or quality. Everyone is familiar with the turnip, the khol-rabi, the numberless varieties of head cabbage, the Brussels sprouts, the cauliflower, the kale, the curly cabbage, the green cabbage, the savoys, the red cabbage, etc. They differ so much morphologically as to seem species.

The vine has no less than 2000 characteristic races, without counting the varieties. The grapes range from white to black, from those that are exceedingly luscious to those that are insipid, from the very acid type to the very sweet, from the most insignificant to those of an enormous size. The leaves vary at least as much as the grapes, from the very regular to the multilobed and spotted, from

---

[1] Cf *Revue de Philosophie*, Oct. 1910, p. 906.

the very smooth to the most hairy, and thus from the more resistant to the cryptogamic diseases to the most sensitive. It is the same for resistance to phyloxera. The stalk and the roots vary also, one sort being adapted to sandy soil, another to stony ground; one plant rises to a great height, another is dwarfed; one requires a very warm climate, another accommodates itself to a climate with an annual mean temperature of 8 or 9 degrees centigrade.

The varieties are no less numerous among the grasses— as blue grass, timothy, oats, rye, wheat, corn; or among the solanaceae as the potato, tomato, tobacco, nightshade, etc. The fruit-trees seem to be unlimited in variety. Thus, we have the multiple varieties of apple, peach, pear, plum, fig, orange, etc., the chestnut, the walnut, the hickory nut, the almond.

The adder's tongue has three kinds of leaves, submerged narrow threads, round floating leaves and aerial leaves below the spike, and so presents a perfect type of variation with the environment. [1] The Jerusalem artichoke varies in form and size, according as it is cultivated in the valley or on the mountain.

Among the flowers we may note the innumerable varieties of roses, chrysanthemums, carnations, dahlias, geraniums, primroses and cineraria.

What is the limit of these variations? and, incidentally, the value of this argument in favor of evolution? Before answering this question we must first distinguish the different kinds of variation, obtained experimentally. We recognize three.

1. *Fluctuation* is a quantitative variation, that is continuous between a minimum and a maximum and can be represented by a curve. It gives the varieties and no more. Galton's law which supposes that selection can displace the average is inexact. [2]

2. *Mutation* studied by de Vries, Blaringham and Cuénot is a sudden and discontinuous variation, producing new

[1] Cf. Caustier, *Histoire naturelle*, fig. 99 and 101, Paris.
[2] Cf. *Revue des questions scientifiques*, 1914, p. 363; p. 358.

races, e. g. the oenothera, the gnato ox, the merino sheep, sheep and dogs with crooked legs, sheep with only the rudiment of a tail and earless sheep. In general appearance they are fixed. Cuénot calls them nascent species. If we may rely on the indefinite inter-fertilization they do not seem to go beyond the limits of species. Morphologically, they are new species, but we do not know anything definite about the origin of the mutation.

3. *Mendelian novelties.* These are produced through rigorous selection, combined with hybridization or development of certain antagonistic characters which make it possible to create new races, as one would create new substances in chemistry by addition, substitution, or subtraction. [1]

We shall give a brief review of the method followed by Mendel, and an account of the laws discovered by him in 1866, and rediscovered in 1900 by de Vries, though already mentioned by Naudin. He chose from among the plants that he wished to cross, only pure races with well defined, easily observable and antagonistic characters. To obtain pure races he assured himself that the species did not vary in four or five generations.

Mendel worked with the edible pea, *pisus sativus*. He first crossed a single pair having different colors and shapes. He found that the type producing yellow seeds crossed with that producing green seeds, giving a yellow hybrid $(F_{.1})$. Letting Y and G stand for yellow and green respectively, we have $Y + G = Y$ in appearance, but Y (G) in reality. The yellow is dominant over the green which is recessive. The self-fertilized hybrid gives in the second generation $(F_{.2})$ some yellows, some greens and the hybrid. $Y(G) + Y(G) = Y + 2Y (G) + G$. There is therefore segregation. The two formulæ sum up the facts and the laws of dominence and of segregation of characters in $(F_{.2})$.

[1] Cf. Grégoire, *Les recherches de Mendel et les Mendelistes sur l'hérédité*, dans *Revue des questions scientifiques*, 1912, vol. LXX, p. 353-390, vol. LXXI, p. 576-629; *Catholic Encyclopedia*, art. *Evolution*, Mendel, *Versuche uber Pflanzenhybriden*, in Ostwalds Klassiker, n. 121. For other works, see bibliography.

From the evolutionistic standpoint, the fact is of little interest, for we thus revert to the primitive type, in this instance of monohybridization, between a pair of antagonistic characters. The following outline will make this clear.

P=parent stock. Y=yellow. G=green. F=generations of hybrids.

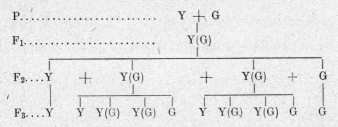

If we combine two pairs of antagonistic characters dihybridization results. YR+GW, i. e. yellow round peas with green wrinkled peas give a hybrid YR in appearance, but YR(GW) in reality. The latter when selffertilized gives 9 YR+3 YW+3 GR+1 GW. Here we have two new pure races YW and GR, but mixed with hybrids. The table given below permits us to forecast mathematically the results of such hybridization and to determine the laws of dominance and segregation.

SUMMARY OF MENDEL'S EXPERIMENTS

To be read as a Pythagorean Table.

Monohybrids.

$D = dominant$, $R = recessive$.

$D \times R = D$ in appearance but $D(R)$ in reality.

DR self-fertilized gives $D + 2D (R + R)$.

PHENOTYPE				GENOTYPE		
Gametes	D	R		Gametes	D	R
D	D	D		D	D	D(R)
R	D	R		R	D(R)	R

Dihybrids.

$DR \times D'R' = DR$ in appearance but DR (D'R') in reality.
DR(D'R') selffertilized gives 9 DR+3 D'R+3 DR'+1 D'R'

Gametes ♂	DR	DR'	D'R	D'R'
♀ DR	DR	DR	DR	DR
DR'	DR	DR'	DR	DR'
D'R	DR	DR	D'R	D'R
D'R'	DR	DR'	D'R	D'R'

Trihybrids.

$ABC \times A'B'C' = 28\,ABC + 8\,ABC' + 9\,A\,B'C + 3\,AB'C' +$
$9A'BC + 3\,A'BC' + 3\,A'B'C + 1\,A'B'C'$

Gametes ♂	ABC	ABC'	AB'C	AB'C'	A'BC	A'BC'	A'B'C	A'B'C,
♀ ABC	ABC	...	...	...	...	...	...	...
ABC'	...	ABC'	...	...	...	...	...	...
AB'C	...	...	AB'C	...	...	...	...	...
AB'C'	...	...	...	AB'C	...	...	...	...
A'BC	...	...	...	...	A'BC	...	...	...
A'BC'	...	...	...	...	...	A'BC'	...	...
A'B'C	...	...	...	...	...	...	A'B'C	...
A'B'C'	...	...	...	...	...	...	...	A'B'C'

These tables illustrate both Mendel's laws and the theory which has been formulated to explain these laws. Mendel recognized that the crossing of two races might be realized by taking indifferently as dominant type the male or the female element. Hence he supposed that in the hybrid flower the two hybrid characters are found reunited in equal proportions in the pollen as well as in the ovule. The gametes of a pure race are never hybrids.

At the moment of selffertilization there are in the case of monohybrids four combinations mathematically possible: $D \times R = DD + DR + RD + RR$.

Experiments prove that when working with a great number of plants, we find these four combinations actually realized in the descendants, and in the proportions indicated.

When we are dealing with a self-fertilized dihybrid DRD'R', we have theoretically and actually 16 possible combinations, i. e. 9DR+3 DRR'+3 D'R+1 D'R'. Four of these are pure races and two of them new, DR' and D'R.

The two tables bring out the following results. In the first horizontal line are placed the male ♂ characters, in the first vertical column the female ♀ characters of the hybrid. The dominant character is written first and the recessive second, e. g. $D \times R = D$ or again $DR \times D'R' = DR$. It is easy to see that in this instance, DR is formed of four elements and is therefore a new hybrid. To illustrate this we write it DR (D'R'). We may note that the diagonal of offspring contains the four pure races including the two new ones DR' and D'R.

In the case of trihybrids $ABC \times A'B'C'$ we have 64 varieties of which 62 are new. Among these there are 8 pure races of which 6 are new. The difficulty of discovering them in the midst of 68 varieties is greater than in the case of the dihybrids, where we have to choose from only 16 and where they represent a fourth of the whole. To have an idea of the fecundity of this method of creating new races, we give the following table : N=the number of new varieties, and R=the number of pure races that may be obtained in the mono-, di-, tri-, tetra-, and penta-hybrids. The letter (n) represents all the combined characters and (r) the number of pairs of characters.

Monohybrids	$N = 2^n = 2^2 =$	4
	$R = 2^r = 2^1 =$	2
Dihybrids	$N = 2^n = 2^1 =$	16
	$R = 2^r = 2^3 =$	4
Trihybrids	$N = 2^n = 2^6 =$	64
	$R = 2^r = 2^3 =$	8
Tetrahybrids	$N = 2^n = 2^3 =$	256
	$R = 2^r = 2^4 =$	16
Pentahybrids	$N = 2^n = 2^{10} =$	1 024
	$R = 2^r = 2^5 =$	32
Hexahybrids	$N = 2^n = 2^{12} =$	4 096
	$R = 2^r = 2^6 =$	64
Heptahybrids	$N = 2^n = 2^{11} =$	16 384
	$R = 2^r = 2^7 =$	128
Octohybrids	$N = 2^n = 2^{16} =$	65 536
	$R = 2^r = 2^8 =$	256

Mendel's laws apply to the creation of new races but not of new species, for the latter are sterile. To obtain new combinations, one must use the dihybrids. In this way there may be accumulated in one and the same subject a whole series of useful characters. A certain disciple of Mendel proposed to obtain a race of vine, capable of resisting both the phyloxera and the cryptogamic diseases, that could produce a superior white or black grape in a colder climate. The result is theoretically possible, and seems to have been partially realized. [1] A number of Americans, notably Luther Burbank, have perfected, in this way, a very great number of vegetables, fruits, flowers, and cereals. These laws apply equally well to animals. L. Cuénot and Bateson have made a very careful study of this. [2]

Further experiments have led to the discovery that certain nonmendelic characters can be added, juxtaposed and symmetrically intermixed. Thus, for example, the Houdanese fowl have feathers that are half-white and half-black. Hence we have here a new method of producing different races.

Could natural hybridization have been an important factor in the variation and in thus the evolution of species? From the stand-point of absolute possibility, we may answer in the affirmative. Considering the actual facts and all the conditions requisite to obtain pure new races, it appears too difficult to obtain new species, and we are disposed to answer in the negative, holding it impossible.

The facts seem to indicate, that outside of the domestic races, the actual wild races never produce fixed new types, and for greater reason no new species. The conditions are indeed, such, that in hybridizing, a judicious choice of types, and a rigorous selection is necessary to preserve the new races. As they are less numerous than the hybrids, they would naturally disappear in the midst of the latter. Now, the hybrids as such cannot produce races, nor fixed species, and yet they exist in nature. Hence their origin seems to have been quite different.

---

[1] Cf. *Revue de Génétique*, by l'abbé Vieules, curé de Nages (Tarn).
[2] Cf. Cuénot, *Le Genèse des espèces animales*, 2ᵈ edit., 1921, p. 213 et sq.

Thus, neither fluctuation, nor mutation, nor Mendelism, nor hybridization alone seem to have the power of creating new species. By means of Mendelism or any other system of hybridization, man can create new races, a fact that is indeed very interesting and very practical, and a fertile field for the scientist, the breeder of animals and plants, and the farmer. It should not be neglected for the sake of seeking a chimerical evolution of species.[1]

§ III.—REGIONAL VARIATION OF SPECIES IN THE PRESENT EPOCH.

Darwin and other evolutionists maintain that their theory is supported by an actual variation of species, taking place in our own time. Thus for both fauna and flora, we distinguish a torrid, a temperate and a frigid zone. In the ocean, we have a litoral, a neritic, a bathylic and an abyssal zone, each with its particular fauna and flora. While in the same latitude, the fauna and flora vary with the altitude, degree of humidity, etc. To conclude from this geographical distribution of animals and of plants, an argument in favor of evolution is but a step which some have not failed to take, affirming with Darwin that the fauna and flora gradually change from one region to another, insensibly passing from one species to another.

This is not the case however. According to Depéret,[2] Neumayr and Waagen, the species produce only races and varieties which group themselves around a central type, but the species always remain distinct from one another. "Observation" says Depéret "shows us that in nature at the present time, certain species vary only slightly, while others are subject to a rather considerable polymorphism that at times is even excessive. It is this maximum variation observed *in a very small number of groups*, that has

---

[1] Cf. J. C. Villis, *Age and area, a study in geographical Distribution and Origin of Species*, Cambridge, 1922.

[2] Depéret, *op. cit.*, chap. xiv, p. 130-148 and p. 65 sq. Cf. the observations of Neumayr on the Melanopsis, the Helix and the Achatinelles.

always served as the principal argument of the defenders of the transformist hypothesis, to show the variability of species.

"We have seen Neumayr apply this consideration with success to some types of land mollusk, the melanopsis, the iberus and the achatinella (fig. 30.) A very close examination of very nearly all the living species shows that they can be subdivided into a certain number of *forms*, or if you wish into subspecies, which certain nomenclators have unfortunately seen fit to classify under distinct names, obliterating the natural bonds connecting with the mother species.

Fig. 30. — *Achatinella splendida.* Sandwich Islands. Sinister and dextral types. Instances of mutation. The black bands vary from total absence to complete uniformity of color.

"But it is important not to lose sight of the fact that these *groups of forms*— which constitute, perhaps the most real and the most striking of all natural classifications— are attached to one *typical species* more broadly conceived and delimited and playing the role, so to speak, of a center of radiation of all these forms. Do these grand species, designated by the not always exact name of *Linnean species*, pass by degrees from one species to another, as some have maintained? Observation of animate nature compels us to answer that they do not. Apart from some rare instance of hybridization, the actual species are not united with one another by insensible transition." [1]

§ IV.—Regional variation during the geological ages.

If we extend our investigation of regional variation to the fossil species in the same geological beds, we shall find the very same thing. For, from Precambrian times to our

[1] Cf. Depéret, *op. cit.*, p. 70 and 141-142.

own day, saving proportions, nature has always made use of the same means, and living creatures have ever obeyed the same influences. The fauna in the Silurian beds of Bohemia, studied by Barrande presents many racial and intra-specific variations, as for instance, among the trilobites, the nautili and other organisms. But we do not find here, either, the transition stages from one species to another. In spite of some variations of detail, M. J. Bergeron identified, in the Black Mountains, the same species that Barrande had found in Bohemia. The Jurassic ammonites of Mt. Crussol near Valencia, studied by F. Fontanes, though of many varieties, all belong to a single very polymorphous species. [1] He also found, in the Pliocene Gulf of the Rhine Valley, the same species of mollusks as are met with in the Italian bearings of the Valley of the Pô, in spite of a difference of size.

Chonchyologists, instead of recognizing variations as of a single type, have too often multiplied the number of species. After making a similar statement, Depéret concludes : "From the mass of facts discovered we draw the conclusion, that variability of species was just the same in ancient times as it is in the present epoch. This variability is revealed in a polymorphism which is at times almost nil, while at other times it is very pronounced in certain species... These forms, too often considered distinct species by descriptive naturalists, are nearly always bound to one another by insensible transitions. But it is important to note that these *groups of forms* have a true objective reality, and nearly always remain clearly separated from the neighboring groups, if we disregard some extremely rare cases of hybridization.

"These are the groups that answer, or ought to answer the true *definition of species* characterized at once, morphologically, genetically and geographically. It is in this sense that we may assert that *the grand species do not pass by degrees from one to another*, either actually in nature or at any past epoch of life on the globe...

[1] Cf. Depéret, *op. cit.*, p. 147-151.

"It would be unreasonable to suppose that the 'variation' could attain in the same epoch a complete separation of two grand species. To undergo a transformation so considerable, from all the evidence at hand, the prolonged intervention of modifying causes (prolonged isolation under the conditions of very different environments) is necessary; it is this action of time with which we are about to deal".[1]

§ V. — Chronological variation, or paleontological varieties.

1. *The Evidence.*

Of all the arguments adduced in favor of evolution this ought to be the most compelling. All else "remains mere secondary evidence" says Prof. T. H. Huxley. "It may remove dissent, but it does not compel assent. Primary and direct evidence in favor of evolution can be furnished only by paleontology. The geological record, as soon as it approaches completeness, must when properly questioned, yield either an affirmative or a negative answer; if evolution has taken place, there will its mark be left; if it has not taken place, there will lie its refutation."

Now we do in fact find in the sedimentary rocks from the Precambrian period down to our own day, the remains of organisms that have lived in the various geological ages. Fossils are met with in all the strata of the earth's crust, as so many witnesses of the life and of the forms with which it was invested (fig. 31). They retrace the history of life and of evolution if it existed. All that is necessary is the ability to read the records.

Now, to tell the truth, these records, though apparently very rich, are, in reality, very poor. Many of the pages of this geological book are missing, either for the reason that they have never been written, or because they have been destroyed by metamorphism or by erosion, or because they have not yet been discovered, or finally,

[1] Cf. Depéret, *op. cit.*, p. 153.

because, the order of their succession, is at times uncertain.
Apart from these restrictions, however, there still remains
a rich store of records, particularly of the marine animals.
Here, at least in certain zones, all the conditions favoring

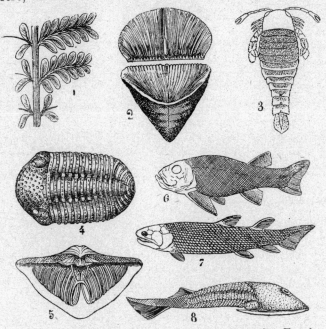

Fig. 31. — Characteristic fossils of the Devonian Epoch,
the 3rd subdivision of the Primary Period.

1. *Palæopteris* (fern); 2. *Calceola sandalina* (coral); 3. *Pterygotus* (crustacean);
4. *Phaeops latifrons* (trilobites); 5. *Spirifer Verneuili* (brachiopod, open
and showing its two spiral arms); 6. *Acanthodes;* 7. *Osteolepis;* 8. *Cephal-
aspis* (Three ganoid fishes).

fossilization are generally realized. Thus, it is not rare
to meet with strata that are literally one mass of entire
fossils.

Since the time of Cuvier, paleontology has made sufficient progress to enable us to present a numerically and
morphologically rich collection of fossils, from the base
of the Primary to the top of the Quaternary strata. It is
from these records that evolutionists draw their strongest

arguments. The following table gives the major geological divisions, and an idea of the successive appearance of vertebrates :

	Present Period		
Cenozuic Era	Quaternary		Man
		Pliocene	
		Miocene	
	Tertiary	Oligocene	Primates
		Eocene. . . .	Placental Mammals
	Cretaceous		
Mesozoic Era	Jurrassic		Birds
	Triassic		Mammals
	Permian		Reptiles
	Carboniferous		Theromorphs
Paleozoic Era	Devonian		Batrachians
	Silurian		Fish
	Cambrian		
Protozoic	Algonkian		Invertebrates
Agnotozoic or			
Precambrian Era	Archean		

This represents the order of appearance of the animals from the Algonkian or Percambrian period to the present day. The latest discoveries tend to push back the date of the first appearance of all vertebrates still farther. This table therefore can be only provisional. [1]

2. *Value of the Evidence.*

It is partly owing to the efforts made to prove evolution, that paleontological researches and studies have been so vigorously pushed during the last 60 years. Darwin had not made use of this argument. He saw its weakness and the gaps which nothing seemed able to fill. His disciples have frequently asserted that paleontology would eventually give indisputable proof of the gradual perfecting of living organisms. They claim that we should find at the base of the sedimentary rocks the very lowest and the most primitive forms of life, and as we ascend in the geological strata we ought to see new, more perfect and more numerous organisms appearing.

[1] *Revue des quest. scient.*, July, 1920, p. 124, art. of Achille Salée.

For popularizers, like Haeckel and his school, Le Dantec, and others, evolution is no longer an hypothesis, but a certain fact that needs no further demonstration. "To prove evolution" said one of these, "is to carry water to the ocean." We have not yet arrived at this point however. Specialists in paleontology are more modest in their assertions, as may be seen from the following testimonies.

The Rev. Teilhard de Chardin has systematized and very well summmarized the ideas of transformists, from Lamarck to Haeckel, and has made a critical study of them though personally fully admitting evolution. [1]

"All the actually existing animals and fossils, could, in the opinion of some, be arranged in a small number of lines, which will, in the course of time, be entirely filled in with increasingly complex types. Thus all those represented by the form N will then assume the form N+1.

"The transformation of organisms in each line, not being subject to interruption, and all of the lines constituting a relatively simple number, it was easy to find with precision, the unfilled spaces. This whole fan-like arrangement of forms diverged and yet developed along the angles with an appreciable velocity, in such a way that some flattered themselves that they could easily know the first beginnings and the actual persistence of vital movement. On the one hand, indeed, the different animal lines traced backward in the scale of transition, obviously, should have converged in the one same point of morphological dispersion, located in the vicinity of the Cambrian beds. On the other hand, even a slight amount of experimentation could not fail to bring into evidence the plasticity of organized matter. Thus, not only the fact, of evolution, but the mechasnism itself, appeared clear. To explain these metamorphoses of life, all that was necessary was to have recourse to adaptation or to natural selection, and to heredity.

[1] *Études*, June, 1921, p. 521-526, 538, et sq.; *Revue de Philosophie*, April, 1923.

"Observation of new facts and a greater regard for truth have brought about a singular revision of these too approximative representations, during the last thirty years." To begin with, we have learned that very many living series, considered as genealogical or phyletic, were only morphological, having been established from the variation of one particular organ only. Thus, for instance, an animal that was considered the ancestor of another, was later on recognized as having lived in the same age with the latter. Or, again, besides the adaptive characteristics upon which the genealogical relations were based, one has noticed such or such an indication of positive divergence which prevents one from placing the two forms in the same line, when not only the hoofs or the teeth or the isolated skull, but all the parts together were taken into consideration.

"The case of the hipparion, at first, considered an ancestor of the horse on account of the hoofs with three digits, but in reality, more complicated than it, as seen from the structure of the teeth, and that of the acerotherium, more primitive than the rhinoceros, because of the absence of a nasal horn, and yet contemporaneous with it, are well known. It would be an easy matter to multiply instances of mistakes made in earlier days that later on had to be rectified." T. de Chardin drew attention to the fixity of certain species. "It was neccessary from the start to give up the idea of a regular, continuous and total evolution. The terebrates of our coast (European) the lingulæ of the southern hemisphere, the limulæ of the Pacific, the trigoniæ of Australia, the cockroaches, the scorpions, etc., are irremediably fixed organisms, fossils of actual living species that have *not varied in a single important trait* from the types that existed in the Secondary, the Carboniferous or even in the Cambrian strata. While certain sections of the animal world are completely renewed, others remain rigorously stationary.

"The nautilus of the Indian Ocean, or the daman of Syria, or the tarsius of Malaisia, or the cryptoproct and the lemurs of Madagascar are known in the fossil state.

and still exist about us, unchanged from the remotest periods. In virtue of the remarkable discoveries of the American paleontologist Walcott, in British Columbia, we know today, that the oldest schists of the world, the Algonkian, already contain highly differentiated crustacians, and in the rich Cambrian strata we are able to study in detail, the soft parts of, not only the crustacians pertaining to the grand orders of the present day, but the annelids, and the sipunculaceæ like those of today, and the extremely specialized holothures.''

Depéret, dean of the Faculty of Sciences in Lyons, and member of the Académie des Sciences, who for more than thirty years has specialized in paleontological studies, has admirably pointed out the difficulties connected with this problem, in a volume published in 1908, and entitled : *Les transformations du monde animal.* He himself, is a confirmed evolutionist but a well informed one. We may borrow some of his conclusions referring the reader to his work for the more special proofs. Chapters xiv and xxiii treat of the value of the paleontological argument.

Alluding to the phylons or genealogical series that some have tried to establish, he declares them to be rare, short, interrupted by gaps and often very arbitrary, because the authors have not always taken into consideration the chronological order, or the organism as a whole. He holds it impossible to find the links between the orders, the classes, the branches and the kingdoms, and maintains that the majority of genera, with the exception of the vertebrates, are represented in the Cambrian strata. He then gives his own rules for the establishing of phylons, or the real and not the imaginary series of the ancestors of an animal. Thus, we must trace them through the geological strata, from the very recent to the most ancient. The process is not without its serious difficulties, since the evolution of a type does not of necessity occur in the same locality, and many of the marine transgressions and regressions have brought about numerous changes of fauna. The difficulty is increased by the fact that only a very small number of animals are fossilized; the others, especially when there is question of land animals, were destroyed.

In spite of these difficulties, however, some have thought it possible to give a genealogical tree of at least a certain number of species. Among the mammals, we note that of the horse, the bear, the elephant, the rhinoceros, the ape, and the swine. We shall review these rapidly, since they are supposed to be the best established.

The Horse. Gaudry was of the opinion he could give

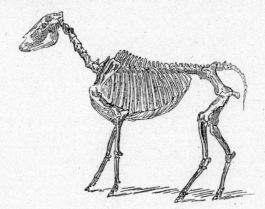

Fig. 32. — Hipparion gracile.

the genealogical series thus : horse, hipparion, anchiterium, paloplotherium, paleotherium, basing it on the progressive reduction in size of the second and fourth digits (figs. 32, 33). More recently, Marsh and Cope have given another series found in the south-western part of the United States. Eohippus, orohippus, mesohippus, miohippus, protohippus and horse. The series is different from that of Europe, and it would indeed be strange if this case of convergence were real. But Depéret finds good reason to criticize the European series, since there is no connecting link between these so widely different genera, and since each of the terms had disappeared without evolving, long before the next term appeared. He holds the period of time from the Oligocene, too short, for the transformation of the paleotherium into the horse. [1]

The Bear. Gaudry and Boule base the proof for the evolution of the bear on the progressive development of tubercled teeth and the correlative reduction of the premolars in different types of Tertiary carnivora. The series is as follows : the amphycion, Middle Miocene hemicyon, Upper Miocene and Pliocene hyenarctos, and the actual oeluropus bears. Now, according to Depéret there existed in the Middle Miocene small carnivora called ursavi, that had all the characteristics of the bears. This being so, Gaudry and Boule have not cleared up the problem of the real origin of the bear group. They have simply followed one dental modification in animals, which have no other bond of affiliation between them.

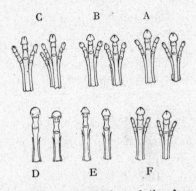

Fig. 33. — Evolution of the fore and hind feet of the equidae.

A. Actual horse; B. *Protohippus* (hipparion); C. *Miohippus*; D. *Mesohippus*; E. *Orohippus*; F. *Eohippus*.

The Rhinoceros. The following is a resume of Gaudry's supposed lineage of the rhinoceros, with Depéret's critique (p. 157, 158).

Palœotherium medium. Eocene. Thin nasal bones, supposedly indicating a fleshy proboscis.

Palœotherium crassum. Bones stronger, leaving no room for a proboscis.

Acerotherium, or hornless rhinoceros. Miocene. Nasal bones very small.

---

[1] The series given by Cuénot, in *Genèse des espèces animales*, p. 384. Small equidae with 4 digits in the Eocene : Eohippus, Orohippus, Epihippus. Small equidae with 8 digits in the Oligocene : Mesohippus, Miohippus. Large equidae with 3 digits in the Miocene : Parahippus, Meryhippus, Hipparion. A large equid with 1 digit in the Quaternary : Equus cabalus.

Acerotherium tetradactylum of Sansan (Gers). Middle Miocene.

Rhinoceros from the Orleans sands.   Oligocene.   Small nasal horn.

Rhinoceros Schleiermacheri.   Upper Miocene.   Nasal bone a little heavier.

Rhinoceros pachygnathus of Pikermi.   Nasal horn and frontal horn.

Rhinoceros etruscus.   Pliocene.   Nasal bones supported by a partially ossified partition.

Rhinoceros tichorhinus of the Quaternary.   Nasal bones full size supported throughout their entire length by a partition.

Depéret remarks : "Without mentioning the many anachronisms, no paleontologist will hesitate to assert that this filiation is in nearly every respect inexact.   There exists no transitional form between the palœotherium and the rhinoceros, for the simple reason that the latter appeared suddenly in Europe, at the beginning of the Oligocene epoch by migration from its place of origin, probably America.   On the other hand the acerotheria are by no means the ancestors of the horned rhinoceros. The appearance of the latter in Europe, at the beginning of the Miocene epoch is also the result of a sudden migration of Afro-Asiatic origin.   Finally, even in the case of the true rhinoceros, the above series indicates a linking of species, as those of R. Shleiermacheri and R. pachygnothus, which have nothing in common, and correspond to a parallel evolution of two distinct branches.   We may then say that Gaudry has studied, not indeed the evolution of the rhinoceros group, but the gradual thickening of the nasal bones destined to support the horns, in one whole series of genera which are not allied.   One might describe almost similar functional series in the other groups of horned vertebrates."

The Ungulates, according to Gaudry.

"Deceived by his constant scheme of alliance (rapprochements) by functional adaptation, Gaudry has not failed to find a link, between the edentates and the ungulates, in a curious family of Tertiary mammals, the schizotherium, the macrotherium and the chalicotherium in which, at their highest stage, the front feet show a fossorial structure. In reality however, there exists no kind of relationship between these strange chalicotheridæ, and the edentates either of the present or of the past. A careful study of the skull, the thigh and fore-thigh and tibia clearly show that we are dealing with a true ungulate, exceptionally adapted to fossorial functions... "

The Monkeys. "Taking up the difficult problem of the origin of the monkeys, Gaudry solves it by the sole consideration of the conical shape of the denticles, which project from the crown of the molars, in many of the existing forms of monkeys, e. g. the dog-faced baboon. He holds that these monkeys have direct connection with certain Tertiary ungulates, the hyracotherium and especially the cebocaerus from the lignites of Vaucluse... No part of this hypothesis will hold. On the one hand the cebocaerus, from all its dental and cranial characteristics, is indisputably a true member of the suidæ, without any connection with the primates, while, on the other hand, the denticles fringing the molars indicate a simple adapta tion to an omnivorous regime, and is found in varying degrees of perfection in the most diverse specimens of nearly all the orders of mammals.

"These examples, that it would be easy to multiply for the other groups of fossil animals, will suffice to explain why paleontologists have rejected these approximative methods, which lead us almost fatally to an imaginary evolution."

3. *The Method.*

The scientific method, having for its object the exact and minute reconstruction of the real phyletic branches, "consists in tracing step by step, in a succession of geological strata regularly superposed and continuous, the chronological variations of one and the same type (species) or of types so close by their natural affinities, that the genealogical relations impose themselves upon every impartial observer. That such series may be demonstrative, it is necessary that all evidence be without any gap whatever." Each of the terms of the ascending or descending series could bear the name of *Mutation*. We could in this way appreciate the value of chronological variation. All that would remain would be to determine what value to give these mutations, in constituting a new species or a new genus.

4. *The Result.*

We might sum up in the following theoretical table [1] the results of paleontological researches :

	A	A[1]	A[2]	B	B[1]	B[2]	C	Fauna of the
	Aa	A[1]a	A[2]a	Ba	B[1]a	B[2]a	Ca	present
Phyletic	Ab	A[1]b	A[2]b	Bb	B[1]b	B[2]b	Cb	Pliocene
Branches	Ac	A[1]c	A[2]c	Bc	B[1]c	B[2]c	Cc	Miocene
	Ad	A[1]d	A[2]d	Bd	B[1]d	B[2]d	Cd	Oligocene
	Ae	A[1]e	A[2]e	Be	B[1]e	B[2]e	Ce	Eocene
								Cretaceous

The table shows how the vertical series evolve within quite restricted limits, but without any point of contact with the neighboring series. The horizontal series represent contemporaneous types morphologically, but not genetically neighbors.

It would seem that if the paleontologists would content themselves with arranging these phyletic branches without prejudice, pro or con, Science would gain in precision what it loses in generalization. We can apply this method of classification to the phyletic branches of the dinotheriums, mastodons and elephants. [2] We see these three types evolving parallelly without meeting at any point. The dentition serves in making the comparison. The common origin remains hypothetical, but has never been demonstrated as has often been said. We may say in addition that the ascendant mutations often bear on a simple detail, as the increase of stature, or com-

[1] Depéret, *op. cit.*, p. 197.
[2] Depéret, *op. cit.*, p. 185-195.

plexity, and that the species disappear at the moment when they have attained their maximum development, as if they were too specialized, to adapt themselves further to the varying conditions of the environment. This remark may he generalized. For the ammonites, trilobites, reptiles and birds give manifest proof of this in the course of the geological periods.

The pretended law of indefinite, continuous progress, no longer seems to agree with these statements, with these facts, which it would be easy to formulate into a law. To have a real paleontological series it would be necessary to follow step by step a species in the series of superposed geological strata. "The first paleontologists to follow this method are Hilgendorf, in his memorable work on the variation of *planorbis multiformis*, from the fresh water strata of Steinheim, and Waagen on his study of the series of Ammonites of the *Ammonites subradiatus* group. The number of *series of forms* that we can reconstruct at present is more limited than we might suppose *a priori*." Depéret p. 69.

"The most striking genealogical series is that furnished by the investigations of Neumayr and Paul on the Paludinæ of the levantine fresh water strata of the Danube basin." Similar variations among other fresh water mollusks are met with in the most diverse families, the melanopsis, the neritinæ and the unios, for example.

We may ask ourselves whether these variations in the form of the shell really go beyond the limits of species. We doubt it when we see chonchiologists demolishing species, and so far from being unanimous in their definitions. These facts, then, have little value as proofs of evolution beyond the limits of species and *a fortiori* of genus.

On page 72, Depéret adds : "If now, we wish to push still further the problem of the important formations intervening in the geological ages, we no longer find proofs as proximate as those which we have noted within the narrow bounds of the formation of species, due to the *series of natural forms* and to experiments on domestic races."

"The paleontologist nowhere shows us a series of types linking widely separated groups as for example, a series from the protista to the mammals, so we must content ourselves with conclusions drawn from analogy and proofs based on resemblance." On page 73 : "Already, in the earliest ages, such as the Cambrian epoch, the presence of all the important fundamental types of the animal kingdom, with the exception of the vertebrates, has been established. Classes, orders and even some genera, common among animals living today, are represented by already highly specialized forms. The class of mollusks is already represented by the four great orders of brachiopods, the lamellibranchs, the gasteropods and the cephalopods. The difference, between the primitive fauna and the actually existing fauna, seems to hold especially with the appearance of animals extinct today, such as the tetracorolliaria, the graptolites, the dipnoi, the ganoidei, the large reptiles of the Secondary era and the large mammals of the Tertiary."

These disappearances cannot be elements of a proof in favor of evolution. "Outside the consideration of the *series of forms*, we ought to attach great importance to certain extinct types that are placed between two zoological groups, entirely distinct today and establishing a link between these groups. No example is more conclusive than that of the archaeopterx, a birdlike form from the lithographic limestone at Solenhofen. Its bill with teeth implanted in the alveoli, its tail formed of a long series of elongated vertebræ, its wings bearing at the extremities free digits provided with claws, the presence of ventral ribs, the disposition of the joint-bones, constitute an assemblage of reptilian characteristics, that permit us to unhesitatingly derive the class of birds from the reptile trunk" (fig. 34). But could we not see here a specimen of a special class intercalated between the birds and the reptiles, without genealogical connection? There are indeed too many missing intermediates to admit the transition of one class from the other. A great number are necessary for the transition from one species to another.

The author thinks that the transition types between the classes and orders, distinct today, are exceedingly restricted in number, and that *from the standpoint of paleontology[1] the major portion of the fundamental types of the animal kingdom appear to have no connection.* Thus, we do not know the primitive type of the great group of vertebrates, nor that of the fishes, nor that of the amphibians, etc.

Hence evolutionists have been forced, like Darwin,

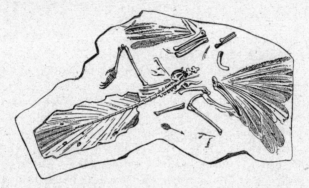

Fig. 34. — *Archaeopterux :* Fossils found in the litographic limestone at Solenhafen. Reptilian tail, vertebrae and limbs. Bird feathers.

Neumayr, etc., to take umbrage behind the insufficiency of paleontological discoveries, and to look forward to the happy chance that will bring to light the types that will fill up these gaps. We shall add that there is no well founded hope of ever completely filling up these gaps, since the first fossiliferous rocks, as, for instance, the Precambrian, have been metamorphosed and have thus seen the almost complete disappearance of the fossils they might have contained. In a word, paleontology is, as it were, a book from which the first and most important pages have been torn, and others present innumerable gaps, or indecipherable enigmas. Thus the hope of ever solv-

[1] Depéret, *op. cit.,* p. 114-120, for Zittel's views.

ing the problem of evolution by means of paleontology
seems to vanish.   We are far from being able to make the
positive statements found in our popular periodicals and
our standard textbooks, wherein we are not even lead to
suppose that there is any difficulty connected with the
problem.   Evolution appears neither continuous nor
regular, nor entire.   If, in spite of these difficulties, one
would still be an evolutionist it is necessary to recognize
the fact, that the path followed by evolution still remains
uncertain.   We cannot build up complete genealogical
trees.   We must confine ourselves to the attempt to
demonstrate transformism in certain particular instances. [1]

5. Certain modern paleontologists ask themselves whether
it is not possible to find, between the mammals and the
reptiles, intermediates constituting a series that is at once
morphological and chronological.   Achille Salée, professor
at the University of Louvain, answers in the affirmative,
in an article in the *Revue des questions scientifiques*, of
July 20, 1920, p. 148.   The group of cynodont reptiles
of the Triassic furnish these intermediates.   The reptiles
are vertebrates that breath by means of lungs from their
birth, and have cold blood (fig. 35).   Mammals are vertebrates that breath by means of lungs and have warm
blood.   Since paleontology cannot supply these characteristics, it is necessary to select some of the salient characteristics that will serve as points of comparison to bring
out the *differences*, between the reptiles and the mammals,
and afterwards the *terms of transition*.

The differences are numerous.   The author cites a
few of them.

The upper part of the skull.

The cranium of mammals is made up of a small number
of bones.   The orbit in particular is composed in great part
of the front bone or frontal.   In the reptiles, the number
of bones in the head is much larger.   There are the prefrontal, the post-orbital and even a post-orbital bone encir-
cling the orbit.   The mammals have neither a prefrontal

[1] Cf. P. Theilhard de Chardin, *Études*, June 1921, p. 572 et sq.

nor a post-orbital bone. The reptiles have an aperture or foramen in the center of the cranium, in which the pineal eye is lodged. This foramen is absent in the mammals.

Lateral aspect of the skull.

In the mammals the lower jaw is directly articulated with the cranium; in the reptiles, there is an intermediary

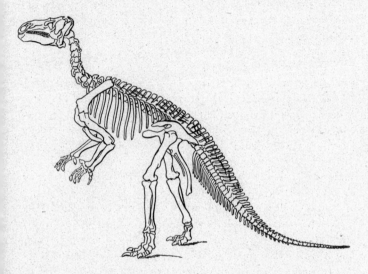

Fig. 35. — *Iguanodon Bernissartensis.* From Lower Cretaceous of Belgium. Adaptation to the life of a land biped. (After A. Salée).

bone, the articular. In the mammals, the mandible is made up of a single bone, the dentary. In the reptiles there are several bones besides the dentary, the subangular, the articular and the angular.

Lower portion of the skull.

All mammals have a secondary palate. The reptiles, except the crocodiles, have none. The teeth of mammals are limited to the bones that form the contour of the jaw-bone. In the reptiles, the teeth may encroach upon the roof of the mouth. The teeth of mammals are differentiated into incisors, canines, premolars and molars, while the teeth arrangement in the reptiles is uniform and conical.

Posterior section of the skull.

The articulation of the head, i. e. of the occipital with the spinal column, is realized, in the mammals, by two rounded protuberances, the two occipital condyles. The reptiles have only one occipital condyle.

The shoulder.   The arm of a mammal is articulated with the scapula, a large bony plate, having a crest which is terminated by a salient appendage called the acromion. This acromion is lacking in reptiles.

The pelvis.   The pelvis is formed from three bones on each side, and, in all mammals, the upper bone or ilion is greatly prolonged in front. Between the two lower bones, the pubis and the ischium, there is an aperture (obturator); in the reptilian type, this aperture does not exist, nor the projection of the ilion towards the front.

From these many characteristics, common to all mammals, we see that the skeleton is clearly different from that of reptiles.

Though these anatomical differences are marked, there are numerous *gradual modifications*. These latter include the following. The orbit is formed from the prefrontal, the frontal, the postfrontal and postorbital, respectively; the foramen and the shoulder bones are gradually reduced in size; the dentary approaches articulation in the measure that the articular, the angular and the subangular are reduced; the secondary palate gradually appears; the teeth, which at first encircle the roof of the buccal cavity are gradually limited to the maxillae and the pre-maxillae; the teeth are differentiated from a uniform type to the varied mammal types; the single condyle of the cotylosaurs is formed from two exoccipitals and a basioccipital; the acromion makes its appearance; the articular socket of the shoulder is first formed from three, then from two and finally from only one bone (146); the foramen between the pubis and the ischium is developed.

Thus through these insensibly progressive modifications the differences are gradually effaced.

It is difficult to explain this gradual succession of fauna, except by slow evolution. We cannot dream, of innumerable creative acts, yet the characteristics are important enough to distinguish species, genera, families and even different orders in the types studied.

There are, between the mammals and the reptiles, certain

Fig. 36. — *Stegosaurus ungulatus.*

From the Lower Cretaceous of Colorado. Adaptation to the quadruped life. (Salée.)

resemblances of a general character. Some are aquatic, some terrestrial, some volant. Some are carnivorous and others herbivorous, etc.

The Secondary reptiles, like the mammals of the Tertiary period became extinct after having attained enormous proportions or extraordinary shapes, as the stegosaurs (fig. 36), the triceropsidae, the diplodocus, and the atlantasaurs.

It would seem that we have here, one of the best arguments in favor of a real evolution. Still the future can modify these positions. If we should discover true mammals contemporary with the reptiles, or *a fortiori*, anterior to the reptiles of the Triassic or even of the Permian epoch, it would be necessary to adduce other arguments for evolution or to seek for another explanation.

6. In this connection let us quote from Depéret : [1] "The age of the appearance of each great group of fossil animals, even the most elevated in the zoological order, recedes farther and farther in time as paleontological discoveries accumulate.

"We have known for some time that from the Cambrian epoch, the majority of the great groups (classes) of invertebrates were already clearly distinct, and that, in consequence, we must almost give up the hope of one day discovering the primitive types of the foraminifera, of the sponges, the corals, the cystoids, the crinoids, the brachiopods, the lamellibranchs, the gasteropods, the cephalopods, the trilobites, the merostomes and, without doubt, even our air-breathing articulates.

"It is probable that, a few years hence, we shall have to say the same of many of the great classes of vertebrates, since we are already certain that the fish originated at least in the Ordovician, the amphibians in the Devonian, the reptiles in the Carboniferous and the mammals in the Triassic periods.

"If there had been in reality, as is probable, a gradual perfecting of the organic world, and if the animal types are the more recent the higher their organization, we shall certainly be obliged to advance again, for the greater number of geological periods, each of the dates which have provisionally marked the beginning of all the branches."

This is avowing that all beings were already specialized, well differentiated, perfect in their kind, at their appearance in the Cambrian epoch. The recent discoveries made in the Precambrian lead to the same conclusions.

Is the research into non-specialized, non-differentiated types, capable of evolving in many directions, well established? Evolutionists think so. [2] We may form a different opinion after an experimental and rational study of the facts. [3]

[1] Depéret, *op. cit.*, p. 251.
[2] Cuénot, p. 387-393.
[3] Cf. Vial, *Revue des Sciences philos. et théolog.*, 1920, p. 5; 1922, p. 5 et sq. Also Termier, *Rev. quest. scient.*, vol. I, 1920, p. 71-77.

7. *To sum up.* The paleontological series, by themselves might be able to prove evolution absolutely, if they were very numerous, very extensive, very real, very continuous, very convergent, and altogether unanimously received. Unfortunately, we must recognize that these series are :

Too rare.—The authors always repeat the same : those of the horses, the bears, the rhinoceros, the elephants, the ammonites, etc. These are indeed few in comparison with the hundreds of thousands of known species.

Too short.—If there is question of connecting an organism with a unicellular type, as evolutionists wish to do, it will not suffice to give merely three or four, or even ten intermediary types; hundreds, yes thousands, would be required to form a continuous series from the actual type back to the most primitive. We are given only a few links in the long chain, and these are confined to one or two strata.

Too discontinuous.—These links are generally not united together when there is question of important transitions as from one class to another, or from one order to another. What is to be said of the value of the archeopteryx that fills up by itself the immense gap, which separates the reptiles from the birds? To pass from one branch to another, or from a mammal to a protozoa, we are offered one twentieth of the terms or links in Haeckel's genealogical tree, connecting man with the moner. The demonstration is quite deceptive.

Too arbitrary.—These series are at times so arbitrary, that it would be impossible for two paleontologists working separately, to give us two concordant series. Even more. The series admitted by one would de declared inexact by the other. This is what has happened with those of Lamarck, of Darwin, of Haeckel, of Gaudry, of Cope, of Boule, of Perrier, and we might say, the same of the majority of those established previous to the last few years. Depéret, after having investigated the origin of mammals for 25 years, declares himself unable to say where to connect the links. But he had no difficulty in demolishing the short series pertaining to the horse, the bear, the rhinoceros, etc., of Gaudry.

There is uncertainty in the logical order, since *resemblance does not signify descent*; in the chronological order, since account has not always been taken of the order of appearance, be it of an organism, or of an organ; in the morphological order, since the resemblances are too superficial, bearing on only one characteristic such as color, size, hair, etc., or on a single organ as the teeth of the bear, the foot of the horse, the septa and sutures of the ammonites, etc.; in the geographical order by joining together forms geographically too widely separated; in the physiological order, since we cannot obtain a sufficiently accurate knowledge of the organs and their functions from the fossils alone. How could we distinguish, or rather, how could we avoid confusing the zebra, the horse, the mule or even the ass, if we had only the fossilized skeletons?

At times too manifestly unreal, indeed purely imaginary, built up in accordance with a previously conceived ideal plan as those of Haeckel, Gaudry, Cope, etc.

Sometimes too manifestly forged in its entirety, as that fabricated by Haeckel. [1]

With these restrictions, there remains considerable evidence to infer a certain evolution, whose limits will be more accurately determined with the progress of paleontology.

§ VI. RUDIMENTARY ORGANS [2]

The variability of organisms often appears as recession. Since evolutionists invoke this in favor of their theory, it would be well to point out the facts and to draw our conclusions from them.

They call such organs *rudimentary* as are so slightly developed as to render them incapable of performing their normal functions. The recession of the organ could go as far as complete disappearance.

---

[1] Cf. Brass, *Ernst Haekel als Biologe und die Wahrheit*; McCann, *God or Gorilla*, 154-157.

[2] Cuénot, *La Genèse des espèces*, p. 179-204.

It can affect the function alone, the organ appearing normal. We find examples of this in all living creatures, from the unicellular animals to man. We can attenuate the virulence of microbes which is to cause one of their functions to retrogress. The same may be produced spontaneously. Among the parasitic worms, we find a very striking example of this in the taenia, originating from the cystecercus in the pig; it seems to have no more than an organ of fixation. While alimentation takes place by osmosis. It is the same with the lumbricoid ascaris, common in children. The parasitic insects that live on the body have become apterous.

The sense organs of some animals that dwell in the

Fig. 37. — Atrophy of limbs in the lizards : *Sphenops capistratus*. The fore limbs are atrophied. (Cuénot.)

dark, e. g. of certain insects, batrachians and fish, have become atrophied, at times to complete loss of vision. Might we not consider as a case of recession the disappearance of the tail and gills in tadpoles? We find a number of interesting instances among the reptiles. The limbs of the saurians, perfectly formed in some lizards, are reduced to mere stumps in the sphenops (fig. 37), the seps and some other forms. They are no longer exteriorly visible in the blind-worm, but are represented by internal bones. In the pythonic serpents, there are but the rudiments, under the form of isolated bones. They disappear completely in the serpents.

The wings of birds exhibit all stages of atrophy, from simple lack of use as in the hen, the duck and the turkey, to total disappearance in the apteryx (fig. 38). The digits of the feet are reduced from 5 to 2.

Among marine mammals, the whale shows several marks of recession. The pelvis and posterior limbs are reduced to a few ossicles. The greatly reduced anterior limbs are transformed into fins. The young whale has teeth which never pierce through. The seals, the otters and the walruses offer further, though less pronounced, examples of recession, with adaptation to marine life.

Fig. 38. — In the *Apteryx*, a walking bird, the fore limbs are reduced to a mere stump.

We find rudimentary organs also in land mammals. The horns of the ungulates present all stages of recession to total disappearance, in the same or in different species, as for example in the bovidae, the ovidae and the cervidae, etc. Recession of dentition and of the fleece is also found in these.

Among the paridigitates as among the imparidigitates,

it seems clear that the digits of the feet have passed from 4 to 2, or from 5 to 3 to 1. The hyomoschus and the hippopotamus have four well formed digits. Swine, bovidae and ovidae exhibit two in recession. The giraffe has only the two middle digits.

Among the imparidigitates, we shall see the elephants with their five digits enclosed in one hoof; the rhinoceros with three digits resting on the ground; the hipparion with two rudimentary digits and the middle toe well developed; and the horse with only one digit.

Examples of recession might be found in the muscular, in the nervous and in the digestive systems. But it is useless to multiply instances.

These are the facts. Do they prove evolution? They do, if there is question of a recessive evolution; they do not, if we mean progressive evolution. Now it is the latter alone that interests us. Everyone will agree that it is possible, to bring about the disappearance of an organ by means of the many different natural causes of atrophy; the difficulty is to effect the appearance of one where none existed before, in a word, to create one. We do not believe physico-chemical forces, though strictly capable of the first, would be able to produce the second. Nevertheless evolutionists suppose this spontaneous appearance of organs.

For us it remains the mysterious enigma of all living beings. Each organism inherits organs from its ancestors, none of the organs are new creations. All the sense organs are an ancestral heritage. Behind and beyond all is creation. That certain recessions should give rise to new forms, even of new species, is possible. We shall see that there is in this a kind of creation intended by the Author of nature. This recession is manifested in the barnacles, the cerripeds, the acornshell-fish, three crustaceans taken for mollusks, in the adult stage (fig. 39.)

The secondary causes might be playing a special role here, but it appears to us quite limited. It would not be necessary, indeed, to exaggerate the importance of rudimentary organs, nor that of the known or the unknown

causes which might produce them. Experience shows,
in fact, that it is not in the power of man to effect
by heredity, the disappearance of the least important of

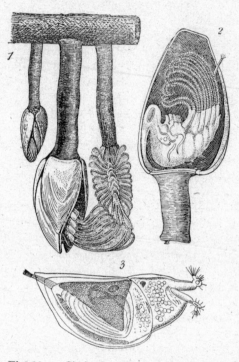

Fig. 39. — Cirripedes (Barnacles) (*lepas anatifera*)

1. Group of anatifae, attached to a piece of floating wood. — 2. Single isolated specimen, with shell opened; — 3. Young free-swimming anatifa.

the sense organs, whether it be the eyes, the ears, the
limbs, or any other.

We should also note here rather than elsewhere, that
the number of rudimentary organs is not so large as
Darwin and his school have pretended. They have often
taken for such, organs whose functions were still unknown,
e. g. the pineal gland, the thyroid gland, the vermiform
appendix, etc., whose true and generally indispensable

function has been eventually determined. Certain organs reputed rudimentary have their explanation during the embryonic period.

§ VII.— ARGUMENT DRAWN FROM EMBRYOLOGY.

All living organisms in their development pass through the unicellular stage, the ovum stage. This cell develops, divides,

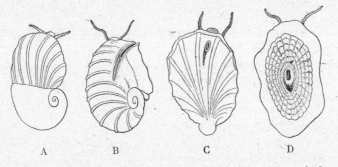

          A   B   C   D

Fig. 40. — Successive forms of the shel) of *Fissurella reticulata*.

A. The larval shell is below and the adult above, surmounted by tentacles; B. 2ⁿᵈ form of advanced shell, with slit on the edge, representing a stage that is characteristic in the *Emarginula*; C. 3rd form of the more advanced shell with perforation that is permanent in the *Rimula*; D. Final stage of the adult shell of *Fisurella reticulata*.

and differentiates, to form, little by little, an organism like that of its parents. Some have tried to find in this individual evolution, stages common to all polycellular beings, in so far as all would be alike at first, but would become differentiated after having passed the lower stages as in the *fissurella reticulata* (fig. 40).

This ontogenic development would be an abridged repetition of the phylogenetic development. The living organism would pass through all the stages through which the species has passed. This is, indeed, the formula of the biogenetic law, so dear to Haeckel and his disciples. If the law were correct, it would be easy to know the ancestors of any organism whatever; it would suffice in fact, merely to study its embryonic development to find there the specific forms of its ancestors up to the primitive moner, and the great riddle would thus be solved.

This law was believed, upheld and taught everywhere until very recently, when some saw fit to question its validity and to demand the evidence supporting this strange law introduced as a possibility by Geoffroy-Saint-Hilaire, Muller and de Serres, and later taught as a scientific fact by Haeckel to bolster up his theory of monism. Embryologists soon began to limit and amend the law ; then they had recourse to tachygenesis or abbreviation of stages; then to the suppression of stages; then to the falsification of stages by the organism, by way of repeating the ancestral phases, just as an unscrupulous student juggles with, mutilates, abridges and falsifies texts and ends up by complete aphasia.

To test the value of this biogenetic law it would be necessary, in my opinion :

1. To establish a true ontogenic or embryological series in the type studied; that is to say, to give a series of representative stages of the organism actually existing, beginning with the ovum, through the morula, blastula, gastrula (fig. 41), etc.

2. To establish a second series of actual or paleontological adult forms, starting also, from the unicellular stage and going to the most highly organized type.

3. These two series having been formed, to compare them with each other, and to verify the perfect correspondance of the successive terms. We are compelled to say that, though it appears easy to establish an ontogenic series, since all that is necessary is to form successive pairs, the series will be arbitrary, depending upon the particular views of each biologist; and unreal, since the embryo is always, an embryo and in consequence incapable of living in this state of incomplete development. The proof for this statement is that if the environment is favorable to its life, the embryo does not remain stationary; if we change the environment, the embryo dies. It is an organism in the process of formation and not yet formed.

The stages passed through are necessary and directly to their purpose. They do not recapitulate anything; the limbs, sense organs, eyes, etc., do not function until they are well developed.

From what we have said above, the paleontological

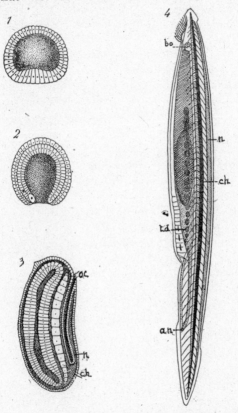

Fig. 41. — Phases of the *Amphioxus* representing the phases supposedly common to all vertebrates.

1. *Planula* phase; 2. *Gastrula* phase; 3. Embryo; *Ch.* Central line, dorsal cord; *n*, nervetube; *oc*, external opening of the nerve tube; 4. adult *amphioxus*; *bc.* mouth; *an*, anus; *td*, digestive tube; *ch*, dorsal cord, *n*, nerve tube.

series which would have to be arranged presents no fewer difficulties. No one would seriously think of building one up at the present time. That of Haeckel has absolutely no scientific value. All others are too fragmentary.

Comparison between the two series therefore becomes impossible, in default of the real terms. Let us add that it would be impossible to identify these series, were they in fact real, since, on the one hand, we have always an embryonic organism which can be compared only with another ambryo, and on the other hand, a free-moving being which can be compared only with another free-moving being that is self-sustaining. Anyone who compares embryos will always find differences, while the resemblances are explicable by the similarity of development. [1]

Haeckel tried to simplify the matter by using another kind of demonstration. He pretended that embryos in the course of their development resemble each other so closely, that it is impossible to distinguish one from another; yes even if they belong to different genera, families, orders, or classes. He gives as evidence, according to Rutinmeyer, His, Semper, Hensen, Bischoff, Hamann and Wasmann, a number of illustrations which are either purely fictitious, or taken from other authors and after retouching inserted in his own works.

But there is something still worse. On page 242 of the first edition of his *Natürliche Schöpfungsgeschichte* [2] (1868), Haeckel thrice repeated the same illustration to show that the human embryo is entirely identical with that of the monkey and of the dog. The same procedure is found on page 248, with reference to the three figures 9, 10 and 11. He represents by one and the same cut, thrice repeated, the embryo of a dog, of a hen and of a tortoise, and on page 249 he says: "If you compare the young embryos of the dog, the hen and the tortoise in figures 9, 10, and 11, I defy you to find any difference in them."

When a theory needs such a procedure, it is already condemned, and when a man of science stoops to such means, he loses all right to respect. [3]

---

[1] Cf. *Revue de Philosophie*, Oct. 1910.

[2] *History of Creation*, etc. Appleton.

[3] Wasmann, *La probité scientifique de Haeckel*, p. 8 sq.

Altough apparently accepting the biogenetic law in an amended and abridged form, Cuenot gives a fair criticism of it, and places it among the superficial hypotheses that are created to supply a need but are rather a hindrance than an aid to science. [1]

A very simple explanation may be found in the very laws of development of organisms from the unicellular state to maturity. This is in fact the opinion of Hertwig : "Each animal promotes only its own development; it ever remains one and the same individual." [2] The stages through which every living organism passes in its development are imposed by the fact that they all start from a single cell. This begins to multiply by division, forming successively two, four, eight, etc., cells. These cells group themselves in different ways, while passing through the morula, blastula and gastrula stages. From then on the embryo becomes more and more complex, differentiates and terminates its development in producing the specific form which gave it birth. That there may be certain resemblances in the development of different organisms, we cannot deny. It is a necessity. But there are fundamental differences, since it is always the same ancestral form that is reproduced.

There is no reason whatever, to look for a repetition, even abridged, of the adult conditions through which the species passed. A complete criticism of Haeckel's pretended biogenetic law may be found in Vialleton's work, [3] which definitively upsets it.

To this argument may be joined that drawn from the phenomena of metamorphoses and alternating generations. This latter idea designates the changes of form occurring in the organism in the process of development, starting from the moment when the latter has acquired all the segments of which its body is formed, to the adult state. It is in this sense, that the term has for some time been

---

[1] *Genèse des espèces animales*, p. 378.
[2] Cf. *Revue de Philosophie*, Oct. 1910, p. 400-411.
[3] Vialleton, *Un problème de l'évolution*, Paris, Masson, p. 205-23.

employed, in connection with the life cycle of insects. The transformation of tadpoles into frogs or toads, of the tadpole-like larvæ of the ascidia into ascidia, or the ammocoetes into lampreys, of the leptocephali into congers, of the pentacrini into comatulæ, and of the caterpillars into butterflies, etc., are all instances of metamorphosis (fig. 42).

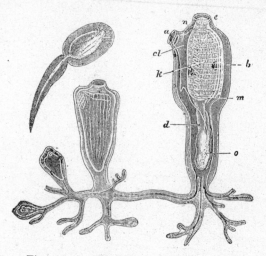

Fig. 42. — Ascidia (*clavalinæ colony*)

Left. Free-swimming larva with tail. When this larva becomes fixed, the tail disappears, *e*, the mouth; *a*, the anus, *b*, the envelope; *k*, respiratory apparatus; *m*, entrance to the digestive tube; *d*, intestine; *o*, ovary; *cl*, cloaca; *n*, nerve ganglion.

We have here a special embryonic development, where the independent life appears very early, and goes through a crisis or fundamental transformation at a given moment, before attaining its final phase. The embryo, not finding in the ovum, the necessary food reserves to complete its development, draws its sustenance from the external medium, instead of from the internal medium, the egg or the maternal organism. It must undergo these modifications before acquiring the appearance of the adult; at times it can reproduce itself in this embryonic or larval state (fig. 43).

The profound transformations which are effected in

these instances indicate the possibility of like transformations in the species, in which the morphological and
physiological changes would certainly be less important.
But, although these metamorphoses are realities, we must

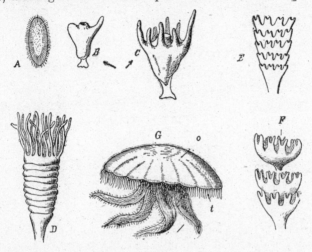

Fig. 43. — Development of the Medusa (*Aurelia œcrita*).

A, Ciliated, free-swimming larva;—B, C, D, E, Fixed individual developing;—
F, Separation of medusae;—G, Medusa, *b*, buccal arms; *t*, marginal
tentacles; *o*, umbrella.

confess that the changes in the species are only hypothetical.

The argument rests on that drawn from embryology, or
the development of the organism from the unicellular
state to the adult condition. The living being builds up
its own organism by unceasingly transforming it both
quantitatively and qualitatively, with direct reference to
the formation of an organism capable of living.

ARTICLE IV

MODERATE OR SPIRITUALISTIC EVOLUTION

The facts which we are about to discuss are the classical
arguments adduced by evolutionists. It would be erroneous to consider them peremptory arguments. To be

exact we should say that they *incline* the mind to think
that the ideal relationship between the species, which
is undeniable, is the result of a real relationship and of a
common descent.   Thus Darwin, who should realize the
real import, would merely say : *It seems to me that... I
am led to believe that... Is it not more simple to suppose
that...*, etc.

Without attaching to these arguments more importance
than they possess, certain spiritualistic evolutionists,
otherwise very firm in their faith, feel inclined towards
evolution or the theory of common descent.   At first
their number was small, but in the measure that evolution
disengages itself from materialism, it is being aug-
mented.

Their form of evolution is called *moderate*, since it rejects
the excesses which have followed in the train of the other
transformistic theories.   It does not admit that life appeared
on the earth as the result of a simple mechanical combination of the atoms which constitute the living protoplasm;
nor does it hold that man might be the result of evolution,
and is merely distinguished from other animals by a more
highly developed organism.

This moderate evolution is also called *spiritualistic*
evolution, since it does not reduce the universe to a mere
machine or to mere matter, but recognizes therein suprasensible forces which are grasped by the mind.   It recognizes a God Creator and the human soul : a God Creator
at the beginning of the world, at the beginning of life, at
the beginning of man and even at the beginning of that
wonderful law, which presides over the evolution of all
living creatures; and the human soul, in the suprasensible
operation, of which man is the theatre and which distinguishes him essentially from the beasts endowed only with
sensation.

According to its advocates, moderate evolution has the
double advantage of taking just account of the weighty
reasons in favor of evolution, and of not running counter
to any of the principles of closely allied sciences.

1.—How moderate evolution takes account of the data of science.

It is an established fact that the progress of humans knowledge conduces to the discovery of secondary cause, in ever increasing numbers, and that God appears less and less as the immediate Author of all the phenomena of nature. Philosophers are agreed in saying that God's glory as First Cause increases in proportion as He appears less active as secondary cause : for, according to an old adage, *melior est causa causae quam causa causati*, "The cause of a cause is greater than the cause of the thing caused." [1]

After Science had demonstrated that the equilibrium and motion of the heavenly bodies was the effect of the general law of gravitation; after having admitted, as very probable and most worthy of God, the grand hypothesis which, according to Kant and Laplace, attributes the formation of the heavenly bodies and their various actual conditions to the physical evolution of a nebulous mass, is not modern Science founded on the belief that God has also established for living creatures a law of evolution in which all forms might be potentially contained?

Moreover, the creation of so complex an organism as that of a mammal through the natural evolution of a shapeless germ, is as marvellous a fact, as the creation of the great genealogical trees of animal and vegetable species. If God is only the First Cause, and not the secondary cause of the evolution of a germ which will develop into

---

[1] We love to cite these lines written by Farges : "Evolution of species, had it existed, could not suppress the numerous arguments that prove to us the contingency of the world and the necessity of a Necessary Being. Yea, more; evolution of species had it taken place, would be in itself a new marvel of order and harmony, that came to add itself to all the marvels of order by which we prove the necessity of an intelligent Ordainer. It would confirm the necessity of this Ordainer rather than suppress it. *Far from suppressing creation it would be one of the modes of creation.*" *Annales de philosophie chrétienne*, Dec. 1897, p. 324, Cf. Bouyssonie, *Revue du Clergé*, May, 15, 1910.

an organism with parts so differentiated, why must He be the secondary and immediate cause and not merely the Primary Cause of all the organic differences which distinguish the species?

Moderate evolution is no less in accordance with the wisdom and power of God. In fact, whereas, creationism supposes that God intervenes incessantly to touch up His work throughout the geological ages, evolution supposes that God created the world, in such a way that it might progress under the aegis of general laws. If, under our very eyes, species are being modified in the creation of new races; if every living being enjoys the incomprehensible power of raising mineral matter to a participitation in life processes, why was the immediate intervention of the Creator necessary for all organic progress in the past?

Undoubtedly, it was under the influence of this consideration that de Nadaillac, one of the declared opponents of evolution, confessed that the evolutionist's conception is more in conformity with religion than the other, since the latter suppose "the Omnipotent, proceeding by sudden and successive creations, and then changing and modifying His work throughout time and space, as a sculptor molds the clay and recasts the outlines of the statue he has in mind", *Congrès scientifique catholique de 1891*, 8e section.

There remains still another element in favor of moderate evolution, which seems to us to have been brought into too little prominence. According to this, the long succession of living beings before the appearance of man, takes on a real meaning. Although no one knows them; although the greater part have perished without leaving any trace, they were the indispensable links in this long chain which reaches down to the present time. When we gather fruit from the branches of a tree, we do not think of the roots which have supplied the sap, nor the bast fibres which have carried the latter to the leaves, which in turn have performed their own proper functions; and yet the cellular units multiply themselves and succeed one another solely, that the fruit may grow and mature.

In the same way, throughout these thousands of centuries during which life pulsated under the genial benediction of God, the forms rose little by little, ever expanding and thus preparing nature for the advent of man.

Finally, and this is the strongest reason it can bring forward, moderate evolution lays under contribution all the arguments drawn from the facts set forth from the beginning of this work. It recognizes the bonds of relationship between the species; it explains them by the theory of descent from a common ancestry. In it the paleontological succession and the laws of embryology preserve all their importance.

If there is question of theories, of Darwinism in particular, it by no means rejects the preservative effects of heredity, nor the eliminating power of natural selection. There where Darwin and all the transformists pass over in silence the causes and the law governing the production of varieties, it brings in the idea of order and the action of a Creator. But instead of seeing God as the secondary cause in each variety produced, it regards Him as the Primary Cause creating the law of vital tendencies; tendencies which though mysterious are the bases for the production of varieties. [1]

2. —How MODERATE EVOLUTION MEETS THE DIFFICULTIES OF A RELIGIOUS AND PHILOSOPHIC NATURE. [2]

The Reverend Father Hy, professor at the "Facultés catholiques" at Angers expressed himself well when he wrote : "Thus, understood as a simple means of creation, which it has pleased God to choose in preference to others,

[1] In the preface of l'*Évolution des espèces organiques* of P. Leroy, Father Monsabré expresses this opinion that the theory of evolution, "far from compromising orthodox belief in the creative action of God, restricts this action to a small number of transcendent acts, more conformable to the unity of the divine plan, and the infinite wisdom of the Almighty, Who knew how to employ the secondary causes in an orderly way so as to attain His ends." p. 4.

[2] This point has been extensively treated by Fr. Zahm, C. S. C., in *Evolution and Dogma*, Daleiden.

the genesis of organisms from a common ancestry is in no way irreconcilable with the most sound notions of philosophy or with revealed dogmas." [1]

Any difficulties that might be raised against the hypothesis in question should be drawn from Holy Scripture, from Catholic tradition or from Christian philosophy. Now it will be seen that these three sources may be reconciled with the hypothesis.

Holy Scripture. — Apart from an official interpretation by the Church the Sacred Text itself does not seem to settle the question. Only one author, to our knowledge, has seen in the text of the first chapter of Genesis a condemnation of all evolution. [2] The majority of exegetes hold that the Bible says, at most, that living beings have God for their author, whatever be the manner of their creation. We should likewise be forcing the text to make it teach the doctrine of evolution. By the words *Let the waters bring forth... Let the earth bring forth...* Moses does not seem to have had the design of establishing that God had created the genera and species, by imparting to the material elements the power of producing them in due time. Besides, the Biblical Commission in its answer of

[1] *Rev. des fac. cath. d'Angers. Les plantes fossiles*, April, 1895, p. 558.

[2] Fr. Brucker, *Quest. actuelles d'Écriture sainte*, p. 221, holds that it is not necessary to force the Sacred Text too much; "Nevertheless believing scientists will not be much aided nor, above all things, much hampered in their labors, by the assertion of the primordial distinction of species, as it is formulated in the Bible. In fact the sacred author nowhere specifies in particular the species which have directly come from the hand of the Creator; he says less about their number. Botanists and zoologists therefore remain *very free* to reconstruct the genealogies of each living kingdom, in accordance with their observations."

Here is the the opinion of Fr. Corluy (*Spicilegium*, vol. i, p. 198): *Tacet scriptura modum quo terra varietatem illam specierum produxerit, an statim, an decursu temporis, an cum specierum firmitate omnimoda, an cum relativa dumtaxat. Sed de sensu disputari posset quem scriptura hic assignet nomini* min. We think that Scripture expressly refers to God all the species, but without determining in which manner God produced them, by immediate action or by evolution.

June 30, 1909, has left this question of evolution free,
since, while enumerating the doctrines which are certainly
contained in the first chapter of Genesis, it insists on only
two : the creation of all things by God in the beginning
and the special creation of man.   It does not exclude other
doctrines; but it does not impose them.

Catholic Tradition.—Though the common opinion of
the Fathers is that all species have God for their author,
we nevertheless see them divided into two opposing schools
on the question of the manner of creation.   Thus St.
Augustine [1] declares that, in these questions, where dogma
is not at issue, the solution appertains to experience and
reason.   As no decision has been given by the Church,
even though Darwinism has raised such violent controver-
sies, spiritual evolution does not appear to be in opposition
to the traditional opinion.

The canon H. de Dordolot, Professor of Geology and of
Paleontology at the University of Louvain, in his work
Darwinism and Catholic Thought, sums up his opinion in
four propositions, the substance of which we give here :
"1. No one can find in Holy Scripture, interpreted in

---

[1] St. Augustine has often been cited as having suspected and
already expressed the theory of evolution.   He shows us that it
was necessary to have a very broad view-point on these matters.   In
his opinion, God created everything by one single act, in consequence
all the species at one time.   Still, as they have not appeared at the
same time, but successively, he affirmed that God created them in
the beginning only *per seminales rationes*.

"Ista quippe originaliter et primordialiter in quadam textura
elementarum cuncta iam creata sunt, *sed acceptis opportunitatibus
prodeunt.*" *De Trinitate*, lib. III, c. ix.

"*In semine ergo illa omnia fuerunt primitus, non mole corporea
magnitudinis, sed vi potentiaque causali. Quid enim ex arbore illa
surgit aut pendet, quod non ex quadam occulto thesauro seminis illius
extractum atque depromptum est.*" *De Genesis ad litteram*, L. IV,
c. xxiii.

Saint Thomas, following the opinion of St. Augustine teaches
that God did not create all the species at a time in fact, but only
*causaliter. Non ergo tertia die productæ sunt plantæ in actu, sed
causaliter.* S. Th. Iª p., q. lxix, art. 2.   It is evident that this
word *causaliter* leaves us great latitude.

accordance with Catholic rules, any argument against the theory of natural evolution.

"2. The teaching of the Fathers (St. Basil, St. Gregory of Nyssa, St. Augustine, and others) is very favorable to natural evolution. They admitted instantaneous creation, and spontaneous generation under the action of natural causes, independently of all living matter.

"3. Application of certain principles of theology and of philosophy to the concrete facts of the sciences of observation forces the acceptance, at least as *eminently probable*, of the theory which would derive all living beings from one or more very elementary types of organisms.

"On the other hand, some difficulties of the scientific order appearing to be opposed to the theory of *absolute evolution*, the hypothesis of a special intervention on the part of Almighty God seems legitimate." We ourselves believe it imperative.

"4. The Catholic theory of the natural operation of secondary causes suffices to account for transformistic natural evolution such as Darwin understood it, and permits of the rejection, as absolutely superfluous, the other special interventions postulated by the creationists or by the moderate creationists."

Christian Philosophy. — By this name we designate that system of philosophy, which the Fathers of the Church during the first centuries, borrowed from the wisest men of antiquity, which the doctors of the Middle Ages exploited and developed with such vigor, and which begins to flourish again in our Catholic schools, after an unwarranted oblivian during many generations. With the favorite axioms of this school, moderate evolution does not seem to be in contradiction.

The School formally teaches that nature implies *order* and *finality*, and that finality proves a supreme ordaining Power, a Creator of the world, of life and of man; but we have seen to what extent this argument is respected by conservative evolutionists in that which concerns the development of species, as well as in that which applies to the development of the individual. It will be enough to give some of the testimonies of spiritual philosophers.

1. On the question of transformism Mgr. d'Hulst [1] expresses himself very clearly in the following terms : "If we object to evolution, at least to the universal extension which some would give the theory, this should be done with a prudent reserve in the name of experience, which just now is silent, and *not in the name of dogma, as long as God is admitted.* For, with God at the beginning of existence, with God at the end of all progress, and with God on the flanks of the column to direct and to sustain the movement, evolution is admissible. If some philosophers of note raise objections drawn from metaphysics, against its possibility, others, no less faithful to spiritualistic principles, refuse to admit the absurdity of the hypothesis. For them, as for the great majority, it is but a question of fact. But without God, all is absurd, and inexplicable, and evolution more so than everything else."

2. According to O. de Sinéty, [2] editor of *Les Études* : "We may hold, not merely as a simple hypothesis, but as an actual fact, that the present system of species, as a whole, has not been immediately created by God, such as we see them, but that they have been slowly formed in the course of ages, through evolution.

"Speci-genetic Transformism (*the transformation of species and of genera*) reduced to a simple negation of immediate creation of systematical species, may be considered as certain... Biologists and philosophers, who would see here only a pure hypothesis, push their scepticism too far.

"Once passed this very reserved statement, which I am going to show, is well established, to grasp fully the extension of evolution, we immediately enter upon the domain of hypothesis. The more daring we shall be, the more we shall admit this extension and the more we shall have separated ourselves from the solid basis of fact.

[1] 5th Lenten conference, 1891, p. 186.
[2] Cf. *Études*, 1911, vol. II, p. 671 et sq.

"Evolution, as a whole, then is not absolutely proven by the biological sciences. It is simply a mental conception, nothing more. It appertains to philosophy and not to positive science, to pronounce for or against the admissibility of this hypothesis.

"What has philosophy to say on the subject? That there exists an essential difference between living creatures and inorganic matter, between an animal possessing sensibility and the plant which is devoid of it, between man endowed with intelligence and the animal which has only sensible knowledge. These differences constitute just so many insuperable barriers to evolution, for the principle of causality exacts that the greater cannot proceed from the less. If a perfection is not contained initially, potentially or eminently in a being, the latter cannot impart such perfection to another.

"In conformity with these principles, we may reject as inadmissible monistic transformism which calls for spontaneous generation at the origin of life; total monophyletic transformism, which holds that all the animals and all the plants originate from one and the same extremely simple initial type ; anthropologic transformism which considers man, in his entirety, as the spontaneous product of universal evolution. These limits fixed, the rest is a vast field for acceptable hypotheses.

"A progressive polyphyletic transformism, which places at the beginning of the great divisions of the vegetable and the animal world, very rudimentary initial types, does not seem absolutely impossible in itself. Why should not the Author of Nature have given to these first forms potential perfections, which they are later on to manifest in their posterity? Do we not see a simple egg-cell giving rise to an organism of greater complexity? It is true, in the case of ontogenic evolution we are concerned only with a single individual, where there is continuity in the particular form which it invests. But, why could not an analogous continuity exist between the different terms of a phylogenetic series, if the first contains, potentially, the perfections of all the others?

"Without going to the length of such transformism, we could propose quite probable hypotheses in seeking to explain by the theory of evolution the genesis of the higher groups in species and in genera, that of families within the orders and that of orders within the classes.

"To appreciate the degree of solidity of these ideal structures is an extremely delicate matter. Philosophers might well leave this to specialists who alone are capable of weighing the pros and cons with a knowledge of the cause. On these points of detail Science is continually progressing, and that which is only an hypothesis today may well become an established fact tomorrow. It is advisable, therefore, to be very reserved, and to await patiently the results of future investigations."

3. P. M. Périer, whose ideas we sum up, asks himself, in what manner transformism is compatible with the dogma of creation? It is question here of an evolution, willed and decreed by God, of an evolution directed by an unceasing and immediate action of the First Cause. Thus understood the hypothesis which accords to preexisting secondary causes a part in the production of types to which we assign the name of species, seems to him quite orthodox, since St. Thomas considered as truly created by God all such beings as have been produced only in their causes; yea more, he expressly foresees the positive appearance of new species through the influence of the active powers imparted by God to the directly created elements. St. Thomas, I^a, q. LXXIII, a. 1 to 3. The mere fact that he admits the possibility of spontaneous generations also proves this.

A propos the work of de Dordolot, P. M. Périer says: "We cannot deny the force of the reasons by which he establishes the fact that the hypothesis of evolution is neither in opposition with Holy Scripture, nor with traditional philosophy, nor with the most rigorously orthodox theology.

"His book reassures disquieted minds. Creationists and transformists, all have equal need of the Creative Power. This is the essential thing.[1]

[1] P.-M. Périer, *Revue d'Apologétique*, June 15, 1922, p. 350.

He continues : "*Materialistic and Atheistic Transformism* is a monstrosity which would never have seen the light of day, had it not been engendered by sectarianism and irreligeon—for, this theory clashes with the most elementary requirements of sound reason.

"Spiritualistic Transformism, in claiming to be a simple fact, in no way pretends to substitute itself for God, nor to present itself as a creative force, immanent in matter as blind as it is marvellous. Equally with the static hypothesis, it calls for the perpetual intervention of God. There is then nothing in it to alarm our orthodoxy.

"Catholics readily recognize that the vegetable and the animal species are not only juxtaposed but are held together by certain bonds—which might go to the extent perhaps of filiation— the nature of which it is difficult to determine precisely; they admit that the bowels of the earth seem to have written upon them *the law of continuity*.

"According to some, to admit that, is sufficient to acquire the right to the title of transformism. This is an advance over former days. And here, undoubtedly, we have the reason why opposition to the evolutionary system is diminishing. We have nothing to fear on the score of our belief, and whatever may happen, the dogma of creation remains beyond all discussion and unassailable."

There is then an evolutionary system, perfectly reconcilable with the most rigorous orthodoxy, provided always that we admit the necessity of a God, Creator of all things. [1]

[1] We find the same thought expressed in the works of very recent date, written by Catholics versed in scientific, philosophic and theological knowledge, as the canon Henry de Dordolot, Professor of Geology and Paleontology at the Catholic University of Louvain; P. Teilhard de Chardin, Professor of Paleontology at the " Institut catholique " at Paris, *Études*, 1921; F. Sinéty, *Études et Revue des questions scientifiques*, 1910; Bouyssonie, *Revue pratique d'Apologétique*; *Revue du Clergé*, 1912; Achille Salée, *Revue des questions scientifiques*, July, 1920, p. 132; P. Lemonnier, *La Révélation primitive et les données de la science*; V. Grégoire, professor of biology at the "Faculté des Sciences de l'Université catholique" of Louvain, *Le matérialisme contemporain*; O. Daumont, *Les preuves, les principes de l'évolution*; Lebrun, *Les théories de l'évolution*, etc.

The School also teaches the invariability of essences. Now, as long as there are living species in nature, so long will there be different essences. Hence living species are invariable; hence species are not transformed. [1]

But is it quite certain that there are as many different essences as there are species in natural history, and even as many as there are genera? Can we give any mark which would permit us to assert that two animals or two plants have different essences? We might cite the morphological differences. But, by what sign can we recognize that a morphological difference marks a distinction of essence, and not merely a variety with the same essence? We might cite physiological differences. But, are they so notable in the different groups of the same kingdom? We might invoke the differences of habits among the animals; but, the same difficulty always arises, of establishing the value of the differences necessary to distinguish the essences.

Between minerals and living beings, there is a clearly marked distinction; between the animals and man there is the same; living beings have life, which minerals do not possess; the animals have sensation which the plants have not; man performs acts by their nature spiritual, the animals cannot do this. We perceive then that one such distinctive mark shows a difference of essence. But it is not the case within the distinct kingdoms themselves, so that certain firm adherents to the pure doctrine of the School would hold that a difference of essence, between the species in the same kingdom, is not philosophically demonstrable. [2]

We should not say that the living species have no common origin because they differ in essence; this would be

[1] This is the fundamental argument given by Farges against evolution : *Annales de philosophie chrétienne*, Dec. 1897, p. 325 and *La vie et l'évolution des espèces*.

[2] Thus, M. Vallet, in his *Prælectiones*, vol. II, p. 206, 5th edi., tries to show merely the essential distinction between the mineral, vegetable, animal and human kingdoms, perceiving very well that the distinctive marks of the species can appear only by accident. M. Bouyssonie, *Revue du Clergé*, 1922, p. 230.

to argue from the unknown. We should rather say : if the species have a common origin, there may, perhaps, be no essential differences between them. Difficult as may be the problem of the origin of species, it is more accessible than that of the distinction of essences

It is about in these terms that moderate evolutionists present their system of conciliation, between the facts verified by science and the eternal principles of sound philosophy. Perhaps the extremists will some day subscribe to this intermediate opinion.

Moderate evolutionists, for all that, still remain perplexed. On the one hand, they are inclined towards evolution, for the following reasons. The world today is, by no means, identical with the world of yesterday. It differs from it by characteristics that become more divergent with time. Nevertheless, the world of today has come from the world of yesterday, by way of natural descent and not in virtue of a catastrophe that might have substituted the former for the latter. Consequently the world progresses and develops under the impetus of the law of evolution. On the other hand, in that which pertains to the living world, evolutionism runs counter to some inconstestable facts which favor a certain fixity of species, and which we are about to set forth.

ARTICLE V

FIXIST ARGUMENTS AGAINST EVOLUTION

The theory of common descent has found two classes of opponents : certain Catholic writers and some professional naturalists.

The defenders of the Catholic Faith noticing that irreligion made use of evolution to attack our dogmas, have had to choose between two modes of procedure in apologetics. Either they would have to consider evolution as indifferent in itself, and so confine themselves to combatting the excessive consequences which illogical irreligion might draw from it.—Some authors, after the example of

P. Bellinck, a learned Jesuit of Namur (see *Études reli-gieuses*, 1868) have taken this position; but their number is small.—Or they would have to identify the evolutio-nistic idea with antireligious thought and so include the two in the same anathema; in the beginning, this is what commonly happened; and numerous refutations ap-peared, resting at the time, on philosophical principles and upon experimental science. Some naturalists of note rose up against evolutionism. Reviving the ideas of Cuvier on the fixity of types, de Quatrefages, Flourens, Agassiz, Faivre, Godron, Hébert, Blanchard, de Nadaillac have to a man rejected both evolution in general and Darwinism in particular. De Quatrefages, an emi-nent professor at the Paris Museum was the principal writer of this school. He expressed himself at all times with moderation in his two important works : *Darwin et ses précurseurs français*, and *Les Émules de Darwin*. [1]

But it is important to note two shades of opinion among the advocates of the fixity of species.—Some conclude sim-ply : *We are ignorant* of the manner in which species were formed; we know only that they are not transmutable, and that neither Lamarck nor Darwin have discovered the true law of their creation. So spoke de Quatrefages. The others go still further and say : Not only are the species not the result of any evolution, but they of necessity re-quire the direct and immediate intervention of the Creator.

For a precise statement of the question we believe it necessary to restrict it to the following.—1. We shall cite only the objections raised against the common origin of living beings; we shall disregard those which pertain to monism, since we treat elsewhere the origin of life and the origin of man.—2. We shall present only the arguments possessing a scientific character, and not arguments drawn from philosophy or religion; for we are persuaded that when

---

[1] We know no book that brings out more strongly the difficulties raised against evolution, than the book of Darwin himself : *The Origin of Species*. No author has better visuallized the objections; he did not disguise their value, he tells each time why he believed he ought to pass over a point.

restricted to the origin of species in each kingdom, the question remains within the domain of science. It is to be regretted that the problem is not always confined to this; for often reasons and facts are applied to the origin of species which refer only to the origin and distinction of kingdoms.

No less regrettable is the confusion which identifies evolutionism with Darwinism.[1] Evolutionism affirms the common descent of species. Darwinism tries to explain the formation of species by natural selection. Evolutionism, according to Lamarck, has not ceased to make progress among naturalists; Darwinism at first acclaimed with enthusiasm has been gradually assailed until today natural

---

[1] In his famous discourse pronounced at Oxford in 1894, on the *Actual Limits of Our Science*, Lord Salisbury directed his principle attack against evolutionism which he confounded with Darwinism. The author recognizes that the doctrine of the constancy of species is, in general, abandoned, today; an important concession overlooked by those who cite against evolution the objections that he had formulated only against Darwinism. — He says that he would not have sufficient time to explain the series of transformations "from the medusa to man"; this critique addresses itself only to those who admit the Darwinian hypothesis of slow transformation. He then refutes natural selection, as the cause of the formation of species; this critique is addressed at the same time against Darwin and Weismann, and not against evolution in general.

In his answer to Lord Salisbury, Huxley remarked that the orator had abandoned the dogma of the immutability of species, that Darwinism criticized by him, was only one of the theories of evolution, and that in consequence, evolution still stands.

Weismann, believing himself attacked by Salisbury, took up the defense of natural selection; he remarked that, even if selection were abandoned, evolution would remain. Moreover, he did not wish this to constitute a declaration of dogmatic atheism; beyond the mechanism of phenomena, there remains a domain that he terms "unknown".

Herbert Spencer, answering in his turn, insists principally on the fundamental error of Salisbury, which consisted in confounding the fact of evolution with one of its explanations. He invites the opponents of evolution who demand proofs, to furnish themselves the examples of direct creation. The article of the English philosopher was presented to the "Académie de sciences" in Paris by Perrier. Cf. *Année biologique*, p. 531-533.

selection is considered but one of the thousands of factors at work in nature to produce differentiation of species. An argument against Darwinism therefore, is not in itself an argument against evolutionism. A passage of some learned author, directed against Darwinism is often taken in a contrary sense when applied to evolutionism. How often some authors, very much attached to evolutionism are quoted through an unpardonable error, as being opposed to a system which they uphold!

Fixists urge against evolutionism properly understood all the restrictions which we have cited in exposing the arguments favorable to evolution. These limitations bear especially upon monophyletic evolution. They would have less force against moderate evolution. To these reasons they join three others, of which we shall give as brief a review as possible. 1. The evolutionistic system is an hypothesis and an hypothesis unsupported by evidence. 2. The facts cited in its favor are susceptible of a contrary interpretration. 3. Certain facts are in manifest opposition to evolutionism.

I.—Evolutionism is an hypothesis.

This proposition presents no difficulty. Evolutionists and fixists are agreed upon this point. Universal attraction is only an hypothesis; the theory of Laplace is but an hypothesis; for a greater reason therefore the theory of descent may in all probability always remain merely an hypothesis. M. Yves Delage does not fear to admit this : "I recognize without the least hesitation that we have never seen one species engendering another, nor a single one transforming itself into another and that no observation has absolutely and formally demonstrated that such a thing has taken place in the past. I mean a true bona fide species, fixed like natural species and maintaining itself like these without the aid of man. " [1]

[1] Delage, *Structure du protoplasme*, p. 184. The author is none the less an advocate of evolution, for he adds :" Still I consider descent as certain as if it were objectively demonstrated." Depéret

M. Blanchard, of the Paris Institute, was convinced that no one could answer the challenge made by him in 1888 in the preface to his book *La vie et les êtres organisés* to all the friends of the natural sciences : "Show me a single instance of the transformation of species." Darwin knew better than anyone else that evolutionism is only an hypothesis, so he avoided catagorical assertions.   For this reason de Quatrefages objected to *the unscientific manner of proposing the theory.* "You pretend" said he, "that this *appears* to you so : it seems to you *preferable* to believe in the change of forms; you are *persuaded* that the actual species descend from common ancestors. But if the contrary *seems to me better*; if I am persuaded that the opposite opinion is more probable, our *inclinations* balance each other." Scientific reasoning proceeds upon entirely different lines.   In the question at issue it would have to cite some well established facts to draw a general conlusion.   Far from blaming Darwin, however, for having employed formulæ expressive of doubt, we should rather bear with him with pleasure; for when a man of science presents an hypothesis with modesty, it is indeed a fact worthy of remark.

If evolutionism is an unproved hypothesis, should it, for that reason, be condemned?   This would be going too far.   To reject it without further examination, it would be necessary to substitute another and better founded hypothesis on the same subject; an hypothesis that is also susceptible of experimental demonstration.

To reject evolutionism in its entirety is to admit fixism or to fall into agnosticism.   The agnostic refuses to have any idea on the subject so we may dismiss him without further consideration.   As for fixism, is it anything else but an hypothesis?   Are there any data of observation or experience showing that the Creator might be intervening immediately in the formation of a species?   Assur-

made practically the same statement, while remaining an evolutionist. We might say the same of a great number of other scientists.

edly not.   Not having any catagorical fact on either side,
therefore, we must interrogate Nature to find out whether
her preference lies on the side of the bonds of relationship
that unite species, or on that of the differences that separate
them. [1]

Is the hypothesis susceptible of experimental verifica-
tion?   As to the past, certainly not.   For, we are reduced
to an interpretation of incomplete paleontological data;
for the present, yes and no—through observation and experience, we establish that the living forms are very plastic
and in consequence exceedingly variable.   These variations
are such "that where there is question of the exterior anatomical dissimilarities existing at times between individual
animals of the same species in the wild state, they might
be the cause of the fixation of distinct and perfectly
characteristic genera." De Quatrefages, *Darwin*, p. 230.

Are these varieties distinct enough to constitute species?
This is a question of appreciation. So much so, that
whereas some would assert that the genesis of new species
has been seen, others would claim that we possess only
races of the same species.

The question of deciding whether new species are created in our day will then be variously solved, according
as the tendencies of the judges be towards evolutionism
or fixism. This is why we repeat that the proposed
solution of the question of the origin of species is only an
hypothesis.

---

[1] Yves Delage, *Structure du protoplasme*, p. 185, in a note, made a
remark that we believe correct : "I am absolutely convinced that
one is or is not a transformist, not *for reasons* drawn from natural
history, but *by reason* of his philosophical opinions." Now there
are two sorts of philosophical opinions on this subject, the opinions
of the materialist who wishes to destroy the idea of a Creator; and
the spiritualistic opinion that holds it more glorious for the Creator
to have created species by way of evolution.

II.—THE FACTS ADDUCED BY EVOLUTIONISTS ARE SUSCEPTIBLE OF AN INTERPRETATION UNFAVORABLE TO EVOLUTIONISM OR AT LEAST DO NOT NECESSARILY IMPLY EVOLUTIONISM. [1]

1.—The organic forms are undoubtedly *variable*, but only to a certain extent. In fact, even under the intelligent and protracted direction of man, the variations cannot go beyond the limits of the race. This is seen in the domestic animals upon which man has been working for so long a time. Besides when his intervention ceases, the created races of themselves tend to revert to the primitive type. Now in the creation of races, nature has many more resources and more power than has man; and still there exists only a very small number of races among wild species. Thus variability of forms is limited and yet evolution exacts that it be unlimited. [2]

2.—There exist some striking resemblances between closely allied species: they are arranged in order, not, indeed in a straight line, but in parallel lines, in such manner as to realize an harmonious whole, one definite plan. But there exist also profound anatomical and physiological differences, and though evolutionism explains the resemblances as readily as does fixism, it cannot so easily account for and produce the genesis of differences. [3]

3.—*The rudimentary organs* are by no means a refu-

---

[1] We can find this proposition developed in three works; Piat. *La personne humaine*, Paris, Alcan, 1897; Farges, *Annales de philosophie chrétienne*, Dec. 1897, and *La vie et l'évolution des espèces*, Paris, Berche et Tralin.

[2] Piat rejects the indefinite plasticity of organic forms; he concludes that it is necessary to place a multiple and not unity at the beginning. Still he recognizes in living beings a great relative flexibility. "The oscillations of the physical world exact in the organic world an analogous oscillating power. Everything was adapted to and could develop only in harmony with this condition. Reduced to its proper measure, plasticity becomes the triumph of finality."

[3] One cannot repeat too often that the living species are not classed in a single ascending line; they are arranged like the limbs and branches of a large tree, on which many parts form parallel series and not one a linear series. To place the species in their natural

tation of fixism. From what Darwin says, we cannot know whether an organ, rudimentary or useless in the adult, does not exercise an important function in the embryo; for example, the pituitary gland, which is atrophied in the brain of the adult man, innervates the pharynx of the infant during the first months. Moreover, why might not these rudimentary organs be the result of a real degradation which the species itself has undergone? This kind of recessive evolution is no proof whatever for progressive evolution.

4.—*The geographical distribution* of species is well explained by the hypothesis of distinct creations. For the Creator could just as wisely distribute the species, according to order in space as He has disposed them, in the order of time, following a plan of increasing progression. In the evolutionistic theory, the distribution of species gives occasion to some difficulties of interpretation which the sagacity of the trasnformists have not altogether solved.

5.—*The paleontological distribution* of species presents only two facts in favor of evolutionism : 1. Certain organisms appear in the order of their organic perfection : the fact, very striking in the plants, is also noticeable in the vertebrates; 2.—We can follow the variations of certain species through the many geological ages.

The fixists explain these two facts conformably to their own system. 1. The most perfect organisms could not live in the beginning; the conditions of the environment would not permit. They appeared only when the conditions became favorable for them. How did they come into existence? Either, God created the species immediately at the moment of their appearance, or else, according to Delbeuf's system, He created at the origin of life the germs of all the living species, and each germ then developed when the circumstances became favorable for it. [1] This

position is to prove beyond a doubt their filiation; but to speak of *a genealogical tree* is to be misled by a *mirage of beautiful words.* Expressions of Farges, *Annales,* p. 315.

[1] Farges seems to rally to this idea following the example of Delbœuf.

system has the drawback of having no foundation in observation or experience. One might even have reason to fear the fate of these myriads of germs which await, under the most critical condition, the remote hour of their development. 2. The species whose number science cannot determine are susceptible of undergoing modifications : this evolution *intra eamdem speciem* explains the differences which some forms, whose relationship cannot be gainsaid, present in the course of ages. Paleontology, moreover furnishes the fixists with facts which they oppose to evolutionism. We shall take them up later on.

6.—Finally, if we cannot deny the *resemblances* in embryos in the process of their development, the fact explains well that all beings acquire their definitive forms through the medium of more or less closely associated forms. These resemblances, moreover, often exaggerated, must of necessity exist. They give testimony of the fact that God puts into His handiwork the impress of finality and of unity : they do not prove the common descent of forms.

III. —Some facts adduced as contrary to the theory of evolution.

We give here only such as appear to us to have the greatest value.

1. *The permanency of organic forms throughout long periods.* The description left by Aristotle show that the species studied by him have in no wise varied, during more than twenty centuries. In the examination of seeds and mummies found in Egypt in the tombs of the ancient pharaohs, forms are found, which have not varied since the Fourth Dynasty. A great number of actual species have not changed since the Tertiary period; instances are even cited of certain Primary species that might have passed through all the geological epochs without any variation what ever.—Hence the species have not the plasticity that some would suppose. Such is Cuvier's argument. On close scrutiny, the bearing of this fact appears quite insignificant.—It proves that all the species do not vary

in virtue of absolute necessity; it does not prove that all the species remain invariable.—The true law, as seen from the history of species, might be stated thus : their stability is assured by the stability of the conditions of life; some notable changes in their biological conditions can give rise to important variations in some species.

2. *Astronomy does not allow evolution the time that it requires* for the formation of species. Lord Salisbury formulates for himself the objection in his famous discourse *The Actual Limits of Our Science.* Lord Kelvin (Wm. Thomson) limits the time that has elapsed since life could freely develop on our planet to 100,000,000 years. But biologists and evolutionists are not extravagant in their demands when they require many hundreds of millions of years for the development of living forms from the primitive moner to man. Hence there is here an evident contradiction between the astronomers and the evolutionists.

This argument might be very conclusive if it were solidly founded. But, on the one hand, Lord Kelvin bases his calculations on very debatable facts, as one may easily verify by reading his *Popular Lectures and Addresses.* On the other hand, the supposition that all variations have been very slow, and that all organic forms originated from one single being, the primitive moner, is altogether gratuitous. One may reject it without injury to evolutionism and its consequences [1].

3. *The primordial invertebrate fauna of the Cambrian and Precambrian rocks presents types that are already well diffe-*

---

[1] The objection drawn from time by Salisbury is combatted by Spencer by means of a striking although too rigorous comparison. Spencer starts from Fritz Müller's law that each individual slowly repeats, during its embryonic development, the phases through which the species has passed during the long ages. Taking for example the human individual, he remarks that its development takes place in 400 000 minutes, or nine months. As astronomers, at least Lord Kelvin, accord 100 000 000 years for evolution of species, a period of 250 years corresponds to one minute, of evolution of the fetus. Would not the species accomplish in 250 years the inappreciable modification which occurs in one minute, in the fetus? Cf. *Année biologique*, 1895, p. 533.

rentiated.   If the various species had sprung by slow evolution from one single primitive form, too long a time would have had to elapse previous to the differentiation manifested by the Precambrian fauna, and geology would find traces of it (figs. 44-49).   Now before the Precambrian rocks, we find no evidence of organic remains. Hence the Precambrian period coincides with the appearance of life.   Hence life was created with a multiplicity of forms appertaining to all groups.

This argument, according to Darwin, Gaudry and Depéret, is very embarrassing for the evolutionists who admit

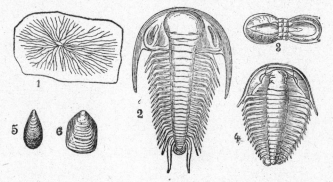

Fig. 44-49. — Type of fauna, termed primordial.

1. Oldhamia (of very uncertain nature.); 2, 3, 4, Trilobites, of the branch of arthropods (paradoxides, agnostus, olenus); 5, 6, Brachiopods that have-traversed the geological ages (lingula antiqua, lingulella Davisi).

only one starting point for all species.   It is of real value for restricted evolution which admits a considerable number of primitive forms.   Still we must not exaggerate the force of the argument, for it is weakened by the two following considerations :—The absence of fossils, before the Precambrian fauna does not prove that life did not exist; primitive species, unadapted to fossilization, were incapable of leaving any trace.   The fossil remains, if they did exist, must have, disappeared for the most part, in the profound changes wrought by metamorphism.   If the species had been arranged in a linear series, the distance would be very great from the trilobites to the equi-cellular protozoa. But the variations could have been produced suddenly as is evidenced by the production of varieties. Hence the different branches of the living trunk could have made their appearance suddenly.

4. *Evolutionists cannot establish the geneaological series* of the actual species in such a way as to attach them all to one common trunk. Paleontology does not furnish the intermediates that would have had to exist and leave their traces in the past. Darwin confessed that this was "the most obvious and most serious objection that one could oppose to the theory". To solve it he could only explain the gaps by the imperfection of the geological archives. He appealed to the future, basing his hopes on the discovery of intermediate types in increasingly great numbers.

5. If evolutionism were true, the living organisms ought not present distinctive characters, or form an orderly collection, but should be *indiscriminately intermingled.—* We must remember that the actual species are only a remnant, that a multitude of forms have disappeared, and that the differential traits are accentuated by the disappearance of the intermediates. From the incontestable order that is apparent in our classification, we cannot help declaring that it cannot be the effect of mechanical evolution or chance, but postulates the ordaining action of a Creative Intelligence.

6. Finally the chief fact that the fixists oppose to evolutionism is the *sterility of crosses of individuals of different species*. This sterility seems to signify that the difference of species is a matter of essence, and so all the efforts made to transform one species into another are as vain as the attempts to square a circle. The species are sterile among themselves, the races of the same species are interfertile. Such is the law of the actual crosses between living organisms. Although not absolute it is so general that we are compelled to take account of it.

De Quatrefages attached great importance to this fact. In his eyes it established an impossible barrier between the species. "Unfortunately", says he, "there comes a moment when Darwin seems to forget the great physiological fact of the sterility between species. At least, he overlooks its importance entirely".[1] Hence the true characteristic of species is the law expressed by Flourens : *If of the same species, the organisms are interfertile, if of different species, they are intersterile.* "

This universal and constant fact cannot find its explanation in evolution. Darwin himself declared that he did not understand it. On the other hand, it is easy

a continuous line of interfertile individuals. But as the intermediates have disappeared, we see only the intersterility existing between the widely separated individuals. For example, we say that all the races of dogs are interfertile, although the extremes might be intersterile. Now if the intermediates were to disappear, and if we were to forget the historical fact of their common origin, we would not hesitate to consider the extreme races as species in their physiological and morphological characteristics.

From this relative law of intersterility, the fixists conclude that all attempts to create new species have been and ever will be in vain. But let us observe: Every time we take two varieties coming from the same stock whatever be the distance between them, the fixists would see in them only races of one same species, and not different species. This being the case, the fixists and the evolutionists will not be able to agree on any fact. When the fixists declare that we create new species artificially, they often state the question inaccurately. They would have that we create new intermediates from different species. But we cannot repeat too strongly that the new species if formed, are created by the exaggerated divergence of two varieties, issuing from the one same stock and not by the fusion of two neighboring branches into a single stock. The intersterility could exist between individuals issuing from the same parents, particularly among the plants. Must we conclude from this that they are of different species, or only that this argument is not conclusive?

ARTICLE VI

THE INSUFFICIENCY OF EVOLUTIONISTIC THEORIES[1]

Let us suppose that in spite of the arguments advanced by the fixists, we were still to adhere to evolution, as do nearly all naturalists and the majority of present day philo-

---

[1] Cf. Delage and Goldsmith, *Les théories de l'évolution*, Paris, Flammarion; Cuénot, *La Genèse des espèces animales*, Paris, 1921; Le Dantec, *La crise du transformisme*, Paris, Alcan; Colin, *Les théories*

sophers, and admit either the unity or the plurality of the primitive living stock, there would still be in this hypothesis of common descent some serious difficulties to solve. The evolutionist must explain "how the innumerable species inhabiting this world have been modified so as to acquire that perfection of structure and coadaptation which justly excites our admiration". (Darwin. [1]) In other words, if there has been evolution, *how* did it operate?

We cannot, take up, in the compass of a single paragraph, all the attempts to explain evolution. Volumes would be necessary. The essays of various authors have proven inadequate, for each writer has his own point of view. The Darwinist and the Lamarckian have reciprocally criticized each other, and have thus brought out the weakness and insufficiency of the opposing theories. Mutual criticisms are even indulged in by the neo-darwinists, neo-lamarckians and mutationists.

Vitalists have with good reason criticized the mechanists, and the spiritualists have shown the inadequacy and contradictions of the materialists. Certain authors have gone into details. Some have shown that no mechanistic theory is capable of explaining the origin of a living being, of instinct, etc., others, the formation of an organism, others the change of species, etc.

When the advocates of evolution tackle this problem of the causes of evolution, they generally recog ze its difficulty, unless they find it more convenient to speak of it as certain popular writers, known for their cocksuredness of assertion. Both of these classes confound the conditions of life and of evolution with true efficient causes. It will suffice therefore to emphasize certain factors of evolution to which recourse has been had to prove their inadequacy.

évolutionistes, Revue pratique d'Apologétique, vol. x; De Sinéty, *Un demi-siècle de darwinisme*, dans *Revue des questions scientifiques*, 1910, p. 1-38, 480-513, *Revue de philosophie*, 1910, p. 215-441.
[1] *Origin of Species*, Introduction, p. 27.

Certain writers simply take the fact of a slow or abrupt evolution for granted and consider it a necessity. The fact, however, has not been proven for all living things, and even if it should be, this would not be an explanation. The same may be said for the transmission of new characters by heredity. We verify the inheritance of specific characters without being able to explain it, *a fortiori* if there is question of new characters. We are even painfully surprised to see certain attempts at explanation of life and of instinct, based on the influences of causes, either insignificant or foreign to the question, and in every case radically incapable of producing the desired effect.

In a preceding chapter, we insisted rather on the special nature of the living organism, so as to bring out the fact that any purely materialistic or even simply mechanistic explanation is insufficient. We shall cite here only the two most prominent theories, that of Lamarck and that of Darwin. Our appreciation of these will hold also for the theories derived from them.

1. *Lamarckism.*—According to Lamarck the variations might be due to *the action of the cosmic environment*, and to *the reaction of the organism itself against this environment.* The change of conditions of life created new needs for the living being. To respond to these needs the animal made an effort. "Frequent and sustained use of any particular organ strengthens, develops and gives it a power proportioned to the duration of such use. Constant disuse of some other organ gradually and insensibly weakens it, causes it to deteriorate and progressively diminishes its faculties, and finally brings about its disappearance." The modifications so produced need only to be fixed by heredity.

Appreciation of Lamarckism.—Lamarck properly went back to the First Cause to seek there the reason for the existence of living things and for their evolution. It is wrong to reproach him for this. The influence that he attributes to the environment is real, but is not itself sufficient to explain the development of life in the evolutionary sense. This is but a condition, a stimulus and no more.

the individual in a constant direction. Neither the environment nor the need creates the organ. If the latter can vary, it is on condition that it exists and has free pontialities. If it retrogresses and disappears, this fact is no proof in favor of progressive evolution which alone is in question.

To find the true cause of the evolution of living things if it actually exists, it is necessary to seek it in their potentialities, and to look for these capacities for development in that which the philosopher calls the vital principle of the plant or animal. But what is the origin of this vital principle? It is inherited from ancestors. But whence did the first living things derive it? From the same source

part which *natural selection* plays in the conservation of the species. Frequently the word Darwinism is taken for evolutionism or transformism. This is a mistake, for Darwin was by no means the creator of evolutionism. Darwinism or the work of Darwin comprises the system of *natural selection* which has been the section most thoroughly studied in this broad question of transformism. We give here a brief outline of it, following the reasoning of the noted English philosopher.

Everyone knows that some organic variations are produced among domestic animals and among cultivated plants. As they have the power of transmitting themselves by heredity, experimenters can, by skilful choice of subjects, create permanent varieties and races so different from the primitive stock, that one might call them new species. From this *artificial selection* combined with hybridization come the races of animals and of plants, which man has created for his own use or pleasure: hornless cattle, marina sheep, animals for slaughter, race horses and draught horses, hunting dogs and watch dogs, etc., 150 varieties of pigeons and more than 2000 varieties of grape vines, etc. Some variations are of necessity produced also in nature, especially when migration or other causes bring about changes in the living conditions. Among these variations, some are useless to the creature, others useful. The former being of no use readily disappear by the destruction of the individuals in which they were produced; the latter, being of great advantage in the struggle for life, have favored the survival of the individuals which were so endowed, and have thus been able to propagate themselves. In this way a true *natural selection* or choice very much like artificial selection, comes into play. The experimenter who chooses the stock and isolates it is replaced in nature by the *struggle for life*, which preserves the better fitted subjects, and by *catastrophies* which prevent the mixture of varieties by separating them.

This process operates in the following manner. *The struggle for life* or vital concurrence is the necessary consequence of the exuberant fecundity of living things. For, if this fecundity were not counterbalanced, the earth would ere long be unable to support its inhabitants, yea would not even be large enough to hold them all. Many perish and yet the individuals that survive are still too numerous, so that each must struggle to preserve its own life. In this struggle, the weakest, or rather, the least fitted, perish. The better endowed, or rather the better protected, remain the masters of the field. Thus, we have a clear insight into the operation of the inexorable law of *the survival of the fittest*. If a being survives, in certain respects quite miserable, it is protected by unknown advantages. It would therefore be erroneous to confound the fittest with the strongest. Cunning, nimbleness, color, stings, an acrid secretion, a tough skin or flesh, apparently defective characters, can serve an animal to outwit its enemies.

This struggle does not bear merely on the matter of food, but also on sexual fitness. Thus, certain animals become extinct with the variety which distinguishes them, since they have not found occasion to reproduce themselves. *Sexual selection* which is practiced with such care in the human species is not unknown among the lower animals. There occurs, then, in each generation a real choice of the individuals possessing the most advantageous modifications. The victors transmit these characters to their descendants, and heredity fixes them in the strain issuing from them. These characters continue as a permanent acquisition, and this in fact, constitutes *the law of permanent characterization*. If, in virtue of *the law of divergence*, the individuals arising from a characterized group form new species, it cannot be by the destruction, but by the modification of previously acquired characters.

Voluntary migration and great cataclysms have isolated the species in process of formation, hindered crossing with individuals of the primitive species, and in consequence, permitted the new characters to become fixed and accentuated. "We can thus understand," says Darwin, [1] "the importance of barriers, whether of land or

---

[1] *Origin of Species*, p. 363.

water, in not only separating, but in apparently forming the several zoological and botanical provinces.''

Criticism of the Darwinian Theory.—This very logically connected system made a great impression when it appeared. As a result, evolutionism became confused with Darwinism and assumed the name. Some prudent scientists like Mivart, Delage, Depéret, Cuénot, et al. however having made a critical study of the system, showed how natural selection is incapable of explaining the formation of species. We shall sum up briefly what is to be thought of this theory which claims to explain evolution. It would appear that nothing, or almost nothing can be retained, since the reality is quite different from this *a priori* conception.

We know that ingenuity, perspicacity, patience, care and knowledge are necessary to create a new race, whether of plant or animal. Man, in virtue of his intelligence can choose the best subjects, the purest races, a single character that he wishes to perfect, and can eliminate with care all the types that might not realize the ideal which he has in mind to create. He can produce crosses most favorable for the accentuation of the character or characters intended. He can insure the perfect isolation of the race which he intends to create, so as to preserve it in its entire purity.

In spite of his intelligence, he runs up against some insurmountable difficulties in producing a new character, in preserving it, in rendering it hereditary or in perfecting it.

Is natural selection capable of doing as much as or more than artificial selection? We believe not, for the following apparently decisive reasons. The intelligence factor, in the Darwinian hypothesis does not exist, and it is chance alone that should bring about the selection, and govern all the operations which it implies. On this score, the inferiority is unquestionably manifest. Chance does not produce order or harmony, nor does it realize a purpose conceived in advance. It can disturb the best established order, but it cannot realize anything like the one in question.

Chance, in the present instance might only be the activity of organisms subjected to the universal struggle, because of the scarcity of food. It has been remarked with apparent reason, that this scarcity of food is not the principal, nor even the ordinary cause of the extinction of numerous organisms. At the various periods, when life began, there was certainly a superabundance, hence no reason for struggle. At the present time, facts without number go to prove that the earth could nourish many more organisms than it actually contains. The intervention of man, the struggle between different species, epidemics, periods of drought or of humidity, of cold, of snow, etc., are only a few of the causes affecting the extinction of species.

Moreover, observation shows that instead of the universal struggle which Darwin's theory supposes, the animals of the same species, as a general rule, render mutual aid and associate with rather than kill each other. Even more. As a factor of progress, the mutual assistance and association will be far more potent than the fratricidal struggle. Many species, in fact, are preserved only in virtue of association, e. g. the bees, ants and termites. We could find examples also among the vertebrates, the fish, the reptiles, the mammals, the herbivora and the carnivora. Man has preserved all the domestic species.

If the fratricidal struggle does not favor progress, could one at least say that the struggle between the different species, between the organic and the inorganic kingdoms, is useful to it? By no means. For it is not in time of famine that strength robustness or beauty will develop. All the survivors will be more or less weakened, and the species will thus have gone backwards rather than forwards.

If the struggle is between different species, one of the two must succumb. Where is there progressive evolution? We can see in this only retrogression, a disappearance of species.

If the objection is raised, that the carnivora can develop only by struggling with the herbivora, and the latter with the plants, we shall answer, that there is no question here of a struggle but of a food supply indispensable to all, to the strong as well as to the weak; but if this struggle became such that one whole category were to succumb entirely, this would immediately be the end of that which had gained the victory, since it would no longer have anything to feed upon.

At present, in the world around us, we see no such mortal struggle, but rather an admirable equilibirum between the vegetable and the animal kingdoms, between the carnivora and the herbivora. Even in the dense equatorial forests, without human intervention, we see living side by side, plants, herbivora and carnivora. There we find a marvellous development of life.

In realizing the progress of the species, the struggle for existence would not favor the strongest, nor the best endowed nor the most fit. The chances of battle are sufficiently apparent, to recognize that it is not necessarily the best that survive. Shells and bombs are not selective. The carnivora no more so. Rather, instead of choosing the weakest they often select the strongest. The swallow that pursues the insects, the whale that gulps down all that comes in its way, leaves no play for natural selection; so much so that, we may say it does not exist in these instances. The herbivora, if they select at all, would merely cause the disappearance of food plants, and permit the rest to continue in existence. Once more it is not a question of a struggle between plants and animals, but a struggle for food, for an indispensable support.

Now it is especially the germs and the eggs that perish. It is difficult to admit that the latter struggle to exist and that a selection is made.

If for the sake of argument, natural selection did all that Darwin claimed for it; if it preserved the fittest, the strongest, should we have in this a factor of progress? Not at all. In fact, the selection would have played the role of a sieve which separates the better grain, but does not perfect it. This has been experimentally proven by the Vilmorins, who have, during a period of sixty years selected grain, without obtaining the least evidence that the race to which it belonged was perfected. True selection separates the pure races, preserves them, multiplies them, but does not perfect them.

We have said nothing of sexual selection, which Darwin considered necessary to join to the struggle for existence, to solve all cases. It is as powerless as the first. It does not exist among beings devoid of reason. Moreover, as the sexes are almost equal in number, all the beings can reproduce themselves, the inferior types as well as those more favored with natural gifts.

For the Darwinian it is not a question of explaining the appearance of a new species; he had first to account for the existence of the innumerable species which his theory presupposes, and upon which natural selection operates to bring about the disappearance of a great number. Whence did they come? Were they themselves the product of selection? This looks much like a vicious circle. If we go back to the origin, we have a single type, or at most three or four types. How did selection take place? What was the reason for the struggle?

We are not yet at the end of the difficulties of Darwinism and particularly of neo-darwinism. The latter supposes an evolution that is slow, continuous and directed solely by chance. We have here as many errors as impossibilities.

Neo-darwinism supposes a unicellular being in the beginning, yes even less than that, a moner. From this, by selection, all the most highly organized beings had to come. Yet, the greater cannot come from the less. In a heap of grain, we may select the wheat, if there be any, or any other grain, but how select in the primitive moner? It hasn't even the appearance of life.

How will the nucleus and its thousands of elements, whose complexity disconcerts the anatomist, the chemist and the physicist, provide for itself? How will the metazoa with their organs, and their so varied and so complex equipment be produced? How will selection produce organs which can only function in a completely developed state? How will it bring about co-adaptation of organs developed independently one of another? How will it succeed in fashioning the masterpieces of the organism destined for vision, audition, perception, locomotion, etc.? One cannot take seriously such theories whatever be their names.

The least object made by man bears upon it the impress of its origin, and yet, some would have it, that a living being, a vertebrate, a mammal, is the product of chance, of natural selection, of the struggle for life, of segregation. Darwin introduced this new factor, which he had reason to suppose indispensable. But here again nature would be incapable of replacing the intelligence of the experimenter. In vain does he invoke chance cataclysms to isolate the new varieties. He forgets that it would be necessary to have as many chance cataclysms as slow modifications fortunately occurring. It would be necessary for the two to always coincide. This is like trying to draw the same number indefinitely from millions of numbers.

If man, in spite of his enlightened intelligence, in spite of his multiple needs, cannot create a single new species, how can one expect natural selection which is infinitely more feeble, to produce more powerful effects, to produce, not only races, but new species, genera, families, orders, classes and branches? This is impossible. If evolution took place, it had to avail itself of factors other than the struggle for life, natural selection, or chance. Neither Darwin, nor *a fortiori* the neo-darwinists have explained evolution. The most ardent evolutionists must admit this. This is what Depéret [1] has to say of the Darwinian theory: "Darwin's vital concurrence, though a very attractive explanation for the extinction of species or the disappearance of intermediate varieties, does not take into account the production of new varieties, so that Darwin himself felt obliged to call to his aid simple chance, that is to say the unknown."

Yves Delage asks himself [2] whether natural selection is capable of engendering specifically new forms. He declares that it cannot. " Natural selection is an admirable and

---

[1] Depéret, *op. cit.*, p. 37.

[2] *Structure du protoplasme*, p. 371 et seq. *The theories of solution*, p. 281.

perfectly just principle.   Every one is agreed on this point
today.   But, where there is no accord, is on the limit of
its power, and on the question of its ability to engender
specifically new forms.   It seems well demonstrated today

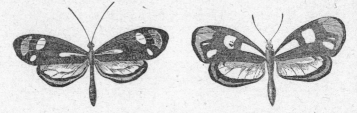

Figs. 50. and 51. Left, South American Leptalides of which birds
are very fond.   Right, a heliconide that secretes a peculiar
nauseous odor to keep of the birds.

that it cannot.   Here are the arguments that prove
it.   1) The causes of variation being weaker than the
causes of fixity, the latter necessarily get the better of
the former.   2) Selection is impotent, since the majority of
the characters that it is supposed to have developed, are

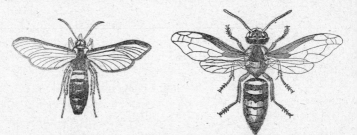

Figs 52 and 53. Left, Lepidoptere of the genus sesiidae, with colo-
ration and appearance of the stinging hymenoptera.   Right, hymenoptera of the wasp family.

useless and do not impart the ability to function.   3) It
is the numerous useful characters that selection has not
been able to produce, since their utility does not become
manifest until they are completely developed.   4) The
variations, even when they are entirely useful, are too

few to create an argument in favor of selection. 5) The selection of accidental variations cannot engender species, since these variations are isolated and since, to constitute a real argument, they ought to bear on several characters at the same time. 6) Selection is impotent, since the variations on which it could exercise itself are continually being destroyed by sexual generation. 7) Selection is not the true cause of the formation of species, for if it were real, however weak its effects, it would transform a species in a period much shorter than that which is apparently necessary for it; and to transform a species in a reasonably long period, the necessary protection is so inadequate that it becomes illusory.

"The conclusion of this critique (p. 391) is that selection is incapable of originating new species. It does however play a certain role. But this is limited to the suppression of radically harmful variations, and to the preservation of the species in its normal condition. Far from being a means of evolution for the species, it guarantees their stability. "

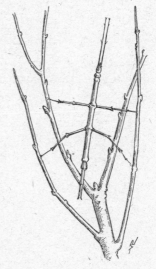

Fig. 54. — Bacillus Gallicus. Example of homomorphy. Adhering to the green twigs the walking-stick is perfectly disguised. (Laby.)

Mimicry has often been adduced as an argument in favor of evolution. Darwinism has tried to explain it. We believe that it was not successful in this attempt, and that here again it faces an enigma for which the theory cannot account. We do not mean any such accidental mimicry as is the result of chance encounter, as that of the leptalides and that of the heliconides (figs. 50 and 51) or that of the wasps and the sesies (figs. 52 and 53), but refer to the instances of homomorphy and homochromy that are rather advanced (figs. 54, 55.)

To conclude. Up to the present, in spite of the many

Fig. 55. — Butterfly from the Malay Archipelago. Whenever it rests on a branch, it assumes the shape easily mistaken for a leaf.

investigations made to discover the secret of the organization and development of life, we can assert that the evolutionistic theories, even those which have been the most popular, have failed to come up to their promises.

ARTICLE VII

THE ERRORS OF MATERIALISTIC EVOLUTION

In the first edition of his *Origin of Species*, published in 1859, Darwin was relatively moderate. His theory embraced only the animal and plant species. He said they had descended through evolution from three or four primitive types created by God. This prudent reserve was not a characteristic of the disciples of the great naturalist. Certain preoccupations of a purely philosophical nature took the Darwinian theory out of the domain of the natural sciences. Soon the whole world was involved in this broad synthesis whose comprehensiveness appealed to a great number of persons.

Then, for the first time, was evolution applied to man. Following Royer, Vogt, Moleschott and Büchner, Darwin was constrained to write a treatise on the animal descent of man. In spite of the excellent and convincing experiments of Pasteur, and in spite of the essential differences between the mineral and the living organism, this school taught as an indispensable dogma the spontaneous origin of life; for God had to be excluded all along the line, from the beginning of life, as well as from its various manifestations. With Haeckel, Herbert Spencer, Littré, Taine, Renan, et al. we arrive at a universal monism, in which the laws of physical mechanics alone, by grouping or dispersing the inherently inert atoms, explain everything from the fall of a stone and the growth of a plant to the conscience of man and the organization of society.

Far be it from us to forbid the naturalist the right to philosophize, for he can not be a scientist, except he investigates the laws which unite the facts and thence rise to the causes which produce the phenomena. But he must not do this haphazard; must not build up hypotheses without foundations, and above all must not give out these hypotheses as articles of scientific doctrine. Now this is precisely what has happened in the question before us. Darwin formulated an hypothesis, grandiose in appearance, it is true, but still withal an hypothesis, and at that, very incomplete since it solved only part of the problem of the genesis of species. And yet, on this very unsteady base, false philosophy under the pretext of scientific unity, erected an immense structure, which the data of modern science and the dictates of common sense have undermined. Reserving for particular discussion the question of the origin of living species, we shall here review briefly what is reprehensible in these excesses.

1. THE THEORY OF EVOLUTION CANNOT APPLY TO MAN.

Before treating this point specially in the following chapter, we shall give here only the fundamental reason that certainly excludes man from evolution. The idea of evolution implies the idea of progress, of development of one and the same thing, of one and the same faculty; but it excludes the idea of new creation. By evolution, we conceive a living being rising in the scale of organic perfection, and even in that of psychological perfection in the measure that this latter is essentially dependent upon the organism, but we do not conceive of a being changing its nature, and acquiring that which it did not prossess in germ in its ancestors. Now man differs from an animal. He is not a more highly developed, more intelligent, more clever, more industrious animal. He is of a new nature, although he has a body, similar in form, to those of the higher animals. In fact, the spiritual operations which characterize him suppose faculties and a nature of a spiritual order, whereas all the operations of the animal, even of the very highest, confine it to the lower sphere of matter and of sensibility. Philosophy studied without prejudice proves this profound difference. The psychological studies of Romanes, the disciple and heir of Darwin, have not shaken this capital thesis. This is why we say that evolution, even if it had realized the progress which unites in one same nature all the animals, could not have created this new thing which we call an intelligent and free man. [1]

2. The theory of evolution cannot apply
to the origin of life.

There is no need to repeat here a question already sufficiently treated. We shall remark only two things. The facts alleged in favor of evolution have nothing in common with the beginnings of life; and the facts and reasonings which are opposed to the spontaneous formation of the first living beings still retain their full force.

That the facts and the hypotheses concerning evolutionism had nothing to do with the origin of life is evident. Indeed, if the facts establish any relation between the living species, they do not at all tend to annihilate the distance already mentioned as existing between the mineral and the plant. When we speak of the influences of the environment, what is meant is the transformation and progress of organisms already in existence, but by no means the transition from the inanimate to the animate world.

It is no less certain, that the facts and reasons opposed to spontaneous generation remain unassailable. For no one doubts, since the experiments of Pasteur, that all the known living beings are generated from parents similar to themselves. And the induction which concludes an absolutely uniform law of reproduction of life at all times, appears the most unquestionable of arguments supported by modern science. How did it happen that evolution was given an extension which the truth did not warrant? It was in virtue of an unlimited confidence in the compass of physical laws and an ill-founded persuasion that the physical universe ought to be self-explanatory. In the domain of the physical sciences, there have been marvellous discoveries. The law of the transformation and of the conservation of energy has thrown much

---

[1] Romanes recognized his materialistic errors later on.

light on all the phenomena of nature. Even in vital phenomena, including human acts, this law is verified with inflexible rigor. But if this law illumines, it must not blind us. Let us not forget that these exchanges and transformations of energy do not constitute the whole of the phenomena; but that the phenomena have modality as well as quantity; that the modality, never capricious, ever orderly, is dependent upon a force other than blind physical energy. In life, for example, the law of conservation of energy regulates the quantities of forces transformed; but a quality inherent in living matter determines its modality. And since this quality cannot be the result of physical forces alone, it follows that inanimate matter as we have already said, can in no way, of itself, become living.

The *persuasion* that Science is dishonored by having recourse to a Creator, is being implanted more and more deeply in the mind of the learned world. This seems to result from a twofold cause : 1) The current of modern incredulity, propagated by a press very foreign to Science. Without noticing it, students fall under its influence. For the preoccupation of safeguarding a scientific reputation inspires a certain human respect. 2) The absence of scientific criticism in certain religious circles; whether through mistaken piety or through lack of education, the interventions of the Creator have been multiplied, and have been given as the solution of difficult problems. In either case, the mind must be educated. It is no disgrace for Science to recognize that the world is not selfexplanatory. This is a philosophical thesis that merits as much investigation as any other topic. If the intervention of the Prime Mover was necessary at the beginning of the first physical motion, of the first vital movement, of the first intellectual act, why shouldn't we acknowledge it?

In Religion, a critical mind and circumspection are necessary, *ne fides ab infidelibus derideatur*, for rash and illfounded statements produce powerful reactions in the opposite direction. We should admit the direct intervention of the First Cause, only when it is indispensable, and even then, only after serious investigation of the arguments. This will not be rejecting or denying God. For, it will ever be a greater glory to Him to act through the creation of causes than through immediate interventions. It is none the less objective and personal. [1]

3. The universal monism of Spencer is not warranted by the theories of the evolution of species.

The philosophers who, following Spencer, Littré, Taine, et al. have upheld, that the same mechanical laws govern the intellectual and moral world, and even the progress of society as operate in the physical world, are merely borrowing analogies and words from the theory of evolution, as it is understood in natural history. The attempt made by Taine, not merely to compare, but to identify the moral with the physical laws, was absolutely devoid of foundation.

As in every false system, we find a modicum of truth also in monism. It is important to bring this out clearly so as to show that monism is not a logical deduction. The physical world, such as it appears to us, evidently seems to be the result of slow and progressive evolution. Created in a state of chaos, matter gradually became organized under the influence of physical forces, according to the cosmogonic hypotheses. The animate world of plants and of animals with that singular variety of forms which it presents today, could thus have been the result of progressive evolution. Paleontology suggests to us that the living beings have gradually perfected themselves; that this evolution might have taken place passively under the action of God, or actively through the impulse of nature and the influence of external conditions. In any case a relative progress has taken place.—Finally humanity itself progressed; starting from a very elementary

---

[1] Cf. de Dordolot, *Darwinism*, P. Teilhard de Chardin, *Études*, June 1921; *Revue de Philosophie*, April 1923; Périer, *Revue d'Apologétique* July 1922, Saulze, *Le monisme en France*.

social status humanity has grown gradually, each generation deriving profit from the scientific or social advantages acquired by the preceding generation. If history
shows, that, among certain people decadence has followed
close upon great prosperity, it is no less true that, as a
whole, humanity rises. Thus, in the physical world, in
the animate world, and in the human world progress or
evolution if you will, is established. But, it is not in
this that monism consists. Monism teaches that these
three worlds make up only one, both by their nature and
by the forces which direct their evolution. Since their
nature is identical, the animate world has risen spontaneously from the physical world; the human world likewise has risen naturally from the animal world. Since the
laws and the forces which preside over their destinies are
the same, the formulae which express the mode of formation of the physical universe express also the manner
of formation of peoples and of society in general.

De facto, these three evolutions are parallel and not
consecutive. The evolution of the physical world started
in the beginning, and it always continued towards a still
remote necessary terminus, under the action of physico-
chemical forces.—Later on the evolution of the animate
world began. But as we have said, life did not originate
in a purely physical action upon inorganic matter. An
influence superior to the inorganic world formed the
first living beings, and conferred upon them the mysterious power of subsisting, increasing and multiplying.—
Finally at a still more recent date, began the human
world in which we find something more than mere
progress of animality, viz. the properties of the intellectual
and moral order which characterize man.

The physical universe evolved by the slow transformation of its potential or available energy. The living world
is thus slowly being transformed, under the action of the
environment and in virtue of its internal powers. The
human world is changed and makes progress through the
elements that each new generation adds to the heritage
of the past.

We see from this, that the idea of evolution, even in its broadest sense, does not lead to monism, which is naught else than a modern form of the old *materialism*.

4. The evolution of species, if it existed, cannot be considered as purely an effect of chance.

With this proposition we return once more to our subject. We regard it as certain, and in demonstrating it, we shall show that evolution should not compromise the proof for the existence of God, that philosophers have always

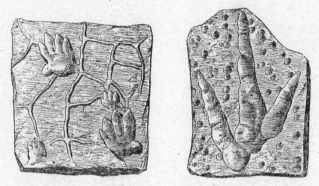

Figs. 56 and 57. Traces of a labyrinthodont and of a dinosaur found in the triassic terrains.

drawn from the order in the world. Our mind is this. If there has been evolution, it took place in accordance with a preconceived plan, following a law of order. We do not wish to prove evolution; but if others believe it proved they ought at least recognize that it took place according to a law implanted by God. Wherever man sees an orderly arrangement, his reason concludes the action of an ordaining power. If he sees a timepiece going, finds a watch in a desert, it is a sufficient proof to him that an intelligent person has passed that way. It will not even occur to him that perhaps this time-piece made itself, or that this watch is the fortuitous resultant of possible combinations of atoms brought together by the wind. When the geologist meets with the imprint of a foot or a hand in the schists and sandstone, he does not hesitate to conclude the presence of some labyrinthodont or of some

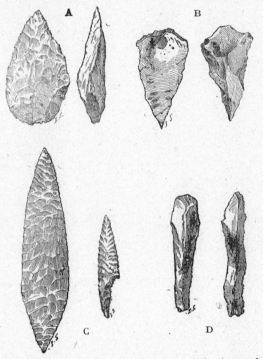

Figs. 58, 59, 60, 61. — Characteristic flints of the four subdivisions of the Paleolithic Age. — A. Chellean spear-head, obverse and lateral view. — B. Mousterian point, obverse and reverse. — C. Solutrian points. — D. Magdalenian scraper, reverse and lateral view.

dinosaur (figs. 56, 57). If a sceptic advanced the opinion that this is not quite clear, that these pretended vestiges might well be but a freak of nature and a curious effect of mechanical forces, the geologist would, affirm and with good reason, that this doubt would be subversive of all science, of all legitimate induction. Likewise the chipped flints found in the Quaternary caverns, prove the intelligent work of man. By means of certain precise characters, it is possible to distinguish the work of intelligent man (figs. 58-61) from those which might be the result of natural forces. Reason can recognize at a glance that which is designed, from that which is not; that which is the work of an intelligent being, from that which is the work of chance. The order of the twenty-four letters of the alphabet is one of 4×10^{26} possible combinations, but no one would hesitate to see an indication of intelligence in their alphabetical arrangement or even their order in a single word. If a mere glance passes as evidence among scientists as well as laymen, why should it be questioned when there is a possibility that the Ordaining Power might be the Supreme Being? Why indeed! The five imprints of this labyrinthodont renders you certain that they had been made by a living animal, and you will hold that the living animal has been the mechanical product of chance? The surfaces of the flints are for you undeniable proof of an intentional shaping, because you discover there, order and purpose; and man, the author of this work infinitely more complex and better ordered, would be the result of unconscious physical agencies?

Order is evident in living nature; it is evident in the correlation and adaptation of parts in each individual; it is evident in that ascending disposition of species which compose the two kingdoms; it is evident in the marvellous development of the seed, where we see each individual attaining with such certainty and regularity the adult form of its species. This order is not explained by the action of the environment, nor by natural selection, nor by the laws of growth and of the correlation of parts; for, all these factors are powerless to effect an harmonious series or to preserve, through the thousands of obstacles, this harmony, once established.

And even though we should show all the degrees of complexity, between the perfected eye of a mammal and the simple eye-spot of the medusa, between the three compartment ear of land animals and the audition spot of a worm, such ascending progress of an organ will never eliminate the idea of an Ordaining Power. The Ordaining Power has left His impress in the lowest as in the highest form of the senses.   Since order appears everywhere, in the organs of individuals as in the series of species, we say that if evolution has occurred, it has been under the action of God, and following a law of development imposed by Him. This law may be unknown to us, but it exists.   It is precisely under this form that moderate or spiritual evolutionism appears, as we have shown above. We thus see to what errors materialistic evolution leads. By a strange misuse of language, it happens that evolution which can be but the history of the development of beings, is considered as a magic force which blindly produces all development in nature. We are in hopes that the anti-religious philosophy which has lead to consequences so unacceptable, will end by giving way, in reflecting minds to spiritualistic philosophy, which sees in the work of nature the hand of a Supreme Ordainer, though without being in a position to state precisely by what way the Creator has produced the diversity of species. [1]

CONCLUSION.

We reject the *monism* of Spencer and of Haeckel, which unifies all beings and explains them by the simple mechanism of atoms, and which teaches the spontaneous passage from inanimate matter to life, from sensible and animal life to the intellectual and moral life of man. [2]

We do not believe that the formation of living species may be the effect of chance, that is to say, of blind mechanical forces. We hold that both the vegetable and the

---

[1] "I cannot repeat here the reasoning that I have developed at length in *Les croyances religieuses et les sciences de la nature*, (Paris, Beauchesne, 1908), chap. IV ; "Evolution can be the history of the world only on condition it is a process of creation in the hands of a Sovereign Intelligence." (Guibert.)

[2] Cf. Senderens, *Apologétique scientifique*, p. 250-264.

animal kingdoms realize a plan conceived and ordained by God. [1]

How did God execute His plan? So far there has been nothing but hypotheses given as answers to this question. On the one hand, the hypothesis of moderate and spiritual evolutionism, on the other, that of fixism. The two hypotheses are but forms of Creationism.

Toward which of these two hypotheses should we be inclined? The serious mind cannot but hesitate to decide. For, on the one hand, it appears to be more conducive to the glory of God, more conformable to His ordinary procedure and more clearly indicated by the observed facts of nature, for God to have created living species by way of evolution, i. e. as the First Cause, rather than by successive creations, or as the immediate cause of each species. [2]—On the other hand, there are so many facts

---

[1] The founders of evolutionism were not far from this idea. According to Lamarck, the laws of nature "are only the expression of the will of Him Who has decreed." *Histoire naturelle des animaux sans vertèbres, Introduction.* Darwin wrote : "I have never been an atheist. I have never denied the existence of God... I believe that the theory of evolution is altogether compatible with the belief in God... The impossibility of conceiving that this grand and imposing universe, with our conscious selves, has been begotten through chance, appears to me to be the principal argument for the existence of God." *Life of Charles Darwin* by Varigny.

[2] This opinion seems to conform very well with the tendencies manifested at the International Congresses of Catholic scientists held in 1894 and 1897. In 1894, the Congress adopted the following resolution: "The Section of Anthropology of the Third Scientific Congress of Catholics at Brussels, commends and encourages the studies of those, who, under the supreme magisterium of the teaching Church, devote themselves to the investigation of the role that evolution has played in the concert of secondary causes that have brought the physical world to its present state." *Comptes rendus,* p. 298.

For the Congress of 1897, held at Fribourg, we extract the following account by de Kirwan, from la *Revue du Monde catholique,* Oct., 1897. "The Reverend Father Zahm, Rector of the Roman College, has, under the title of *Theology and Evolutionism,* developed this thesis that there exists an orthodox evolutionism which not only does not exclude final causes but, shows their necessity in a

that can not enter, or can enter only by violence, into the evolutionistic synthesis, and the various theories, invented to explain evolution, have failed so miserably, that we cannot tax with ignorance nor with a reactionary spirit, such as put no credence in the idea of evolution.

If God created the species through evolution, did He make them start from one primitive type or from many? In the actual state of science, it appears to us more probable that when creating life, He placed in nature several simple primitive forms. We know nothing about this; but this supposition is adduced in order to shorten the time which descent from a single stock would demand, and especially to simplify the problem of evolution and to remain more in accord with the facts.

still more striking manner... If evolution thus understood is not accepted by all... after all, it is always and will probably be nothing more than an hypothesis—at least it is, in general, no longer rejected *a priori* by any scientific mind... Whereas it has been quite necessary to recognize in the various camps, that provided it is confined to strictly scientific limits and disengaged from arbitrary and excessive hypotheses, these theories contain absolutely nothing contrary to the truths of faith, but rather strengthen it, the discussions on this subject, without ceasing to be animated, have become less passionate. ''

CHAPTER V

ORIGIN OF MAN

§ 1.—Meaning and bearing of the question.

Our series of studies leads us to treat of the origin of man. If the question is for many reasons, difficult, its importance will not permit us to overlook it. In the mind of naturalists for whom the human species is only the highest of the animal species, this new study would only be going over the same ground again. The problem of human origin should of necessity have the same solution as the problem of animal origin. As for us, who find in man a privileged nature, we hold that his origin should also be marked by a special privilege. Even though the Creator might have produced living species by way of evolution, He would not be illogical in His works if He had formed "His image" in man by a special intervention. Knowing that the problem exists, we are going to examine *how the first man made his appearance.*

To come directly to the point, we eliminate, for the present, the question of the unity or the multiplicity of human origins. Whether the different races descend from one primitive stock or from many, the point with which we are concerned remains the same.—Is it evolution or is it the Creator that has produced these groups of intelligent and free beings that constitute the human species?

As the matter resolves itself into a question of fact, authentic documents should be the best source to consult. It would be rash to assert that these documents are absolutely lacking. We cannot help being struck by the legends which are in circulation among all peoples that uncivilized life has become much degraded.   They undoubtedly differ in many respects, but all agree in placing the human origin in the hands of the divinity.   May we not see in this common tradition the more or less confused recollections which humanity has preserved of its beginnings?

According to Christian Faith, the Bible contains in its purity the history of man's origin : Whatever effort may be made to weaken the high import of the first chapter of Genesis, we, on our part, shall always see, in it, this doctrine clearly enunciated, that God, by a special act, created the first man.   It is not a work of historical or exegetical criticism that we are engaged upon, but only an unpretentious work of a naturalist.   Thus, leaving aside the discussion of documents of an historical character, we shall faithfully investigate, toward what solution the right inductions of a scientific nature incline.   We shall have the pleasure of verifying the fact, that Science, when it does not deviate from its course, is not disturbing but rather reassuring to Faith.

Before Darwin's time, no scientific doubt was cast upon the creation of the human species.   The attacks directed against Christian belief emanated from a materialism, more sectarian than reasoned.   Lamarck, undoubtedly, had applied his evolutionistic principles to man in his *Philosophie zoologique*, and had examined by what process the chimpanzee, for instance, could have been transformed into an organism with a human form.   But the conclusion that he came to after his study shows quite well what his opinion was.   "Such would be the reflections that one might make" says he, "if man were distinguished from animals only by the characters of his organization and if his origin were not different from theirs." [1]

When Darwin's work *The Origin of Species* appeared in 1859, the materialistic school of philosophy hastened to apply the principle of natural selection to man.   The illustrious English savant found he had to tag after his numerous

[1] Cf. de Quatrefages, *Charles Darwin et ses précurseurs français*, Paris, Alcan, p. 365.

disciples; for some time after, in 1871, he published his *Descent of Man.*

This notion of the animal origin of man could not fail to be taken up, with great enthusiasm and be widely diffused. It is especially under this form that the idea of evolution was spread among the people. The very favorable reception that was given it is readily understood. The devotees of pleasure found here a pretext to free themselves from the moral law; the theorists, inimical to the existence of a soul and of a God, found a very opportune means of explaining a world without God, and man without an immortal soul.

Today evolution as a doctrine is so generally accepted by naturalists, that it is difficult to question its conlusions, without being considered an *ignoramus* and behind the times. It is a whole from which we may not detract a single part. "We must accept all or leave all" said Darwin, and his disciples expressed themselves in a similar strain. How then accord the same prominence to all the assertions of the theory? Why not distinguish that which is susceptible of evolution from that which is not? Are there not some hypotheses well grounded, some purely gratuitous and some dictated solely by prejudice? It is with a certain amount of surprise that we find such keen minds as Spencer, Perrier, Boule et al. not making so fundamental a distinction, as that existing between the soul and the body, and teaching that the entire man comes from the animal, because we cannot make a distinction between the human organism and that of the higher animals.

To safeguard the esteem that true Science merits, will it be necessary to subscribe to this materialistic thesis? Can the spiritual philosopher no longer be the student of natural philosophy? In the question before us what will be the attitude of the advocates of the divine origin of the human species?

Those who reject absolutely the evolution of the plant and animal species, do not even consider the problem in connection with the origin of man. For, if God has had to intervene directly, for each living form, there is all the more reason why He should intervene for the creation of the first man.   They have no need for the arguments that will be set forth in this work.   They invoke them, however, to confirm their thesis.   Perhaps in imitation of de Quatrefages [1] they may be tempted to exaggerate. Desirous of comprehending in one common law the formation of all species, they might conclude that the divine origin of the human species proves also the immediate divine origin of all living species.   But since the nature of man is so peculiar, so independent of the animal nature, why may not the human origin be unique and independent of the law which rules the animal species?

Those who admit that God has probably created the living species through evolution, distinguish in man the two elements of which he is composed, the soul and the body. All the spiritualists admit that the human soul is directly created by God.   As to the body which becomes a human body in virtue of its union with a spiritual soul, one may ask in what manner God was its author.   Either the human body was directly fashioned by God out of purely inorganic matter, that is to say, evolution *had absolutely no part* in the formation of man; or the human body was, in the designs of God, prepared for in advance, by a slow natural evolution, and God created man by infusing a spiritual soul into an already animate organism.   This would be saying that for *a certain part* of man, there had been evolution in his formation.

In this latter hypothesis we may make another distinction, the reason for which will appear later on.   At the moment when God decided to create man, He either took an animate organism such as had been prepared by evolution, or He completed His preconceived plan, by giving the organism the characters, more special to the human species, such as the cerebral development, upright posture, etc.   These different hypotheses have been formulated among Catholics.   Hence we have thought well

[1] See *Revue scientifique*, Aug. 23, 1890, p. 231.

to mention them, so as to bring into fuller light the meaning of the question. No author brought out more explicitly the possibility of attributing the origin of the human body to evolution, than did Saint-Georges Mivart. [1] In his opinion God would remain the Author of the entire man, of the body as well as of the soul, but He had produced them in different ways—the body in accordance with the law of evolution, the soul by a special and immediate creation.

From what precedes it is evident that we must treat separately the origin of the human soul and that of the human body. By proving, contrary to materialistic evolution that the soul comes from God by way of direct creation, we shall have, by that very fact, established that man is not the result of blind and fatalistic evolution. By studying the similarities between the human organism and that of the animal, we shall see that even Science inclines us to believe, as the Bible says, that God must have fashioned the body of the first man.

Taken as a whole, the question has an importance which we hardly need insist upon. The solution given carries with it important philosophical, religious, moral, social and international consequences. From the philosophical standpoint, it is man's nature that is at stake. If man has a spiritual and in consequence an immortal soul, he comes only from God; if he is only the last element in a series produced by evolution, he partakes of the nature of the beast and has no immortal soul. As every being derives its end from that which gives it being, the destiny of man will not have more value than his beginnings. In the case of an animal origin of man, what is the meaning of religion? It becomes, in its many forms, but a mere

---

[1] Mivart, *Genesis of Species*, chap. xii; *Theology and Evolution.* — It is but right to say that Saint-Georges-Mivart was one of the strongest champions of the divine origin of the human soul; on this fundamental point, he has taken issue with Romanes the disciple and continuator of Darwin. It was to refute him that he wrote his excellent book entitled: *The origin of human reason,* London, 1889. Romanes himself ended by recognizing his materialistic errors.

secretion of the human brain. Being altogether based
on the necessary relations of the creature with his Creator
religion disappears with the doctrine of creation.

Furthermore, moral law ceases to exist. In fact, the
moral law no longer exists where there is no Supreme
Power, to ordain and sanction. Duty which has no other
foundation than sentiment of the internal need which
man has of being honest can have neither consistancy, nor
authority, and man is no more responsible for his acts than
are the animals of which he is the highest type. Relieved
of all moral responsibility, unincumbered by the belief
in an hereafter, why should he restrain his passions? To
see what social and international consequences result from
these pernicious theories, it is not even necessary to
reason them out. It is sufficient to consider the facts. Is
it not evident that, under the influence of these new ideas,
public morals have been debased, crime has developed,
brutal egoism has increased, might has tried to usurp
the place of right, etc.?

If we wish man to preserve, in his life, the dignity and the
virtue, to which, in spite of all, the human conscience
remains invincibly attached, it is necessary to teach him
ideas about his nature other than those of materialistic
evolutionism.

§ 2.—ORIGIN OF THE HUMAN SOUL.

To show whence comes the human soul is to solve the
problem of the origin of man. It is the soul which characterizes man. Not only does it determine the nature of
his faculties and of his operations, but it also communicates
to the organism itself the qualities which distinguish it.
The material elements taken by themselves would be indifferent to any particular organization; they become a human body only through the principle that controls them.
The organs are indifferent in the execution of acts of
purely animal life; the physiological energy which they
expend assumes the orientation which the interior principle of the being impresses upon it. The nature of man

being determined by the nature of the soul itself, it follows
that the origin of the soul indicates the origin of man himself. When the first man appeared, whence came his
soul? For us it is a *certain thesis that it was created by
God*, and that it could not have been the result of evolution. The importance of this statement rests on the solidity of the following reasoning. If the human soul, the
source of life in man, is of a separate nature, if it is more
than just a degree higher than the animal soul, it cannot
have been produced by evolution. Now the human soul
by nature is so transcendent that it cannot be considered
as being of the same order as the soul of animals. It is
clear that the solution proposed will have to be held as
true, if these two propositions are demonstrated. The
first needs less attention since it is not contested by the
evolutionists. They are quite agreed that evolution
merely develops that which already exists, perfects that
which is already acquired and adds only a new degree in
the same order of beings. Evolution modifies an existing
nature, it cannot create a new nature. This principle is
fundamental in the School. It is to safeguard it that the
evolutionists have been logically led to universal monism.
They began by suppressing the difference of nature between
man and the lower animals. This chasm once bridged
by an hypothesis, evolution could freely proceed from one
term to another. Hence they followed with the suppression of the real distinction between animate and inanimate creatures. This done, evolution could admit as
a biological necessity, despite all the facts to the contrary,
the thesis of spontaneous generation. The surest means
of annihilating the differences of nature was to admit
in its entirety the mechanistic conception of the universe.
Everything then, from the falling of a stone to the conscience of man (Haeckel) became reduced to simple forms
of mechanical motion in the inert atoms.

It seems evident then that the first proposition of our
reasoning is equally accepted by both sides. Thus it is
only with the second that we have to deal. Romanes and
his materialistic school were well aware of this. This is

why the problem at issue hinges on the nature of the human soul. The soul of man, say the materialistic evolutionists, whatever it might be otherwise — immaterial principle of activity or resultant of material forces, is only a perfected animal soul, as the soul of the adult is the cultivated soul of a child, as the soul of the civilized man differs only in degree from that of the present or the primitive savage.

For us, on the contrary, there exists a true *difference of nature between man and the beast* [1]. We shall set forth the positive arguments which sustain this thesis, before examining the objections opposed to it. This thesis has not always been advocated with equally solid arguments. Thus de Quatrefages clearly admitted the real distinction between man and the beast, but he gave as signs of it religiousness and morality noticeable in man and not intelligence which he conceded to animals as well [2]. Now these two qualities are not true human faculties, but only modes according to which the faculties of cognition and of volition express themselves. If then the cognitive and the volitive faculties are of the same nature in the animal as in man, it should be possible to say that the intelligence of animals will some day perhaps produce religion and morality, since it lacks merely the proper degree of development. De Nadaillac is far from identifying man with the brute beast. [3] *Conscience* and *progress* are assuredly weighty arguments in favor of the difference. But, in rejecting the difference of nature between the intelligence of the beast and that of man, doesn't de Nadaillac undermine the very foundation of the edifice he is erecting? For, let the animal increase a little in intelligence, and this

---

[1] "When Linné speaks not only of *physical* man, but of the entire man, he puts him in opposition to all the animals, and that, in such terms, that the notion of a *human kingdom* imperatively follows." De Quatrefages, *L'espèce humaine*, 12th edit., p. 17.

[2] De Quatrefages, *L'espèce humaine*, chap. i. *Races humaines*, p. 252.

[3] De Nadaillac, in *Le Correspondant*, Jan. 15, 1892; *Intelligence et instinct*, 3d article.

intelligence will create conscience and bring about progress. For the same reason we regard as insufficient the difference that is based on the higher operations of the mind alone, on the reasoning faculty, as the argument is stated by certain modern spiritualists. Indeed it is the same faculty which produces the idea, the judgment and reasoning. If we concede to the beast an intelligence capable of perceiving ideas, by that same fact, we admit the possibility of judging and of reasoning.

On this hypothesis, we cannot see why the beast could not reach the reasoning stage, as does a child. Contrast with this the strong position of the disciples of Aristotle and of the School. Thus, Mivart undertaking to defend against Romanes, the specific difference of the human soul and in consequence its divine origin, courageously adopted the distinction of two orders of cognition, the true basis of traditional philosophy. [1] The following is a brief outline of his argument. The nature of a being is manifested by the faculties which proceed from it. The faculties are known by the operations they produce. While the operations are of the same nature as the objects which they comprehend. Thus, it is quite logical to mount from the nature of an object, known and willed, to the nature of the being which knows it and wills it. Consequently, a being which knows objects abstracted from all matter, as principles, ideas, the universal abstractions, the beautiful, the good, the true, the right and the wrong, etc., is a being immaterial by nature, a spirit capable of existing by itself, as it is capable of acting by itself. Now man, in all the human races and at all ages of humanity, has given proof that he exercised such spiritual operations. He is everywhere endowed with the power of abstraction and generalization. He is an intelligent being in the strict sense of the word; he has ideas. On the contrary, the beast, which shares the sense faculties with man, which knows and pursues sensible objects, has no power over suprasensible things, cannot know immaterial or

[1] Mivart, *The origin of human reason*, Introduction, 1889.

abstract objects. It has sensible images but not ideas.

Thus then our problem reduces itself to an examination of two facts : *man is endowed with intelligence along with sense faculties; the animal has only sense faculties and is devoid of intelligence.* This is the culminating point of philosophy. It is here in fact that all discussions terminate at the present time. The opposite solutions lead into absolutely blind paths.

We are conscious of the fact that the question demands a development beyond the compass of an article [1] for to place the spiritualistic solution in as clear a light as possible it would be necessary to discuss a great number of concrete facts, which appear to be in contradiction with it. At least, we shall trace the route to be followed through this maze of difficulties.

The first fact to establish is the reality of the intellectual power of man.

Conscience is the enlightened master that gives us information about our operations and thus about our nature. If we examine our interior acts, we find that they are of two kinds. Some belong to the category of *sensation.* They have for their object, matter and its sensible qualities. They embrace the particular, dimension and color. The senses are the organs through which they operate. Our eyes see, our ears hear, we experience pleasure, pain, hunger, thirst; the images which are vividly presented to our internal senses are in a certain way formed in our brain—The others belong to *entirely spiritual faculties.* They have for their object the immaterial, the abstract, the general, the true, the good, the beautiful, all that is independent of dimensions, of color, etc... Such acts are in no way the product of the corporal organs although in the present state, they cannot be realized without a certain participation of the body. They are elaborated by the spiritual faculties, but these faculties

---

[1] Cf. Card. Mercier, *Origins of contemporary psychology*; Farges, *Le cerveau, l'âme et ses facultés*, Paris, Berche et Tralin. All works on spisitualistic psychology.

act only on the images presented by the sense organs.

This distinction of a twofold faculty in man is certainly the result of a thorough philosophical analysis; but what may not be easy for every man to discover by his own inherent powers, may be possible for each to establish and to verify in himself by reflection. Thus, conscience reveals two stages of being in us : the one which we have in common with the beast, the other which is proper to us and which characterizes us. At the same time, the sense of our own unity imposes itself upon us with such force, that we recognize the same principle as the author of all our operations. Such is the reflective act by which the soul becomes conscious of itself, of its spirituality and of its unity.

But an internal cause so exalted, so singular as is the human soul, cannot fail to express itself outwardly by effects equally high and characteristic. These products of the spiritual soul, identical in all races and at all ages of humanity, permit man to argue the identity of nature in all such beings as resemble him in organism. Articulate language, morality, religion, intellectual progress, industry, the arts, etc., such are the exterior phenomena through which radiates human intelligence.

Articulate language is both the sign and the result of abstraction and of generalization. Whoever speaks is a being that thinks; for all the words of a language, the pronouns as well as the nouns and the verbs, are general and abstract formulae disengaged from particular objects. Reciprocally, whoever makes acts of abstraction will be in possession of a language. Not that every act of abstraction produced in the mind necessarily manifests itself in words, but we cannot conceive how a being living in society, can have general and abstract ideas without ever using formulae to express them. Moreover, these formulae are not all modulations of the voice; they may be conventional signs executed by the hand, the eyes, or in an altogether different manner, by writing, painting, sculpture, etc.[1]

---

[1] Cf. Senderens, *Apologie scientifique*, p. 362 et sq.

Now language, this infallible witness of the mind, the human species possesses in every clime. It is more or less rich, more or less harmonious, but it is found everywhere. Thus, even though the sounds of the common language cannot be perceived by a deaf mute who may also be blind, rather than keep the thoughts of his soul pent up within himself, will resort to mimicry, each movement of which will have a general and abstract meaning. Language exists even among savages. However poor it may be, it is composed of general formulae, and is, besides, always capable of being enriched. [1]

Morality is another consequence of intelligence. The notion of good and of evil supposes consciousness and of responsibility. That alone is free, and distinguishes good from evil, which knows the relation of conformity or of opposition between an act which it performs and the law which it knows. Now morality, like language, is also found among all the human races. The sentiment that it inspires is not merely a fear of punishment, but shame for having broken an immutable law revealed by conscience. Undoubtedly, the positive laws are quite variable from one nation to another; undoubtedly also the practises on the essential points, as modesty, propriety, respect for human life, are very different according to the degree of civilization; but the remarkable thing is, that there is not a people, no matter how barbarous, that has not adopted some customs, and established sanctions which attest the existence and assure respect for moral sentiment. [2]

Religion comprises both the belief in superior beings capable of exerting an influence over our destiny, and the persuasion that a part of ourselves survives after death. According to the opinion of de Quatrefages, atheism is met with among men solely in an *erratic* state. Man is naturally religious. He must be trained not to become

---

[1] For further development see Piat, *La personne humaine*; de Bonniot, *La bête comparée à l'homme*, Paris, Retaux.

[2] Cf. Mgr. Le Roy, *Religion of the Primitives*.

religious but to become atheistic. Surely, instruction is necessary to develop the religious sense under a particular form, but before all instruction, the human soul is instinctively religious. This tendency is also the result of human intelligence. Seeking to know whence he came and who has made the world, man feels that he is the child of a Supreme Cause upon whom he is in daily dependence; regarding his destiny man feels he cannot die entirely. While the religious sense is foreign to the rest of the universe, it is universal in humanity.

Intellectual progress in the individual and in the species is a fact absolutely characteristic of the human species. The animals are not susceptible of progress, because as Ch. Richet says "they are condemned to a *psychic fixity.*" Whence comes this fixity, if not from the inability of animals to make abstraction and to generalize? Whence does man derive his faculty of development, if not from his mind which permits him to rise from particular facts to general and abstract ideas? All creation occasioning progress consists in the domination of a general idea over matter or particular phenomena. While the animal is a slave of nature, intelligent man dominates and subdues it.

Man has created industry, agriculture, the arts. This subjugation of animate and inanimate beings to his needs and his caprices is therefore also a sign of man's intelligence. Man of all the races and he alone, fashions wood, iron, stone, etc., constructs habitations which in no way resemble each other and which surpass his physiological needs. He alone lights a fire and makes clothing for himself. He alone creates works of art, whose purpose is to express the beautiful and not to realize the useful. He extends his empire over the animals, tames the most ferocious and trains for his service the more docile...

It would be superflous to multiply or to develop these marks of human intelligence further. As they are met with in all men and are lacking in all animals, they establish an impassible line of demarcation between the one and the other class. Moreover, they have proving force only in so far as they lead to this conclusion: there exists in man some spiritual faculties which are lacking in the beast. A conclusion that we believe solidly established on the grounds we have given above, viz. the nature of objects, reveals the nature of the faculties which comprehend them: the objects which man grasps and which he alone knows, being of a spiritual nature, it follows that the human faculties are likewise spiritual. But a spiritual soul is not of the same order as a principle of pure sense activity, and so cannot have arisen from it by simple development. It follows from this, that the first human soul, not being merely a progress but a *new entity*, could come into existence only by the intervention of a creative power outside of nature.

We must not overlook the arguments of the opponents of our thesis but point out, if we can, how a faulty interpretation leads them into error and holds them there.

§ 3. — DIFFICULTIES CONCERNING THE HUMAN SOUL

Since our doctrine on the origin of the human soul is based on its transcendency, we must examine by what arguments our opponents bridge the chasm which separates man from the brute. They reproach us, indeed with depreciating the animals and of overestimating the inferior human races. Among the animals, they say, we find, at least in a rudimenrary state, all the faculties of man. The savage is an intermediary between the civilized being and the beast, still retarded in his development; moreover do we not see the infant repeating one after another all the phases through which the human intelligence has to pass before attaining to its present high state?

The mind of animals. [1]—Darwin in *The Descent of Man*,

---

[1] This question has been very carefully studied in the work of the abbé Piat, *La personne humaine*, bk. II, chap. III and IV, Paris, Alcan, 1887; De Bonniot, *La bête comparée à l'homme*, Paris, Retaux, 1889; H. Joly, *L'homme et l'animal*, Paris, Hachette; *L'instinct*, Paris, Fontemoing; Wasmann, *Rev. de philosophie*, 1910, p. 314, et sq.

2nd ed., p. 10 et al., had already made great efforts to discover in the acts of animals a trace of an intelligence which generalizes and makes abstraction. Romanes, his disciple, has developed the thought of his master in his work entitled *The intelligence of animals.* [1] Perrier taking up the theses of both, concludes in favor of real intelligence. [2] The Marquis de Nadaillac, who it is true, rejects the idea of identity between human nature and animal nature, [3] arrives at the same conclusion in a series of very well documented articles. According to Perrier, animals possess all the human faculties: exterior perception, memory, imagination, power of induction, of abstraction and of generalization; they may have some curiosity, a certain sense of beauty, even indeed of religion and of morality.

Although it does not enter into our plan to discuss in detail all the facts alleged in favor of the higher faculties in animals, we shall at least give the principles which enable us to solve this very old but ever new problem.

It is far from our intention to undervalue animals with a view to exalting the dignity of man. We shall not say with Descartes that animals are machines which the hand of the Creator has skilfully assembled and whose springs are so well adjusted that the purely mechanical releases give the illusion of spontaneity, of sensitiveness, of perception and of volition. The most elementary common sense compels us to admit that animals have cognition, set themselves in motion, resolve, become excited, defend themselves, build habitations for themselves, etc. St. Thomas as a faithful disciple of Aristotle goes so far as to attribute to them a faculty of combining images which might be "a certain imitation of the judgment found in man." But in connection with animals we distinguish two kinds of faculties. One class, called sense faculties,

---

[1] Romanes, *The intelligence of animals.*

[2] Perrier, *Le transformisme*, Paris, J. B. Baillière, 1888; *La Terre avant l'histoire*, Paris, 1921.

[3] De Nadaillac, articles *Instinct and intelligence* in *Correspondant*, 1891-1892.

consists in the power of knowing, loving, seeking that which strikes the senses, of retaining and of combining the images impressed on the cerebral organ. The other, called intellectual faculties, consists in the power of abstracting the idea from the image, and of pursuing the immaterial good, of combining ideas with each other; which latter act leads to reasoning, to morality, to religion and to progress. As we have said previously, we attribute to animals all the sense faculties, but in man alone, do we find the intellectual or spiritual faculties; we believe that all the acts of animals are confined to the domain of sense. Contrary to the doctrine of Locke and of Condillac, we hold that human thought is something other than a simple collection of transformed sensations.

As to certain observed facts, we think that the authenticity of many of the most remarkable ought to be controled. Numerous anecdotes of intelligence in animals have been collected. But were the sources absolutely reliable? If they were, were they based on sufficiently attentive observation? Even if the observation had been serious and careful, how may times has not the act of the animal been perfected by the intelligence of the observer? By anthropomorphic inclination, we attribute our reasoning and our sentiments to animals. As we pass through the same sense conditions that we observe in them, we suppose that they pass through the same intellectual states, which in us are superimposed upon sensation. This conferring of prerogatives is purely gratuitous, yes even faulty. For, not only do the animals not prove that they have the same intellectual states as we, but they prove rather the contrary.

Indeed all the well authenticated facts are reducible to sensation, that is they do not require a faculty independent of a material organ. We do not discuss the facts of the imagination, of dreams, of memory of perception, of love or of hate, since we recognize the existence of these faculties. The difficulty bears on the facts which seem to be instances of induction, of reasoning, of morality, of religion, etc. Darwin cites an instance of how a monkey, that had learned to lift the lid off a box with a stick, ever after, used a stick as a lever, each time that it wished to dislodge some heavy object. To act thus, had the monkey really *abstracted* from the first object the *general idea* of resistance to effort and that of leverage? Is it not simpler to admit that each resistant object raised in the mind of the monkey the image of a stick and the operation to perform?

When Darwin supposes that the peacock in spreading its tail has a *sense of the beautiful* does he not make a very gratuitous assertion? For, is not the spreading of the peacock's tail the necessary result of muscular contraction under the impulse of passion, rather than the effect of a deliberate intention to cause admiration?

That animals warn one another of danger, that they mutually defend one another, that they divide their prey into equal portions is all possible, but does it follow from this that they are moved by a moral sense of duty? When man does these things is it always through love of duty? Is it not often through a simple sense effect, of sensible attachment, through fear of sensible consequences? It requires strong prejudices in favor of the system, to find traces of religion in a horse, that rears up rather than advances in the dark: or in the dog that rolls on the ground when it hears the crash of thunder. Man and animal are equally subject to fright. Fear may take the same form in both, but religion is altogether different from fright. It is born of beliefs that belong to the realm of intelligence. It may be, and is without signs of fright: it may, however, and does provoke salutary fear. In general, the majority of animal actions are easily reduced to sensation: obviously none of them appertains to intelligence properly so called. To judge the more difficult cases, we must rely on clearly known facts. For if the animals were really intelligent, and had a rudimentary reasoning faculty, as some pretend, they would perform acts that would be admitted as evidence. That which we cannot read in their consciences we should at least be able to deduce from external manifestations. They should have formulae of language by which we might interchange ideas with them. They have only sense expressions, cries, songs, gestures revealing their various passionate states. [1] Garner has detected in the monkeys, modulations of the voice expressing the passions of hunger, fright, sensual love, etc., but did he interchange ideas with them? They should have a certain sense of responsibility. They should give indications of liberty in preferring suprasensible good to the pleasures of the senses. But is it not known that an animal never hesitates between two pleasures, or rather between pleasure and a sensible pain? They should derive profit from the work of their ancestors. They should make progress above all, in the school of man. But is it not known that the education of an animal is confined entirely to the senses, that it consists altogether in the relations established between material signs, etc.? We might extend these considerations indefinitely. They all lead to this same conclusion, the animals do not show the effects a spiritual intelligence would necessarily produce, if they possessed it even in its most rudimentary form.

Contrariwise animals show clearly that they are lacking in intelligence; that they *do not know how to reason.* [2] A very great number of facts have been gathered which show

[1] Duilhé de Saint-Projet, *Apologie*, p. 397, points out the traits that distinguish the language of animals from that of man — 1º It is a purely emotional and not rational language. — 2º The animal does not freely manifest its impressions, *non intendit manifestationem*. — 3º The brute is physiologically and absolutely incapable of lying. — 4º The language of the animal is not perfected. See the very interesting study by the abbé Piat, *La personne humaine*, bk. II, chap. IV.

[2] In *Cosmos*, of Mar. 21, 1891, we meet with a number of facts showing that the most cunning animals, such as the monkey, the elephant, the dog, the bee, the ant, lack the reflection that characterizes intelligence. The author gives in this article an excellent study of the subject here treated.

Cf. Fabre, *Souvenirs entomologiques* or *Fabre's book of insects*, retold from Alexander Teixeira de Mathos, Tr. from Fabre's Souv. entom., by Mrs. Rodolph, Stawell, Dodd. He proves that the army worms, beetles, bees, and spiders are totally lacking in the intelligence necessary to solve the most rudimentary problems. These animals and others nevertheless have a marvellous instinct.

hat animals as clever as the monkey, the elephant, the horse, the dog, the bee and the ant, lack that reflection which always characterizes intelligence. I readily comprehend, how the simian race might be too backward to invent matches, or to produce the skilful combination of setting splinters of wood on fire, but when the monkey has seen a fire built in the home of its master and has at hand all the elements for repeating a lesson gone over so many times as in the preparation of a meal, why should it be incapable of a series of acts that otherwise an intelligence must link? Its instinct for imitation will cause it to perform acts sensibly bound together, as the opening and shutting of a door, but in absence of any training of the senses, it becomes incapable of acts which demand personal reasoning. [1] One has often been struck by a certain connection between successive acts of animals; and so has been led to see in this the result of reasoned foresight. As Fouillée [2] expresses it, the series of acts provoked by the appetite begotten of a need, shows the same linking as for organic needs. Each new appetite is in necessary relation with the impression that preceded it. The chain of successive acts is regulated for the conservation of the individual. This connection that our mind discovers after the fact had not of necessity been foreseen by the animal.

From these considerations it follows logically that we are not belittling the animal by confining it within the realm of sensation, sensibility and sense-knowledge, and that the barrier which separates it from man is not

---

[1] This monkey was enclosed in a cage in such a manner as to prevent his opening the cage, it being necessary to push one of the bolts to the right and another to the left. He pushed the two in the same direction and never succeeded in finding the simple combination. Thus also do the savages from Central Africa lay the most conspicuous snares. This snare consists in an urn with a narrow neck containing maize. The monkey can easily introduce its hand, but cannot pull it out when filled with grain. It has no idea of letting go of the corn to set itself free.

[2] Fouillée, *Origine de l'instinct,* in *Revue des Deux Mondes,* Oct. 1886.

encroached upon. But is the barrier so intact on man's
side? Is man really as great as we have said? Is he
not overrated?

The intelligence of savages. One cannot deny the miserable condition of uncivilized nations. Relegated to
some inhospitable corner of the globe, they pass their time
roaming the forests and frequenting the banks of lakes and
streams, or the shore of the ocean, hunting and fishing to
obtain the means of satisfying their hunger. Their language is meagre. Their social organization very rudimentary. Intellectual life has very little place in their
existence. One may say, all their energies are used up
in struggling against death.

Some theorists, whose ideas we cannot accept, regard
the savage as a backward individual, as a retarded member
of the human family, midway between the ape and civilized man. That which is scarcely the outline of an idea
in the animal has already undergone a certain development in the savage. He is represented to us, then, as
a living witness of one phase of the progress that humanity
has made. In the same way as the savage becomes
civilized without change of nature, so the anthropoid
ape became the uncivilized man by simple development
of the same faculties. Thus is bridged over that chasm
which was supposed to exist between man and the brute
beast.

Before entering into a lengthy discussion of this question
of primitive man and the uncivilized man, we shall merely
indicate the principles upon which the solution is based.
For us the savage does not bridge the chasm as is stated.
Whatever be the degree of his inferiority or lack of culture,
he bears unmistakable marks that rank him with the human
family and separate him from the brute. Associate with
him, follow him in the chase, enter the hut where he is
sheltered, enter into relations with him, and you will
soon discover in him an intelligence capable of generaliz-
ing and making abstractions of which a white man might
be proud.

His language is not made up of simple cries expressing

sensations and passions. It is composed of general formulae, few in number [1] it is true, yet numerous enough to
enable you to exchange ideas with him. Let him learn
your language, and, in a short while, he will submit himself to
your instruction. He will follow you into the realm of
metaphysics. You may perhaps even make of him a scientist, a manufacturer, a merchant, an apostle. See how
cunning he is, how he sets his traps. He catches all the
animals, but no animal ever catches him and none reduces
him to servitude. He builds a fire. He clothes himself
in garments. He manufactures implements for the chase,
and if he has leisure, his arrows even go beyond the useful
and give evidence of an artistic sense. We may truthfully
say that we find in him, though in a rudimentary and
imperfect state, all that civilized man possesses including
religion and morality. In the uncivilized man, as in the
civilized man, there is an identity of nature. Only the
development of it differs. But both are separated by the
same characteristics from the beast which possesses merely
sense reactions.

Now look at the uncivilized races in history. Whether
you take the modern savage, or whether you study the
remains of the uncivilized men that inhabited France during
the stone age, you will in either case come to this conclusion
which to us appears of the highest importance, viz. the
savage is intelligent although he may be a backward mem-

---

[1] Still the language is more complicated than is ordinarily supposed. De Quatrefages took for example the Tasmanians, whom he
judged "inferior to the Australians" and whom the traveller Lubbock considered beings scarcely endowed with reason. Now the
Tasmanians had really a wealth of languages. "Let us state in
the first place that all the witnesses testify to the multiplicity of
languages spoken by these islanders... Not less than eight or ten
languages, or dialects are known to some two hundred individuals
taken from various parts of the island... The prisoners, compelled
to live in common instruct one another and thus form a sort of
composite or common language... The Rev. Nixon, Bishop of
Tasmania, had gathered eight children speaking eight languages with
entirely different words..." De Quatrefages, *Hommes fossiles et
hommes sauvages*, p. 330.

ber of the human race, or one that has degenerated.   Indeed
we hope to show later on that the actual Australian, the
miserable Fuegian from Tierra del Fuego, the unfortunate
Morioris, are at present in a lower state than that through
which they have passed; that they have in their language
and in their customs, vestiges of a much higher civilization.   Like-wise the men of Chelles, Saint Acheul, Moustier,
Chapelle aux Saints, the Madeleine, Cro-Magnon and Menton... have left in French soil the remains of a civilization,
which, though rudimentary in certain respects, was nevertheless human, because of the signs of intelligence displayed
in its production.

To sum up.   From whatever aspect we may consider
him, primitive man or the savage is a man of low culture,
but yet a man in the fullest sense of the word.   Whereas
the best trained dog, the most highly educated ape, the
most clever cat, etc., is in a way civilized, but in spite of this
still remains only an animal.   Thus the natural barrier
that we have seen raised between man and the beast remains intact from either side.

The faculties of an infant. [1] —In conformity with their
principles evolutionists pretend that the infant, in the
process of development, repeats all the phases of transition
through which humanity has slowly passed while evolving
from the brute state.   Like the animal the infant is at
first capable only of sensations.   In the measure that it
grows it acquires the faculties which characterize the
man.   Though a mere animal at first it gradually becomes
a man.

The progressive development of the infant is too evident
a fact to be insisted upon.   But the interpretation that
evolutionists give it is absolutely fantastic.   We shall
give one that is conformable to our theory of knowledge
and also entirely logical and unassailable.

---

[1] This subject has been well treated by Saint-Georges-Mivart in his
various works, *The origin of human reason*, chap. v; *Reason and the
infant;—Man*, chap. v-viii; Senderens, *Apologie scientifique*, p. 348
and sq.

To reproduce a thought man needs images, multiple images, combined images. Not only does the thought consist of this combination of images, but the mind elaborates a thought only by employing numerous images as so many documents. Now before the human intelligence can elaborate and manifest thoughts with precision, it is essential that the senses be educated, that the brain be duly developed, that its various component parts be formed and well differentiated. All this requires time. Sometimes, if the infant remains without instruction and is not made to think, this time may extend beyond five or six years. At other times, if the education is well conducted or the temperament more favorable, the first glimmer of thought will appear at a much earlier period. Certain precocious children have given signs of intelligence as early as two years or even earlier. We do not say that the intelligence commences or is developed in the child, but that it is exercised and acquires ideas in proportion as the child grows. The child is born with an intelligent soul; his intelligence acts when the conditions are right.

Shall we say that such is the condition of the intelligence in apes, and that it is merely not exercised by them?[1] If this is so, let us try not indeed to hasten, but merely to realize by a careful education the transition to a state of activity. Who does not see that our efforts will be in vain? Who does not see that the infant is not in the brute stage of its individual evolution, but that it follows the laws of development proper to its human nature?

To sum up this part of our study, we shall say that arguments alleged in favor of the identity of nature in

---

[1] Mivart, speaking of Romanes' objection that the intelligence is equally existent in the beast and in the child, borrows the following excellent scholastic distinction : "In the child, intelligence *exists* really but it is *in potentia ad actum*; the proof for this is that in the measure as the child develops, the exercise of the intelligence is manifested. In the beast intelligence is only *in potentia ad esse*, for God could perhaps (?) have placed it there; the proof that it is nonexistent is that no exercise of it is ever manifest." Mivart, *The origin of human reason.* p. 215.

man and the brute are not very weighty, and that our thesis
of a real distinction has not been shaken, and so we have
reason to invoke a force superior to evolution for the crea
tion of the human soul.   Was the human body that re
ceived the first human soul, also the direct result of a divine
creative act?   This second question we shall now consider.

§ IV.—ORIGIN OF THE HUMAN BODY.
TRANSFORMIST ARGUMENTS.

In the sixth work of creation, Genesis represents the
Creator proceeding by two distinct acts to form the first
man.   First, he fashioned the body of man "from the
slime of the earth" (Gen., II, 7).   Then He animated it
with a vital breath, communicating to it the life of a spirit.
This spirit, we have proved, could not be the result of a
nature in a state of progress.   God had to create it by an
act of His omnipotence.   But the body, this "slime" to
which He imparted human life—what was it?   How was it
fashioned into a human body?   Two hypotheses are possible.
Either God made all the parts of the human organism by
fittingly disposing the inorganic elements; or He chose to
raise to the dignity of a human being the most perfect
organism resulting from a long evolution of living matter
during preceding ages. [1]

It is this second hypothesis that the evolutionists
embrace.   Some, who are materialists in their philosophy
teach that along with the human body the whole man
evolved from the animal state.   We have already shown how
they make the mistake of not distinguishing between the
body and the soul.   The others of spiritualistic persuasion,
claim that the "slime" of which Holy Scripture speaks
might have been an organism previously prepared according to a definite plan of God through evolution.   It is
with these alone that we have to deal. [2]

---

[1] Lemonnyer, *La révélation primitive*, Paris, Gabalda, p. 121-145.
[2] The Rev. Brucker vigorously opposes this opinion.   "Is this
restrictive interpretation acceptable? No.   First because the very

Those Catholics who follow Mivart [1] have applied evolution to the human body, but cannot adduce any real evidence on a subject that is beyond human science. They

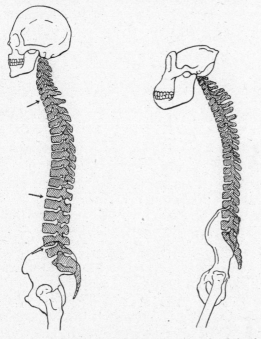

Figs. 62 and 63. — Head, vertebral column and pelvis of man and of gorilla. (M. Boule.)

ive only arguments that establish the possibility or probability, but no real scientific proofs. These arguments

xpressive text of Moses certainly says more than that taken by very reader who approaches it without bias... In the recital which ngages us (Holy Scripture) not only does not in any way indicate hat there is question of a *mediate* action of God, (but) it multiplies s by design the marks that give the idea of a special, direct intervention... Our interpretation of verse 7 is singularly confirmed by ther texts in goodly number, in which the formation of the first man s referred to in more or less detail." *Questions actuelles d'Écriture ainte*, p. 235, 236.

[1] "My *Genesis of species*" says Mivart "was published in 1870,

as we shall see are drawn from the works of evolutionists
and are in part based on some reasons of fitness that ar
of little importance. Like Darwin, transformists invok
in favor of their theory : 1. the similarity of organic struc
ture in man and the higher animals ; 2. the absence of any
real gap between the organism of man and that of the apes
3. the facts of human embryology; 4. the rudimentary
organs; and 5. atavistic phenomena. [1]

That there is a certain organic ressemblance between the
body of man and that of the higher animals is undeniable
Long before the rise of transformism, it was universally

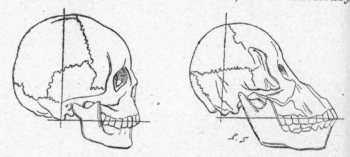

Figs. 64 and 65.—Skulls of orang outang and of man compared.

admitted that man had no special organ that was not to
be found in the mammals; that his brain is distinguished
less in form than in development from that of the apes.
Never have the spiritual philosophers who defined man as
"a reasonable animal" sought in the body of man the
basis for a specific distinction between man and the brute.
They have always frankly confessed that in the structure
of his organs and in his vital functions man is a vertebrate,

and I do not hesitate to advance in this book the idea that the body
of Adam had to be derived from an animal other than man, in which
a reasonable soul had subsequently been infused. Great outcries
have been made against this idea, but I sent my book to the Sovereign Pontiff, and, soon after, Pius IX kindly accorded me the doctor's
hat which the regretted Cardinal Archbishop of Westminster sent
me in a public ceremony." *The nineteenth Century*, Feb. 1893.

[1] E. Perrier, *Le transformisme*, chap. III, Paris, 1888.

a mammal, a primate. Though the organs manifest considerable resemblance, they nevertheless present some profound differences of adaptation and of development characteristic of the human species. Thus, the structure adapted to an upright position, the curvatures of the spinal column, the very special shape of the vertebræ, the ribs and the pelvis, (figs. 62 and 63), the anatomical differences of the hands and of the feet, the disposition of the hair, the shape of the nose, the development of the brain, the shape of the skull and the manner in which the bones are joined (figs. 64 and 65) the special dentition, etc., are so may traits that have induced scientists to class the human races in the one same species. This species is the only one of the genus. This genus is the only one of the family; This family of the bimana joins the quadrumana only in the order of the primates [1]. Cuvier long ago said : "Man is the only animal that has a very large skull and a very

[1] To bring out the isolated position of man in the classification of animals, we give that of the Primates to which he belongs anatomically.

ORDER	SUB-ORDER	FAMILY	GENUS	SPECIES
Primates :	Bimana	Hominidæ	Homo	Sapiens
	Quadrumanae or Monkeys or Apes	Catarrhinæ or Old World Monkeys with 32 teeth	Anthropoids	Chimpanzee Gorilla Orang outan Gibbon
			Cynoids	Cyncephales Macaques Ceropithecus Semnopithecus
		Platyrrhinæ or New World Monkeys with 44 teeth	Cebidæ	Sajous Sapajous Ateles Saîmiris Sakis
			Arctopithici	Ouistitis Tamaris.
	Lemurians or Prosimians	Lemuridæ	Loris Makis	
		Tarsiers Cheiromydæ Galeopithecidae		

small face; the animals deviate more and more from these proportions as they become more stupid or more ferocious. " Boule [1] personally demonstrated the profound anatomical differences between man and the brute, particularly with reference to the feet.

"A difference which the great English anatomist Owen considered as fundamental, is observed in the conformation of the foot. In the anthropoid apes, the first digit is very short, much shorter in fact than all the others, and is advantageously placed opposite to the latter so as

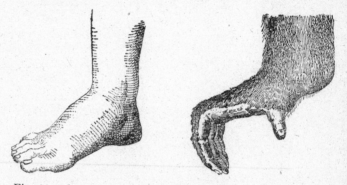

Figs 66 and 67.—Comparison of foot of man and of the monkey.

to function as a thumb. The foot thus becomes a hand... In man, the big toe, is the largest of the digits. It is pressed close to the others and cannot be opposed to them. We are dealing with a true foot, that is to say, with an organ of support. This adaptation to a function so exclusive is repeated in all the bones, and so are morphologically different from all the bones of the posterior hand, or if you will, of the prehensile foot of the anthropoid apes" (figs. 66 and 67).

So Owen concludes : "In spite of the existence of some transitory phenomena, observed in certain apes and certain men, all these characters are practically so determined as to render impossible any confounding of the highest of the

[1] *Les hommes fossiles*, p. 78, Paris, Masson, 1921.

living apes with the lowest of actual men." Paleontology, whatever one may say of it, has not effaced these anatomical differences in the opinion of Boule. "We must confess that paleontology has not revealed any indisputable transition form, any material proof of a descendent coming from an ape form to a human form."

Darwin tried to weaken the importance of these *differentiating marks* by showing that "each of them taken singly is found in a certain number of the higher animals" and are lacking in a certain number of men belonging to the inferior races. Here is how he argues : "Among the apes," says he, "the extreme types do not necessarily resemble each other. The difference, it is true, never goes as far as in man, but it exists in certain cases. Sometimes, as in man, it is the lower member, that seems to become a foot; sometimes, the reverse of that which is met with in man, it is the thumb of the fore-hand that ceases to be opposable. In man there is a tendency for the big toe to become opposable; this fact is often noticed in the human embryo, but only persists in certain uncivilized races."

The method employed by Darwin, in looking for resemblances between man and the ape is absolutely faulty. To have any value it should look for a type that possesses them all rather than a group of beings, each of which has some one of them. The resemblances of which he speaks are exaggerated. The big toe, for instance, never tends to become opposable. It might turn slightly away from the others to become prehensile but no more. In the quadrumana the hand never has a tendency to become a foot. It is a hand made for grasping. When applied to the ground it rests on the edge or on the knuckles.

According to Darwin and Haeckel, the organism of man, *during its embryonic development* follows the same course as that of the higher animals. Like them man passes through stages in which he shows points of resemblance with the states that are permanent in certain inferior animals. Doesn't this show that he repeats in an abridged form the stages through which the species passes before obtaining its final perfection? Do we not, even, see " certain organs developing temporarily only to disappear before the end of the embryonic period, although they continue permanent in the lower groups, as for instance the Wolfian bodies corresponding to the kidneys in the fish, the second aortic arch, that only begins to exist in the reptiles, the lanugo that, up to the sixth month, covers the entire fetus with the exception of the palms of the hand and the soles of the feet, is similar to the permanent fleece of certain mammals?" Thus he showed the relationship of the human body with the animal organisms. We shall merely answer that man, being like the animals subject to the law of development, ought to pass through similar, but not identical stages. [1] In fact, all the beings are so completely differentiated from the beginning that even the germinal cells differ from one another.

This fact of passing through the most simple stages like the animal is a condition, a necessity of development, and by no means a repetition of ancestral traits. These stages cannot be arrested since they are not viable in him or in any other organisms.

This connection between man and the other organisms, is said to be, even more apparent in the *rudimentary organs.* These imperfect organs, which are rather numerous and absolutely functionless in man represent organs that play a more or less important role in certain animals. Might not this be a sign of a common ancestry for men and animals? Might not such organs have become atrophied in the branch from which the human species has sprung, while continuing to develop in the other branches of the same stock? Darwin cites the motor muscles of the outer ear (*The Descent of Man*, p. 31), the remnant of the nicti-tating membrane or third eyelid so well developed in the birds (*Hist.*, 35), the hair, (*ibid.*, 37) and certain arrangements of the bones (71 et sq.). The pretended rudimentary organs of man are less numerous than Darwin and his school maintained. The development of physio-

---

[1] Cf. Vialletton, *Un problème de l'évolution*, p. 225-232, Paris, Masson.

logy has brought out that these supposed rudimentary organs, including the vermiform appendix, in reality a gland, actually function during life, while others seem necessary for the life of the embryo. Some, are common to both sexes, although characteristic of only one of them, as if the organism in the course of its development was susceptible of indifferently acquiring one sex or the other. So one may say that there is nothing which might be considered a positive proof of a former state essentially different from the actual.

Indications of animal ancestry are also sought for in the monstrosities or abnormalities of the human body. Every one knows that *atavism* is a natural law, in virtue of which a living being tends to reproduce the characters of its ancestors. This phenomenon of heredity often operates in very strange ways. Thus, an exceptional trait of one parent may be transmitted to the offspring for several consecutive generations, then will disappear for several generations, only to reappear again unexpectedly in certain isolated cases. Now since some unforeseen characters that make their appearance suddenly in certain children, are really inherited from some ancestors who possessed them, one may, in virtue of these facts of atavism, reconstruct the history of a family or of a species. Now, the human organism is subject to certain variations, and these abnormalities do not appear altogether without order. In fact, they generally tend to resemble some inferior type and most frequently that of the apes. When an important anomaly appears, it is always accompanied by many others in the same direction. Thus, according to Carl Vogt, microcephalic idiots have also prominent eyebrows, sloping and depressed foreheads and very prognathous jaws.

Let us say with de Quatrefages, that these anomalies give more evidence of being monstrosities than real atavistic facts, and that their connection is inevitable, hence without value. They are often due to a simple arrested development. [1]

---

[1] Cf. *Revue des questions scientifiques*, vol. xxxv, p. 563 et sq.

Struck by the following facts that we are about to analyze, certain Catholic authors have been inclined to hold that the human body, after all, might have been formed by way of evolution. The text of the Bible has not appeared to them so explicit as to exclude this opinion. It might well be, say they, that God formed the body of man, mediately through the agency of natural laws and not immediately from inorganic matter. For, whether the matter was in an inorganic or an organic state, it was still the "slime of the earth". [1] In this hypothesis there would be a certain grandeur, in considering the human body which is the most perfect of organisms as the climax of evolution of all living beings, and the result the Creator had in mind from the beginning to give to nature its intelligent master. Thus, we should have a better understanding of the physical relations of man with

---

[1] Here are a few important quotations on this subject. "I shall not permit myself to censure the opinion of the English theologian Mivart so long as it shall be respected, or at least tolerated by the Church, the only judge competent to determine and to qualify the theologico-dogmatic propositions, and to decide if they are in harmony or not in harmony with Holy Scripture." Card. Gonzalès, *La Biblia y a Ciencia*, vol. i, p. 542.—Father Dierckw, quoting the words of the eminent cardinal and theologian, declares "that he takes pride in holding the same wiews as Cardinal Gonzalès." *Revue des questions scientifiques*, July, 1894.—Canon Duilhé de Saint-Projet, after having stated his preferences for the "traditional doctrine touching the immediate formation of the body of man," adds : "But, in our soul and conscience, we do not believe we have the right to impose it for the present as certitude of divine faith. We do not allow ourselves to qualify with any unfavorable note the contrary opinion.   We do not believe we can say to Catholics seeking for the truth in good faith : "You are not free to think otherwise, you are not free to investigate." *Apologie scientifique*, p. 272, note. —At the Catholic Congress of 1894, the same author made practically the same declaration. *Comptes rendus*, section d'anthropologie, p. 10.—At the Catholic Congress in Paris, in 1891, Mgr. D'Hulst said : "Of the other limits to the transformistic hypothesis, rigorous orthodoxy imposes only the dogma of the immediate creation of each human soul by God : outside of this, if there is any rashness in these hypotheses it is by scientific arguments that they are to be combatted." *Comptes rendus*, 1891, section d'anthropologie, p. 213.

the rest of nature. We see all beings linked together in one harmonious whole; the millions of species that have disappeared before the advent of man, would thus have an explanation were we to consider them the elements of a mighty tree at the pinnacle of which God would place the human organism. Some, it is true, feel a certain repugnance to this idea, that the organic ancestors, not indeed of man, but of the human body, should have been beasts, more or less allied to the apes, but has not St. Thomas taught that each human individual before receiving its human form passes through phases of plant and animal life? [1] Such are the reasons of fitness given by the authors who believe in the possibility, and even the probability of an animal descent for the human organism. All this is purely hypothetical, as appears from what we have already said. [2] What little plausibility there may be in it loses a great deal of its value in face of the serious objections of the opponents.

§ V.—Arguments against the materialistic evolution of Darwin, Haeckel, Romanes, le Dantec, etc.

The arguments we propose to give are drawn in part from certain evolutionists, and in part from the simple principles of reason. The problem of man's origin was not solved by Darwin, much less by Haeckel. Every true scientist must admit that the arguments brought forward cannot convey conviction, in as much as they are weak, superficial and in contradiction to very evident facts and the data of reason. Evolutionists themselves recognize this as we may gather from their own writings. [2] Witness

---

[1] Here is the text of St. Thomas in which he expresses this opinion which was also a classic in the Middle Ages : *Anima igitur vegetabilis, quæ primo inest, cum embryo vivit vita plantæ, corrumpitur, et succedit anima perfectior, quæ est nutritiva et sensitiva simul, et tunc embryo vivit vita animali*; *hac autem corrupta, succedit anima rationalis ab extrinseco immissa, licet præcedentes fuerint virtute seminis.* , *Contra Gentiles*, lib. II, c. LXXXIX.

[2] Cf. Depéret, *Transformations of the animal World*, p. 40.

the following. [1] "This burning question of man's origin has been too often raised against Darwin, either by scientists or more often by philosophers and methodologists for the author of *The origin of species* to evade a decisive answer. It is perhaps, in this answer, that the contrast that characterizes the work of Darwin on so many points, so clearly stands out. On the one hand, there is the admirable ingenuity of Darwin in his comparative studies of the anatomical, intellectual and psychical character of man and of animals, on the other, the really surprising weakness of positive arguments and of precise facts, relative to the real reconstruction of the human branch." In the body of his text Depéret gives the argument and concludes (p. 43) : "It is to these truly rudimentary estimates, drawn, for the most part, from the works of Huxley, Kowalsky and Goodsir, that the unique attempt by Darwin to reconstruct the genealogy of one of the branches of human beings is reduced. Will it be too severe to conclude, that paleontologically, at least, the question of the origin of species still remains unchanged?" We shall cite an argument used by Wallace to demonstrate the intervention of a higher power in the formation of the human body. These considerations have all the more value for us, since Wallace is one of the most ardent advocates of evolution and shares with Darwin the glory of having, through his theory of natural selection given a scientific aspect to transformism. Undoubtedly Wallace derives the human body from the animal, but in his eyes, this body owed the faculties which characterize it, to a divine intervention. God might have intervened directly to give the human form to an organism prepared by evolution.

Without admitting all the ideas of the learned Englishman, we can draw profit from his argumentation to show that science itself inclines to the idea that God intervened immediately in the formation of the human organism.

---

[1] Wallace, *Natural selection — Essays, The World of life.* —See de Quatrefages, *Espèce humaine*, p. 85, and *Origine de l'homme*, dans la *Revue scientifique*, Aug. 1890.

Wallace starts from the principle *that natural selection produces nothing that might be harmful or even useless to the species.* This principle is so fundamental in the transformist theory, that in the opinion of Darwin himself, one simple contrary instance would be enough to overthrow it. Selection, in fact, above all aims at "immediate and personal utility". It can only eliminate and not preserve a harmful or useless character. "Then", says Wallace, "if we find in man characters that have become hurtful to him since their first appearance, it will be evident that they could not have been produced by natural selection. It would be the same for the special development of an organ, if this development were either merely useless, or exaggerated as regards its utility. Similar examples might prove that another law or another force than natural selection had come into play."

The principle once established, Wallace studied the human organism and drew attention to the *characters that are either useless or harmful to the organism that have developed in the process of its formation.* We give some examples drawn from his work. According to Wallace and the entire transformist school, the present savage represents the condition of primitive man. We shall see later on what must be thought of this. For the present, let us merely follow the author. "Now", says he "the present savage and in consequence primitive man presents a perfect *anatomical identity* with civilized man. Still the organs, that in civilized man, exercise a high functional activity were relatively useless to primitive man. The hands so skilful in delicate work, the larynx so well formed for the varied and complicated sounds of modern music were an absolutely useless perfection in primitive man. This perfection was an assembly of latent qualities that would not be required until much later." We must say as much for the brain. The quantity of cerebral matter, is known to have a real connection with intellectual phenomena and this quantity is measured by the cranial capacities. Now in primitive man, as in the modern savage, the cranial capacity is sensibly the same (about 1500 cc.) and ever removed by the same distance from the cranial capacity of the apes, which have on an average only 500 cc. There is then in the savage and in primitive man, an excess of force, an instrument that surpasses the needs of the possessor, a power or source of activity that is not utilized, but that will be put into operation only in proportion to the progress of civilization. Since natural selection has for its essential character the elevation of each species to an organization conformable to its needs and of *never exceeding them*, it cannot bring about an organic development in view of the future.

Among harmful characters, Wallace mentions the almost complete nudity of the human body. How could natural selection deprive man of so useful a protection as the hair? He also claims that the shape of the foot is a disadvantage to man. It would have been very useful to primitives to have the big toes of the feet and the thumbs of the hands opposable to the other digits in the four members, as in the quadrumana.

In the domain of the intellectual faculties, nearly all the characters are beyond the scope of natural selection. Selection might perhaps, have been able to develop the notions of *justice and benevolence*; for though they are useless to the individuals, as contrary to the law of the strongest, they are eminently useful to society. But the abstract notions of time, place, eternity, infinity, or the artistic sense or the mathematical mind, could not have been of any use to man in his primitive state.

The origin of the *moral sense* is no less inexplicable. The savages attach a notion of holiness to certain actions considered as good and moral, in opposition to those which are considered as merely useful. Selection cannot make the moral sense prevail over the utilitarian sense : it cannot cause a duty or a promise to be preferred, even to the preservation of life.

The origin of *the religious sense*, of which Wallace does not speak is just as mysterious. The generous sacrifices of the martyrs dying in defense of their faith, the renunciation by religious of even legitimate natural inclinations are certainly not inspired by the desire to conquer in the struggle for life.

The examples given, suffice to establish the fact that *natural selection cannot explain the formation of man.* Limiting ourselves to the organism, we must say with Wallace, that he is not the work of Nature alone. But if selection does not suffice, is *it absolutely necessary to have recourse to a Superior Power?* "Yes," says Wallace, and these are his reasons : selection is the only natural means that science can propose to account for the origin of living beings, and it is insufficient to produce man. In man everything seems to be prepared in advance for his future needs. The aptitude of the brain, the perfection of the organism. Now the natural forces respond only to present need. They are incapable of foresight, hence "a directive action is exercised on man". Hence the human body is not the result of blind selection.

In concluding our analysis of this argument, we shall observe that the evolutionary origin of the human body must present some rather serious difficulties,solely from the standpoint of the transformist laws, if so ardent an evolutionist as Wallace separated and remained separated from nearly his entire school, on this point. These difficulties will stand out more clearly, when we come to study the arguments proposed by de Quatrefages.

The third argument, the basis for which we draw from this eminent anthropologist is an *argumentum ad hominem.* [1] Provisionally accepting as demonstrated the principles of transformism, it leads to a conclusion diametrically opposed to the animal descent of the human organism. Let us suppose that the different races originated from the same common stock. Agassiz, it is true, thought that the human groups had begun by so many distinct creations, but this opinion has always been rejected by Catholics. Vogt held that the different simian stocks had given rise to the various branches of the human species, but in this he

[1] De Quatrefages, *L'espèce humaine,* chap. xi.—See also the excellent work of de Nadaillac, *Le Problème de la vie,* chap. vi and vii.

stands apart from the great majority of writers on evolution. Nearly all, particularly Darwin and Haeckel believe in the unity of origin for the human races.

Haeckel, to whom Darwin voluntarily referred his readers who were curious to know the human genealogy, places man in the twenty-second link of a long chain that begins with the simple moner. In the seventeenth degree of evolution appear the marsupials—lower mammals like the opossum and the kangaroo. The prosimians, represented today by the lemurs and the loris, mark the eighteenth. The nineteenth comprises the tailed catarrhines as the cynocephali (hamadryas) the cercopitheci (guenon) and the semnopitheci. The tailless catarrhines or anthropoid apes, as the orang outang, the gorilla, the chimpanzee and the gibbon form the twentieth. Between these anthropoid apes to man, the interval is quite large. To bridge it Haeckel created a twenty-first stage with the man-ape or pithecus, to which he allowed no language or self-consciousness. Finally man himself appeared in the twenty second stage.

These preliminaries so briefly set forth here show how de Quatrefages argumentation proceeds. The *law of permanent characterization*, accepted by all evolutionists, tells us that an organism, once modified in a determined direction, will no longer be able to vary in another antagonistic direction. Two distinct organic types can readily originate from one common ancestor not yet definitely characterized (supposing one exists), but they cannot descend one from the other. Now in man, and in the apes, the organs correspond exactly with one another, but they are disposed according to a very different plan. Thus all parts of man are arranged for a being that walks, while every part of the ape is adapted to one that climbs. It is contrary to the principles of transformism to make a walking animal descend from a climbing animal. Therefore it is necessary to go back beyond all the simians, beyond the prosimians even, to find a type not yet characterized as a climber. Thus we arrive at the didelphic type of kangaroo that oc-

cupies the seventeenth rung of Haeckel's ladder. But the
didelphs or marsupials themselves are already characterized
anatomically and physiologically. Hence we must go
back still farther to find the common ancestor, and even
then we always meet with the same difficulty.

What do modern evolutionists think of Haeckel's genealogical tree? Depéret gives his opinion of it in his *Transformations du monde animal.* In exposing Haeckel's
hypothesis he says that all these genealogical views are
extremely superficial, and for the greater part at least, we
may say altogether inaccurate. On page 57 he says "If we
submit the twenty two stages of Haeckel's human genealogy to the control of paleontology, we must first note, that
the first nine stages are altogether unknown in the fossil
state." The tenth, eleventh and fourteenth are not the
ancestors of the subsequent stages, since these latter are
contemporaneous if not anterior.

"Haeckel, arriving at the fifteenth stage, fimds himself
confronted by the problem of the first appearance of the
mammal type. He solves it by imagining two hypothetical
types, complete in all respects and without analogy in
the living world, nor among fossilized animals, called the
protamniotes and the promammalia. These types are
intended to fill up the great gap that separates the lower
mammals or monotremes from the salamandriform amphibians with which the author tries to connect them."
Arriving at the mammals, the seventeenth stage, Haeckel
admits that the primitive mammals have had to pass the
monotrematous and marsupial stages, but the transition
types between the marsupials and placentals are entirely
unknown to us.

To Depéret the eighteenth or prosimian stage, similar
to the lemurs derived from the marsupials, does not appear
any better demonstrated than the transition from the lemurs
to the catarrhines. "One must confess that the exact
origin of the order of apes is entirely unknown to us."
On page 60, "We have shown in the preceding pages the
very general weakness of the paleontological arguments
invoked by Haeckel in all the chapters of his work, and

the complete collapse of the majority of his fundamental hypotheses".

If paleontology does not confirm the theories of Haeckel, must we adhere to his embryogenetic or ontogenetic method, and accept as demonstrated the biogenetic law upon which he has built up his whole system? We do not think so. This law is only an undemonstrated and undemonstrable hypothesis as Vialleton recognized and proved and as we have mentioned above.   The best he could do to bolster up his theory of embryonic resemblance, was to make a threefold reproduction of the same cut and give each a different name, and then to challenge the reader to find the least difference between them. [1]

Having discovered in this same work and in the *Anthropogenic evolution of Man*, some purely fictitious and some altered drawings, His says of Haeckel "that he juggled heedlessly with facts" and should be denied the right to "be counted among reputable scientists". Rutimeyer calls this falsification "a scientific hoax". [2] No evolutionist of any prominence accepts Haeckel's series, because of its superficiality and too great simplicity. The various genealogical trees built up by other evolutionists, since Darwin and Haeckel, do not seem to have any more value, if we take into account the divergencies and contradictions that we find in them.

Boule, [3] in his work *Les hommes fossiles* (1921) declares as inadmissible the more recent genealogical trees of Gregory (1916), Keith (1915), Pilgrim, (1915) Sera (1917) and Bonarelli (1919). "A comparison of their tables only increases, if possible, our reserve, for there are in these various graphs, considerable, even fundamental differences. The most prudent conclusion we may come to, is that the group of anthropoids is still "up in the air", and that we do not yet know exactly whether to insert the human

[1] The first edition of his *History of Creation*, p. 242-248.
[2] Quoted by Wasmann : *La probité scientifique d'Haeckel*, p. 8 sq.
[3] Cf. *Les hommes fossiles*, p. 448 and 107; Teilhard in *Revue de philosophie*, April, 1923, p. 116 et sq.

line on a branch or on one of the neighboring offshoots. There are as many hypotheses as authors.

Boule shows in fact how some evolutionists connect man with the pithecanthropes, others with the anthropoid apes, such as the chimpanzee, gibbon, orang outang, gorilla; others with the cynomorphic apes, as the macaques,

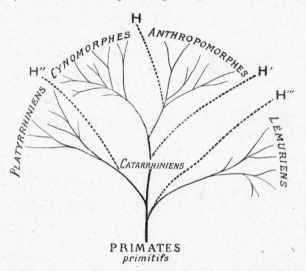

Fig. 68.—Diagram (by Boule) showing the different hypotheses invented to show the genealogical relation of Mend (H) with the other groups of Primates.

ceropitheci and semnopitheci; others with a single unknown catarrhine; others join him to a branch of the platyrrhines either among the cebians or among the arctopitheci, while a number hold it necessary to go back even farther either to the lemurs of the present day or to some unknown primitive lemurian type (fig. 68).

Despairing of their cause, some authors seek the hypothetical ancestor among the rodents, the suidæ (swine), or the marsupials. There are as many gratuitous hypotheses as authors. Let us patiently wait until evolutionists agree among themselves before discussing any particular genealogical tree. Science can not be made up of such uncertain hypotheses without forfeiting its claim to the name of science.

Since one or several *intermediate* organic types had to precede actual man and must supply the links that bind him to the common stock; and since these types in the process of becoming man should be represented by types that have acquired and preserved characteristics in each stage of their organization; how does it happen that no living branch represents the trunk which produced the human species? Must it be said that these intermediate types were imperfect and so had to disappear in the struggle for existence? But, why have not the ancestors of the anthropoid apes disappeared also? Why should the human intermediates have had less chance to survive than the intermediate apes?

Now, as a matter of fact, no living species represents the desired intermediates. Haeckel frankly says that the pithecoid man no longer exists. He must have existed, but he is no longer represented. What, if we looked for the intermediates that are to unite us with the marsupials? It would be a strange aberration to take uncivilized man as the missing link, since, both from the standpoint of organism and of intelligence, he is a man in the fullest sense of the word. Mereover, no serious scientist has ever taken them for pithecoids. All that has ever been said, is that they were backward members of the human family. We shall see later on in what sense this assertion must be taken.

If the human organism is connected with the animals by one or more links, geology ought to reveal to us the remains or the traces of the intermediate ancestors. As actual man is far removed from the marsupials or even from the tailed catarrhines, and as a transformation of species takes place only very slowly, these intermediates should have existed a very long time ago, and should have left numerous traces as have all the other animals. But the paleontologist is obliged to confess his ignorance of the ancestors of man.

The traces of early man are numerous. But, far from

supporting the thesis of the animal origin of man, all the evidence from this source tends to overthrow it. Indeed, as far back as one may go, man is always decidedly a man. We cannot verify this slow and ascending progress of an organism emerging from animality. Thus, the oldest human skulls have unmistakably the same shape, the same capacity as our own; the smallest, those of the Neanderthal race are far removed from the simian skulls and at least the equal of human skulls of modern times. Likewise there is not a human bone that does not clearly bear a human impress. [1] Whenever we come across the fossils of man, we find also the traces of his industry—weapons, tools, pictures, signs of fire... Hence, as we shall see later, as soon as man appears he resembles in all respects, both in body and in intelligence, man as we find him among all the living races today.

From the standpoint of organism man in our classification of living beings and of fossils, is and remains the only one of the species, the only one of the genus *homo sapiens*, the only one of the family humans and the only one of the suborder bimanæ.

If we should take into account, in these classifications, his whole nature, that is, include his intelligent and free soul, man according to de Quatrefages would constitute by himself alone the human kingdom. In the opinion even

---

[1] On the subject of the *Driopithecus* that de Mortillet regarded as the precursor of the human species (anthropopithecus) of which Lartet writes "that it is the only fossil monkey that has been compared with man" Gaudry said in 1890 before the " Académie des Sciences" : "The *Driopithecus*, judging from what we possess, is not only far removed from man, but is even inferior to many of the actual monkeys. As it is the highest of the great fossil monkeys, we ought to recognize, that up to the present *paleontology has not furnished any intermediate between man and these animals*".

Cf. Boule, *op. cit.*, p. 84 and fol. He is of the same opinion. The discoveries made by Dubois, in Java, in 1891 and 1892, do not solve the problem of an intermediate either. Here is what Virchow said in 1895 : "I cannot admit that this pithecanthropus is the link between the monkey and man."

of Boule, who excludes the Neanderthal man, the pithecanthropus and all the actual apes from the line of man's
ancestors, the characters of resemblance that evolutionists
must discover between man and the apes, in passing from
the Neanderthalic and the Pithecanthropic types are
really too *superficial* to admit a transition from one to the
other.   Boule attaches great importance to the shape of
the skull of the Chapelle-aux-Saints man of the Neanderthal race.

We must not forget that the human race is as plastic
as all the animal species; that any particular variation can
be brought about under the influence of environment and
living conditions and converge towards a more specialized
form, which it would be incorrect to liken to a simian
form.   The characters that separate the Neanderthal
from the simian type are far more important than the
more or less superficial resemblances.   The hypothesis
that the Neanderthal race is a degenerate race is more
scientific, more explicative than that of a supposed evolution of whose antecedents or of whose derivatives we
know nothing.   Furthermore, we shall repeat with Boule,
the actual races do not descend from the Neanderthal
race, hence the argument is without value.

The Piltdown race, if one existed, [1] presents very few
degenerate characters, and Boule does not hesitate to
hold it a normally constituted race and the true ancestor
of actual races.   Certain details of conformation are unim-
portant.   One may find the more important ones in the
actual races.   From what has been said, it follows that
man was the same throughout time and space, and that he
possessed his actual organic perfection from his very beginning, and that in consequence, he constitutes an isolated
type, superior to any of the animal species.   This then
is the reason for saying in the beginning of this work,

---

[1] Cf. McCann, *God and Gorilla* for Piltdown man exposure.   On
page 8 he says : ' The Piltdown remains disclose the ease with which
"missing links" between apes and men can be fabricated by resort
to wide stretches of imagination in support of preconceived opinions.

that Science itself inclines to the belief that the Creator at the moment when He resolved to form man, fashioned him directly or at least completed an organism that was to be vivified by a spiritual soul.

In establishing as a scientifically sound thesis, that God is truly the Creator of man, since the human soul has to be imparted by Him and not come by way of evolution, we have merely confirmed the Biblical doctrine. If the commentators on Holy Scripture hold that the Sacred Text formally teaches that God immediately fashioned the body of man, we shall have to sacrifice nothing in the domain of science, and we shall willingly adhere to their opinion. If they think the text is not explicit, we shall say then, that we too feel some uncertainty on this point, for of themselves the scientific reasons are incapable of definitively binding us to either hypothesis. The only very clear statement of the Church on this question of the origin of man is the answer of the Biblical Commission given June 30, 1909. We have already cited it *in extenso* in the first chapter. In the third answer, it says that the Bible teaches us "the special creation of man". We have shown, that this solution even from the scientific stand point, is beyond question. But the Biblical Commission does not say—and undoubtedly lacks some of the elements necessary for a decision—what material God used to create man. It seems, that for the present the Bible and the Church leave the matter open to conjecture.

To sum up this rather lengthy study. There is no doubt that man was created by God in virtue of a special intervention. Whatever be the teaching of evolutionists on the subject of animal, or plant species, man is not the result of evolution .

Granted that man is specifically such, because of his soul, it is in the creation of the human soul that God has created man.

Without departing from the data of Science and of reason, we can give as the best established, the opinion of those who make the Creator intervene even to fashion the body of man, and to impart to him the traits that characterize his organism so that, even from the stand point of his body man descended neither from the apes nor from any other animal.

As for knowing what "slime" God took to form the human organsim, it is a point on which we have no evidence.

CHAPTER VI

UNITY OF THE HUMAN SPECIES

§ I.—Classification of the human races.

Before taking up or even outlining the question that we are about to treat, we think it necessary to give a few brief notions about the different classes of humanity. This will be the surest means of giving a correct idea of the similarities that connect, and the differences that separate the human races, when we come to give a fuller appreciation of them further on.

This section is positive and is evidently beyond discussion. Every one can tell whether a living being belongs to the human family or not. The information on color, anatomical form, etc., of a people is within the compass of all.

Numerous authors have attempted to classify the human races. These classifications differ notably, because they have not been built up on the same fundamental characters. As there exists no character that can be regarded as clearly dominant, it follows, that each classification is more or less arbitrary and artificial. We shall take up the principal ones.

That of Linnaeus was based upon geographical distribution. It distinguished the European, the Asiatic, the American and the African type. This order was, after all quite natural, for generally speaking, Europeans have some anatomical features that distinguish them from Asiatics, etc... Yet how many different types there are in Europe, Asia and America!...

Blumenbach classified the human races into five groups.

As a basis he relied chiefly on the color of the skin, but did not overlook the other characters. Dumeril did not merely use color as the sole element of his classification, but taking the traits as a whole he recognized five principal groups, Caucasians, Hyperborians, Mongolians, Negroes and Americans. According to Virey, the human genus is divided into two groups, the first having a facial angle greater than 85° comprising a white race, a swarthy race (the Mongolians) and a copper-colored race (the Americans); the second having a facial angle less than 85° comprising a dark brown race (the Malays) a black race (the Ethiopians) and a blue-black race (the Hottentots). According to Bory de Saint-Vincent, Geoffroy Saint-Hilaire, Haeckel and Huxley, the classifications should start with the texture of the hair as the most important characteristic. Thus Haeckel distinguishes races with glossy hair and races with woolly hair. The glossy hair is either stiff and wiry as in the Australians, Hyperborians, Americans and Malays, or curly as in the Dravidians and Mediterranians. The woolly hair either grows in tufts or is distributed over the entire head like fleece. But, in the groups so formed are found men with anatomical features so different, that one cannot consider this classification as anything but artificial. For example, the Dravidians with long heads and dark complexion have glossy, curly hair like the Celts who have round heads and fair complexion.

Cuvier based his classification on color. De Quatrefages closely followed him. The major divisions are based on color and the minor on other anatomical characters. In this way we obtain three main groupes: Whites or Caucasians, Yellows or Mongolians and Negroes or Ethiopians. This classification is open to criticism. Indeed among the negroes some have an elongated skull and others like the Negritos have a rounded one. Certain families with a fair complexion must be placed in that class because of their ethnical characters. Likewise among the yellow races we find men of white complexion. Some have an oval, others a round face and not all of them have slanting eyes. This difficulty of making a natural classification is due to the mixture of characters in the different races, and to the absence of clearcut lines of demarcation among them. This fact is important for our thesis.

In describing the principal human families we shall

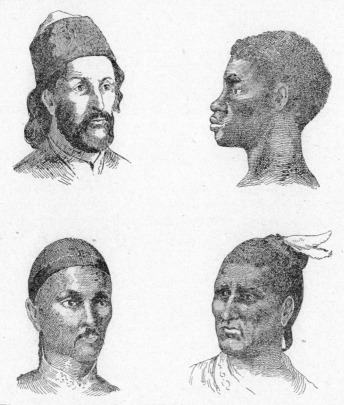

Figs. 69, 70, 71, 72.—Types of the four human races : white, negro, yellow and Indian.

follow with Dr. Verneau [1] the classification of A. de Quatrefages, for, though old, it is the simplest and not any more arbitrary than the others (figs. 69, 70, 71, 72.).

The Whites or Caucasians.   The whites in general comprise all the races that have the fairest skin.   However,

[1] Verneau, *Les races humaines*, Paris, J.-B. Baillière.

owing to a pigmentary layer, the skin may vary to a considerable extent. Sometimes the layer is very thin and the skin is so transparent that the red corpuscles of the blood give it color. At other times the pigment is thick and gives to the skin a brown complexion. At times even, as among the Hindoos, it becomes so thick that the skin is as black as that of the Ethiopians. The color of the eyes and of the hair is extremely variable. The hair of the whites is silky, glossy or curly; it is not woolly like that of the negro, nor wiry like that of the yellow races. It has an elliptical cross-section.

It is especially by the anatomical formation of the head that we distinguish the whites. The skull is well developed, the forehead broad and lofty, the eye-brow ridges less prominent, the openings for the eyes are horizontal, not slanting, the nose straight and projecting, the cheekbones have not the unlovely prominence of the negro, the jaws do not project forward, the chin is not receding, the lips are not very thick, and the facial angle is very nearly 90°.

The white races occupy almost all Europe, half of South-West Asia and North-Africa, while some tribes are found in the south-east and north-east of Asia and on the north-west coast of America. In taking possession of America, the Europeans peopled it whith Caucasians. De Quatrefages divides the whites into four principal branches : the Allophylic branch represented in Europe by the Basques, the Finnish branch represented by the Laplanders and the natives of Dauphiny, the Semitic branch represented by the Hebrews, the Arabs, the Egyptians, the Kabyles, the Touaregs, the Aryan branch, represented by the Hindoos, the Greeks, the Moscovites, the ancient Germans, the Celts...

The whites as a rule speak inflected languages, while the religion most generally practiced among them is monotheism, under the forms of Judaism, Mohammedanism and especially Christianity.

According to the figures of Omalius d'Halloy, the whites comprise 42 per cent of the total population of the globe, i. e. about 508,000,000 persons. The *World Almanac* for 1925, gives 821,000,000 for the Aryan whites and 75,000,000 for the Semitic whites.

The Yellows or Mongolians. The yellow stock includes the races in which the color is very noticeable. However as in the preceding stock, the complexion may vary considerably. "It ranges from white to yellowish brown or even to olive green. The hair is long, thick and wiry, and has an almost circular cross-section. The beard is as a rule very thin, and is black like the hair of the head. The Mongolian skull is usually very brachycephalic, i. e. with a very short anterio-posterior diameter. The face is broad, the cheekbones prominent, giving the countenance the shape of a lozenge. The eyes seem oblique and narrow, because the upper eyelid forms exteriorly a sort of loop. The nose, less prominent but broader than that of the whites, is however not flat like that of the negro. The lips, likewise are medium. The prognathism of the jaws, where it exists, is less than that of the negro.

The yellow races occupy nearly all Asia, except the south-west. In the north-east some tribes of whites are intermingled with the Mongolians. In the west, on the confines of Europe, there is a mixture of whites and yellows particularly in Russia. The native races of North-America and of Greenland are descended from the Mongolian types, without speaking of the mixed Oceanic American races that we shall mention later on. Monosyllabic languages are the general rule among the Mongolian races. Buddhism and Brahmanism are the dominant religions. However, neither the language nor the religion are exclusively confined to this group. Omalius d'Halloy assigns to the Mongolian race 44 per cent of the total population of the world, it being according to his estimate in the neighborhood of 530,000,000. The *World Almanac*, for 1925, gives 654,000,000.

The Negro or Ethiopic stock. Exclusive of some tribes with yellow complexion, the negro type varies from slightly dark brown to the purest black. The hair of the head and of the beard is black and woolly. The beard is sparse and curly. The hair of the head is more abundant.

Sometimes it is disposed in tufts separated by naked spaces, sometimes it forms a continuous fleece. It has a very flat, elliptical cross-section that causes distortion and curling. The skull is dolichocephalic, that is, elongated from front to rear. The cranial capacity is on an average less than that of the whites. The forehead is slanting and receding. the eyebrows are prominent, the eyes large and of a dark color, the nose short and very flat. The thick lips exaggerate the already very prognathous jaws. This gives the chin a receding appearance.

The negroes are spread over the whole of Africa, the southern portion excepted, the South African Islands and all but the central part of Madagascar. They are to be found in the islets of Southern Asia, in Japan and in the Malayan Archipelago. Australia and Melanesia have no other native population. The agglutinate tongues are nearly universal among the negroes. Their religious cults are quite varied; fetischism flourishes among them. Omalius d'Halloy considers the number of negroes to be 136,000,000 i. e. about 11 per cent of the human race; but he wrote at a period when the large African population was still unknown, so that the figures must be very far from the reality. The *World Almanac*, for 1925, gives for the Negro and Bantu (black) race 130,000,000. *Mixed Races.* Under this name de Quatrefages includes the races, whose characters show a mixture of the preceding types. The Oceanic races, spread as far as Japan and Madagascar, comprise about 27,000,000 individuals. The native Americans, formerly called red-skins, i. e. the Indians, dispersed over the whole American territory and principally in the frigid zones, number no more than 10,000,000. The *World Almanac*, for 1925, gives 28,000,000 American Indians in North and South America, including pure bloods and half breeds. According to Omalius d'Halloy's computation, the total population of the globe would be 1,200,000,000 inhabitants. But more recent scholars rightly give higher figures. Thus Peterman admits a minimum of 1,397,000,000 while Wagner and Belom go still further to 1,436,000,000 (in 1883). The most recent estimate is also the highest.

Thus the *World Almanac*, for 1925, gives 1,748,000,000. The figures taken from the *World Almanac* are those of the American anthropologist Dr. A. Hrdlicka.

What is more important is not so much the exact number of individuals as the proportion of individuals of each race, and the density of population in each type.   Now, if we represent the whole human race as 100, we find that there are about 42 whites, 44 yellows, 11 negroes and 2 Oceanic mixed and 1 native American mixed.   Again, if we represent the inhabited territory of the globe by 100, we find that the area covered by each is 22 for the whites, 28 for the yellows, 18 for the negroes, 3 for the Oceanic and 29 for the mixed native Americans.   From this it is easy to compute the proper density for each race.   In territory occupied by one native American, we could have 19 negroes, 21 Oceanians, 50 yellows and 61 whites.   These figures of themselves indicate the natural trend of migration of dense populations.

We have spoken only of the actual races, because what we have given suffices for our present purpose.   We shall see very soon, what are the characters of the extinct races.   Do these human groups that exhibit among themselves resemblances so important that they are clearly distinguished from the animals, but that also show differences so profound that they are divided into various classes, form a single species with many varieties, or rather many independent species?   This is the question that will now occupy our attention.

§ II.—WHAT IS THE STATUS OF THE QUESTION OF THE UNITY OF THE HUMAN SPECIES ?

We cannot solve the question without first defining it. But this is very difficult, as the term species has such a variety of meanings. So the best way to understand the problem is to follow its history down to the present time. It is important to note that the question of unity of origin is correlative with that of the unity of species.   The authors that have written on this subject all suppose that the unity of species follows the unity of origin and *vice versa*. Indeed, the oldest definition of species was thus expressed : "Of the same species are the individuals that are anatomically alike and descend from one common stock." Consequently, some did not hesitate to class, in the same species, individuals quite different in exterior characteristics, if they are known to be derived from the same ancestor. The individuals whose resemblances would cause them to be united in the same species, would be attributed to one same primitive stock.

Up to the seventeenth century, the belief in the unity of origin led to the belief in the unity of species for the whole human genus. When, in 1655, La Peyrère before his conversion to Catholicity gave out the hypothesis of the *Préadamites* and the plurality of the human species, he had in mind precisely to establish the plurality of origin. He thought he had discovered in the Bible an essential distinction between the men created on the sixth day along with the animals, and Adam, the father of the Jewish people, taken from the slime of the earth after the repose on the seventh day. Between the Preadamites and the Adamites or Jews, there was then a difference of species and a difference of origin. [1] This opinion, which was afterwards retracted by the author, had but few supporters in the xiith century, but in the following century it was revived and exploited by the irreligious philosophy that looked for errors in the Bible. Voltaire was at the head of this movement. "Only a blind man" said he "can doubt that the whites, the negroes, the Albinos, the Hottentots, the Laplanders, the Chinese and the Americans are entirely different races." [2] Under the name "races", he understood precisely the idea of species, for his purpose was to combat the unity of origin of the human groups, adopting implicitly the definition of Linnaeus "that there exist as many different species as God created types in the beginning."

---

[1] La Peyrère, *Systema theologicum ex Præadamitarum hypothesi*, 1655.

[2] Voltaire, *Essai sur les mœurs*, Introduction, p. 11.

Voltaire could only weaken the thesis of the unity of origin by undermining the theory of unity of species. In the firts half of the xixth century, politics became mixed up in the question without shedding much light upon it. The Americans carried on the traffic in blacks on a very extensive scale. The European nations made numerous demands that the American government put an end to this inhuman practice. In 1844, Calhoun replied that the traffic was legitimized by the fact that the blacks were not men of the same species as the whites. The American Secretary quoted the opinion of numerous Polygenistic scientists. Indeed, apart from all this political and philosophical preoccupation, certain scientists were teaching the plurality of the human species. Virey, Desmoulins, and Bory de Saint-Vincent in France, and Gerdy, Morton, Nott and Glidden in America, were evident advocates of polygenism. At the same time, Linnaeus, Buffon, Lamarck, Cuvier, Blainville, the Geoffroy-Saint-Hilaires, Muller, Humboldt showed themselves no less attached to monogenism.

In all these discussions, the idea of species is never separated from that of the unity of origin. The polygenists dwelt chiefly on the organic differences that separate the human groups. It did not seem possible to them that types so different as the negroes and the whites could be derived from the same common stock. "Certainly" said Virey "if naturalists saw two insects or two quadrupeds so differently constructed in their external forms and permanent color as the white man and the negro, in spite of the half breeds that arise from their mixture, they would not hesitate to call them two different species." These words make us understand the question as then stated. According to A. de Quatrefages, it was specially treated by paleontologists, entomologists and conchyologists, etc... Now these naturalists are prone to call species all the varieties having wellmarked differential characters. They care little about the value of these characters, and especially do they neglect too much the physiology of a being, to occupy themselves merely with its morphology. How often has this system classified a male and a female, or even two successive stages of the same individual into two distinct families! From this confusion has risen the almost infinite number of species in paleontology and conchyology...

De Quatrefages clarifies the situation somewhat by giving equal value to the exterior form and to the physiology of the organism. The physiological element, par excellence, was in his eyes, *filiation.* Hence, he defined species as the "assemblage of individuals, more or less alike among themselves, that can be regarded as having come from a single primitive pair by an uninterrupted and natural succession of *families* [1]". Thus, we see the great champion of monogenism giving as a sign of unity of species the fact of unity of origin. Consequently the two questions remain correlative.

The principal adversary that de Quatrefages had to contend with was the Catholic scientist Agassiz, professor at Harvard University. Irreconcilably opposed to transformism and to the variability of living forms, he believed he could more readily assure the constancy of animal and plant life, by affirming the fixity of human types also. For him, the human races, incapable of being formed by natural influences, had to be separately created by God, and as there exist as many species as God had created in the beginning, the multiplicity of origin follows directly the multiplicity of species.

The numerous writings of de Quatrefages have made monogenism triumph, and the question would be regarded as finally settled, if it were not that the rise and propagation of evolutionistic ideas has given it an entirely new aspect. Indeed all the arguments of the monogenists rested on the hypothesis of the reality and of the constancy of species. Now it is just the existence of species that is rendered doubtful by transformists. According to their theory, the species are not natural, isolated and parallel groups from so many primitive types independently creat-

---

[1] De Quatrefages, *L'espèce humaine,* chap. II.

ed by God, but are only varieties that are more or less
separated at present, yet always related, though in various
degrees, since, like the branches of a mighty tree, they all
have risen from a single trunk. In this hypothesis the
words *variety*, *race*, *species*, *genus*, etc., are only conventional
terms having as their object merely to indicate the degree
of proximity of living forms.

We need not discuss the objective value of transformism, but as it has a great number of adherents and is
based on reasons and facts that cannot be despised or
summarily dismissed, and as we desire to place the question of human origin beyond all discussion, we must take
into account this new attitude of mind existing among scientists of today. Hence we separate the question of the
origin of species from the idea of species. If the question
of species is set aside, the question of origin will still
remain.

What matters it whether the human groups are called
varieties or races, or species? What is important is man's
unity of origin. The question of species is only one of
words, since it no longer involves the question of nature.
The question of origin is the only one that concerns us here,
for if men have the same origin, it will naturally follow
that they have the same nature. In answering the question
of the unity of origin, we solve also that of the unity
of species as formerly intended.

Let us note well, that the change of appearance does
not offer any serious difficulty. Indeed, the question of
species has ever been raised to solve that of origin, hence
the monogenists of a former day will have no cause for
complaint. Nor will Catholic apologists, since the purpose
they have in mind is precisely to establish the unity of
origin. The arguments that we shall employ are those
of monogenism itself, but from a different point of view.

Here is a clear statement of the question : "Do actual
human races show such differences, that they could not
descend from the same primitive pair?" To solve it, we
shall follow the method of de Quatrefages. We shall
seek, among the plants and animals, some groups that

certainly descend from the same original stock, and shall
compare them with the human groups. In making this
investigation, we shall verify the fact that the differences
between the human races are less pronounced than between
the various animal and plant races, that certainly descend
from the same pair, that the physiological resemblances are
such as characterize related varieties, and that after
all it is easy to explain the formation of traits, even the
most accentuated that differentiate the human families
today.

We put the seal of scientific approval upon the conclusion that we shall draw in favor of the unity of origin, and
it will be a real satisfaction to confirm by the investigations of true science, a truth that Catholic dogma has taught
us and which is quite formally expressed in Holy Scripture.

If this conclusion were to bring us into conflict with
certain scientific persons, it would be none the less acceptable. But it gives us real pleasure to state that it is admitted even by scientists, who take an opposite stand on this
question of the origin of man. For, the majority of materialistic transformists, for whom man is but a perfected animal, teach that all the human branches are derived from
the same animal branch.

§ III.—VALUE OF RACIAL DIFFERENCES. THEY ARE INSUFFICIENT TO ESTABLISH PLURALITY OF SPECIES.

All the arguments of polygenists reduce themselves to
the following statement. "There are too many differences
between the negro and the white man for them to be of the
same species, or to have had the same origin." Now the
contrary proposition seems to express the truth more accurately "It is so difficult to find a characteristic difference
among the human races, and the differences that are noted
have so little importance, that it is impossible to consider
them as of distinct species, and to assign them to several
primitive stocks."

Absence of characteristic differences. Let us suppose, for
instance, that there are several human species and that

each of them goes back to a particular primitive pair. We shall then have these results : a) The primitive pairs were characterized by real differences, for if they were absolutely alike, why speak of several species and several separate origins? b) The descendents of these different pairs bear the faitful impress of the distinctive marks of their ancestors, throughout all the variations subsequently occurring in their organism. Such is the result of the law of heredity and of the law of permanent characterization; c) These well-preserved distinguishing marks are traits by which we shall separate the species; just as all the pigeons have one characteristic that specifically distinguishes them from all the rest, etc.; so the whites, the negroes, the yellows, if they derive their origin from different pairs, must be readily recognized by some traits that clearly range them into separate classes. Now, this is precisely what is not the case. De Quatrefages, in spite of his lengthy and learned works, has declared that it was impossible to make a natural classification of the different races of man. Why is this so? In the first place, it would be necessary to find among the races, a gap which in no way exists. Place side by side, a white man and a negro, a yellow man and a red-skin, and you are at once struck, as Voltaire affected to be, by the diversity of the four types clearly characterized. But gather a million men from all climes and arrange them according to color in the same line, and you pass by insensible shades from the very fair complexion of the European peasant to the most intense black of the African that roves under the torrid skies. Take any characteristic you please, the color of the hair, the facial angle, the stature, the cephalic index, and you always arrive at the same result : the long line in which the men are ranged is without a gap; while, on the contrary, a gap always separates the human line from that in which are ranged individuals of neighboring species. Not only is the line uninterrupted, but a notable intercrossing of characters is apparent. This fact is of more importance than the preceding. Here is what one may notice. Let us suppose we had all the men arranged in a single row according to the color

of their skin.   We should find them exhibiting a mixture
of all the other characters.   We should have orthognathous and prognathous types of every degree, and if we
repeat the procedure for other characters, such as the
hair, the stature, etc., the result will always be the same.
Every mark taken as differential, infallibly increases the
admixture of all the others.

Now this would not have happened had the human
races descended from different primitive pairs.   For, these
ancestral differences preserved in the descendents, would
serve to establish among them fixed lines of demarcation.
This is exactly what takes place in the animal species.
Though there be crossing of the races, at least all the races
of one species have some trait in common, that clearly
distinguishes them from all other species.   It is impossible,
therefore, to find characteristic differences among the
human races.   All anthropologists implicitly admit this,
since all confess that there is no solid basis upon which to
build up a natural classification.   Now suppose the differences really existed and should be so characteristic as to
permit of classification, we must confess that they are of
too little importance to constitute a species.   In fact, if
we look over those that are adduced, we shall see that they
are less accentuated among the human races than among
the animal races, that we certainly know to be derived
from the same stock.

Color.   The color of the skin is the phenomenon that
strikes one most readily and most forcibly.   It was precisely on difference of color that the first polygenists relied
to overthrow the notion of the common origin of the human races.   Now the color of the skin is in itself a physiological fact of little importance, which is easily produced
under the influence of environment and regime, and is
neither more general, nor more accentuated in the human
species than in the animal species.

A few brief notions on the structure of the skin will
help us understand the phenomenon of color.   The skin
is composed of two layers, the dermis and the epidermis,
superimposed one upon the other. The colorless dermis is

tinted red by the blood vessels which traverse it; the epidermis is composed of a more or less transparent superficial layer, and of a deeper one or mucous membrane which secretes a pigment.   This pigment, lying between the dermis and the epidermis is constant in all the races; but its shade is quite variable.   It is almost colorless in the whites, yellowish in the Asiatics, very dark in the negro.   But in the same race, even in the same individual, according to the kind of life led and the part of the body, the pigment is variable in thickness and in color.   Thus the pigment increases and turns brown in the wind and in the sun; it decreases and becomes transparent in those living in close confinement and of sedentary habits.   This great variability deprives the question of color of all its importance. We shall presently show how this variability itself is of great assistance in explaining the formation of the races.

But even the circumstance of color, were it of greater importance or less understood, would lose all its force by comparison of the human with the animal races.   The same contrast of colors is met with in the animals, which evidently belong to the same species and are derived from the same original pair.   Thus "our races of fowls present the three extremes of color found among men.   The French fowls have a white skin, those from Cochin-China tend towards yellow, and some are black" (de Quatrefages). —Moreover, melanism may appear suddenly in our barnyards and be transmitted by heredity, thus forming a new race.   The bovine races are extremely variable in color.   While among dogs and horses, all of which most certainly belong to the same original stock, the color is no less variable than in man.   We can understand then, why Voltaire could misuse the color of the human races to ridicule a truth taught by the Christian religion; but we do not understand how a scientist could make use of the same argument to call into question the unity of human origins.

The hair.—Haeckel attaches so great importance to the hair that he has made this the basis for a classification of the human races.   He has been violently criticized by a number of scientists even of his own school.   "There

are many other characters just as important" says
Hovelacque, "and one cannot, without being deficient
in all method, select only one character, and neglect all the
others." Let us merely remark with de Quatrefages,
that the human hair shows less variation than that of
animals rightly classed under one species. For example,
the human hair, in spite of its varied appearances, preserves
the nature of hair, but the fleece of our sheep is replaced
by a short curly wool in Africa. "In America it is the
same for the Madeleine sheep (moutons de Madeleine),
when they are no longer shorn; while on the contrary,
in the high plateaux of the Andes, the wild boar acquires
a sort of thick wool." If such variations do not make us
doubt the unity of species and of origin in the animals, why
then should they make us doubt the unity of the human
origins, when the variation is less?

However, the ease with which the color and the form of
the hair change in the same individual, according to age
and environment, prevents naturalists from placing any
reliance upon a character so changeable and so superficial.

Anatomical characters. — There is no anatomical difference which has not been invoked in favor of polygenism.
All the objections based on this head are solved in the same
way. These organic modifications, even if they might
characterize the races, would be insufficient to determine the
species, since they are always less accentuated than the
corresponding peculiarities to be met with in the same
species among animals. We shall have occasion to bring
out this fact more prominently, when reviewing the principal organic differences which distinguish men.

It is surprising how variable is the stature of human
beings. We find some Buschmen measuring less than
1 meter in height and some Patagonians that attain a height
of 1.92 meters. It is true that even the average heights
are very far apart in the different races, since the average
for the Buschmen is 1.37 meter, and for the Patagonians 1.72. The variations are quite notable in the animal
races derived from the same stock. Thus, among dogs, the
little spaniel measures 0.30 meter in length and the mountain

dog 1.33 meter, is four times as large. We find some
rabbits measuring 0.20 meter and others 0.60, i. e. three
times as large. Among sheep, goats, cattle and horses
the difference is no less marked.

The spinal column, varies but little in man. At the very
most the addition of only one vertebra has been noted;
yet even these cases are individual and by no means characteristic of the human group. In the animal species the
variations of the vertebral column are profound and con-

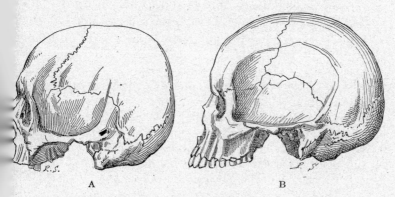

A   B

Figs. 73 and 74.—A, Brachycephalic; B, Dolichocephalic.

stant. There exist some "races of dogs, of goats and of
sheep in which the tail is so reduced in length as to constitute
but a short cocyx" (de Quatrefages). In the African pig
the vertebrae number 44, while the English pig has 54.
Thus again we see great variations even in the same
race.

The structure of the *members* is no less constant in all the
human races, apart from certain teratological exceptions,
e. g. six digits on one hand or one foot.—On the contrary
what profound differences in the members of certain animal
species! Thus, in dogs, the fore-paws have five well formed digits, while the hind-paws have four perfect and a
fifth rudimentary digit. This last digit disappears entirely in certain races of small dogs, while in certain large
races it becomes equal in length with the others. From

being cloven footed, which it is normally, the pig may become single-hoofed, that is a middle digit develops between the two complete digits, each of which has its own hoof, at the same time a single hoof develops which encloses the three digits. (Cf. de Quatrefages, *Espèce humaine*.) The differences which the conformation of the head assumes have no great significance. Every one knows that there exist two opposite types of human heads; the *dolichocephalic*, in which the head is elongated from front to rear, and the *brachycephalic* in which the head is broad and short (cf. figs. 73 and 74.) But between these two typical shapes there are innumerable mesaticephalic heads serving as transition forms. There are also numerous intermediate shapes between the *prognathous* individuals who have the jaws very prominent, and the *orthognathous* whose faces are flattened, with the maxillae less projecting. There is not only an insensible transition from one form to another, but each form is found in all the races, so that Haeckel declared that the cranium could not be considered sufficiently characteristic to be used in classifying the races. Prognathism and dolychocephaly characterize a considerable number of Europeans, and are particularly easily developed under the influence of a more or less uncivilized existence. On the contrary, orthognathism exists especially in children of the inferior races, and perseveres in a great number of individuals. Still, were the cranial forms clearly marked according to races, as those of Neanderthal, it would not be necessary to attach too great importance to them, for if these variations are comparable with those which are found in the animals, would they serve to characterize the races evidently descended from the same stock? It would be necessary to reproduce here the text and the drawings of a chapter of de Quatrefage's, *Introduction à l'étude des races humaines*, in which he brings out these differences.

What a variety of shapes in the skulls of 150 races of pigeons, which are all descended from the same wild rock pigeon! What a difference there is between the heads of the *bos triceros*, of the *gnato* ox of La Plata, of the European or ordinary ox; likewise between the head of the Spanish grey hound, and that of the mastiff, or of the bull-dog; as also between the head of the wild cock, of the white-crested cock, or of the buff Cochin! No human skulls exhibit such profound differences.

The cranial capacity as a measure of the volume of the brain offers no stronger argument for polygenism. For, if we hold to averages only, we note two equally constant facts: they are always very far from the average measurements of simian skulls, while they always approximate one or other of the human races.—Thus while the average capacity of skulls of the highest apes always ranges round 450 cc., the average capacity of negro skulls, e. g. of the Australians, Nubians, Tasmanians, etc..., according to figures compiled by Broca, approaches some 1,400 cc. in men, and 1,250 cc. in women. This shows that the gap between the highest apes and the lowest men is very wide, and without any intermediate average permitting the transition from one to another. Between the extreme averages of the human races, the difference is slight. Broca estimates the average capacities of the very highest types the Auvergnian, Bretons and Welsh around 1,600 cc., and the average of the lowest that of the negroes and Australians, etc., in the neighborhood of 1,400 cc. Furthermore, these differences would lose all meaning if instead of taking the averages, we should consider the individual figures. For, although the brains of negroes are in general very small, we find some small and some large brains in all races and in all countries. Even, if the intellectual faculties were measured by the cranial capacity, the differences could not characterize two distinct species. But, if we remember that above 1,100 cc. the size of the brain has little bearing on the intellectual value; and that we find instances of remarkable minds and of limited faculties, in all sizes, we shall realize still better that from this standpoint, the brain cannot serve as a specific basis for determining the human races.

Perhaps we may have better luck in considering the *facial angle*. We call by this name, the angle formed by two lines, one of which extends from the base of the nose to the middle of the entrance to the external ear, and the other from the prominence in the center of the forehead to the most prominent part of the upper jaw. This angle, which Camper invented to distinguish the human races, cannot give good results, so it is no longer taken into account. It cannot throw any light on the cerebral value, nor indeed with greater reason, on the intellectual power of the individual.—Let us remark, that even if it deserved any consideration, the facial angle would not upset the theory of monogenism. It varies in fact from 70° to 90° in men, and it is in general more acute in negroes than in whites; but here, as in the preceding instances, we shall find at each stage a mixture of individuals of all races. If at times, certain authors have made the facial angle of apes approach that of men, they were deceived by some defective manner of measuring the angle. [1]   Indeed, whenever they have compared the facial angle of young apes with the facial angle of the adult man, they have taken the ridge of the eyebrows for the frontal prominence.

Disparity of the races from the moral and intellectual standpoint.—That there have been, in fact, superior and inferior races and that there exist profound differences between men, from the point of view of knowledge, customs, industry, refinement, etc., *no one will deny*, but that we may deduce from this the plurality of species and of origin is absolutely contrary to the facts themselves. Take whatever people you will, civilized or uncivilized, make sure that all the individuals of which it is composed descend from one common stock, then compare the individuals with one another. There is not one nation, not one town even, in which you will not find all the degrees of intellectual and moral development. On the contrary, among the most degraded tribes, the Fuegians, the Australians and the Buschmen, will be found very highly

---

[1] See Topinard, *Anthropologie.* Quoted by Vigouroux, *Les Livres saints*, vol. IV, p. 73.

developed individuals perfectly capable of being instruct-
ed in the sciences of the most advanced nations. This
should not surprise us, for the differences mentioned do
not constitute a divergence of nature, but only different
degrees of development of an identical nature.   In fact,
what do we find in civilized people, that we do not note in
uncivilized tribes? What spiritual quality is lacking in
any race?   All the races have articulate language, industry,
works of art, expressions of general and abstract ideas, a
religious cult, a moral code.   All are susceptible of education and of progress. The most degraded men can be
raised to the level of others, and thus give evidence of a
real identity of nature.

Moreover, these intellectual and moral characters are
extremely *variable* in the degree in which they exist.
If this degree arose from nature it would be constant in the
same race. Now such is not the case. The races and
the peoples are susceptible of being elevated or debased
the same as individuals. Some nations, once very prosperous and possessed of a high degree of civilisation are very
miserable today. It is an evidence, as we shall show later
that the nations that are degraded today, have had for
their ancestors men of the highest culture. On the contrary, the Welsh and Saxon races have made progress
over their forebears. This disparity of races then
is no solid argument in favor of plurality of origin. It
is quite accidental by nature and quite variable in
degree.

Diversity of languages. Towards the middle of the XIXth
century, in the heat of the discussions on the unity of
species, very many polygenists thought they had found in
the diversity of human languages, an argument in favor
of a multiple origin. It is not possible thought they, for
children of the same father, to learn to speak languages
absolutely opposed. Renan even went so far as to write :
"If the planets, whose physical nature seems to be like
that of the earth, are inhabited by beings constituted like
ourselves, we can state that the history and the language
of these planets does not differ from ours any more than

the history or the language of the Chinese differ from it." [1]

Renan himself recognized the weakness of this argument when he made the following avowal : " From the fact that the languages actually spoken on the face of the globe are divided into absolutely irreconcilable families, are we authorized to draw from this certain ethnographic conclusions? To say, for example, that the human species has made its appearance at different places; that there has been one or many appearances of the human species? We must certainly answer this question in the negative. From the division of languages into families, we cannot conclude the division of the human species... Philology teaches nothing about it." [2]

This conclusion is quite correct. In fact, if some irreconcilable languages should prove the distinction of origin of the peoples who speak them, it would not follow from this that the African negroes had descended from different ancestors. All anthropologists ascribe to them the same origin. An argument proves nothing when it proves too much. Since there has been linguistic division, when, at the beginning, some peoples could not have been divided, it follows that linguistics is not a just criterium to decide the question of the origin of a people.

To understand how all men, having the same nature, still speak different languages, we must remember that articulate language is essentially conventional. Natural language, or the spontaneous expression of sensations and of passions is the direct result of nature. Thus it is evidently the same everywhere. In all climes the expression of joy or of pain is, because of its constancy, easy to recognize. As for artificial language, identity of nature demands that one should exist, even among the most degraded of peoples, but by the very fact that it is conventional, it is variable with the environment, the custons, etc... as all the other manifestations of human intelligence.

---

[1] Renan, *Histoire des langues sémitiques*, Paris, 1855.

[2] In *Revue politique et littéraire*, March., 16, 1878, Quoted by Vigouroux, *Les Livres saints*, etc., vol. IV, p. 96.

Some simple facts reveal the secret of the formation and differentiation of languages. A nation that is prosperous enriches its language by cultivating the arts and the sciences. When nations decline, their language is promptly impoverished. The more united a people is, the more the unity of its language is preserved; the more it is broken up, the more do particular dialects multiply. Commerce unifies languages, just as isolation differentiates them. Each adds its part to the modification of the language; these differences are accentuated in the measure that separation becomes more complete. Is it surprising then, that the human families roaming isolated through the primitive forests, and along the shores of ancient rivers, had developed languages as opposite as the modern languages?

But, then, why do we not find traces of a common language? Ought not the essential roots be found alike for all the descendents of primitive man? To this question we may give a threefold reply : 1. To all appearances, the language of the first men was very meagre; the small number of primitive roots, even if preserved would be difficult to discover. — 2. Philology is not in a position to prove that the actual languages are absolutely autonomous. Between the primitive languages and the actual languages there has existed a number of intermediates of which no document remains, which nevertheless would be necessary to reconstruct a history of language.—3. Since it is a fact of experience that a people without fail loses certain words of its language as it grows older, and especially as it becomes decadent, is it not enough to know that this loss applies also to the primitive roots, and so makes it impossible to discover the common starting-point?

What we have said of the intellectual and moral disparity of the races and of the diversity of languages, we might say of the ideas which the different peoples have formed of the divinity. The religious mind exists in all races, throughout the ages. This common element takes various forms; but these variations in belief are of an accidental character, and not a sign of nature. There are no races monotheistic or polytheistic by nature. Both conditions are found among all races; hence they cannot characterize the species. From all that precedes, we may conclude that there is not one single difference establishing a real line of demarcation between the human races; at least that not one single difference is so fundamental that the human races should not be classed in the same species and be derived from the same primitive stock.

§ IV.—RACIAL RESEMBLANCES. THEY ARE SUFFICIENT TO CHARACTERIZE THE UNITY OF SPECIES.

Although it is difficult to find such characteristic differences between men, as may not merely distinguish the several species, but even separate the races, we shall have no difficulty in finding resemblances and family traits which unite them. Anatomy, physiology, and psychology all prove, that in the measure, that the human races are distinct from the animal species, by so much do they resemble one another. The marks by which a man is distinguished from an animal apply in various degrees, it is true, yet none the less certainly to all men.

From the *anatomical* point of view, we could not say anything more to the point than these words of de Quatrefages; "Dolichocephalic or brachycephalic, large or small, orthognathous or prognathous, Quaternary man is always man in the full acceptation of the word... The more one studies, the more one is convinced that each bone of the skeleton, from the largest to the smallest, carries with it in its shape and in its proportions a certificate of origin impossible to mistake." (*L'Espèce humaine*, p. 220.) This illustrious anthropologist speaks, it is true of Quaternary races compared with the actual races, but what he says applies with still greater force and this too was in his mind—to actual races compared with one another, for the anatomical differences are more accentuated in the races of modern times than they were in the races of former ages, and they are not of a different nature.

Physiology leads to the same result. The organic phenomena, which show real differences in the nearest animal species, are identical in all the human races. The temperature of the body, the average duration of life, the inclinations, the instincts, the voice and the nature of the cries, the period of gestation, etc., all show the traits of close resemblance that characterize beings of the same species, and having the same origin and not of beings of different species.

As, among all these physiological characters, that of *filiation* or of interfecundity of races is the most important, we must give it special attention. Whatever be the interpretation one may put upon it, it is a *fact* beyond all question or discussion that all the human races are interfertile. For more than three centuries the mixture of races has been going on, in all parts of the world, always with the same result, the union of human individuals of the most widely separated races have been fertile.—This fecundity is by no means the result of a sort of violence analogous to that which produces fecundity between animals of different species. It is the natural result of spontaneous alliances, brought about by real physiological bonds uniting all the human races. These alliances are even so easily entered into, that in 1861 the California legislature had to interdict with severe sanctions the union of certain races. Since then, 29 states have prohibited marriages between negroes and whites, 4 between whites and Indians; and 6 between whites and Chinese. Finally these offspring, metis or halfbreeds, are endowed with continuous fecundity. This is seen from the great numbers of mixed breeds or intermediates born from such alliances between distinct races. Thus, in the last century the Dutch and the Hottentots produced the mixed race of Griquas which have disappeared because of further crossing. At present, a mixed race is being formed between Australians and Europeans. Two thirds of the population of Mexico are a mixture of Spanish and American Indian blood. Between the English and the Maoris there is being formed a mixed race in New Zealand.—

We may add that frequently these mixed races are more prolific than the pure races. This was remarked by Le Vaillant at the Cape (Cape Town), by Hombron in Peru, and by Captain Jouan in Greenland. In the question before us, these facts are differently interpreted, according as one leans towards or is opposed to transform- ism, but either interpretation admits the unity of species and of origin.

De Quatrefages, a declared foe of evolution reasoned thus :—1. Man being an animal by reason of his organism should, from a physiological standpoint, be subject to the general laws which regulate living beings; every doc- trine that makes man an exception should be considered false.—2. In the study of living forms, both plant and animal, the mark by which we recognize the different spe- cies is the existence of continued interfecundity. Compared with the phenomenon of filiation the morphological char- acters have very little value. According to this mark one may say of the same species, although of different races are the morphologically distinct individuals that can form alliances which are indefinitely fertile; of different species are the individuals that in spite of certain morphological resemblances cannot contract alliances between each other, or only contract sterile or partially fertile alliances.

If this rule is applied to man, the facts of inter- fecundity cited above prove that the human groups are not different species, but merely races of one and the same species. And as unity of species supposes unity of origin, the human races descend from one common stock.

In the eyes of the transformist, whatever be the shade of opinion he may adopt, this argument, to retain its prov- ing force must of necessity be given in another way.—In fact de Quatrefages supposes here the reality and the fixity of living species. It is just this that evolutionists question. Moved by these considerations the advocate of the common descent of the human species would aban- don de Quatrefages' procedure and would reason in the following manner : 1. In the plant and animal species only nearly related forms enter into fertile union, only groups but recently separated from a common branch, where the divergence has not had time to become accentuated or produce intersterility. On the contrary, groups long separated or forms attached to distinct branches of the trunk will be either absolutely intersterile or possessed of only a very limited fecundity.—2. Hence, the marvellous interfecundity which holds among the human races proves that they are very closely allied, closer than the groups classified by naturalists, under the heading of species quite recently detached from a common branch of which they preserve by heredity all the fundamental traits.—3. Intersterility would rule among the human races if they had been separately formed on distinct branches of the animal kingdom. Moreover the intersterility which exists between man and the nearest animal groups proves that, if the human organism had once been united to the animal there has been a very considerable period of time, since it has acquired that autonomy which actually distinguishes and isolates it.

Now we are far from accepting this reasoning. But, as the unity of origin appears to us of prime importance, we have tried to show that its certainty dominates all modern discussions on the origin of living forms. Even for a transformist who would admit the animal origin of man, there would be the necessity of recognizing that all men, ancient and modern, descend from the same primitive pair. As for us, who think that evolution of animal and plant forms would not of necessity imply the evolitive origin of the human organism, we shall have all the more reason to admit origin of all men from a single pair.

We have frequently remarked the identity of nature which characterizes the *psychological phenomena* in all the human races. In spite of the differences of degree, this similarity is so marked that we need not insist upon it again.

From all this it seems we might well admit the unity of origin. But certain religious polygenists will say resembances do not of necessity imply the same origin,

for God could have created in different places types which
resemble each other.   Undoubtedly He could have done
so.   The question at issue is not whether He could, but
whether He did.   Now both the Bible and Science tell
us that all men descend from the same stock.   Transformist polygenists will ask: "Could not evolution begin by
producing the same type by way of two branches?"
Yes, under the hand of a skilful intelligent Creator, a
fact which the transformists in question do not wish to
admit; but not under the action of chance alone; nor even
in accordance with the principles of evolution, since two
branches living wide apart, could only accentuate their
divergence.   All that remains therefore is to complete
our demonstration, to prove that monogenistic science
easily explains the formation of the human races.

§ V. — The formation of the human races.

We must admit that it is impossible to find an absolutely
pure primitive type among the actual races.   For since
the creation of man the environmental conditions have
changed many times; the mixture of types has gone on so
readily that the primitive traits could not be preserved.
Some authors, among them de Quatrefages, have attempted
to reconstruct the physical characteristics of the first
man.   Taking as the basis for their investigation, the
facts of atavism, they hold as probable "that our ancestors had hair of a color approaching a more or less russet
shade of red", that the yellow pigment was dominant in
their skin, that the eye was slightly oblique like that of
the Mongolian, and that the upper jaw had a certain
amount of prognathism.

The human species very early broke up into many
races (figs. 75-78), for the crania of the Quaternary epoch
manifest among themselves differences no less noticeable
than in the crania of actual man.   The Mauer, Neanderthal, Piltdown, Moustier, Grimaldi, Cro-Magnon and
Chancelade races differed from one another as much, or
even more than the white, yellow and black races of

today. It is very remarkable that the modern races are not absolutely identical with the Quaternary or fossil races. Anthropologists regard modern men as formed from races of relatively recent origin among which are

Figs. 75, 76, 77, 78.—Ancient types, painted on the Egyptian monuments of the XVIIIth Dynasty (1635-1434 B. C.).

found individuals that are linked by ethnical characters, with the Quaternary races. If the modern races are very recent, one may well ask which originated first, which gave rise to the others. De Quatrefages, [1] always basing his statements on the facts of atavism, holds that the negro race was not the first, nor is it the branch from

[1] *Introduction à l'étude des races humaines*, Paris, 1889, p. 160.

which the other races have sprung, for numerous facts appertaining to the negroes, such as the complexion and the color of the Buschmen incline us to the belief that they descend from the yellow race; while for the yellow and white races no facts recall the negro race, but a number, do link the white race with the Mongolian. Among the whites, the Aryan race is generally regarded as the last one formed. Whatever be the relative antiquity of the races, it is important for us to establish under what influences were formed the ethnic characters which distinguish them, such as color and changes in anatomical formation. Dr. Verneau [1] following de Quatrefages' teaches that the varieties can be produced either through the influence of environment, or abruptly and spontaneously, or through crossing. The plasticity of the plant and animal organisms under the influence of these agencies aids in the comprehension of the phenomena that are produced in the human species.

The influence of environment. — Under the name of environment, we understand all the conditions of existence, climate, food, servitude or freedom, etc., etc. The environment is termed natural, when man has not intervened to produce it; it is called artificial, when man has regulated the conditions according to a preconceived plan. In the absolutely natural environment, plants and animals are said to be wild; in the artificial environment the plants and animals are termed domestic. Now in either case, the living forms vary with the environment. Every one knows to what extent plants vary, when they are placed in different localities. According as they grow in the valley or on the mountain, in a hot climate or a cold, on the seashore or in the interior, the plants of one species show notable differences. To recognize in them the same specific type, one must compare the forms of transition which have sprung up in the intermediate states between the two extremes. In his garden the florist obtains, by

---

[1] Verneau, *Les races humaines*, Paris, J.-B. Baillière; de Quatrefages, *L'espèce humaine*; *Introduction à l'étude des races humaines*.

the creation of a special environment, the most singular varieties of one and the same species. He is not acting on the plant itself. His influence is indirect, because he effects only the conditions.

The animal organism is no less plastic under the action of the environment. The numerous domestic races created by man in the various species of cattle, horses, dogs, pigeons, swine, etc., are sufficient evidence of it. Thus the foxes of Africa and those of Siberia are of the same species as the foxes of France. The lions of Sennaar are of the same species as those of India and of Barbary. The pig assumes a woolly fleece in the cold air of the Cordilleras; the ox loses its hair in the hot plains, etc.

As man is subject to the same biological laws as other living things, he cannot escape the modifying action of environment. We have some facts which enable us to verify directly the powerful action of environment on man. De Quatrefages instances the Anglo-Saxons that moved to the territory of the present United States, nearly three centuries ago. After about a dozen generations, the American no longer resembles his ancestors. Naturalists have examined this subject in its minutest details. Already in the second generation the American English show alterations which approach the local races. "The skin dries up and loses its rosy hue, the glandular system is reduced to a minimum; the hair becomes black and glossy; the neck tapers off; the head diminishes in size. On the face, the temporal fossae increase, the cheek bones become prominent; the orbital cavities grow deeper; the lower jaw becomes massive. The bones of the limbs become longer; while their cavities contract, so much so that the gloves manufactured in France and in England for use in the United States must have exceptionally long fingers. The female pelvis, in size and appearance, approaches that of the male" (de Quatrefages).—These modifications are surely very striking. That which proves best that they are the effect of environment, is the fact that they have a general tendency to approach the English type of redskin. Another fact shows that in America both negroes and whites "tend to turn into red-skins" (Élisée Reclus). For one hundred and fifty years, the negro has undergone the same remarkable changes. His complexion is lighter. "With respect to his outward appearance he has covered a good fourth of the distance which separated him from the white race. He has lost his characteristic odor, so by that mark alone one could distinguish an African from an American negro. " [1]

The French that emigrated to Canada have changed in the same way, taking on the characters of the local races. And in this latter instance as in those which precede, it is not one of degeneracy. Far from it. Beyond question, the negroes in consequence of their sojourn in America, have made progress both from the intellectual and the moral standpoint. The American is in no way inferior to the Anglo-saxon. The French Canadians form a race possessing great physical strength, capable of enduring the greatest fatigue, proud under a foreign domination and endowed with marvellous fecundity.

These examples, which it would be easy to multiply, from other sections of the world, prove that new races are being formed and that as a consequence, the different races have originated in former times under the influence of environment alone.—In the cases cited, the differences are undoubtedly less accentuated than in the older races, but we must remark that we are here experiencing the division of a branch into offshoots, and that the divergence is as yet too slight to be very noticeable. If the fundamental

---

[1] In response to an inquiry on this subject, Dr. Ales Hrdlicka, Curator of the Division of Physical Anthropology at the Smithsonian Institute, and the foremost authority in America on the subject of the early Americans, writes : "As to the color of the American negro—there are some indications that a slight lightening, even in the full bloods, may be taking place, but the subject is very difficult of precise determination and no real scientific work on the point has as yet been carried out. As to the negro odor... that is in very much the same category. Your question about any evidence in the descendants of early white families of America, of a gradual approach to the Indian type of physiognomy may definitely answered with no."—Translator.

races are farther apart today, it is because long ages have accentuated the slight differences produced in the very beginning.—Let us state also that we must not expect that environment changes the whites into negroes and reciprocally.

The white man, the yellow man and the negro are three extremes of the branches long in divergence, each of these branches is apt to produce offshoots which diverge in turn, but still preserve the fundamental traits already acquired by the race. This is an application to the human races of the great law of permanent characterization.

Thus, although man has, more than all other creatures, the power of escaping the actions of environment, he unfailingly falls under its influence. The multiplicity of races in the human species is as natural as in all other species of living creatures.

Spontaneous variations.—Under the name of spontaneous variations we understand those organic modifications which may appear abruptly without our knowing the cause. Among the animals the instances are not rare. The sheep of Mauchamp, remarkable for their silky fleece, are supposed to have originated from one exceptional individual whose breeder carefully preserved the traits through selection. Melanism, especially, can arise spontaneously and constitute permanent varieties. Thus in Bogota, there is a variety of black fowls derived from a race imported from Europe and which did not show the trait. According to Gordon, it is not only in New Granada that we find black fowls but also in the Philippines, in Java, on Cape Verde island, though all may be otherwise derived from different races. We find some even in Europe where melanism could have originated only spontaneously.

Man is not exempt from these sudden modifications. Among men as well as among other living beings, new races can appear through hereditary transmission of such traits spontaneously formed. Let us cite merely two instances drawn from Dr. Verneau's work. [1]

---

[1] Verneau, *Les races humaines*, p. 39.

In 1817, an individual named Edward Lambert, although born of perfectly normal parents, was covered with a sort of scaly carapace of more than a thumbs thickness. This peculiarity he possessed during his whole life so that he was called the human porcupine. Married to a woman who was free from this defect, he nevertheless transmitted the trait to his six children and to his grandchildren. It is not known what has become of the members of this family, but if they had intermarried, followings the rule of strict selection, in all probability they would have originated a race of men with a carapace.

The spontaneous appearance of supernumerary digits is often cited. In the family of the celebrated mathematician Colburn, this anomaly has persevered through four generations; and yet, in each generation the abnormal individuals had married with normal persons. Might not a proper selection have created a special race of polydactyl men? We cannot assert positively that the human races of ancient or of modern times originated through such spontaneous variations, but there is surely a possibility of it that we should not overlook.

Crossing.—Crossing is the art of producing new types by interbreeding individuals belonging to distinct races of the same species. Though practised to a great extent by nurserymen and breeders of animals, it is very rare in nature. The general rule is that the cross has forms which partake of the characters of both parent races, or follow the laws of Mendel. They possess continuous fecundity. From these two statements we may conclude that crossing fulfills the necessary conditions for the formation of new races. Do human crosses exist? Do they display great fecundity? Are mixed races advantageous to the human species? From the thorough study of this subject made by de Quatrefages we can answer in the affirmative to all these different questions. Some human crosses had to exist in very remote ages, for this is the only way we can explain how certain Quaternary races assumed several types at a time. As soon as the first human races were produced through spontaneous variation and change of environment, the mixture of types began to take place. Although the human families were much more isolated than they are today, still contact was not absolutely lacking. From the time that ships brought Europeans to all shores, the mixture of distinct races grew apace. Owing to the railway systems, steamships, automobiles, etc., communication is becoming still easier and the mixing of races is going forward on a very great scale.

That the mixture of whites and blacks, the extreme human types are prolific, no one any longer doubts, the existence of mulatoes is a living proof of it. But what has been most frequently discussed is the fecundity of the mixed races when intermarrying.

It is now accepted that they are prolific, not only when uniting with individuals of the parent races, but also when intermarrying with each other.

From thousands of instances we shall cite only the Griquas that originated on the Cape of Good Hope, from a crossing of the Dutch settlers and the native Hottentots. They became so numerous as to excite apprehension, and were banished to the other side of Orange Free State. Here they developed a prosperous colony which increased very rapidly. On Pitcairn Island in the Pacific, a colony of English and Tabitians have produced a mixed race which has multiplied among themselves with extraordinary rapidity. Moreover the mulatoes amongst themselves were often more prolific than the whites and the blacks. The mixed races are not a condition of human decadence. They may be, rather, a renewal of the human species. In fact, they not only possess fecundity but even physical prowess, plastic beauty and intellectual ability. It is not, therefore, a mixture of different bloods that will cause the decline of the human species, but rather physical misery and intellectual and moral perversion. We shall see in fact in the course of our study that the history of humanity offers us examples, both of progress and of decay. Work, sobriety and virtue produced

strong races; idleness, good-living, effeminacy and corruption of morals caused the fall of the greatest nations.[1]

CONCLUSION.

The problem of the unity of the human beginnings
seems to us now quite cleared up. We regard as scientifically certain the thesis that all human races descend from
the same primitive pair. We were aware of this from the
very catagorical teaching of our Holy Religion and from
the very clear text of Holy Scripture. But the modern
mind is such that it loves to see its beliefs in accord with
science. Now in the present instance, these exigencies
are quite satisfactory. Despite the title of this chapter,
it is not the unity of species that we have proven but the
unity of origin. The notion of species has become very
obscure, that of origin has remained clear. Elsewhere
we have said, the unity of species was of interest to us
only in as far as it leads to the unity of origin.

In applying to the human groups, the biological laws
which govern animals and plants, we arrive at the following
conclusions. The differences which characterize the human races are less important than those which distinguish
the animal and plant races, the identity of whose origin
is certain. Between the human groups there exist some
anatomical, physiological and psychological resemblances
for which unity of origin alone can account. Finally
the factors, which concur in the creation of animal and
plant races act also on man, and their action is quite
sufficient to explain how a single primitive type could
have originated the different races that we know.

---

[1] Some authors would like to have *heredity* counted as a factor
in the formation of the human races. Assuredly its role is essential,
since it is this that assures the preservation of a new character in
a variety. But this is precisely because no race can be formed
without adding heredity to the number of factors. That which
we are trying to discover, is just the factors which produce a variation
in the species : for this variation once produced, it is fixed and may
be transmitted to the descendants by heredity.

Polygenists have often invoked in favor of their theory he impossibility of peopling America and Polynesia with the descendents of a single couple created on the Asiatic continent. But de Quatrefages has rightly offered his objection. Both from an analysis of ethnic types and from geographical studies, it has been shown that America and Polynesia could have and must have been colonized by people coming from Asia at different times. Knowing that a single man has been the progenitor of all mankind, it will be interresting to investigate how far back we must place his creation, and what was the intellectual and moral status of humanity in the beginning.

CHAPTER VII

ANTIQUITY OF THE HUMAN SPECIES

§ I.—Whence the elements for the solution of the problem

At what date occurred the creation of the first man. Although this question is of less importance than that of the origin and of the unity of the human species, still it arouses our most lively curiosity. As there have been very different solutions in these last years, it is interesting to examine which of them comes nearest to the truth. Whereas certain anthropologists place man back more than 300,000 years, we shall show that the most exact calculations oscillate about an average much lower than these exaggerated figures.

But, whence come the data which lead to an acceptable solution of the antiquity of man? Perhaps we shall astonish certain readers when we say that it is to natural history that we must look for the most ancient, as well as the most authentic documents, and the most exact elements in the solution of the problem in question. We shall bring this out in a few words.

History in its strictest sense can give us only very recent and therefore very insufficient data. Everyone knows in fact, that history proper does not extend very far back. For the most favored of nations, does it of a certainty go back two thousand years before Christ? We shall return to this subject anon. By its very nature, the history of a people only goes back, at the very most, to the period of the origin of this people. Now before the origin of a nation, even the most ancient, how many centuries have elapsed during the patriarchal life of the isolated families?

To history we must add *the monuments*. The monuments can give us authentic dates, but how far removed from creation were these haughty tyrants of Egypt and of Chaldea, who had the important events of their reign carved in bricks or on stone?

Antedating history we find *popular traditions*. There is no people that does not possess traditions about its beginnings. In all races, there exists a sort of cosmogony recounting the origin of the world in general and of man in particular. These traditions are far from being despicable. Through a thousand variations created by the imagination, one cannot fail to discover the trace of a common remembrance of our origin. Though it is difficult to separate the truth from the great amount of dross, a truth formerly known might yet be discovered there. But a question of dates cannot be solved in this way. For to what extent can we suppose they had not altered? If they were otherwise worthy of credence they would at the very utmost give the age of a people. We shall find nothing in the different popular traditions that gives us the age of humanity.

The Bible seems to be an exception. Indeed the Sacred Book worthy of all respect because the Holy Spirit has inspired and directed its composition, appears to fill in quite well the gaps which everywhere separate the first days of man from history. It gives us some figures which, when added, place the origin of humanity back some six or eight thousand years. All exegetes are agreed in asserting that there is no true biblical chronology, that relying on Holy Scripture alone one cannot fix the date of creation. Instead of citing here a hundred testimonies that one can find for himself in the learned work of Vigouroux, *Les Livres saints et la critique rationaliste*, [1] we shall merely give the principal reasons upon which this assertion is based.

To begin with, Holy Scripture nowhere states how many years or centuries have elapsed since the creation

[1] See vol. III, 3rd edition, Paris, 1891.

of man. By adding up the ages of the persons mentioned in the sacred history, exegetical writers have constructed a chronology.—Now these calculations are far from being concordant. Some have been accepted for more than 200 years, of which the shortest gives 3,483 and the longest 6,984 years from the creation of man to the birth of Christ. There is, therefore, a discrepancy of 35 centuries or of 50 per cent between two interpretations of the same document. To take merely two versions which have the most authority in the Church, the Vulgate, which is officially recognized, and the Septuagint, which is held in high esteem, the difference would still be more than 12 or 15 centuries. The Church itself does not impose any chronology. On the one hand it declares authentic the Vulgate which gives 4,004 years before Christ, and in the Roman Martyrology the birth of Christ is given as in the year 5,199 after the creation of the world.—Evidently we must conclude from this that some mistakes of the copyists have crept into the transcription of the figures in Genesis, else how explain so many variations in the different versions of the same primitive text?

Then, even supposing that the sacred writers had intended to fix the date of creation, the loss of the exact number written by him leaves us in a state of uncertainty. [1] But according to reliable exegetes, it is very probable that there are gaps in the genealogical trees of the early patriarchs. [2] This opinion is based on two facts of considerable importance; some similar omissions have been noticed in some of the other books of Holy Scripture where the data can easily be controlled;—a memnotechnical reason seems to have determined the number 10 in the patriarchal genealogies before and after the deluge. [3] Orientals, besides, have a tendency to suppress intermediates in their genealogical lists. These considerations

---

[1] *Les Livres saints et la critique rationaliste*, vol. III, 3rd edit. p. 470. "It is impossible in the present condition of the text to recognize the exact numbers written by Moses."

[2] *Ibid.*, p. 473.   [3] *Ibid.*, p. 479.

lone would suffice to render the date of the creation of
man absolutely uncertain.

So let us accept this conclusion of Father Vigouroux... [1]
"One can merely declare to scientists : Establish, by
good arguments, the antiquity of man and of ancient
peoples; the Bible will not contradict it. The genealogies
of Genesis are probably incomplete, hence they can not
serve as a real basis for chronology. Scripture does not
propose to teach us directly about the precise date of the
heavens and of the earth, no more so than of our first
parents. Does she not wish to make us understand that
he leaves these questions to be discovered by men, provided they remain within the bounds of prudent criticism,
when she tells us through the mouth of Ecclesiasticus :
Who hath numbered the sands of the sea and the drops
of rain and the days of the world?' Eccles., I, 2."

We desire to state here that the position taken by present day exegetes is not a surrender to scientific progress.
For, in the XVIIth century, the most competent exegetes
said with Petau : "We have no means of knowing at
what date creation took place, and an express revelation
of God would be necesary to find it out. Such then are
in error who not only venture with assurance to state it
precisely, but treat with contempt those who believe it
possible to add to or subtract from their calculations." [2]

Does not this rapid sketch of the bearing of the data
of the Bible suffice to show : that it is necessary to seek
outside of revelation for the means of determining the
age of man; that in this investigation Faith leaves us
great latitude? It is the part of common sense to remain
within "the bounds of prudent criticism."

There still remains the task of examining the natural
sciences, to obtain from them the solution of the double
problem of the *relative age* and of the *absolute age* of
humanity. Relative chronology is that which classifies the

---

[1] *Les Livres saints et la critique rationaliste*, vol. III, 3rd edit., p. 517.
[2] Peteau, *De doctrina temporum*, lib. IX, c. VI, vol. II. Cf. Vigou
rou, *Ibid.*, p. 469.

facts in the order of their sequence, without attempting
to assign the real date in a certain unit of time. Absolut
chronology gives us positive dates, at least for the uni
of time, the year. Relative chronology can tell us in wha
geological period we find traces of man, without guaran
teeing that he may not have been older. Absolut
chronology through the natural sciences furnishes onl
a probable approach, by no means mathematical i
character.

§ II. — Relative chronology of humanity.

We know, through stratigraphic geology the relativ
age of the various rocks which constitute the earth'
crust. We have already given the general table of th
geological ages (p. 86). The question before us a
present is to know at what level man made his first appear
ance. No one dreams of placing it at the beginning o
plant or animal life, in the Precambrian Era, nor even in
the Secondary Period. But there have been and stil
are found advocates of man's existence in the Tertiary
Period.

We hold with the majority of scientists that man does
not go back farther than the Quaternary Period. To solve
the problem, it would be absolutely necessary to agree
upon the upper limit of the Tertiary, and then upon the
value to be attached to the documents adduced in favor
of man's existence at a determined level.

1. Limits of the quaternary period.

The Tertiary is divided into the Eocene, Oligocene,
Miocene and Pliocene. According to geologists, it is
quite difficult to determine the precise limits of and to
draw a line between the subdivisions of the Quaternary
period, the geological importance of which is very insignificant in comparison with the preceding. Among the
geological phenomena which have characterized the Qua-

ernary, the most important is indisputably that of the
numerous glaciations, the last of which is still taking
place under our very eyes.

The relative age of this phenomenon is easy to determine. We may take then a glaciation as the end of the
Tertiary Period or the beginning of the Quaternary. The.
difficulty consists in determining upon the precise glaciation. We know today that there have been at least three
in Scandinavia, four in the Alps and in the Pyrenees, and
at least an equal number in North America. Haug in
his *Traité de géologie* makes the Quaternary Period begin
with the first Alpine glaciation. In 1901, Penck distinguished four glacial periods, calling them by names taken
from rivers in the Danube basin, the Günz, the Mindel,
the Riss and the Würm. Thus we have a series of four
glaciations separated by three interglaciations : 1. The
Günzian Glaciation; First Interglaciation; 2. Mindelian
Glaciation; Second Interglaciation; 3. The Rissian Glaciation; Third Interglaciation; 4. Würmian Glaciation;
Postglacial Period.

Thus, for Haug, the Quaternary began with the First
Alpine glaciation, and is thus divided into quite homogeneous periods by this phenomenon. Other geologists
and especially the prehistorians will not admit this starting
point, because it impinges upon the Tertiary, as it is generally delimited. They make the Quaternary begin with
the third Alpine glaciation called the Rissian. The
duration of the Quaternary is thus restricted.

There is no reason why we should not accept this starting
point as it is the one most generally admitted by prehistorians. As we shall show over and over again, these glacial
phenomena ought to give some indications as to how these
four Alpine glaciations correspond with the three Scandinavian glaciations. The one that gives some difficulty
is the first, the others seem to be synchronous with those
of the Alps. The same holds true for the interglaciations.
To avoid confusion in speaking of the first, the second
and the third glaciation, we recall that Boule admits only
three. We admit four with Haug, Depéret, Penck,

Ohermeyer and numerous other geologists conformabl
with the table given below.

These glaciations have had an importance so conside
able, and such a reaction upon man, that we must sho
their *extention*, their *path*, their *causes* and their *biologic(
consequences.* Moreover, we find in these glacial pheno
mena, or in those which accompany them, a means o
estimating the absolute age of humanity.

The Rissian invasion, with which the Quaternary bega
was more important than the Fourth. The Scandinavia

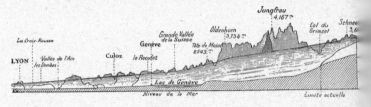

Fig. 79. — Quaternary and actual Alpine Glaciers compared.
(De Lapparent.)

glacier extended towards the south-east, south and the
south-west. It covered immense territory; all of Centra
Russia, Northern Germany, England, Holland and the
North Sea. Its southern limit extended to the 51º N. Lat.
The American glaciers covered 4 or 5 times more territory.
All Canada, the eastern states of the Union, extending as
far south as the 42 parallel of N. Lat.

The Alpine glaciers of Valais, Oberland, Mont Blanc,
distinct today and covering some 4,000 square kilometers,
formed an immense glacier covering 150,000 sq. kilos.
which covered Switzerland and many departments of France.

The glacier of the Rhône extended its terminal morain as
far as Lons-le-Saunier, Bourg, Villefranche, Lyon, Vienne
and Bourgoin (fig. 79); the Pyrénées and the Central
Massif were likewise covered by glaciers. We shall find
traces of these glaciers at the present day, in the " terminal
morains," [1] long winding ramparts of detritus left behind

[1] Cf. E. Haug, *Traité de géologie*, vol. i., p. 443, Paris, Colin.

when the ice receded in the amphitheatre morains of the Alps or of the Pyrénées, in the valleys under the form of rocks polished by the glaciers, in the four or five fluvio-glacial terraces easily recognized on the shores of the Danube, of the Rhine, of the Rhône, of the Garonne, of the Seine and of the Loire. [1]

In the valleys, in consequence of the glaciations, or of the melting of the glacier, there was produced through the action of water, first a deposit of gravel and of sand

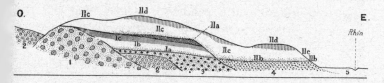

Fig. 80.—Cross section of the Rhine Valley at the level of Strasbourg. (E. Haug.)

1, 2, 3, 4 : The four fluvial terraces corresponding to the four Ice Ages. *Ia, Ib, Ic,* Ancient lœss. *IIa, IIb, IIc,* Recent lœss.

on the fluvial terraces, then a channeling or erosion of the valley.

The slopes of the Garonne, Rhône, Rhine and Seine valleys give evidence of this (fig. 80). A lowering of the temperature was the effect rather than the cause of these glaciations. The fauna and flora varied with these changes of climate; fauna of cold climates would migrate south during the glaciation, and those of warm climates would move north during the interglaciation.

The causes of these glacial phenomena still remain obscure. The hypothesis which appears the most plausible is that they were due to orogenic and epirogenic movements. After the Alpine upheaval, entire ranges, as the Canadian and the Scandinavian ranges, have continued to oscillate, that is to be subject to positive and negative movements. This is evident from the traces of very

---

[1] Depéret, *Revue générale des Sciences*, 1923, p. 130 et sq. For other works in English, see Bibliography.

numerous marine transgressions and regressions, and contemporary glaciations.

An upheaval in the Scandinavian range would have had the effect of transforming it into a powerful condenser of all the vapors which should come from every direction, and which would be precipitated as snow. The accumulation of snow changed to ice. Its weight forced the glacier to move as a stream with a velocity varying from 0.50 m. to 10 meters a day, and even more in certain glaciers of Greenland, Alaska and the Himalayas. A negative oscillation of a chain would have removed the source of the glacier with all its consequences. Geologists have well established the chronological parallelism of these various glacial oscillations in all the mountainous countries of Europe. One same cause has operated to produce these same effects at the same time in countries geographically so close... Moreover, the identity of the fauna and the flora, established on the terranes abandoned by the glaciers during the interglacial periods, leave no room for doubt.

Though widely separated, the identity of succession of phenomena permits identification of the ages at which they took place. For the climatic conditions which existed over all Europe, should have been the same in America at the same period. The Scandinavian range separated from the Canadian by the Atlantic belongs to the same orogenic formation. It is quite probable that they continued to oscillate together in the Quaternary. If the glaciations have had another cause, it must have been very general, to judge from the extent of the European glaciers. Everything tends to the belief that it had taken place in America at the same period.

The fauna which then inhabited Europe could not have been the same in America, the hippopotamus and the cave-bear that lived in France and in England during the Ice Age still live in Africa.

2. First signs of man.

We cannot say that man left characteristic traces of his presence wherever he existed. But there are some indications from which we certainly can deduce the presence of man. There are primarily human bones which infallibly argue man's existence, since as de Quatrefages says "there is not one human bone which does not bear on itself the certificate of its origin".—Then there are the implements and other articles of human manufacture, art or industry; chipped flints, bones fashioned into awls, needles, spears; collars and pendants used as ornaments; designs of men or of animals carved upon the bones of reindeer, of stags, of horses; the accumulations of debris from the chase or preparation of food in the caves in which man sought refuge; the traces of fire on the chipped flints, or in the caves; the designs in ochre on the walls

Fig. 81.—Chellean instrument or flint worked only at one extremity.

of his natural shelter. In the opinion of all prehistorians, the most ancient and perfectly authentic traces of man's existence are furnished by the flints of Chellean shape. The typical Chellean flints are in the form of flat almonds, shaped with great nicety on the two faces; they extend to a more or less tapering point; are very thick at the base and in the middle; thin and sharp on the edges and at the extremity. Often, particularly at the beginning, the base of the flint was left untouched that this heavy implement might be wielded without injury to the hand (figs. 81 and 99).

In 1888, Boule stated in his *Essai de paléontologie humaine* that the first human traces were found only after the great Rissian glacier. In this, he followed the English and German glacierists. Still he adopts it as his own opinion. Fort he countries covered by the glaciers the argument is quite compelling. The Chellean implements have always been found on the shifting rocks of the great glacier, of the third glacial extension, or at the base of the shifting rocks of the last. Nothing has ever been met with in the more ancient deposits, in the moraines of the third glacial invasion. In the regions covered by the ice, whether in Germany, in England, or in Scandinavia, it is believed that a definite lower limit has been reached; man seems to have arrived in Europe only after the end of the great glacial invasion (fig. 82).

For the extra-glacial valleys, where human utensils are found in the alluvial deposits of ancient rivers, the chronology is rather difficult to establish. Still, it is thought "that Chelles and Saint-Acheul are third interglacial deposits" and this conclusion agrees best with the actual status of paleontology and stratigraphy. It is enough to state the fact. In the next chapter, we shall show the climatic conditions in which the Chellean man lived. But certain anthropologists hold to a much greater antiquity for the human species; some even going so far as to place him in the middle of the Tertiary period. We shall see presently what is to be thought of this.

3. DID TERTIARY MAN EXIST?

This question of the existence of a Tertiary man cannot be solved *a priori*. From the point of view of the natural sciences, the arguments from reason that one could allege for or against have about equal value.

It is certain that the Tertiary period afforded an environment favorable to the human organism. The climate was hotter and more humid than at present; the plants and the animals most useful to man covered, at that time, the whole face of the earth. On the other hand

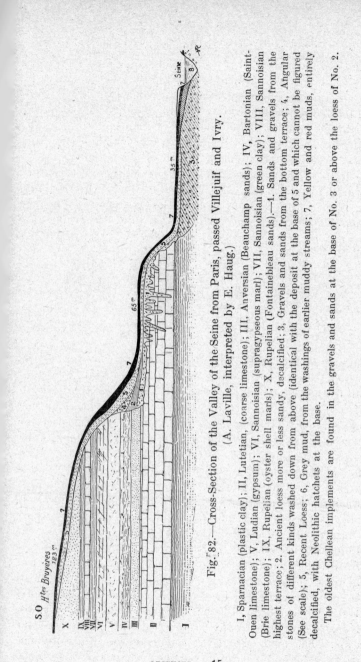

Fig. 82.—Cross-Section of the Valley of the Seine from Paris, passed Villejuif and Ivry. (A. Laville, interpreted by E. Haug.)

I, Sparnacian (plastic clay); II, Lutetian, (coarse limestone); III, Anversian (Beauchamp sands); IV, Bartonian (Saint-Ouen limestone); V, Ludian (gypsum); VI, Ludian (supragypseous marl); VII, Sannoisian (green clay); VIII, Sannoisian (Brie limestone); IX, Rupelian (oyster shell marls); X, Rupelian (Fontainebleau sands).—1. Sands and gravels from the highest terrace; 2. Ancient loess more or less sandy, decalcified; 3, Gravels and sands from the bottom terrace; 4, Angular stones of different kinds washed down from above (identical with the deposit at the base of 5 and which cannot be figured (See scale); 5, Recent Loess; 6, Grey mud, from the washings of earlier muddy streams; 7, Yellow and red muds, entirely decalcified, with Neolithic hatchets at the base.

The oldest Chellean implements are found in the gravels and sands at the base of No. 3 or above the loess of No. 2.

there is no reason why God should have created man as soon as the earth was able to support and nourish him. Undoubtedly, the whole world was inhabited in the third interglacial period, but it was inhabited by sparsely distributed families. The creation of man in the beginning of the Quaternary is early enough, for the populating of the globe at the end of the third glaciation.

It is on these facts alone that the solution of the problem depends. From the preceding facts there results a strong presumption against the existence of Tertiary man. For, since the existence of man is everywhere

Figs. 83 to 86.—Tertiary flints from Thenay (Loir-et-Cher).

signalized by real and abundant evidence during the whole Quaternary Period, why have we only few and altogether questionable signs for the preceding period, if it is not for the reason that he had not yet made his appearance? If man had really lived in the Tertiary period when the environment was so favorable to his expansion, would it be credible that he should have failed for so long a time, to leave indisputable evidence of his presence? This argument appears to have considerable weight. Let us then examine the facts. In the first place, there are the flints from Thenay (Loir-et-Cher) (figs. 83-86). In 1867, the abbé Bourgeois, director of Pontlevoy, presented to the International Congress of Anthropology and Prehistoric Archeology, at Paris, numerous chipped flints found by him in the clay beds of the Miocene era at the base of the Beauce limestone. He believed them chipped by man. The majority are cracked by fire, many retouched into scrapers and awls. The members of the Congress were quite divided in their opinions. Some believed that the clay beds had been subjected to alterations posterior to the Miocene era; others that the flints had not the marks of intentional chipping; still others merely concluded that man thus dated from the lower Miocene era. The last group, de Quatrefages in particular, have compared these flints with the implements which the Mincopies in the Andaman

1. Humus.	1	
2. Shell-marl, mass of marine fossils.	2	
3. Fresh-water limestone.	3	
4. White, fresh-water marl.	4	
5. Bed of fresh water limestone.	5	
6. Marl.	6	
7. Clay-bed with limestone boulders.	7	
8. Marl.	8	
9. Folliated marl containing the flints discovered by the abbé Bourgeois.	9	

F. 87.— Section of a pit dug by M. Bourgeois on the Thenay plateau.

Isles make at the present time by cracking flints in the fire. Certain anthropologists have attached such importance to the abbé Bourgeois' discovery and to other similar facts, that we think it worth while to give them a critical examination.

With geologists and de Lapparent, we assert, in spite of numerous contradictions, that these clays are undeniably Miocene (fig. 87). But if the flints are of human origin what became of man during the many centuries that separate the Lower Miocene from the Third Interglaciary period? If he really lived at Thenay why did he not populate France and leave unquestionable traces? An attentive study of the flints forces us to deny their human origin.

For they do not bear the marks by which we recognize the work of man; the percussion marks, the design, the touching up, the sharp edges, the signs of use, the regularity of shape. None of these marks can be found on these thousands of fragments. On the highways, in the masses of gravel cracked in the sun or mechanicalyl crushed, we meet with fragments more indicative of intelligent labor than the flints of Thenay.—The cracking does not bear clear traces of the action of fire. Even if it did, it would not of necessity be due to the action of man; the alteration of the flint by the sudden variation of temperature could produce similar fragments. The notches are even more readily accounted for by purely mechanical agents; by striking against rocks, the flints could have had their sides modified by friction, so that small pieces chipped off would give the appearance of touching up.—Arcelin has found similar fragments in the Eocene clays of Mâconnais.—The abbé Breuil [1] has shown that the Eocene flints of Belle-Assise near Clermont (Oise) though naturally chipped leave the impression of a rudimentary shaping. Rutot took them for eoliths. The fragments had remained attached to the nucleus. In the Eocene epoch, there could be no question either of man or of an anthropopithecus.—It is by the millions and in heaps, and not merely in isolated spots that these flints are found in the marls of Thenay. We do not understand why, or how, man made so many implements, whereas we can very well conceive how identical conditions have produced the same effect on so many kidney-shaped flints.—We do not really see of what use these flints could have been to man; especially in the number found which have some vague resemblance to scrapers and awls. We have often found among naturally chipped flints some which might have been more readily used than those of the abbé Bourgeois. Never has any trace of a human body been found in the vicinity, to confirm the very

[1] Cf. Breuil, *Anthropologie*, 1910, p. 385.

debatable existence of man at this epoch. We know, in fact, that the oldest human bones do not go back beyond the third interglaciary period or the Chellean period.

We may conclude therefore, that the presence of man in the Miocene is not only not proven, but even that the contrary seems solidly established. For it is incredible that numerous remains should not have been found, had he been in existence. Higher, in the upper Miocene of Otta in the valley of the Tage, Ribeiro (figs. 88-90) also thought he had found human traces in some quartz and flint fragments.—But, de Quatrefages observes "the

Figs. 88 to 90.—Tertiary flints   Figs. 91 and 92.—Tertiary
found near Lisbon.   flints found near Aurillac.

members of the Congress at Lisbon were divided on the origin of the fragments." This throws the intentional shaping into doubt. They have been found upon a Miocene bed and not within it, and as this bed is itself at the surface of a plateau, there is great reason to believe that these flints are undeniably Quaternary.—Indeed, on such a basis, could one formulate or even hasard a theory of a Tertiary man? At *Puy-Courny*, near Aurillac (figs. 91 and 92) Rames discovered, in the upper Miocene, some flint fragments that de Quatrefages asserts have been the work of human handicraft. He thought he recognized in them hachets, discs, points, scrapers, short blades, etc... These objects fashioned from horny and spark producing flints could not have *been chipped out*, says he, by natural forces alone in the midst of four other varieties of flint coming from the same strata. The abbé Breuil rightly sees in these only the result of the pressure produced by two strata of basalt which enclose the stratum of silex. In fact we find the cracked flints with the fragments, in situ.

It seemed to de Quatrefages that "the latest objections relative to Tertiary man should give way before a rather attentive examination of some incisions found

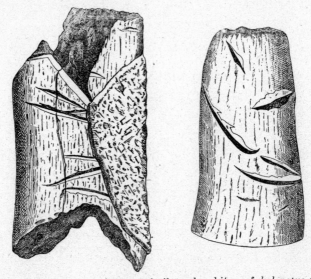

Figs. 93 and 94.—Fragments of rib and cubitus of *balenotus* with numerous incisions.

upon the bones of a balenotus discovered by Capellini [1] in the *Pliocene* clays of Poggiarone near *Monte Aperto* (figs. 93 and 94). Capellini attributes these incisions to a sharp-edged tool used by man to strip the flesh off the balenotus stranded on the left side. A mammal or a fish, says he, would have left two traces of its bite corresponding to the two jaws; a sharpedged tool, which cut off a fragment of bone, ought to produce a smooth inclined surface on the side where the natural fragment was detached. Still many objections are raised against that which he con-

[1] De Quatrefages, *Introduction à l'étude des races humaines.*

siders man's work.   Thus, acording to Dr. Magitot, the
blows struck with the sword of a sword-fish on the whale
bone would have produced cuts similar to those remarked
by Capellini.   According to G. de Mortillet, these cuts
have been made by the teeth of
carnivorous dog-fish; the same
locality possesses specimens of
these teeth.

The most serious difficulty is
the fact that the balenotus has
been found in a stratum above
which there had to be some 12
meters of water during the Pliocene epoch.   In the language of
geologists the neighboring hills
had scarcely emerged and could
not have been inhabited by man
at the time. [1]

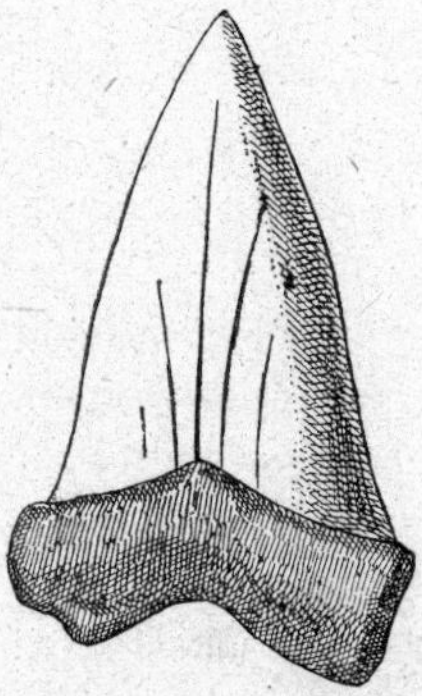

The Eoliths.   The question of
Tertiary flints struck by man
seemed definitely answered, when,
in 1889, it was again reopened.
Prestwich, an English geologist,
became its champion. His example
was followed by others, and

Fig. 95.—Tooth of carni-
vorous squaloid, found
at the same site with
the bones of *Balenotus.*
According to G. de Mor-
tillet, teeth like these
made the incisions dis-
covered by Capellini.

throughout all England no lack of so called worked flints
were soon discovered.   The Belgian geologist Butot made
himself the defender of these flints dubbed " eoliths ".
They are, in his opinion natural shapes directly used by
man, and may be recognized, through the intentional
touching up in the thousands of flints found by Butot
and his friends.   It has been proven, however, that
natural forces could have produced similar flints by friction
against each other.   So the theory of eoliths was
definitively abandoned again.   But like all other hypotheses it has once more been revived.

In 1910, Moir thought he had found at the base of the

[1] De Nadaillac, *Le problème de la vie,* p. 193.

Pliocene at Ipswich in the "Red Crag" certain flints more nicely chipped than the eoliths. The biologist Sir Ray Lancaster took a favorable view of them. Boule unhesitatingly ascribed them to the action of natural agencies, rather than to the intervention of an intelligent being. These flints are called rostrate keels.

We might remark that some such mechanical action as the ocean waves at the foot of cliffs, could produce eoliths. According to the abbé Breuil, it is like the action of the glaciers. We have seen a whole series of these eoliths that were produced by these agencies. They all lack the characteristic marks of human handicraft. This warns us to be always very cautious when there is question of flints that show little evidence of being touched up. [1]

It is useless to take up all the pretended discoveries, for the discussion would always lead to the same conclusion. We can, then, for the present state that there does not exist in positive science any trace of Tertiary man. What has been claimed has not even the weight of serious probability. There is then not one proof that man lived prior to the Quaternary period.

It is quite likely that, de facto, he did not exist any earlier in Europe. For excavations have been made in so many places that, had he lived, his existence would have been discovered. Why, indeed are the traces of man so evident and so constant at the beginning of the third interglacial period, while there is not even a suspicion of them before that time? We confess, however, that our argument is purely negative and that it is not sufficient to establish a thesis. From the fact that man was not discovered before the Quaternary, it does not follow necessarily that he did not exist before that time. Prehistoric archeology is still in its infancy; it has scarcely come into existence; we have not the right to close our eyes in advance to the surprises which it may have in store for us.

The abbé Breuil found at Ipswich, at a very high level

[1] Cf. Boule, *Les hommes fossiles*, p. 120, 122.

in the Upper Pliocene, certain flints which appear chipped, but the indications of this seem so uncertain, the absence of the typical forms so evident, that we do not believe it possible to attribute them to man. At any rate, they would be only from the limit of the Tertiary and of the Quaternary. Moreover, the glacial movement could have modified the local stratification.

§ III. — ABSOLUTE CHRONOLOGY OF MAN.

The problem of the absolute age of humanity is still the preoccupation of our day. A glance at the following figures will suffice to show how varied are the estimates made by different authors.[1] For the Quaternary epoch, the figures range from 10,000 to 1,620,000 years. For the Ice Age, from 6,000 to 1,290,000 years. For the Post-glacial Period 5,000 to 100,000 years. We shall show how exaggerated are the maximum figures. Some would hold that religious motives have influenced the minimum figures. We do not think this is the case for there is no chronology in the Bible. The scientists who have given the minimum figures are above all suspicion. May not the evolutionists who have given the maximum figures be influenced by the desire to prove that man evolved slowly, emerging with difficulty from an inferior condition? We prefer to examine the problem altogether objectively; to study the facts and to draw only such conclusions as they warrant.

Starting from the fact admitted by all prehistorians, that man existed at the beginning of the Third Interglacial period, we shall inquire at what absolute date this lowest limit might be put. Let us interrogate history for the historical period, and geology for the prehistoric period.

---

[1] Cf. Boule, *Les hommes fossiles*, p. 60.

1. Historical chronologies. [1]

Let us first consult the historical chronologies. They
cannot, as we have already remarked, take us back to the
beginning of humanity; but they may aid us in fixing a
limit beyond which traces of human origin are certainly
found. If we hold, for example, that four thousand
years before the Christian era certain nations were fully
civilized, we shall understand why it is necessary to go
back much farther for the first appearance of man.

It will be sufficient to study the nations whose traditions
and monuments proclaim a great antiquity. So we shall
say nothing of America or of Oceanica whose legends,
even if we take them into serious consideration, lead us
back no more than two thousand years. We shall likewise
pass over the documents of European history; at most
they would carry us back three thousand years; whereas
we are sure that Asia and Egypt offer the most ancient
of all chronologies.

We shall make a rapid survey of the traditions of
China, of India, of Egypt and of Chaldea. For each of
these nations, we shall show, that even if their pretensions
are very much exaggerated, we cannot deny them an
antiquity unsuspected up to modern times.

We must evidently relegate to the domain of fable
the 2,267,000 years which certain literary works assign
to the existence of the Celestial Empire. Even, while
according the Chinese traditions the credence which they
do not merit, we shall not encounter figures that would
be disconcerting. In fact, according to Sigismond de
Fries, one of the most recent historians of China, the
history of the Chinese people is divided into two parts; a
mythical period and an historical period which latter
begins in the year 775 B. C. This date, he says, is the

---

[1] Cf. De Nadaillac article entitled : *Les dates préhistoriques* in
Correspondant, Nov. 10 and 25, 1893. For Vigouroux, and other
works, see bibliography.

first fixed point from which one may begin a comparative chronological study. This does not mean that everything would be legendary in the period which this author terms mythical, but no certain date can be assigned to the events. This uncertainty arises from many causes. The authentic monuments are missing; the Chinese annals present numerous contradictions; finally, in the year 231 B. C., the founder of the Tsin dynasty consigned to the flames all the books recounting the history of his predecessors. Whether it had been preserved, or reconstructed from the tales of old men, one of these books, the Chou-King, still gives us some data on the past history of China, but all authors warn us that these sayings can be accepted only with the greatest reserve.

But, supposing it were altogether trustworthy, the historical documents which it gives us, only deal with the period between the years 2,698 and 627 B. C. If we accept what in China is called "the highest antiquity" which begins with the reign of Fo-hi, the inventor of writing, we must go back according to some 2,952 years, according to others 3,568 years prior to our present era. This figure will then be the very earliest possible date at which we could arrive.

Before this epoch, China was undoubtedly inhabited, but its civilization was not yet developed. Its inhabitants lived in a condition similar to that of our own ancestors in Europe during the Stone Age. They dwelt in caves, used stone implements, were ignorant of metals and subsisted on raw meat. These men are called Miao-tze or "sons of the uncultivated soil". Their descendents still live in the mountanous regions of China, whither they have been driven and held first by the Pun-ti race, later by the yellow race which still inhabits the country. According to Nadaillac, whom we follow, this invasion of the Mongolian race would go back only twenty-three centuries before the Christian Era. This new race quickly attained to a high degree of civilization in which it has remained fixed down to the present day. We know from their traditions that the Chinese at a very early date learned how to determine the solstitial points and the equinoxes, to alloy copper and tin, to make money, to work copper and iron and to dye fabrics.

From all this obscurity in Chinese tradition, two things stand out prominently : *a*) that 30 or 40 centuries before the Christian Era, China was already inhabited and so it is necessary to place the first dispersion of mankind at a very remote period; *b*) that in allowing, as de Nadaillac has done, three thousand years, for the period of human existence, we satisfy to a great extent all the otherwise hypothetical exigencies which Chinese tradition suggests. In fact, supposing that the Miao-tze had been masters of China six thousand years ago, would not the addition of four thousand years suffice for the development and spread of humanity over all Asia?

The past history of India, as little known as that of China, does not require such high figures. The millions of years which Hindoos ascribe to themselves are as fabulous as those of China. We must seek outside of these unfounded myths for a true chronology. The documents worthy of any credence, scarcely go beyond 1,000 or 1,200 years B. C. According to certain authors, we cannot even establish an historical chronology prior to 800 B. C.

The principal monuments concerning the Hindoos are : 1) The trilingual inscriptions found at Persepolis, in which Darius, king of the Persians, refers to the land of Hindusch as having been brought under his sway;—2) Some fragments of the Greek writer Megasthemus who visited India as embassador of King Seleucus Nicator about the year 300 B. C.;—3) The inscriptions of Asoka made in the year 250 B. C. are the most ancient native documents; —4) The Vedas, celebrated literary productions of ancient Hindoos, were composed at various periods; the oldest goes back beyond the XVIth century B. C., but otherwise gives us no historical information;—5) The old epic called Mahabhârata, and the drama Sakountala which have revealed to the Occident the high civilization of the Hindoos are, it seems, still more recent than the Vedas. According

to Sassen, an authority on India, the victory which terminated the war spoken of in the poem, should be placed
between the Xth and XIIth centuries B. C. Other monuments as the megaliths similar to the Breton dolmens are
of altogether uncertain date.

But long before the date derived from the monumentst
India was inhabited. Flourishing cities had been buil,
whose very names have been forgotten. Numerous implements, knives, arrows, etc., attest that as in Europe the
stone age had existed for many centuries before the age
of metals. It is commonly admitted that the Aryans must
have invaded India at least 2,500 years before Christ.
But before the arrival of the Aryans, the yellow race had
already made incursions into the Indian Peninsula, and
had found there negroes of the Ethiopic type, who themselves had dispossessed the Negritos whom de Quatrefages
believes had been the first inhabitants of India.

This enumeration suffices to prove to us that India
was inhabited many centuries before the first certain
dates of its history. Yet we need not multiply these
centuries indefinitely, nor attribute to India more than
the maximum for China.

The necessary documents for an Egyptian chronology
are derived from three sources : a) the Greek writers;
b) Manethon's history and c) the recently discovered
monuments.

a) There are too many contradictions in the Greek
writers that treat of Egypt, to make them reliable. Plato
thought that Egypt had already arrived at the height
of its development 10,000 years before his time (De Legi-
bus, I). The priests of Heliopolis had declared to Solon
that their monarchy had been in existence 8,000 years.
Later, Herodotus learned from the priests of the same
temple that the records of their kings go back more than
eleven thousand years. Varron accords two thousand,

---

[1] Cf. Meyer, Geschichte des alten Aegyptens, Berlin, 1887; Breasted,
The ancient records of Egypt. 5 vols. Chicago, 1906-7; A History
of Egyptians, New York, 1905. For other works, see bibliography.

Diodorus of Sicily five thousand years to the Egyptian monarchy.

b) Three centuries before the Christian era, Manethon, an Egyptian priest, was charged by Ptolomy Philadelphus with the task of writing the history of his country. This history was destroyed in the burning of the Alexandrian Library. But some fragments preserved by Josephus and Eusebius have at least transmitted its chronology. The work attributed to Egypt an existence of 30,000 years before the reign of Alexander. This long period was divided in the following way : [1]

1. Reign of the gods	13 900
2. Reign of the heroes	1 255
3. Reign of other kings	1 817
4. Reign of the thirty Memphites	1 790
5. Reign of the ten Thinites	350
6. Reign of the shades and of the heroes	5 813
7. Reign of the thirty dynasties and 370 kings	5 000

This assemblage of gods, shades and of men has long since caused the chronology of Manethon to be relegated to the domain of fables. But as modern discoveries are confirming the truth of these narratives in that which concerns the 30 dynasties, this last part of his work inspires greater confidence. If we admit the 30 dynasties and the 370 kings who have reigned over Egypt from Menes to Alexander the Great (336-323), we can fix with certainty only the duration of this period. The figures given by the authors that have studied the question vary from 2,691 (Wilkinson) to 5,702 B. C. (Boekh); F. Lenormant gives 5,004, Meyer 3,315, de Barenton 2,735. Even while accepting this highest number as decisive, the antiquity of Egypt would give us no concern. But we ought first be sure of its accuracy, for it has been arrived at by the addition of the years that have been assigned to each King's reign, as if the dynasties had never been simultaneous nor some of the kings contemporaneous, whereas we see from

---

[1] Table taken from Vigouroux, *Les Livres saints...* 3rd edit., vol. III, p. 524. It is the table made by Eusebius.

the monuments during certain periods that several kings reigned at a time.

The monuments also show that the length of the various reigns had often been exaggerated by Manethon.

c) The authentic monuments are the very incomplete royal lists; the hierogliphic inscriptions recounting the exploits of the Egyptian kings; the steles, tombs, etc.   We shall not describe them here. [1]   It will be enough for our purpose to state that the oldest are the tombs of the three first dynasties.   Thus the original monuments, while entirely confirming Manethon's dates do not carry us back beyond the reign of Menes, that is to say to a maximum of 5,000 years before Christ.   But it is important to note that this limit of Egyptian history is in a period of complete civilization.   The Egyptians knew how to work the mines, to cast statues from bronze, to spin and to dye linen, and to raise animals before the Fourth Dynasty. [2]   They had a very advanced scientific knowledge.   The British Museum is in possession of a papyrus of the Twelfth Dynasty of about the year 2,000 on which is found a treatise on surveying.   Religion which appears to have been Monotheistic was in honor in the first dynasties.   The statues of 342 successive high-priests, which Herodotus saw at Heliopolis in the Fifth Century B. C., undoubtely carry us back to the beginning of the thirty dynasties and the 370 kings.

Whatever we may think of the first condition of man, it is evident that a very long time has elapsed since the first dispersion of the human family, and since the arrival of the first inhabitants of the land of Egypt.   For, a civilization as advanced as that of the Egyptians, four or five thousand years before the Christian era, could be the result only of a very slow social evolution.   However, we shall still freely say with de Nadaillac, that there is nothing

---

[1] Cf. Meyer, *Geshichte des alten Aegyptens, Guide to the British Museum*, p. 186.

[2] Cf. *Guide to the Egyptian collections*, in *The British Museum*, p. 109-203.

in all this to compel us to place the creation of man, any further back than ten thousand years; as four thousand years from the time of creation to the first Egyptian dynasty, is quite sufficient for man to populate the globe and to attain to a state of civilization.

Chaldean and Assyrian monuments give us the most precise data. Before the middle of the last century, we knew Chaldea only from the history of the Babylonian Berose, who lived in the third century before our era. The age of 466,000 years which this historian ascribes to his nation, no longer receives any credence. Even Cicero treated as dreams and brazen falsehood the pretensions of the Chaldeans. The cuneiform inscriptions recently deciphered give us the names of most of the kings, anterior to the monarchs whose history was already known, but they only take us back at the very most, to six or seven thousand years from the present day.

We shall mention here only two of these discoveries. The first refers to Sargon king of Assyria and to Naram-Sin, his son, who reigned in the north of Chaldea about 3,739 B. C. At this period, art was already well advanced and governments very well organized; astronomical formulæ and the calculation of eclipses, found on cylinders, attest to a remarkable scientific progress. The portraits of these kings were very artistically done. [1] Nabonahid or Nabonid, the last king of Babylon, was dethroned by Cyrus in 539. Many inscriptions have been found on cylinders which report his restoration of the temples. On one of these, Nabonahid says that he will restore, at Sippar, the temple of Samas, built by Naram-Sin the son of Sargon 3,200 years before his time. This figure announces this foundation in the year 3,739 before Christ and 5,864 before 1924.

From other sources, we know that Naram-Sin is a contemporary of the Bronze Age and posterior to the Neolithic. We find, in fact, in the excavations at Susa,

[1] Cf. *Guide to the Babylonian and Assyrian antiquities*, British Museum, London, 1908, p. 229.

an industry that is certainly of the Bronze Age, since this metal is found up to 25 meters from the base of Tell *in the numerous tombs that it contains*. At this level, were found a few pieces of pottery which denote an exact knowledge of an industry that was far from being in its infancy. Moreover, the ornamental designs of animals and of men that adorn these ceramics lead us to suppose them to be the product, not of a primitive people, but of a nation long civilized. Now the ceramics, according to Pottier, resemble those which are contemporaneous with Naram-Sin (3,739), at Lagash (Tello). Thus, it would date around 4,000 years before Christ. Lower down is a more ancient type of pottery which goes back to 5,000 years before Christ. Still, if as certain Assyriologists believe, the date of Nabonahid is too great by 1,000 years, it would be necessary to adopt the figure 4,000 B. C. This date represents also the end of the Neolithic period for this country. [1] The second takes us back still farther towards the beginning of this Chaldean civilization which seems to have antedated all oriental civilizations. These are the stelas, bas-reliefs, statuettes and inscriptions pertaining to Our-Nina and E-Anna-Dou, his grandson, both much older than Sargon. According to the tablets, Our-Nina wishing to erect a temple worked there with his own hands. Already at that time bronze was in use. [2]

It is probable that Our-Nina, the tenth king before Sargon, goes back farther than 4,000 years before Christ. Of the age that preceded him, there exists no document possessing any chronological value. But how many centuries intervened since the first appearance of man? Without any monument we cannot conjecture; not even approximately. Ought we add four thousand years, or ought we add more? We cannot be certain.

---

[1] Cf. *Dict. Apologét.* (art. *Babylone*).—Pottier, *Études historique et chronologique sur les vases peints de l'Acropole de Suse*, p. 12 et sq. Paris, Leroux.

[2] Cf. de Nadaillac, in *Correspondant*, Nov. 10th, 1898, p. 485.

If we wish to draw a conclusion from the preceding facts, we must say : *a*) that the pretensions of Asiatic peoples to a remote antiquity are absolutely legendary; —*b*) that the authentic monuments of the most ancient countries do not go beyond 5,000 years prior to the Christian era;—*c*) that the arts and sciences already well developed at these historical dates, make it necessary to place the beginning of humanity at a very much earlier date;—*d*) that the monuments of men do not furnish any date for an exact appreciation of the duration of time anterior to history;—*e*) that, if the geological documents do not point that way, nothing obliges us to assign to humanity an existence of more than 10,000 years.

2. Chronology based on geology.

We can divide into three periods, the time which elapsed since the formation of the interglacial, or Chellean deposits, in which we find the first human traces.

The first would be the interglacial period; the second the glacial period; and the third the actual or post-glacial period. We can reduce these three periods to two, by prolonging the first to the maximum extension of the glacier, and by making the second begin with the end of the glacial period. Thus, we shall have the glacial and the post-glacial periods.

Some years ago, scientists postulated for man's existence thousands of centuries. Haeckel allowed him more than 100,000 years; Burmeister supposed Egypt inhabited for more than 72,000 years; Draper attributed to the European man more than 250,000 years; finally de Montillet in 1913 still taught that man was in existence for about 240,000 years. Walcott, 400,000 and Penck and Osborn, 500,000.

These figures have been upon so arbitrary and so weak a basis that real science has long since rejected them. There is also a tendency to diminish notably the duration of the human species. Such indeed is the statement of the American scientist McGee, made in 1892 during the Geological Congress at Washington. This is also the opin-

ion of W. Upham who says : "Observations at the present
day permit us to believe that the end of the glacial period
is much more recent than we have believed."

The recent prehistoric discoveries have given occasion
to new extensions of time. [1]

We shall review briefly the attempts at geological
chronology which have served to estimate the duration,
both of the present epoch and of the Quaternary period.
Let us define the notion of a geological clock. We must
first fix on some definite starting-point and on the limit
of the period which we wish to measure, then some natural
clock or phenomenon progressing with constant and
commensurable velocity during the period of evolution.
This may be a phenomenon of erosion, of sedimentation,
of transport, etc. The precision of these measurements
depends on the facts of the case, viz. the starting-point,
the terminus and the regularity of the phenomenon.
Very frequently, the velocity is variable and consequently
uncertain; the limits are indeterminate. We shall cite
some of the chronometers used. Some are very defective,
others incorrectly interpreted; we shall give the preference
to the glacial phenomena and to those of fluvial erosion
which seem to be the most regular.

1. *Post-glacial Period.*—According to Arcelin "a duration of 7,000 to 9,000 years is generally admitted today,
both in Europe and in America for the post-glacial period,
reckoned from the beginning of the glacial recession to our
own day [2]". These figures are based on many observations made by numerous geologists. Though each observation is but hypothetical and possesses an element of
uncertainty, the concordance of their results is a fact
remarkable enough to invite our confidence in the method
employed. These methods consist in the study "of permanent natural phenomena producing effects which taken

---

[1] Cf. Boule, *Les hommes fossiles*, p. 60.

[2] Arcelin, *Quelques problèmes relatifs à l'antiquité préhistorique*,
read before the International Congress of Catholic Scientists, at
Brussels in 1894, published in *Revue des questions scientifiques*,
Jan. 1896.

together can be measured and so furnish data". It is thus that de Quatrefages, would define natural *chronometers*. A good natural chronometer, for the estimation of the post-glacial period would be a geological formation beginning with the recession of the glacier and continuing since then, without interruption and with certain regularity, and so affording very authentic data.

The celebrated geologist Lyell took as a basis for his calculations the erosion caused by the fall of Niagara. When, after the beginning of the glacial recession the river had changed its course, it flowed over the plateau which extends from Lake Erie to Lake Ontario. The falls were then near Queenstown, 12 kilometers (7 1/2 miles) from their present position. The 12 kilometer (7 1/2 mi.) gorge has been quite regularly worn away by the action of the water during this period. Lyell maintains that the falls recede around 30 meters (81 ft.) a century. "Hence", said he "some 40,000 years would have been necessary to cut a 12 kilometer gorge into the plateau." Since Lyell, other scientists have studied the same phenomenon, and hold that the erosion had been much more rapid than Lyell thought. W. Upham would have it 10,000 years which figure Gilbert reduced to 7,000. [1] In this study of Niagara Falls we suppose that the end of the Ice Age in America corresponded with the same period in Europe. As we have said, this identification is probable, since the same cause has had to produce the same effect in the same time. For the post-glacial formation of the Niagara gorge we adopt the figure 8,000 given by de Lapparent. We believe this still too great, for at the beginning the action of the water was more considerable because of its much greater volume. If the annual erosion had been two meters instead of 1 m. 50, 6,000 years would suffice. [2]

These represent the entire time that elapsed since the maximum of the glacial extension. Hence it measures

---

[1] Cf. de Nadaillac, *Le problème de la vie*, p. 213.
[2] Cf. De Lapparent, *Les silex taillés*, Paris, Bloud.

the duration of the glacial recession and that of the entire postglacial period down to our own day. From the geological stand-point, this duration ought to be very nearly equal to that which had preceded it, from the beginning of the third interglaciary to the maximum of the glacier extension. In the following schema the whole question is seen at a glance.

```
3rd Interglaciary  4th Glaciation        Present
|----------------|-------|------\------------------|
A                B       C      D                  E
|    Pre-glacial         |   Post-glacial          |
```

The recession of the falls of Niagara extended from C to E and took 8000 years.

Now, if we suppose AC = CE, the duration of AC should also be 8,000 years.

Other estimates were made in America. Thus the falls of St. Anthony in the Mississipi leads to the figure 8,000 years for the post-glacial period.—Dr. Andrews, basing his calculations on the erosions produced by the waves of Lake Michigan, says 7,500.—Emerson after an attentive study of Lakes Bonneville and Lahonton gives 10,000 years as the maximum. Other estimates all lead to nearly the same result. A second calculation based on the glacial advance and recession would give similar results. We might divide the interval AE into 3 sections which, for geological reasons, we might consider equal. The attempts to measure the duration of one glaciation BD, give quite concordant figures, in the neighborhood of 6,000 years, 2,000 for the advance (figure exaggerated), 2,000 for the stationary period, and 2,000 for the recession. This figure of 6,000 multiplied by three would thus give the duration of the entire period, or 18,000 years. Though arrived at in an entirely different manner and certainly exaggerated, it agrees quite well with the preceding. We have supposed the synchronism of the 4th glaciation in America and in Europe. It is admitted by geologists, de Lapparent and Haug in particular. The latter gives the arguments in his Traité de géologie, p. 500 et seq. It is shown today that the Scandinavian range had been twice invaded by the ocean during the Quaternary. The first time at the recession of the great Rissian glacier, and the second time at the recession of the last Würmian glacier. The first invasion had left marine deposits, characterized by the *Yoldia* found at the present time at heights varying from 0 to 270 meters. The second marine transgression left littorals which are found at lower levels, ranging from 0 to 65 meters, [1] in the Scandinavian range. The same phenomenon is found in Canada. Similar trans-gressions and similar fossils, placed at varying altitudes, show that the maximum elevation of the Canadian range is found between the Hudson Bay and the mouth of the St. Lawrence in the glacial region.

Moreover, the theory of epirogenic movements easily explains the simultaneous oscillations of the Finno-Scandinavian range and of the Canadian Shield (bouclier) (?) separated by an area of incline, the Atlantic. One might go farther still, and admit as very probable, that the positive oscillations of these ranges have apparently the same duration as the negative oscillations, and that the multiple oscillations ought apparently have the same duration. All oscillation is, by its nature, isochronous. To the positive oscillation corresponds the glaciation, to the negative, the melting of the glacier. Haug considers these oscillations of the earth as the most plausible cause of the glacial phenomena. So much for the geological phenomena with its share of uncertainty. [2]

We can, moreover, parallel the different prehistoric periods with these same geological phenomena. The Chellean and Acheulean periods are interglaciary, the Mousterian period corresponds to the glacial advance; the Aurignacian and the Magdalenian to the glacial recession; the Neolithic to the postglacial period.

In consequence of these relations, the Aurignacian would date around 8,000 years ago, the Chellean around

---

[1] Cf. Haug, p. 502, for map of the isobases of the ocean at Yoldia.
[2] Cf. Haug, *Traité de géologie*, p. 501 et sq.

16,000. But as we have already said, we believe these figures are exaggerated. We shall return to them later on.

In Europe, some at first, wished to base their calculations on the peculiar deposits known in Denmark under the name of *kjœkkenmœdings* or *kitchen midden*, or *refuse heaps*, in which are found heaped pell-mell by ancient peoples, shells, the remains of fish, birds and mammals, stone implements sometimes rudely chipped, sometimes artistically fashioned. But it has been impossible to rely upon them as a trustworthy chronometer, both because of the lack of data and for the reason that the relative date of the beginning of the deposits is unknown. Better results seem to have been obtained from a study of the Danish post-glacial skovmoses or peat beds. These beds or pits occupy sink-like depressions in the Quaternary silt, and at times reach a depth of ten meters. As man frequented these skovmoses from the time the first layers of peat were formed in these sinks, and as he accidentally left a great number of objects and implements which he had been using, there was formed a sort of "chronologically constructed museum" (de Quatrefages) in which each generation has left some trace of its existence and vestiges of its social condition. On exploring this peat, layer by layer, we may reconstruct the history of the ancient Danish peoples. We find there successively, traces of the Iron Age, the Bronze Age and the Stone Age.—If we knew with exactness the average annual increase of this peat the skovmoses would furnish excellent chronometers. But as the authors give figures that vary from 1 to 10, we readily perceive how the results found are very debatable. The scientist Steenstrup had assigned 4,000 years to the formation of these beds; but if some have doubled this number we have no right to contradict, especially if we take into account the subsidence which in time took place in the lower layers. [1]

In Switzerland, investigations have been made into the age of the "lake cities" through the recession of

[1] Cf. De Quatrefages, *L'espèce humaine*, chap. XII.

the lakes. The lake-dwellings were built on piles in the
water. Some of these piles have been found three kilometers (1 7/8 mis.) from the shore of the present Lake
Bienne, near the bridge of Thiele. How long has it taken
Lake Bienne to recede three kilometers in consequence of
all sorts of deposits? In 1100, the abbey of St. John was
erected on the shore of this lake; in 1850 it was 375 meters
away; hence the shore line has receded on an average of
50 meters a century. From this it is easy to deduce that
it required 6,000 years to recede three kilometers. This
figure it is true does not take us to the beginning of the
recent period, for the dwellings of the Thiele are not the
oldest lake-dwellings in Switzerland. They carry us back
to the recent Neolithic period.

According to G. de Mortillet, the most important
chronometer formed from deposits in water courses is
that of the cone of the Tinière. The Tinière is a torrent
in the canton of Vaud, which empties into the lake of
Geneva at Villeneuve. It is post-glacial. At the point
where it issues from the mountain and empties into the
plain, it forms a vast cone of detritus. When a railroad
made a cut 113 meters long and 7.7 meters in depth,
three undisturbed strata were found. A Roman stratum
containing tiles and Roman coins at depth of 1.20 meters;
a stratum from the Bronze Age at 3 meters, and a stratum
from the Stone Age at 5.7 meters. Morlot who has described this excavation with the greatest care, comes to the
following chronometric conclusion :

Age of Roman stratum	10 to 15	centuries
» of Bronze age stratum...............	29 to 42	—
» of Stone age stratum	47 to 70	—
» of entire cone	74 to 110	—

In the beginning, the formation of the deposit was
more rapid. Thus the age of the entire cone which ought
to go back to the end of the glacial period would not surpass
the average which we, after Arcelin, [1] have indicated, even

---

[1] De Mortillet, in the *Dictionnaire des sciences anthropologiques*,
supposes that these results have been "revised and corrected"

after increasing the figures given by Morlot. Arcelin himself arrived at similar results. From a study of the Soane it is seen that at present the river cuts a channel in its bed through the Quaternary alluvia. The layers of muddy deposits from these erosions of the river bed raise the shore line. The blue Quaternary marl is clearly distinguishable throughout from the modern alluvia. At 33 different localities, Arcelin studied the natural cuts of these banks, laid bare by the river torrents. He constantly found at the same levels some objects appertaining to the Roman period, others to the Bronze Age and still others to the Polished Stone Age. Knowing the age of the Roman stratum, he was able to compute the approximate age of the other strata. We give his results : [1]

Duration of Roman stratum	1 500	years
— of Bronze age stratum..................	2 250	—
— of Polished stone stratum	3 000	—
— of Quaternary marls....................	6 650	—

These figures are considered as the minimum by de Quatrefages and by Arcelin himself. [2]

From all these attempts we conclude that an average of 7,000 to 9,000 years suffices to account for the phenomena of the post-glacial period, or the period which elapsed since the first recession of the Alpine glaciers.

Can the alluvia or the filling up of the lakes give us reliable data? Assuredly, providing we do not exaggerate. The filling up of the Lake of Geneva would date from the end of the fourth glacial extension, i. e., from an epoch pertaining to that whose antiquity we wish to measure viz. DE. Now according to Forel, the Lake of Geneva whose volume was once 6,884 million cubic meters, is almost one third filled in. Forel estimates that the

by Arcelin so as to make them accord with the Bible. We should be surprised at such an injustice done to so conscientious a scientist as Arcelin, if we did not know that every page of this dictionary was inspired not by science, but by antireligious hate. This sectarian spirit is revealed in every article.

[1] De Quatrefages, *L'espèce humaine*, chap. XII.

[2] Arcelin, in *Revue des questions scientifiques*, Jan. 1895, p. 8.

waters of the Rhône carry 221,670 cubic meters of silt during the 90 days of summer. By supposing that this might be the annual average of the river, since the recession of the glacier, the filling in of one third of the lake would have required in round numbers some 10,000 years.

2. *The Preglacial Period comprising the interglaciary and the drift period.* — For these past ages, the data are still very vague and the results obtained very uncertain. Our purpose being, not to write only of matters that are decisive, but to make known the actual status of science, we shall add only a few words more on these so inaccessible ages of antiquity. Some authors have looked to astronomy for the principle of solution. They hold that the alternate glacial conditions were determined and regulated by the variation of the eccentricity of the earth's orbit, and the procession of the equinoxes. For, in virtue of these variations, there would have been alternation of very long and very cold winters with very short and very hot summers. But astronomers and physicists are unanimous in rejecting this hypothesis. For: 1) this supposed cooling could not explain the abundant snow-fall during the Ice-age; 2) these astronomical variations being regular, it would be surprising if these variations did not take place before or after the Quaternary period; 3) the eccentricity that is invoked to explain the Quaternary glaciers would place the fourth glaciation back more than 200,000 years. Now as de Lapparent says, not more than 8,000 to 10,000 years have elapsed since the disappearance of the last ice in America, and we can say the same for that in Europe. Astronomy cannot furnish a chronometer for estimating the duration of the Ice Age. In any case, it would give us no exact data on that special period whose length we are investigating.

It would also be imprudent to have recourse to the *succession of fauna* contemporaneous with Quaternary man. We know for a certainty that in the first Paleolithic, Chellean and Acheulean phases, man *in* Central Europe at first lived associated with the *elephas meridionalis* (fig. 96) later with the *elephas antiquus* (fig. 96)

the *rhinoceros Merckii* and the *hippopotamus major*; in
the second Mousterian phase, with the *mammoth* or *elephas
primigenius* (fig. 97) and the *rhinoceros tichorhinus* (fig. 98);

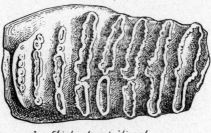

1 *Eléphant méridional*

2 *Eléphant antique*

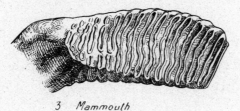

3 *Mammouth*

Fig. 96.—Rear molars of the three principal species of fossil
elephants. (Boule.)

1. Elephas meridionalis.
2. Elephas antiquus.
3. Elephas primigenius or Mammoth.

and during the last reappearance of the glaciers, in the
Upper Paleolithic with the reindeer or *cervus tarandus*.
But can we say how many ages are necessary for the
appearance or disappearance of a fauna? Are we in a
position to say in what this substitution of a hot climate

fauna by one from a cold climate precisely consisted?
From the fact that the fauna about us has not changed
during 5,000 or 6,000 years, have we the right to conclude
that a change of fauna requires hundreds of thousands of

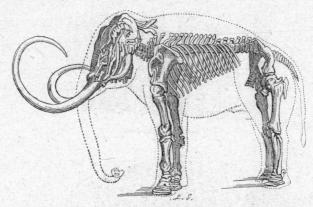

Fig. 97.—Skeleton of *Elephas primigenius* (Mammoth).

years? A change of climatic conditions would suffice for
the substitution of a northern fauna for a torrid zone
fauna, *in a few years*.   The fauna has not evolved in the

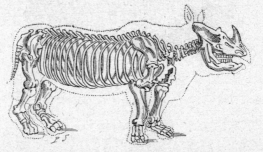

Fig. 98.—Skeleton of rhinoceros (*tichorhinus*).

locality. It has migrated.   Hence we must not look for
any chronological data from paleontology. We have no precise chronology of the preglacial period. The best that we
can do is to give an *estimate* that is colored by the *excessive*
figures proposed by certain authors, but without wishing

to give them as exact figures. Mortillet [1] makes man go back 230,000 or 240,000 years. He bases his calculations on the *drift of the glaciers* and on the changes effected in the lime-stone at Biolay near Aix-les-Bains, France.

The great Alpine glaciers carried a number of heavy stones a distance of 280 kilometers (175 miles) to Lyons. If we suppose the Quaternary glaciers had the same velocity as the existing glaciers, 62.66 meters a year, we shall find that their transfer was made in 4,468 years. But this number, says de Mortillet, is much too small to account for the entire period.—1) It measures only the extension of the glacier; it must at least be doubled to obtain the duration of the advance and recession, say about 9,000 years. —2) This figure measures only the duration of one glacial oscillation. There were many oscillations of this kind in the Quaternary period. At least three. By tripling this figure we obtain 27,000 years. —3) The velocity of 62.66 meters a year is the velocity of glaciers on steep declivities, the less inclined the declivity the slower the glacier movement. Now Quaternary glaciers had only steep declivities at the starting point. For the most part they flowed in the valleys at a very slight incline. On an average the declivity of the Quaternary glaciers was really five times less than the slope of actual glaciers; hence the velocity was thus five times less. Consequently the oscillations of the Quaternary glaciers certainly require more than 100,000 years.

We cannot admit all the elements of this calculation. According to de Lapparent, the minimum velocity of the Sea of Ice is 0.305 meters a day which should give an annual velocity of 109 meters, or say 100 meters a year. To move over 280 kilometers (175 miles) only 2,800 years instead of 4,468 would have been required.—If we double this to take in the recession and advance, the whole amounts to 5,600 years.—We have no right to triple the number obtained by the great glacial extension, since man was present only during a single glaciation.—We do not

[1] *Formation de la nation française,* Paris, Alcan, 1897, p. 234.

think it necessary to quintuple, nor even augment the figures obtained from a consideration of actual glaciers, when dealing with the Quaternary glaciers. We must rather diminish them. The velocity of the glaciers is a function of the mass of ice in movement. Indeed, the great glaciers of Alaska and of the Himalayas have velocities from two to ten times greater than those of the small Alpine glaciers. [1] The Quaternary had therefore a velocity much greater than 100 meters a year. De Geer holds that the Scandinavian glacier moved at a velocity of 0.56 meters a day or 200 meters a year.

We give these estimates and these figures, not as anything decisive, but solely as a study to show the reader how enormous numbers can vanish as by magic, before the powers of reason.

The chronometer which G. de Mortillet considers the most trustworthy, is the erosion of the limestone on a hill situated a little above Aix-les-Bains in Savoy. The hill has been polished by the ancient glacier of La Haute-Isère. Wherever the rock has been preserved from the action of the atmosphere and of water by a layer of loam, the polish is still quite noticeable. But considerable weathering has taken place wherever the layer has been subjected to atmospheric action. The Romans, some 1800 years ago, quarried the stone and used it for the buildings erected by them in the neighborhood. The surfaces left exposed at this period have been crevised by atmospheric agencies only to a depth of 2 to 3 millimeters. On the contrary, the older corrosions in the same limestone attain an average depth of one meter. If in 2 000 years the corrosion bas been one centimeter, at most 200 000 years would have been required to effect a corrosion 100 times as great. Thus there should have been 200 000 years, since the great glaciers retired from the valley of Aix.

This chronometer can not be exact as there is an evident

---

[1] Cf. *Revue du Clergé*, 1912, p. 683 sq.

source of error in the proposed calculation. We suppose
that the atmospheric agencies were always operating
with the same intensity. Now in the glacial period remarkable for abundant rains and great variations of temperatures, the corrosion would have been produced more
rapidly than at present. We suppose that these agencies
alone have produced the entire result. But, there were
fissures which existed before, and which were only increased
by erosion. We would not dwell on these facts here, if
there were not at the present time a new tendency to
lengthen the time of man's existence on earth.

Among the most weighty reasons adduced are the
following : 1) The density of the population in prehistoric
times and even in the Lower Paleolithic period; 2) The
necessary time for the development of human industry;
3) The importance of archeological remains left by man;
4) The differences noticeable in the existing races in the
Lower Paleolithic period; 5) The importance of the geological phenomena produced under the eyes of man; the
glacial phenomena and their consequences; the channeling
of and sedimentation in the valleys; volcanic phenomena;
orogenic movements; important sedimentary deposits, for
example : ancient *loess* and recent *loess*.

Let us give a brief answer to each of these difficulties.
1) If the population doubled only every hundred years
starting from a single pair, 4,000 years would suffice to
give the actual population of the globe, about 1,748,000,000.

2) The Chellean industry precedes the others, but is
not so inferior to them, that it would be necessary to
interpolate thousands of years, for a transition to the
Mousterian or the Magdalenian. The fashioning of the
flints is very advanced in the Chellean period and is similar
to that of the Mousterian as it is known today. If the
industries do not originate one from another, but have
distinct origins and merely happen to be superposed on
French soil, in the European catch-basin, there is no longer
any need for assuming thousands of years. Indeed as
long as man lived by the chase he had to migrate rapidly
towards the better hunting grounds. These migrations

ultimately and permanently increased the population within the confines of Europe.

3) Wars incited by the food question rapidly spread destruction over the most poorly armed races, and this recurred at different times. These wars would in themselves explain the sudden and rapid changes of industries or of civilization, if we were to verify them one after another.

4) The study of prehistoric archeology or of the remains of prehistoric human industry, does not seem to favor over much the advocates of a very long period of time. As proof of this, we have the following. Of the accumulated remains of prehistoric human industry in *caverns*, we know of none which surpass 20 meters in height. On the sites of towns such as Susa the debris does not exceed 35 meters. The excavations made to the very foundation of Susa have nevertheless shown the presence of bronze or of copper, or of pottery which is known to be contemporaneous with a civilization that does not go back further than 6,000 years. The deposits in the most important caverns range from the Mousterian to the Neolithic periods, without reaching a height of 20 meters. It would appear, therefore, that a duration of 6,000 years was amply sufficient for the accumulation of this mass of debris. We must know that the troglodytes left all the refuse from the kitchen and from their work in one place, and this with other rubbish finally obstructed the cave. Prehistoric archeology therefore does not seem to exact an antiquity as remote as some have recently pretended, when speaking of 10,000 years for the Neolithic, the same for the Upper Paleolithic, and of a much longer duration for the Lower Paleolithic, without mentioning the time that elapsed between the appearance of man and the Chellean period. We believe it nearer the truth to adopt the figures found by means of geological data.

All the prehistoric industries can be comprised in a maximum period of 18,000 years.

The following schema illustrates our meaning. It represents the three periods: the interglacial (A) the glacial (B) and the recent (C). In A we have the Chellean and Acheulean

industries.   In B the Mousterian, Aurignacian, Solutrian
and Magdalanean industries.   In C the Neolithic industries,
the metals and the historic period.

Ch.	Ach.	M. A. S. M.	Neo. M. H.
A		B	C

5) The formation of the human races that we find in
the Lower Paleolithic does not necessarily imply a very
long duration.   These races could have appeared suddenly,
as did the animal and plant races.

6) The strongest argument in favor of a high antiquity
for man is drawn from geological phenomena contemporaneous with man, which should have required many tens
or even hundreds of thousands of years.   But we have seen
that some of the facts adduced, such as glaciations, interglaciations, changes of fauna, are not demonstrative. The
others, as final channeling of the valleys, deposits of lœss,
alluvia, volcanic eruptions are not conclusive.   According
to certain geologists and prehistorians, man might have
witnessed the channeling of the valleys, enclosed between
the high and low terraces.   The average, difference of level
is fifteen meters.

Some would conclude from all these facts that an extremely long time was necessary to accomplish this.   First let
us say that the water courses were much more important.
It is not an exaggeration to suppose them at least ten times
more extensive, if we may judge from the valleys which
they have formed.   The Somme was once a kilometer
wide; the Seine, according to Belgrand had a flow of
27,000 to 70,000 cubic meters per second instead of the
present 75 to 2,000.   The work done was in proportion to
the velocity and to the volume of water.   Hence the
channeling must have been rapid; we have seen this for
the Niagara and for the Mississippi.   Moreover de Lapparent does not admit that the channeling below the highest
terrace was done under the eyes of prehistoric man, for
it is anterior to the Pleistocene.

We find indeed at Chelles, almost at the present level

of the Marne the Chellean industry hidden under a thick stratum of gravel. It was therefore necessary that the valley should have been channeled at this epoch. Hence, the argument drawn from the channeling of valleys under the eyes of man has no value. The gravels in the valleys have been changed, but this could have been done very rapidly in a few thousand years. It is sufficient even for a flood to transport materials and to deposit them under masses of silt at another spot.

The fact of finding the jaw-bone of Mauer under 24 meters of fluvial sediment should not lead us to argue a fabulous antiquity for it. Nothing is so variable as the velocity of these deposits. Might we not consider the sediments accumulated by the winds during this period? We may say that the action of the wind increased from the fact that the glacier denuded a region, pulverized the materials and gathered these at favorable points, whence the winds carried them rapidly to great distances in the valleys, and deposited them in deep layers under the form of loess and clays.

The orogenic movements of which man was a witness does not require any greater duration. Volcanic phenomena are indeed the most sudden and the most rapid of all, and we do not see that this compels us to postulate for them a long duration. Whether the volcano ejects pulverized materials or vomits forth lava, it does this with an incomparable intensity and rapidity. The recent eruptions of Mt. Vesuvius and of Kilauea in Hawaii in May 1924 are proof of this.

The phenomena of *erosion* in the often very fluid matter ejected from the volcano, are such that veritable torrents of mud pour down the slopes of the volcano and become submerged. Hence a human skeleton or a tool might be buried under 20 to 50 meters of slag or of lava, and so is no proof of a very high antiquity. It is useless to push the argument any further.

Man is of relatively recent date. We do not consider it worth while to go back further than the number of years already indicated. The very high figures often given seem to be exaggerated. De Lapparent [1] whose authority in geology is universally recognized inclines towards the more moderate figures. In the work which he published some months before his death *Les silex taillés et l'antiquité de l'homme*, he accepts the proof that the figures of a hundred or two hundred thousand years are absolutely exaggerated, and lack all foundation in the data of science. He himself gives no estimate, but the author has heard him say many times that in his opinion more than 15,000 years was certainly necessary.

CONCLUSION.

We take it on the word of the most authoritative exegetes that the Bible does not impose any chronology. The liberty which results from this appears to us very important, for, on the one hand, the desire to find the Bible at fault had not been without its influence on the minds of those who assigned to man a fabulous antiquity; and on the other, the preoccupation of safe-guarding an old interpretation undoubtedly led Catholics, in spite of certain scientific data, to hold to figures that were too low.

The recently discovered monuments in Egypt and in Chaldea show us that a very advanced civilization was already in existence in these countries 4 000 or 5 000 years before the Christian era. Without teaching us anything about the beginning of humanity they lead us to place the origin of man rather far back.

The first human races go back almost to the Quaternary period. The pretended traces of Tertiary man lack probability.

Since the appearance of man, the time elapsed is divided into two parts, the Postglacial that a very common and otherwise well founded opinion does not extend beyond 7 000 to 9 000 years; and the Quaternary or the Preglacial epoch of which it is impossible at present at least to appreciate its exact duration. The study that we have made of

[1] Cf. *Traité de géologie*, p. 1641.

certain calculations shows that it is necessary to guard against uncontrolled and exaggerated results.

Granting that the veracity of the Bible is not involved in the question, we have no reason *a priori* to set at naught the figures that true Science might be able to propose on the antiquity of man. But in the present state of Science, we have the right to say that no very approximate number can be given.

CHAPTER VIII

CONDITION OF PRIMITIVE MAN FROM PREHISTORIC AND ETHNOLOGICAL DATA.

§ I. — PRELIMINARY REMARKS.

The question of the condition of primitive man is intimately bound up with all that has preceded. In fact, if man has risen through a slow evolution from the ranks of the brute beast, we should find in a review of his past history all the intermediate phases of his physical and intellectual progress, from the anthropoid with a mere rudiment of intelligence to what he is today. This, evolutionists hold, is possible. On the contrary, if as we have taught, man was created by God with all the faculties that pertain to his nature, we ought to meet, from the very outset, a human being completely formed; he ought to be identically the same throughout the ages, both in organism and in intellectual make up. Of course, being plastic under the influence of environment, his organic type would become differentiated in the various races; but these modifications are purely accidental. Likewise being endowed with intelligence and so capable of progress, man would create in the course of time, works in an ascending scale of perfection. But from the very beginning his works will have been the result of characteristic spiritual faculties.

Such will be the thesis that we shall develop. In proving that, from the beginning of his existence, man was really intelligent, we shall confirm the privileges that distinguish him : the spirituality of his soul, his manifestly divine origin, the specific unity of the human group. Whatever be the date of his creation, whether very remote or very recent, we shall always have sufficient time to explain the formation and the development of even the most advanced nations.

To uphold their theory, materialistic anthropologists have recourse to two sorts of arguments. — They appeal to the documents of prehistoric times; they try to find in the most ancient human remains, whether bones or implements, the signs of a state intermediate between animal nature and human nature. — Then from a study of modern uncivilized peoples, they consider them as undeveloped and still in the way of becoming civilized.

We shall have recourse to the same sources of information. After having described the works of primitive industry and given the characteristics of the most ancient races, we shall, to some extent, establish that the identity of the physical and intellectual type is clearly apparent through the thousand variations of an entirely secondary nature. Then taking up the present uncivilized races, we shall show, that these races, though indeed undeveloped or degenerate, are of a nature as complete as our own. Finally, to avoid all confusion, we shall study in particular the traces left by the first human races in Europe. They have been more seriously and more extensively examined than in other parts of the world; they lend themselves to a classification which though not entirely certain, still facilitates investigation. Moreover in other countries, the primitive remains of man are sensibly the same. Finally as the Chellean industry goes back to the third interglacial period, the European documents ought to bring us pretty near the beginnings of humanity.

We shall give the facts drawn from the prehistoric ages. These facts are numerous enough to permit us to form some idea of the primitive European. They do not, it is true, settle all the questions which our curiosity may raise, but they will have given us much information, if they prove that man has always been what he is today, an intelligent being and that the differences between the primitive man and the actual man, do not bear on the development of the faculties themselves. It is really *prehistoric* man and not *primitive* man that we meet with as the colonizer of Europe, but with the Chellean man we also come as near as possible to the primitive man.

§ II. — PREHISTORIC TIMES.

The knowlege of the existence of man on the earth before historic times is an achievement of modern science. It seems that some very old traditions, among the Greeks and the Latins, have kept alive the remembrance of the Stone Age, the Bronze Age and the Iron Age. The polished stone was called *ceraunium* (κεραυνὸς = thunderbolt). These notions have persevered to the present day. In the sixteenth century they still considered them as species of fossil or strange freaks of nature. At the end of the sixteenth century, Michael Mercati discovered the true nature of the polished hatchets. In the course of the seventeenth and eighteenth centuries, these stone weapons were compared with the tomahawks of the American Indians. [1] Buffon recognized in them the first evidences of the art of man in a purely natural state.

Up to the nineteenth century only the polished stones were known. The chipped stones were discovered later associated with a fauna that had long since become extinct or had migrated elsewhere. Hence Cuvier himself, who died in 1832, had not yet found the proofs of prehistoric man.

Tournal, after several years of research, wrote in 1829 that geology alone was going to give us a proof of the high antiquity of man. In 1833, the Belgian Schmerling found some chipped bones and worked flints that he believed to be antediluvian. But it is to Boucher de Perthes (1788-1868) Director of Customs at Abbeville that we must give the credit of having given the proof of man's antiquity. In 1846, he published his work *De l'industrie primitive ou des arts à leur origine*. In it he declares that the ancient

---

[1] Cf. Boule, *Les hommes fossiles*, p. 1-27, Paris, Masson, 1921.

alluvia of the suburbs of Abbeville abounded in stones shaped by antediluvian man, and buried at various depths with the bones of large animals of an extinct species.

He had many violent opponents among the prominent scientists of his day, including Élie de Beaumont, Secretary of the Academy of Sciences, but was encouraged by Al. Brongniart and Constant Prévost. Dr. Rigollot of Amiens, after having opposed him, accepted his opinions in 1854 when he himself found in the gravel pits of Saint-Acheul some " hachets " resembling those picked up by Boucher de Perthes.

In 1859, numerous English scientists came to Saint-Acheul to study the facts on the ground, and one of them, Lyell, published his celebrated work : *The antiquity of Man proved by Geology.* Albert Gaudry came to Amiens and succeeded in finding " nine hatchets " from the diluvian period at a depth of 4.50 meters together with a special fauna comprising the rhinoceros, the elephant and the hippopotamus. The Academy and its secretary did not wish to submit to the evidence. In 1860, E. Lartet, after having excavated the cavern of Aurignac, addressed a note to the Academy of Sciences entitled : *On the geological antiquity of the human Species in Western Europe* : the title only appears on p. 599 of vol. i, Comptes Rendus. Lartet had already produced an essay on *Paleontological chronology* which ought to be revised and completed. In 1864, he discovered, in the grotto of the Madeleine, an ivory blade on which some prehistoric man had carved a mammoth, giving at once a high idea of his artistic attainments and of his antiquity. Together with the Englishman Christy, Lartet excavated the grottos in the Végère valley, and discovered the marvellous carvings and paintings of the Magdalenian period. A number of investigators went to work, including P. Gervais, de Vibraye, A. Milne-Edwards, Louis Lartet, Piette, E. Cartaillac, G. de Mortillot. In foreign countries, especially in England, great interest in prehistoric problems was manifested. Books, reviews and international congresses collected and discussed the topics raised by this new science. Since Lartet's time the movement has grown considerably. The abbé Breuil occupies a conspicuous place among prehistorians, and his numerous works have brought about his appointment to the Chair of Prehistoric Archeology at the Institute of Human Paleontology, founded at Paris by the Prince of Monaco.

J. Dechelette published from 1908 to 1914, his noteworthy *Manuel d'Archéologie préhistorique* [1] in which are summed up and synthesized the works of his predecessors. It is a work that every one, who wishes to become acquainted with this new science, should read. Valuable collections of prehistoric objects are today gathered in national or private museums, to facilitate the study of prehistoric times. We can give here only a very summary appreciation of prehistory and the principal results so far obtained.

Materialists believed they had found in this science the long sought argument for the brute origin of man. His high antiquity, his peculiar nature, his primitive condition, all argued in favor of their theory. The spiritualistic scientists could not be disinterested in these vital questions and they have already given proof, by their works, of their interest in the subject.

§ III. — AUTHENTICITY OF PREHISTORIC DOCUMENTS.

The documents of prehistoric times may be placed into two categories: the archeological documents or remains of human industry and the paleontological, or prehistoric skeletons.

We shall take up successively but rapidly the most important of these. But it is highly important that we assure ourselves of their authenticity. Where there is question of the product of human industry, we must know whether they are really the work of man, of prehistoric man. When we are dealing with human fossils, we must be sure they are prehistoric.

I. *How can we recognize the intentional work of man in a*

[1] Paris, Picard.

prehistoric object, so as not to confuse it with a natural object which was never subjected to human handiwork ? Among the products of human labor we find chipped and polished stones, metallic objects, engravings, paintings, sculptures, buildings, etc. The only difficulty that arises is in connection with the chipped stone where the work was very hastily executed. It might be well to give some rules or indications how to recognize the intentional work of man.

1. Symmetrical, regular, complex and constant forms indicate at once intentional work. The chance forces of nature produce asymmetrical, irregular, quite simple and non-constant forms.

To cite some examples of intentional chipping :

a) Symmetrical forms are referred to an axis, according to a preconceived plan, as the beautiful Acheulian (fig. 105) or Solutrian points, the Solutrian (fig. 134) or Neolithic (fig. 169) arrowheads, as well as certain Mousterian points (figs. 107, 108). The symmetry may bear on the general form, or on the touching up of the article in question as in the Magdalenian blades, and the nodules of all periods (fig. 115).

b) Regular forms are realized in all the symmetrical forms, and in others in which we notice, either particular dimensions or a regular curve, or a particular angle, as in the Aurignacian chisels and the Mousterian or Neolithic scrapers (fig. 109).

c) Complex forms have been produced only as a result of numerous operations on a flint rock, or on the lamina which has been detached; such are the Chellean punches, the Levallois fragments (fig. 107) the Campignian paring knives (fig. 107).

d) Constant forms called also typical forms are characteristic of each period. Certain of them are so rudimentary that we should hesitate to accept them as the work of man, were it not for the fact that they are found in quantities in one or more localities. Thus, among these we may mention the Mousterian chips with their sloping planes, their percussion marks, their sharp edges, which, strictly speaking, might be the result of an accident once or twice, but could not be regularly so by mere mechanical impact (figs. 107, 1, 2, 3).

e) The formless or nontypical flints not fulfilling these conditions should not be considered documents, at least when they are not found among authentic articles in caves, on the hearth, in the grave, in the workshop of the flintworker, in a word, in a prehistoric locality (figs. 105, 106).

All the Tertiary eoliths (figs. 83, 91, 92) lack these characteristics and are to be eliminated. They serve only to throw confusion into Science, which ought to be based on indisputable facts.

2. Examination of the flints enables us at times to discover the man's mode of chipping, the way the instrument was used, the use for which it was destined.

3. The traces of touching up in view of prehension, of transformation, of re-adaptation are sufficient to characterize an intentional work. Prudence, on this point, therefore is indispensable. We risk taking for intentional retouching the merely accidental chipping of natural and often recent fragments. This is what the advocates of the eoliths have done. As an example of retouching for the purpose of prehension, we may mention certian implements specially adapted to the right or left hand (figs. 100, 101).

4. The implements very frequently give evidence of having been used to cut, to saw, to pound, to pierce, to rasp, to polish, to smooth, etc. Here again we must avoid confusing these signs of human handicraft with what natural mechanical forces could produce through friction, impact or pressure, etc.

5. The polished specimens of the Neolithic period leave no room for doubt (figs. 157-162).

6. The same holds true for some toothed, perforated or notched bone, or reindeer or stag horn implements (figs. 137-142).

7. The writings, carvings and paintings themselves testify to the intellectual activity of man. It suffices merely to prove their antiquity (figs. 116-130).

II. *How can we be certain that the articles are prehistoric and not the work of some forger ?*

1. The surest way is to *find them in situ*. Stratigraphy will indicate the relative age of the strata of rock in which they are imbedded, and the age of each specimen itself. Here we may always have a specimen much older than the rock; if it has been *carried* by a stream of water, it has lost its sharp angles; if the article still has the latter it has not drifted and so is no older than the stratum in which it is buried.

2. We may trust to human testimony, when it is worthy of credence.

3. If the object is at the surface of the ground, it becomes impossible to obtain even its relative age. At the very utmost one may have a more or less proximate estimate of its age from its appearance, i.e. from the amount of discoloration, incrustation or chemical alteration since the time of its manufacture, as in the flints found in Egypt on the surface of plateaux. This discoloration, however, is not always present, since there are varieties of flint which are not subject to it.

4. The *typical form* of the flints will at times permit one to refer it to a particular prehistoric period, as each has its own characteristic and typical forms. But a shrewd forger could imitate them. It is no uncommon thing for these men to produce new forms, in which the deception however is clearly evident. But the greatest difficulty arises when trying to distinguish a paleolithic specimen from one that is more recent, since men in certain localities continued to chip and polish stone well into the Neolithic period. In such cases, it would be necessary to resort to stratigraphy. A single Neolithic specimen proves that the others at the same level belong to the same period. The absence of a polished stone, however, does not indicate with certainty, the Paleolithic period.

§ IV. — CLASSIFICATION OF THE QUATERNARY PERIODS. PREHISTORIC INDUSTRIES AND RACES.

That the reader may have a clearer understanding of prehistoric times, we shall give here a table in which are summed up the geological, paleontological, archeological

DIVISIONS	PHENOMENA	FAUNA	INDUSTRY	RACES
Holocene or Actual Quaternary	Recent Alluvia Peat-bogs / Climate much like the present	Actual Species / Domestic Animals	METALS { Iron, 900 B. C. / Bronze, 2.500 B.C. } / Neolithic { Recent / Old } / Azilian	Races in appearance similar to the actual races.
QUATERNARY — PLEISTOCENE OR OLD QUATERNARY — UPPER Postglacial	First grotto deposits. / Upper loess deposits.	Steppes fauna Dry cold / Reindeer Tundra fauna Wet-cold	PALEOLITHIC — UPPER { Magdalenian / Solutrian }	Chancelade race, / Cro-Magnian race,
MIDDLE 4th Glacier	Cave deposits / Formation of the basal terraces and Wormian moraines. / Lower loess deposits.	Cold climate fauna. / Mammoth or Elephas primigenius / Rhinoceros tichorhinus, etc.	Aurignacian / Mousterian	Grimaldi race, / Neanderthal race,
LOWER 3rd Glacier, 3rd Intergl.	First Alluvia in the caverns. Calcarious tufa. Alluvia of the 2nd terraces. Rissian moraines	Torrid climate fauna. Hippopotamus, Elephas antiquus. Rhinoceros Merkii.	LOWER { Acheulian / Chellian }	Piltdown race, / Mauer race.
TERTIARY — Pliocene	2nd Interglacial period. 2nd Mindelian glacier. 1st Interglacial period. 1st Gunzian glacier.	Elephas meridionalis. Rhinoceros Etruscus. Equus stenonis, etc.	Unknown.	Unknown.
Miocene. Oligocene. Eocene.				

and anthropological data of the period.   We are indebted
to Boule for part of it.   It is generally accepted by prehistorians, in particular by the abbé Breuil and by Déchelette.
We must not forget that these divisions are not as clear cut
in reality as they appear to be in the classification.   There
was no interruption of industry, from one period to another,
of one fauna to another, of one race to another, but a
gradual transition.   Moreover new discoveries may alter
the lines of demarcation at present admitted by a relatively
recent science.

§ V: — PREHISTORY.

Prehistoric archeology, or prehistory studies this period
of the life of the human races anterior to the most ancient
historical documents.   It makes use of the debris of industry strewn over a great extent of territory, or buried in the
rock strata.   The chronological limits of prehistoric times
varies with each region.   In Egypt the historical period
goes back to 4 000 B. C.   In France it does not go beyond
the fifth century previous to our era.   The history of the
Scandinavian countries scarcely begins with the ninth
century.   In America, with its discovery.   Certain tribes
are still in the prehistoric period, since they are unacquaint-
ed with writing.   We shall deal particularly with France,[1]
since it is the best explored region.   To avoid repetitions
and to group together similar facts, industries and

---

[1] Explorations and accidental fines in America have yielded no
authentic remains of early Quaternary man.   In a letter to the
translator, dated Feb. 1st, 1927 Dr. Ales Hrdlicka writes : "So far as
Quaternary man in America is concerned.   I may only say that to
this moment no generally acceptable piece of evidence of that nature
has been produced : but there have always been and are now, and
will doubtless continue, individuals, as a rule not professional anthropologists, who claim to have found a man of antiquity.   Upon
critical examination in all of these cases to date it is found that,
either the evidence has been misinterpreted, or the conditions were
such as to make a clear decision one way or the other a mere question
of opinion. "

races, we shall proceed according to the following plan :

1. The Lower Paleolithic comprising the Chellean, the Acheulean and the Mousterian periods;

2. The Upper Paleolithic including the Aurignacian, the Solutrian, Magdelenian periods;

3. The Neolithic goes from the period of transition to the Azilian;

4. The Metals : Copper and bronze, or the protohistoric period.

1. Lower paleolithic

Chellean, Acheulean, Mousterian.

I. Chellean Epoch. — It is not at the very beginning of the Quaternary that we find the first traces of man, but only after the Third Glaciation (the Rissian) during The third Interglaciary which we may call the Chellean from the name of the industry which characterizes it. The name is derived from the locality of Chelles, Seine-et-Marne, France, situated near the river Marne, at some meters below the present level, under a mass of alluvia averaging from 10 to 12 meters. In these alluvia comprising several strata we find the Chellean industry[1] at the base, and the Acheulean higheŕ, up. On the neighboring plateaux, we meet with the industry of the Upper Paleolithic.

Caumont[2] found on the terraces of the Somme at Saint-Acheul these same three industries superposed. He believes that he discovered at the base an even more primitive industry which he calls Prechellean. The existence of Chellean industry has been remarked by d'Ault of Mesnil in the Champs-de-Mars at Abbeville, and by Boule, Chauvet and Capitan at Tilloux (Charente-Inférieure).

The characteristic implement of the period is a flint nodule, a rubble-stone of quartzite or of some hard stone fashioned by chipping off long fragments from both sides, so as to form a more or less tapering point. It is very thick

---

[1] Cf. Déchelette, p. 61-90 on the Chellean and Acheulean epochs.
[2] Cf. *Anthropologie*, 1908, p. 528-572.

in the middle and, at the base, but very sharp around the edge and at the point (fig. 99).   Often the natural surface

Fig. 99. — Chellean Implement from Abbeville.
(Ault du Mesnil Coll. Drawn by A. de Mortillet.)

of the nodule has been preserved at the base to enable a person to grasp or manipulate it without injury, when

using it as a punch or as a hunting knife. The fragments
which are knocked off in the manufacture of these implements are also used, but ordinarily without any touching
up. Ât Ville-franche (Rhône) however, the Chellean
industry consisted of large chips carelessly retouched, often

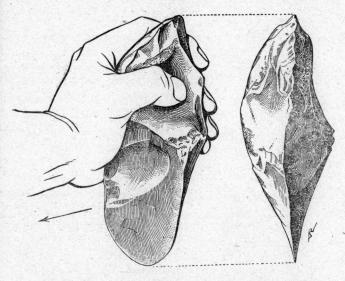

Fig. 100. — Flint hunting-knife from Saint-Acheul.

The touching-up permits it to be held with the left hand, as is shown by the
obverse and lateral wiew of drawing. (*Collection of Seminary of St. Sulpice,
Issy.*)

in the shape of scrapers; [1] at Taubach (Saxe-Weimar) there
are only chips without any definite shape [2].

The genesis of the punch seems rather simple. By using
a rubble stone or some other hard rock as a hammer
prehistoric man could have noticed that the chips became
detached from it, and acquired very sharp edges, when the
blow was regulated, thus obtaining a more perfect implement. The Chellean implements are so varied in their
forms and their dimensions, that they certainly had very

[1] *Anthropologie*, vol. VI, p. 285; vol. VII, p. 595; vol. IX, p. 184.
[2] Reinach, in *Anthropologie*, vol. VIII, p. 53.

different uses. Some terminate in a large transverse blade like a chisel, or in a blunt point like a pick. In others, on the contrary, the blades are lateral, developed into an 'arc of a very regular circle, representing the serviceable part of

the implement. Others, finally, are 'elongated into a pointed chip like a dagger, having sharp lateral blades and terminating in a more or less sharp point. These implements were often admirably adapted to right or left hand use. A special touching up effected this (fig. 100).

Were there any that were intended to be used with handles ? We believe so. For certain forms from Saint-Acheul resemble the points of a lance or of a javelin, so perfectly that it is impossible to assign to them any other purpose. Some specimens are often so well formed that they are almost identical with the Neolithic (fig. 101). The variety of use and the perfect adaptation to the use for which it was destined, the difficulty of manufacture, the necessity of contriving all this — all proves that primitive man was not an

Fig. 101. — Neolithic knife with sharp blade, and oblique at each end. *(Issy Seminary Collection.)*

inferior being. We have evidence here of his having been very intelligent, since he knew how to put to good use a very clumsy material, and to triumph over apparently insurmountable difficulties. The locality of Taubach [1] (Weimar) is interesting for the reason that here lie deposits of the Third Glaciation and in consequence according to

[1] Cf. S. Reinach, in *Anthropologie*, vol. VIII, p. 58, and Déchelette.

Klaatsch also the interglacial deposits. It shows us that
man was a hunter, and that he lived on the flesh of the
elephant, of the rhinoceros of Merck, of the bison, of the
bears and of the hyena. He already built a fire to cook
his food and split bones to extract the marrow.

Of the social and religious customs of the Chellean man
nothing is known.

Some recent discoveries in the grottos at Grimaldi near

Fig. 102. — Skeleton of *Cervus megaceros*.

Menton have confirmed the stratigraphic facts of Chelles,
Saint-Acheul, Taubach, etc. In one of these, called the
Prince's grotto explored under the auspices of the Prince of
Monaco, the Canon of Villeneuve recognized a continuous
series of Paleolithic industries from the Chellean to the
Magdalenian periods. Here, as well as in other localities,
it becomes evident that the Chellean utensils called Mousterian exist in abundance. We shall show what was the
extent of the Chellean, in speaking of the Acheulean which
was its normal development.

The Chellean fauna is well known today. In the Champ-
de-Mars at Abbeville and at Tilloux (Charente-Inférieure)
we find the very primitive *elephas antiquus* which was first
confused with the *elephas meridionalis*. Along with it was

found the *machairodus latidens*, a large cat with enormous
and serrated upper canines, the *trogotherium Cuvieri*, a
large rodent closely resembling a beaver.   The rest of the
fauna includes, as at Chelles (Seine-et-Marne) the classic
Chellean location, the *rhinoceros Merckii*, *hippopotamus
major*, *cervus megaceros* (fig. 102) *bison priscus*, *ursus
speleus*, *hyena spelea*, etc.

A fauna, so rich in great pachyderms and herbivora such
as stags, oxen and horses, and a flora that included the
willow, the ash, the Judas tree, the large-leaved spindle
tree, the wild grape vine and the Canary Islands laurel,
suppose a very warm and humid climate.

The rivers carried numerous alluvia that filled up their
beds, and often caused them to change their course
during a flood, and to abandon the gravel banks upon
which man later took up his abode and left the remains of
his industry.

Chellean Man. — 1. The nonauthentic human bones. —
In spite of the abundant evidence of Chellean industry
found over almost the entire world, and in spite of the long
duration of this period, the human fossils are extremely
rare.   Up to 1908, they were almost unknown.   The earlier finds, according to Boule, are either uncertain or of a
more recent period.   Such is that of the Canstadt skull
found in 1 700 near Stuttgardt (Wüttenberg).   Its origin is
obscure and its antiquity more than doubtful.   Such also
the human bones discovered, in 1844, in the ashes excavated
from the volcano of Denise near Le Puy.   There may have
been a burial in the rock of the period very remote from
the Quaternary.   The morphological, physical and chemical examination of these bones is to be made again.   The
jaw-bone of Moulin-Quignon discovered in 1863 does not
give any evidence of authenticity.   Boucher de Perthes
was the victim of a fraud.   The Olmo skull also discovered
in 1863 near Arrezo in Tuscany, is likewise of too uncertain a geological age.

Nor does Boule admit the antiquity of the skeletons of
Clichy (1868) and of Grenelle (1870), since their stratigra-
phical position was not verified at the moment of the

liscovery. Were they burials or not ? In 1888, some
portions of a head and some other parts of a human skeleton
were taken out of the Pleistocene gravel beds at Galley
Hill in Kent, at a depth of eight feet. It was associated
with Paleolithic flints. The shape of the skeleton is that
of a modern Englishman, says Keith. Boule finds no
sufficient evidence of its antiquity, for no geologist was
present when it was discovered, nor studied the character

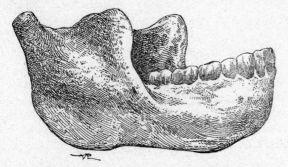

Fig. 103. — Mauer jaw-bone. *(From a photograph by Schaentensack.)*

of the site. The skull is deformed and is not fossilized but
resembles those of recent burial. [1] In 1912, a human
skeleton was discovered under similar conditions at Ipswich
in Suffolk. It is not prehistoric.

Besides these, there are the Mauer jaw-bone which is
certainly of this period, the Weimar teeth and jawbone,
and the Piltdown skull which is perhaps a little more
recent, probably of the Saint Acheul period.

2. The authentic human bones. — The Mauer jaw-bone
(fig. 103) found October 21, 1907, 27 meters below the surface
of the earth in the fluvial sands of a tributary of the Neckar,
near the village of Mauer, 10 kilometers south-east of
Heidelberg. The geological section of the rock, from top to
bottom, shows the following series of strata. Upper lœss,
lower lœss, Mauer sands, clay sediment, Mauer sand,
containing the human jawbone at 24 meters depth.

[1] Boule, *Les hommes fossiles*, p. 142.

The Mauer fauna is that of Chelles, consisting of the elephant (elephas antiquus), the Etruscan rhinoceros, a horse that is intermediate between the Etruscan and the present horse, etc.

This jaw-bone is considered as belonging to the Third Interglaciary, anterior to the last Ice Age, and marking the beginning of the Chellean period. Some authors have desired, but without sufficient evidence, to place this jaw-bone as far back as the Second Interglaciary. It is almost entire and is well preserved. At first sight, one is struck by its dimensions, its massive and extraordinarily robust appearance, by the great length of the vertical sections, and by the complete absence of the chin. The dentition is entirely human, the canines are small, the molars have the dimensions and characteristics readily found in men of the present time. It so resembles that of the Neanderthal race, as to give the impression of direct relationship. [1] It is a specimen to keep in mind when studying other discoveries.

2. *The Acheulean Period.* — The Acheulean period takes its name from the locality of Saint-Acheul [2] (Somme) and is only a progressive development of the preceding, both from the standpoint of fauna and of industry. The elephant (antiquus) gradually disappeared with the hippopotamus and the rhinoceros Merckii. The mammoth (elephas primigenius) and the rhinoceros with septiform nostrils (r. tichorhinus, cf. figs. 97, 98 above), both covered with a heavy fleece, began to flourish. Along with them existed great numbers of horses, as well as the bison, the aurochs and deer, *cervus megaceros* and *canadensis*, whose flesh supplied the bear, the tiger and the cave hyena with food. Sucha faun a supposes a much colder climate. The distinctly arctic flora likewise proclaims an encroach-

---

[1] For further technical details see Boule, *Les hommes fossiles* p. 153 et sq.

[2] Cf. Commont, *Les industries de l'ancien Saint-Acheul*, in *Anthropologie*, 1908, p. 527-572, where may be found cross sections and numerous reproductions of this primitive industry, from the Chellean to the Magdalenian.

ing cold area.   Yet the atmosphere still remained very humid, and while abundant rains produced great masses of alluvia, the snow on the mountains prepared the last great glacial invasion.

The typical Acheulean tools were composed of the

Fig. 104. — Lanceolate Acheulian implement.   *(Ault du Mesnil Collection.)*

amygdaloid instrument of Chelles, and some different varieties of carefully touched up fragments.   Man aimed more at symmetry and at lightness for his implements.   He gradually made the blade of his punches straighter and transformed them in this way into real weapons (fig. 104). The Acheulean punch is differentiated into several types, the use of which must have varied with their size and shape,

thus greatly extending the field of the prototype's usefu]
ness. — Many are almond shaped (amygdaloid type)
others are oval or elongated to a sharp point (the lanceolat
type). The laborers at St. Acheul have dubbed them cats
tongues. — Their size and thickness are also quit

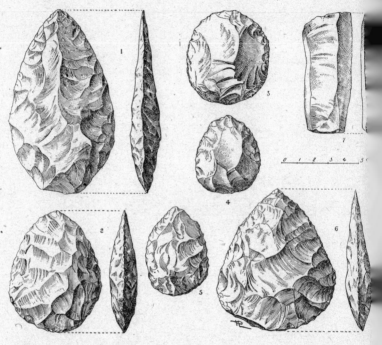

Fig. 105. — Amygdaloid and discoid Acheulean tools; Obverse and
lateral view. *(Issy Seminary Coll.)*

variable. At the beginning of the Acheulean period, the
massive punches are most numerous at St. Acheul.
Towards the end of the period as at La Micoque (Dordogne),
for instance, the utensils scarcely exceeded 5 or 6 centimeters in length. Many of these latter served as lance
and javelin heads, knives and awls. Certain punches
are nearly round and pass almost insensibly into the disk
type characteristic of the Upper Acheulean (fig. 105).

All the foregoing implements are made by roughhewing

int rubble stones. The chips that resulted from this;
ere used to a great extent in the Acheulean period, after
aving been subjected to skillful retouching. At La
Iicoque for one punch chipped on both faces, we meet
ith twenty chips finished into points and scrapers. If we
ollow the Acheulean man by the remains of his industry,
e find him dwelling at times on plateaux, then on the
anks of rivers as at Saint-Acheul; then again on the side
f steep declivities with a southern exposure (La Micoque).
t the end of this period he took up his abode in the small
aves as at Eyzies, in the grotto of the church at Guilhem,
t Rinxent (Pas-de-Calais) and in Kent in England.

In the vicinity of La Micoque, we see that the Acheulean
nan lived by the chase and fed chiefly upon horse meat.
The scrapers and awls which abound at this period lead
is to believe that man prepared, for his own use, the skins
of the animals that he ate.

The Chellean or the Acheulean industry preceded the
other industries at all places where research has been
conducted. It appears unlimited wherever flint abounded. In France it is found in nearly 600 communes and in
53 departments. Saint-Acheul has produced thousands of
specimens. It is found in England on the shores of the
Thames and the Ouse; in Belgium, in Spain, in Portugal, in
Africa, from Algeria to the Cape, in Syria, in Palestine and
in Hindustan. It is absent in the regions covered by the
Quaternary glaciers since these regions remained for a long
time uninhabitable.

Human paleontology furnishes us with two documents
that go back at least to the Acheulean and probably to the
Chellean.

1. The Weimar jawbone was discovered May 8, 1914 at
Ehringsdorf, near Weimar at 11.90 meters below the surface
in the tufa covering the lower lœss. It is remarkable for
the entire absence of chin and very pronounced prognathism. The last rear molar is very small, already indicating a tendency to disappear. It was associated with
the Merckian rhinoceros, the red deer, the horse, the ox,
and the cave bears.

Schwalbe unhesitatingly ascribes the specimen of Weimar to the Neanderthal group. This jawbone is certainly human, although of an inferior type; it differs notably from that at Mauer.

2. The Piltdown Man *(Eoanthropus Dawsoni)*. [1] — December 18th 1912, the geologist Charles Dawson and the paleontologist Smith Woodward of the British Museum presented to the Geological Society of London some human bones, from the Lower Quaternary, found at Piltdown in Sussex, England. The various more or less complete fragments of the skull, and the entire jawbone were successively discovered very close together at the same level. As these bones were not found in close proximity, we may well ask whether they really belonged to the same individual.

Stratigraphy, paleontology and archeology would classify the Piltdown sands in which these human bones were found, as Chellean. The bones are contemporaneous with the deposit. We have therefore a rare specimen, the remains of a Chellean or Acheulean man. [2] A detailed examination of each of the bones leads to the conclusion that they are human, and of a type much closer to the present man than to those of the Neanderthal race. In fact, the orbital ridges are not more prominent than in the present white race (fig. 106).

The discovery in 1916 of another fragment — a section of the frontal bone of another individual, has confirmed the above. The forehead is vertical, the occipital is rounded, the shape is regular and harmoniously arched from the cranium; the glenoid cavity is vertical and deep while the minimum cranial capacity of 1 300 cc. agrees with the above. From all these very clear osteological characteristics the Piltdown skull so evidently belongs to a man, that only a close study of it can differentiate it from that of a man of the present day.

---

[1] Cf. McCann, *God and Gorilla*, p. 9, and quotation given above.
[2] Cf. P. Teilhard de Chardin, *Revue des Questions scientifiques*, 1920, p. 252.

If we pass to the study of the jawbone and the dentition, here is an entire change. [1] So complete indeed that Boule as considered it the jawbone of a chimpanzee, especially n account of the large sharp-pointed canine that is much vorn on the inner side, and from the symphisis of the nandible prolonged on the inside like an osseous lamina. Still English and American paleontologists look upon it as

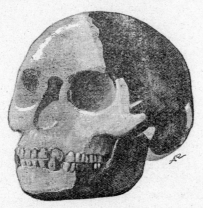

Fig. 106. — Piltdown Skull. Restoration by Smith Woodward.

human [2]. It would be easy to find men at the present moment with more developed canines and with a chin as receding.

[1] Boule, *Les hommes fossiles*, p. 158.
[2] Not all American and English scientists accept the Piltdown bones as those of an extinct human being. Dr. Ales Hrdlicka, curator of the Division of Physical Anthropology, United States National Museum, Washington, D. C. writes : " The most important development in the study of The Piltdown remains is the recent well documented objection by Professor Gerrit S. Miller of the United States National Museum, to the classing together of the lower jaw, and the canine with the cranium. According to Miller, who had ample anthropoid as well as human material for comparison, the *jaw and tooth belong to a fossil chimpanzee.*" Smithsonian Report, 1913, p. 191-552. Sir Ray Lancaster, emphatically denied the claim of Mr Dawson and Dr. A. Smith Woodward on the ground that the jaw-bone and the skull had never belonged to the same creature. Cf. McCann, *God and Gorilla*, for further testimonies and discussion.

The existence in the Chellean, or at least in the Acheulea
period of a human type so close to the actual type, and s
different from the one of the Neanderthal race, does no
sustain the evolutionistic theory that requires an intermed
iary between man and the beast.   The inferior characte
istics of the Neanderthal man of the Mousterian period d
not exist in the one of Piltdown.   We may for the presen
suppose that the Neanderthal race far from being primitiv
is rather degenerate as Boule maintains.

In the Piltdown gravel are found flints that at first wer
taken to be of the Mousterian type, chipped only on on
side.   This confirms what we have already said about th
variety of the Chellean shapes.   In this same gravel be
were discovered a sliver detached from the bone of
proboscidian and which is no less than forty centimeter
in length and ten in width, pointed at one extremit
and rounded at the other.   Its shape denotes it a rea
implement.   Thus bone would have been fashioned at thi
period, contrary to the opinion that this was not don
until the Aurignacian period.

3. *The Mousterian Period*. — The Mousterian perio
takes its name from the little grotto at Moustier, in th
commune of Peyzac (Dordogne) situated on the shore o
the Vézère.   This locality was studied by Lartet and
Christy.

The fauna of this third prehistoric period characterized
by the *elephas primigenius* or mammoth gives evidence of a
cold climate.   Of the animals which have survived many
have migrated to colder regions or into the mountains, as for
instance the *ursus ferox*, the musk ox, the *cervus canadensis*
of North America, the saiga antelope of the frozen steppes
of Central Asia, the reindeer, the wolverene, the blue fox
and the lemmings of the polar regions of Scandinavia, the
marmot, the wild goat, the chamois of the high mountain
ranges of Europe.

The flora also indicates a cold climate.   In spite of the
cooling down of the temperature, the atmosphere was still
very humid.   This explains the scarcity of the reindeer,
the musk ox and the lemming which prefer a dry cold.

The Mousterian *industry* made use of the earlier tools and created new forms, which were less elegant perhaps, but certainly as practical. The Mousterian point (fig. 107) replaced the amygdaloid implements that had become

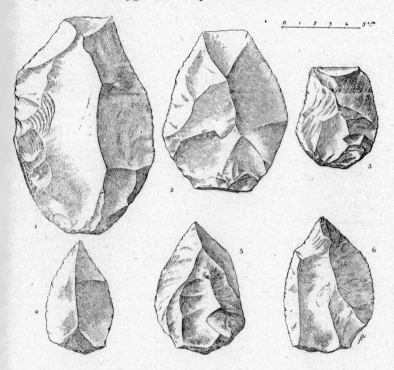

Fig. 107.— Acheulean and Mousterian flints called Levallois chips. 1, 2, 3, Paring-knives; 4, 5, 6, Mousterian points. *(Issy Seminary Collection.)*

scarce. Numerous chipped fragments are met with, that are adapted by skillful touching up, to the most varied use, arrow heads, saws, scrapers and awls. These were chips removed by hammering from a matrix rock or nodule. A few blows on the side, ordinarily on only one face (fig. 108) characterized these fragments. The *scraper* (fig. 109) was touched up at the lateral edge on the arc of a circle. It must have served to cleanse and beat the skins of animals.

The *knives* or fragments elongated on the parallel sides, of which the edges were not touched up so as to leave them sharp, served to skin animals or to cut them up. A slight touching up on the edges of some fragment produced a blade slightly denticulated that could be used as a saw.

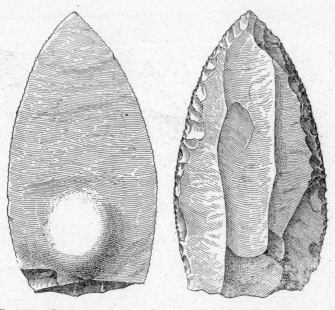

Fig. 108.—Large Mousterian chip, worked only on one side; un-chipped side

The same Mousterian chip; chipped and retouched side.

The head of a lance or of a javelin could be had by retouching on the two edges, in such a way as to obtain a sharp-pointed extremity. These points might have been attached to the end of a staff, in a manner similar to that of the lances of the natives of New-Guinea. The variety of tools is even greater than in the two preceding periods.

Although the Mousterian industry was very wide-spread in Europe, in Western Asia and in Africa, we cannot say that there had been anywhere one morphologically well characterized as Mousterian. Impelled by the rigorous cold, Mousterian man clothed himself in skins, inhabited shelters with a southern exposure or little caves where the refuse from his fireplace accummulated. Being a great hunter, he attacked even the mammoth, the numerous remains of which are found for example at Cœuvres (Aisne).

Was he buried after death?[1] We can answer with certainty in the affirmative. The two skeletons of Spy, in Belgium, have often been considered as having been taken from a grave of this period, but we know today of authentic burials at Chapelle-aux-Saints (fig. 143) at la Ferrassie, at Moustier and at Baoussé-Roussé, etc.

Fig. 109. — Mousterian scraper.

Mousterian Man (Neanderthal Race). There exist quite authentic [2] bones of the Mousterian race, permitting us to attempt a real reconstruction of this human type. Let us speak first of the locality whence they are taken. The Neanderthal skeleton (fig. 110 and 111) comes from the little Feldhofer grotto on the right bank of the Düssel. It was found in 1857 at 0.66 meter depth, in the old and very much sunken and as yet untouched clay (lehm). In another grotto situated only 130 paces away, were found the remains of a rhinoceros and of a hyena, in an identical deposit of debris.

At Enguisheim, near Colmar, on the left bank of the Rhine, a portion of a human skull was discovered in 1865 at a depth of 2.50 meters, in the virgin clay (lehm) with the remains of the mammoth and the *cervus megaceros*.[3]

At Marcilly (Eure) in 1884, a fragment of a skull was taken from beneath 7 meters of brick shale. The neighboring brickyards contained Mousterian flints and numerous

---

[1] Cf. Mainage, *Les reiigions de la préhistoire*, p. 165.

[2] Abbé Breuil, *Les plus anciennes races humaines*, in *Revue des sciences philosophiques et théologiques*, 1909, p. 728; Boule, p. 178.

[3] This Enguisheim skull is insufficiently dated; it might have been from the glyptic phase; its shape approaches the bones of this peri od.

remains of marmots. Another skull that was much more
complete was discovered in 1893 in the same geological
conditions at Bréchamp (Eure). [1]

In 1866, in the grotto called « Trou de la Naulette »
(Commune Furfooz Belgium) on the left bank of the Lesse,
was found a famous jawbone. The soil was divided by
seven stalagmitic layers. The jawbone was covered by
5 meters of such layers and was associated with other

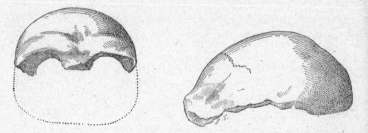

Figs. 110 and 111. — Neanderthal cranium, Front and side view.

human bones, as well as the long bones of the *mammoth*
and the *rhinoceros tichorhinus*.

The cave at Malarnaud, in the valley of the Arize (Ariège)
also yielded a human jawbone (fig. 203) in 1889, which lay
2 meters under a stalagmitic coating, associated with the
ursus spelæus, felis spelæa and rhinoceros tichorhinus.

Two skeletons (fig. 112) found in a rock shelter at Spy,
in Belgium, lay at 4.50 meters depth under a layer of
continuous and very resistant brecia, along with Mousterian
flints and bones of the mammoth (1886).   In the grotto
of Fées, at Arcy-sur-Cure (Yonne), in the year 1859, de
Vibraye discovered a fragment of a human jawbone in
a layer of Mousterian flints on top of a bear's den of an
earlier date and beneath a Magdalenian bed. [2]

Another skull, badly deformed by the pressure of the
soil, was found at a depth of 15 meters along with Mouste-

---

[1] Boule considers them doubtful.
[2] Abbé Parat, *Anthropologie*, 1901, p. 125.

rian flints, and the bones of an elephant in a lacustrine clay of the Olmo, in Italy. [1]

The Gibraltar skull, discovered in 1848 in the ossiferous breccia of Forbe's Quarry, is related to the Neanderthal race. Let us note still further a mandible of Isturitz in the Lower Pyrenees discovered in 1895; fragments of from

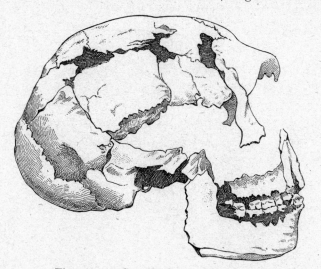

Fig. 112. — Spy skull, n. 1 (Fraipont).

two to twelve skulls at Krapina in Austria in 1899; three fragments of human jawbones at Petit-Puy-Moyen (Charente) in 1906.

More recently, some Mousterian skeletons preserved in relative entirety were discovered in August 1908 by the abbes Bouyssonie, and Bardon at Chapelle-aux-Saints (Corrèze) (figs. 204 and 205). Another at Moustier (Dordogne) in 1908. In September 1909, Capitan and Peyron discovered two Mousterian skeletons at La Ferrassie near Bugue (Dordogne) (fig. 113). In the vicinity of the Quina (Charente) a skeleton likewise Mousterian (fig. 114) was

[1] Hamy, *Bulletin mens. de la Soc. d'anthr. de Paris*, IIId series, 1878, p. 112. Boule shows the uncertainty of its geological age.

discovered by Dr. Martin in 1911.   In 1912, at La Ferrassie, he found two skeletons of children.   At the Mousterian level in the grotto des Enfants at Grimaldi, two skeletons of a negroid type were discovered in 1901.

A skull of the Neanderthal type was found in 1921 at Broken Hill in Rhodesia, among broken bones and tools of chipped stone, at the bottom of a caved-in grotto on top

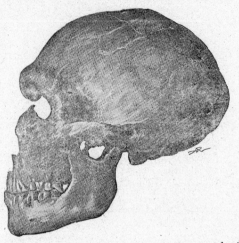

Fig. 113. — La Ferrassie (Dordogne) skull discovered at the base of the Mousterian; Neanderthal type *(Boule)*.

of the debris. [1]   It is difficult to prove that these last human bones are of the Paleolithic Age.   That which is especially interesting, is the resemblance these skulls bear to those at Chapelle-aux-Saints.

From these remains of the Mousterian men and from the older ones already mentioned we can get an idea of the human type that goes by the name of Neanderthal.

The Mousterian man had a very depressed skull because it projected in the rear.   On this account, there was a great development of the posterior part and a narrowing of the anterior portion.   The skulls in fact narrowed later-

[1] Boule, in *Nature*, 1921, p. 384.

ally in back of the orbits. The thickness of the cranial bone is about 1 centimeter.

The average cranial capacity of the Neanderthal skulls is 1 400 cc., and is little less than the present average of 1 500 cc. This is far from the 500 cc. of the apes. The posterior part of the skull is large, bulky and undulating. The frontal is depressed, and narrow. The salient super-

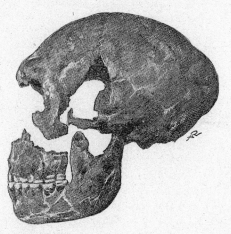

Fig. 114. — Quina (Charente) skull, discovered by Dr. H. Martin in a Mousterian bed. It belongs to the Neanderthal race.

cilliary ridges are highly developed often enormously so as at Spy, Neanderthal, Moustier, Ferrassie, la Quina and Chapelle-aux-Saints.

The orbits are scarcely broader than high, indicating a round eye. The upper jaw is very strong and well developed. The nose very depressed below the prominent superciliary, must have been broad and flat. The lower jawbone is also very powerful. The horizontal portion is flat and thick, and rises to a lump on the outer side and presents a broad plane surface below. The chin is absent. The triangular chinbone is not prominent, the line of suture of the two mandibles extends backward. The Arcy jawbone, however, is an exception. The teeth are strong;

the molars increase in size from front to rear.   Further the rounded ribs curve sharply, indicating great strength of the thoracic muscles and a strong and expanded chest.   Strength also characterizes the clavicles, the scapulae and the pelvis.   The stalky and thick humerus has a strong twist and very pronounced depressions for the insertion of the muscles.   The very prominent coronoides and ole-cranial cavities are not perforated.   The radius and the ulna, although very thick are proportionately less than the humerus.

The very powerful heavy and thick femur shows depressions and projections denoting very great muscular strength.   The short thick and strong tibia has a highly developed and slightly inclined upper surface.

The hands are large and broad; the feet still more so. The size of the Mousterian man was about 1.60 meter.   All these characteristics are very interesting, because of their bearing on so old a race, and concur in revealing the Mousterian man as a small but powerful being.

Life in the Paleolithic Period. — Is it possible to obtain some idea of the kind of life led by the Paleolithic, Chellean, Acheulian and Mousterian men, dwelling in caves and living by the chase ?   Yes, if we consult the narratives of the traveller Pallas, who in the eighteenth century visited all the people that were living under similar conditions.   At the western extremity of Siberia, he came across the Wogoules who dwelt in caves and lived solely on hunting and fishing.   Agriculture was unknown to them.   In times of famine, they crushed bones, and by cooking them prepared a sort of bouillon.   He also saw the Tchouktches on the peninsula lying between the Arctic Ocean and Siberia. They dwelt either in subterranean dugouts or in caves, closing the openings with reindeer skins.   Metal was unknown to them, their knives were made of sharpened stones, their bodkins of pointed bone, their dishes of wood or leather.   They defended themselves with the bow and arrow made of bone, the pike and the sling.   The women tanned the skins, scraping them to remove the hair, rubbing out the fat and making them pliant by carefully pressing them.   Their needles were made from fish-bones; the tendons of the animals killed in the chase served them for thread.

The Kamtchadules lived in the same way. Some islanders were still more primitive. They did not even possess the dog as a domestic animal. Their under ground dwellings often 100 meters long and six to ten wide and divided into compartments, sheltered up to 300 persons. Others occupied caves and rock shelters which they closed as well as they could with drift wood cast up by the sea. One would suppose he was describing Perigord's Mousterians. [1]

2. Upper Paleolithic.

The upper Paleolithic period is also called the *Age of the Reindeer*, because of the great numbers of this species of deer in the fauna of this period. Edouard Piette has termed it the Glyptic Period, because of the first engravings and carvings on reindeer horn, on bone, on ivory and on stone that are to be met with in that period. These are the oldest works of art of which we have any knowledge, and for this reason they deserve special mention.

The south-west departments : Dordogne, Gironde, Haute-Garonne, Hautes-Pyrénées, Basses-Pyrénées, Arièze and Charente possess the best and most numerous sites, consisting of rock-shelters and natural caves. The valley of the Vézère a tributary of the Dordogne alone has thirty. Among the most important are the grottos of Eyzies, the Mouthe, of Combarelles, Font-de-Gaume, the Grèze, the Madeleine, the Moustier, Laugerie (Dordogne). Besides these, there are also the grotto of Pair-non-Pair in the Gironde, of Marsoulas in the Haute-Garonne, of Niaux in the Ariège, of Gargas in the Hautes-Pyrénées, etc. Spain also has a very great number of sites among which is Altamira. [2]

A close study of these numerous sites has led prehistor-

---

[1] Cf. Pallas, *Description de toutes les nations de l'Empire russe*, quoted by de Morgan in *L'Humanité préhistorique*, p. 28, Paris.
[2] Cf. Déchelette, *op. cit.*, p. 92 and 241 sq.

ians to admit three subdivisions or three epochs in the
upper Paleolithic :

a) A lower level called Aurignacian, from the name of the
grotto at Aurignac in Haute-Garonne;

b) A middle or Solutrian stratum from the site of Solutré
(Saône-et-Loire);

c) An upper or Magdalenian stratum from the site at La
Madeleine (Dordogne).

The whole Upper Paleolithic is characterized by a special
fauna and industry; by the appearance and development
of art, and finally by a new human race, different from that
of Neandérthal, viz. the Cro-Magnon type.   Before passing
in rapid review each of these epochs and noting what is
most characteristic in them, let us first see what they have
in common.

1. *The fauna.* — The rhinoceros and the mammoth were
gradually disappearing.   These cold climate animals
had lived in these regions during the glacial invasion.
With the Aurignacian epoch, the retreat of the glaciers and
a change of fauna begins.   The presence of the reindeer
seems to indicate a climate of the steppes.   With it abounded the polar fox, the marmot, the saiga, the antelope, the
bison, the musk ox, the ibex, the chamois, the horse, the
lemming and a few specimens of the cat and dog tribes.

The upper part of the Paleolithic is marked by a gradual
return of humidity; the reindeer during this time quits
these regions; the deer, the wild boar and the beaver multiply; the first peat bogs are formed.

2. *Dwellings.* — In this period, man selected deep
caves for his dwellings, but it is only at the entrance
of these that we find traces of fireplaces and the
chipped flints.   Man left the debris of his industry on the
spot, mixed with the ashes of his fireplace, kitchen refuse,
the bones of the animals he had used for food, the rubbish
of the grotto, the deposits from the streams that at times
penetrated into the grotto.   All these elements are generally cemented and agglomerated by clay or calcarious
deposits, and constitute veritable prehistoric archives.   At
times, however, the sites are in the open as at Solutré, at

the base of an escarpment where Aurignacian man had killed more than a hundred thousand horses (fig. 133). Beyond question, other sites, less important than these, have escaped the investigation of the prehistorians, or have been destroyed by agricultural development.

3. *Industry.* — The tools are distinguished from those of

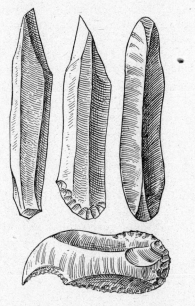

Fig. 115. — Simple Magdalenian gravers.   Scraping gravers, double gravers, and hooked graver.

the preceding period by certain new characteristics. Yet the primitive forms whose utility was the same in all ages were not abandoned. In the Recent Paleolithic epoch, man used principally flint fragments, cut according to design, rather than large rocks. Thus, we see that man knew how to make from flint rocks a series of regular blades with a precision that is marvellous. These blades were often used as such, because of their sharp edges. They are real knives, we might even say razors, so sharp were their edges... They are often touched up, either at the point to produce gravers or tools of the most varied shapes, or on the sides to smooth down their one edge to make them easier to hold, etc. (fig. 115). These blades have very different lengths, ranging from two to twenty centimeters or even more. Their thickness varies from three to twenty millimeters or more. These proportions enable us to distinguish them from the generally broad and thick Mousterian, Acheulean and Chellean fragments. These specimens constitute only a very small percentage of the implements of this period. We meet with awls, taps, javelin points, spearheads, scrapers, planes, chisels, arrow heads of different shapes, etc. It is enough to see a great collection of specimens like that of Riviere, derived in part from the grottos of the Vézère, to have an idea of the skill of the artificer and the precision of his technique. Many nodules of 5,10 and 20 centimeters in length show traces of a series of lamina, regularly detached around the whole circumference by skillfully directed blows. The artificer had to select a suitable spot for the blow, had to calculate the necessary force and the direction it would take, otherwise he would obtain only misshapen, irregular and useless fragments. We need merely try this ourselves to perceive the difficulty we might say the impossibility of the task. It is on this account that we set a high value on the professional skill of these workers in flint, at least the equal of men of our day. They have had the merit of conceiving the tool, of realizing it and of using it, although they had at their disposal only apparently useless material, and very rudimentary means with which to work it. In fact, in the upper Paleolithic as in the Chellean, it was always flint rock that is cut up by means of a simple stone hammer.

An industry that had long been held as recent, appears abundant at this level. It is that of working with bone and deer or reindeer horn. This material sometimes advantageously replaced the flint and permitted the fashioning of new tools such as harpoons, bodkins, needles, etc. It could be engraved and carved, was less fragile, and this will explain its continued use during this entire period.

4. *The Arts in the Upper Paleolithic.* [1] — To give as adequate an idea of the arts of this epoch, as possible, in a small compass, we cannot do better than give an extract from the work of the abbé Breuil, who has made the best study, classification and reproductions of the art of this period.

"The sculpture, painting and engraving have left

Fig. 116. — Elephant carved on the walls of the grotto at Combarelles (Dordogne). Art and its beginnings, by Capitan and Breuil.

innumerable and valuable documents which give a high idea of the artists of the second race. In the Lower Aurignacian or at the very least in the middle, we find only carvings and these rather numerous. So that it has been supposed that the first artistic efforts had been to copy exterior forms. Art would have evolved from sculpture in high-relief to bas-relief, to terminate in engraving.

"This conception does not seem entirely justified. Along side the primitive carvings, we already find some engravings and some paintings. The proportion is reversed as we advance toward the Upper Magdelenian, but the high-relief does not disappear altogether.

[1] Cf. *Dictionnaire d'Apologétique*, art. Homme, col. 479.

"The progress in painting is quite evident.   Man began
by tracing the outline of the animal, later on he added to
this the model; finally after a short period in which he
used a flat color, he came to produce pictures in polychrome.

"He does not seem, at least, in France, to have arrived
at the stage of "composition" or the grouping of several
objects in one picture.   But he reproduced groups found
together in nature itself; the male pursuing a female, two
reindeer facing each other, a drove of horses, a man fighting
a bison, etc.   Still in eastern
Spain which formed part of
an   artistic   province,   we
encounter paintings of hunting scenes on the walls of
the rock shelters, etc.

"The objects reproduced
are always animals, in particular the bison, the reindeer, the horse, the mam-
moth (figs. 116, 117, 118)
the rhinoceros, the boar, the

Fig. 117.— Bear carved in
the Glyptic rock. Art and
its Beginnings.

ibex, the swan, the salmon and some serpents.   The representations of plants are uncertain.   Except the human hand
which is often reproduced, painted or surrounded by paintings on the walls of caverns.   Man was only rarely the subject of the plastic arts.   The entire body appears in some
large red or black drawings at Portel in Ariège.   He is less
rare in the rupestrine paintings of Spain.   In sculpture
many specimens appear in the Aurignacian, but disappear
completely in the Magdalenian.   In this latter epoch,
engravings are still frequently made on stone, bone, or
reindeer horn, but carvings of animals no longer occur.

"These works of art are of very different sizes.   Some
paintings and engravings at Cape Blanc attain or even
surpass the actual dimensions of the reindeer, the bison
and the horses depicted.

"The plastic arts seem thus to have rapidly attained to
a high perfection.   Perhaps it was because they had
originated and developed under other skies.   Only very

few subjects, which might be considered as the first attempts
of a novice rather than a crude artist, have been found.
There are some representations of men that might give this
impression, and yet they are contemporaneous with the
best reproductions of animals.

"By way of contrast, it is interesting to note beside

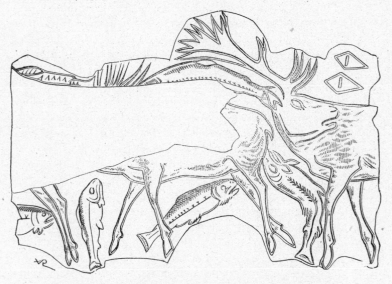

Fig. 118. — Stags and salmon carved on stag's horn.
Grotto of Lorthet (Hautes-Pyrénées) *(Piette.)*

the scrupulously realistic reproduction, an intentional
modification, that is the progressive delineation of forms.
The designs become simpler or more exactly, are altered
to the point of becoming unrecognizable. Between the
motif of lines in appearance purely geometric, and a horse or
a fish, it is necessary to place a whole series of intermediates
to be able to recognize the relationship. Thus, we may
be prepared for a great amount of liberty in art, especially
in the decoration of objects. But it appears that
the Cro-Magnon race made no use of this facility, at least
in France.

"One might ask himself whether this simplification of

design had not brought about the invention of *writing*.

"Various objects have been collected which were used for carving and engraving on bone, ivory, wood and stone, or in the production of paintings and engravings on the walls of grottos (fig. 115).

"To carve this hard material, man made use of flint in the form of a chisel, or more frequently a simple knife blade. To color the objects he had to gather from the surface of certain rocks, oxides of iron or of manganese which gave him various shades of yellow, of red shading off more or less to brown, and black. Perhaps he had recourse also to vegetable dyes. When he had to use this for drawing, he cut it into a pencil. In other cases, he ground up the colors and mixed them with water or with grease. Stone plates that served him for palettes, hollow bones that he used to lift up the powdered ochre, and grease lamps that lighted the recesses of the grottos for him, have been found."

The abbé Breuil has personnally restored the greater part of the prehistoric paintings which he discovered or of which he had been informed, particularly in France and in Spain. Faithful copies of this work which suppose as much skill as patience and courage, may be seen in the Museum of Human Paleontology at Paris or in the various publications of the abbé Breuil. [1]

Sculpture. — In the systematically explored beds in the Pyrénées region, the Aurignacian stratum begins with a level devoid of bone or ivory artifacts, but it yields a mass of flint chisels which lead us to suppose that the men of this epoch had already carved materials such as wood, which are no longer preserved. Above this layer there appears suddenly some masonry carved in high-relief, already very specialized, in no way characteristic of an art in its infancy. The material used is very often ivory or reindeer horn, at times even stone. The oldest statuettes are certainly those of Brassempouy (Landes). They nearly all

---

[1] *Caverne d'Altamira, Cavernes de la région cantabrique, Font-de-Gaume, Combarelles,* etc.

represent women of a very peculiar type, which recalls
the steatopyga (a remarkable accretion of fat on the but-
tocks of the Buschmen). Other human representations
come from Menton, the Dordogne, the Ariège, Moravia.
In the same way have been represented mammoths,
reindeer, bisons, ibexes and horses. These carved objects
are sometimes pendents or amulettes as is indicated by
the holes for suspending them. Sometimes they are used

Fig. 119. — Fragment of a stattuette from Brassempouy;
head covered with a net veil. *(Piette.)*

as dagger hilts. The high-relief carving brings out some
important facts. Barley was already known (Piette). The
grotto at Lourdes and the shelter at Bruniquel (Tarn-et-
Garonne) yield barley spikes carved on ivory. The
statuettes of women (for the most part entirely nude) show
us certain garments in use at the time. One wears a
cincture around the waist; a fragment of another statuette
from Brassempouy shows a sort of hood falling to the
shoulders (fig. 119); two others from Brassempouy and
Menton are wearing a headdress of net-veiling which falls
over the ears and neck. The heads of the Brassempouy
and Menton images show a very Neanderthalic profile;
receding fore-head, accentuated superciliary ridges and
pointed but receding chin. [1]
The sculptures were also a striking manifestation of
human intelligence. Piette has found carvings represent-

[1] Cf. Piette, in *Bull. Société anthr. de Paris*, 1894.

ing even skulls and emaciated horses, which show us a preoccupation in these artists to know, and to represent the anatomical structure of their favorite subjects.

In the upper part of the carved masonry the bas-relief replaces the high-relief. This is the first step in the process of artistic evolution. It may be that having arrived at the high-relief stage, where convention is reduced to a minimum, since the subject is reproduced in its relative proportions, man is of necessity led to the bas-relief. His labor will cost him less trouble, since there will no longer be any fullface aspect to carve and it will be possible to make his subjects assume bolder attitudes. Such is the beautiful piece of ivory of the two ibexes from Mas-d'Azil.

Very frequently at this level, we meet with a serpent carved in bas-relief surrounded by graphic signs. We give below a reproduction of some of the most beautiful of these carvings of the Upper Paleolithic (figs. 120, 121, 122).

Engraving. — According to abbé Breuil it was in the Aurignacian epoch that engraving on bone took its rise or at least manifested itself for the first time. The abbé Parat found at this level in the Trilobite grotto (Yonne) a piece of slate upon which several designs are engraved. It is easy to recognize the rhinoceros tichorhinus. It is the very oldest engraving of the Reindeer Age. The grotto of La Croze, in the commune of Tayac, has fournished primitive engravings of bisons, horses, ibexes and mammoths.

In the valley of the Ain, at the rock shelter of the Colombière, L. Mayet[1] made the important discovery of a site of the end of the Aurignacian period where he was able to collect a veritable museum of prehistoric art, consisting of the oldest known specimens of engravings upon stone. We may see represented there on boulders from the Ain, the majority of animals of the Quaternary period that are now either extinct or have migrated, the great bear, the musk ox, the rhinoceros tichorhinus, the reindeer, etc. Also a curious delineation on mammoth bone of a human being.

[1] Cf. *Comptes rendus Acad. des Sc.* Dec. 12th, 1921, p. 1245.

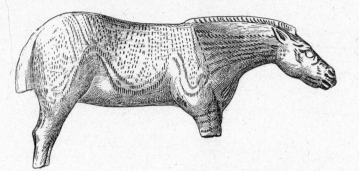

Fig. 120. — Horse carved in ivory.   Grotto of Lourdes.   *(Piette.)*

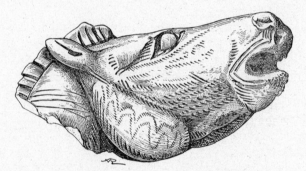

Fig. 121. — Head of horse carved in reindeer horn.
Grotto of Mas-d'Azil.   (Ariège) *(Piette.)*

Fig. 122. — Two reindeer carved in ivory.
Bruniquel (Tarn-et-Garonne).   *(The abbé H. Breuil.)*

These are documents of the very first order of the human paleontology of these regions, and a proof of the keen intelligence of this prehistoric race.

The industry and the engraving [1] are principally of two kinds. *Engravings with carved and grooved outlines* and simple engravings. The first class were carved on thin bone laminae in silhouette form, and were finished by hatching and skilful tracing with a chisel (fig. 123). Among

the designs are horse and ibex heads. The grooved engravings were made by carefully hollowing out the plane surface on which was the outline of an animal, so that these forms would stand out in slight relief from the surface. The details were added with the chisel. To this class would belong the hollowed carvings in the

Fig. 123. — Head of horse found by Mascaraux at St.-Michel d'Arudy. *(Piette.)*

walls of the grotto at Pair-non-Pair (Gironde), for the hoofs of the carved horses and goats were found in strata belonging to the Aurignacian beds. The tools of this bed include large, smoothing stones, bone awls, chisels, along with some scrapers that are lighter than those found in the older beds.

The other engravings merely traced on a smooth surface are still more remarkable. In this last stage of artistic evolution the material labor is reduced to a minimum, while that of the intelligence on the contrary attains its full development, since the surfaces and the reliefs are interpreted only by a combination of lines and hatches. The animals represented are always the reindeer (fig. 124), the horse, the bison, the ibex, the antilope, the seal, the elephant, etc. [1] Man is sometimes represented. An engraving at Laugerie-Basse (Dordogne) shows him in pursuit of a large bison. Another at the Madeleine (Dor-

[1] Déchelette, *op. cit.*, p. 220-238.

dogne) represents him with a stick in his hand standing between two horses. Often enough the fore-arm and hand are found graven on bone along with geometrical markings. These and some other signs such as spirals, bars, broken, lines, circles, etc., often repeated side by side are undoubtedly symbolic emblems. According to Piette, we must see in these, the trade-mark or the signature of the artist (cf. fig. 118, p. 523).

The grottos frequented by man were often remarkably

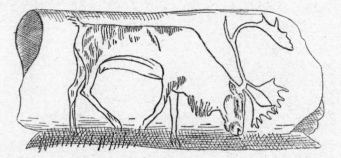

Fig. 124. — Portrait of a reindeer at pasture, engraven with a pointed flint on reindeer horn. Grotto of Kesslerloch at Tayngen, Switzerland.

and consistently decorated. At times with engravings of large dimensions, at other times with real *frescos* painted in red ochre and black. *The engraved grottos* are those of the Mouthe (Dordogne), found by Rivière, of Combarelles (Dordogne) discovered by Dr. Capitan and the abbé Breuil. These two grottos alone contain more than 150 engravings of animals (elephants, horses, stags, reindeer, etc.).

Painting. — Grottos with real frescos are known; that at Altamira (fig. 125) near Santander in the north of Spain and that at Font-de-Gaume (Dordogne) (figs. 129, 130) also discovered by Dr. Capitan and the abbé Breuil, are the most remarkable. We reproduce some of these masterpieces of prehistoric art, executed at the bottom of dark caves, without a model, without any touching up,

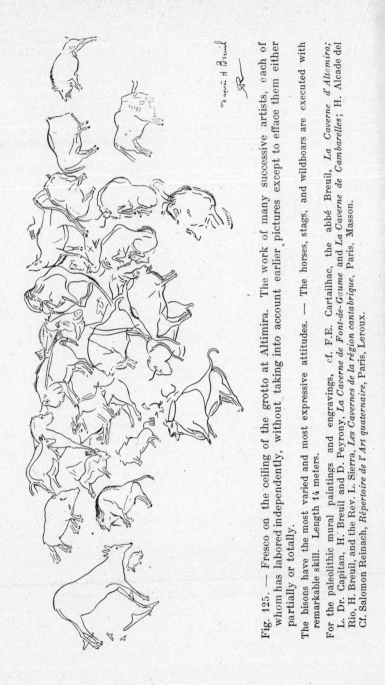

d'après H. Breuil

Fig. 125. — Fresco on the ceiling of the grotto at Altimira. The work of many successive artists, each of whom has labored independently, without taking into account earlier pictures except to efface them either partially or totally.

The bisons have the most varied and most expressive attitudes. — The horses, stags, and wildboars are executed with remarkable skill. Length 14 meters.

For the paleolithic mural paintings and engravings, cf. F.E. Cartailhac, the abbé Breuil, *La Caverne d'Altamira*; L. Dr. Capitan, H. Breuil and D. Peyrony, *La Caverne de Font-de-Gaume* and *La Caverne de Cambarelles*; H. Alcade del Rio, H. Breuil, and the Rev. L. Sierra, *Les Cavernes de la région cantabrique*, Paris, Masson. Cf. Salomon Reinach, *Répertoire de l'Art quaternaire*, Paris, Leroux.

with a steadiness of hand that does great credit to the talent of the artist (figs. 126, 127, 128, 129, 130).

In 1911, the Count de Bégouen discovered at the bottom of the grotto of Tuc d'Audouberg (Ariège) two bisons of natural size, modeled in clay. The execution is identical with that of modern artists. It is a real masterpiece of prehistoric art and another proof of the intelligence of Paleolithic man.

These decorated grottos are not illuminated by daylight

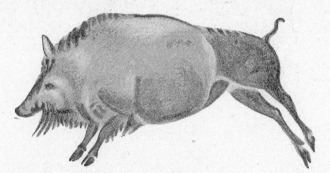

Fig. 126. — Wildboar in polychrome.   Grotto of Altamira.
(The abbé Breuil.)

except one at Pair-non-Pair, which seems to be the oldest, and also some grottos in Spain. The men of this epoch must have had lamps. Rivière has in fact found a real stone lamp at the Mouthe. Certain of these engravings are situated four meters from the ground floor. Some sort of ladder therefore was necessary. Finally these grottos being narrow and several hundred meters long, with only a limited amount of air and very damp sides could not have served as a permanent habitation. It would not be rash to suppose these places were intended for religious assembly. Ethnography furnishes us with modern instances of this. [1]

Authenticity. — The authenticity of sculptures, engraved and painted objects cannot offer any difficulty when they

[1] Déchelette, *Manuel d'Archéologie*, p. 269; Mainage, *Les Religions de la préhistoire*, p. 316.

Fig. 127. — Hind in polychrome. Grotto of Altamira.
(The abbé Breuil.)

Fig. 128. — Bison in polychrome. Grotto of Altamira.
(The abbé Breuil.)

are met with in truly prehistoric deposits. This is the case
for all the objects considered.

That of the mural engravings and paintings neces-

Fig. 129. — Wolf in polychrome.   Font-de-Gaume (Dordogne).
(The abbé Breuil.)

Fig. 130. — Two reindeer facing each other. Point engraving,
   from the grotto of Font-de-Gaume (Dordogne). Size 2. 1 m. × 1. Sm.

sitate a more careful study. Still stratigraphy comes to
our aid.   At Pair-non-Pair, La Grèze and Teyat paintings
and engravings have been found on the walls of the grottos
either partially covered over by stalactites, or by the
rubbish of the cavern. Furthermore, the uniformity of

style leads us to admit the authenticity of the designs traced on the walls or on the ceiling.

The fauna represented also furnishes an excellent argument, since it has either long since become extinct or has migrated. Thus we find the reindeer, the bison, the rhinoceros and the mammoth. It corresponds, moreover with bones found in the Paleolithic caverns. [1]

The abbé Breuil extended his investigations still further. He has succeeded in verifying the successive steps of Quaternary art, even when the paintings or the engravings are superposed on the same wall. The artists have, in fact, many times repainted the same surface, though not without having quite frequently effaced part of the previous work. It is this circumstance that enabled him to reconstruct the history of the art. [2]

One might ask what motive actuated the artists of the Reindeer Age in decorating their very dark caves. Unfortunately they have not disclosed to us their secret, and we believe that we shall discuss their intentions for a long time to come. The simplest hypothesis would be to hold that they cultivated art for art's sake, but why had they so often placed them at the furthest and darkest extremity of their grottos ? Why not, if they lived there and used artificial light there ? Some paintings however have been found at the very entrance to some of the grottos, or in the rock shelters. This is of frequent occurrence in Spain. The care which they bestowed upon the drawing of the animals that were familiar to them indicates an artistic preoccupation. We might also see in these a memento of their hunting exploits. They might have drawn the animal they had captured. [3]

[1] Cf. Mainage, *op. cit.*, p. 81-84.

[2] H. Breuil, *La Caverne d'Altamira*, Paris, Masson.

[3] List of ornamented grottos, arranged in the order of their discovery with the name of the discoverer; 1° Altamira, (Spain) de Santuala, 1875, as an archeological bed, 1879 as an ornamented grotto, designs reproduced and published by abbé Breuil, 1905-1906; 2° Chabot (Gard) Chéron; 1879; 3° La Mouthe (Dordogne), Rivière, 1895; 4° Pair-non-Pair, (Gironde), Daleau, 1896; 5° Marsoulas

Another explanation might find in these painted grottos sanctuaries or places of worship. This is a possibility. The interpretation of the designs is not so easy. We shall refer the reader to the work of P. Mainage : *Les religions de la Préhistoire.*

1º *The Aurignacian Epoch.* — In 1860, Lartet explored the little grotto at Aurignac (Haute-Garonne) and discovered there an entirely new industry, that of bone. This had long been confused with that of the Madeleine which is much later. Still, the Aurignacian industry was only recognized as distinct from the others, after the extended researches and discussions incident to the labors of the eminent prehistorian the abbé B. Breuil [1] at the Congress of Monaco in 1906. Stratigraphic data furnished him with his principal argument, new implements, another. The Aurignacian was found in the Allier (Chastelperron); in

(Haute-Garonne), Regnault 1897; 6º Les Combarelles (Dordogne), Capitan, Breuil and Peyrony, 1902; 7º Font-de-Gaume (Dordogne), Capitan, Breuil and Peyrony, 1902; 8º Mas-d'Azil (Ariège), Breuil 1902; 9º Bernifal (Dordogne), Breuil 1902.; 10º Teyat (Dordogne), Breuil 1902; 11º La Calévie (Dordogne), Breuil, 1902; 12º Cavalanas (Spain), Alcade del Rio, around 1903; 13º Castillo (Spain), Alcade del Rio; 14º Hormos de la Pena (Spain), Alcade del Rio, around 1903; 15º La Hoza (Spain), Alcade del Rio; 16º La Grèze (Dordogne) Capitan, Breuil and Ampoulage, 1904; 17º San Isabel (Spain), Alcade del Rio, and Breuil, 1906; 18º La Venta de la Perra (Spain), Alcade del Rio and Breuil, 1906; 19º Gargas (Haute-Garonne), Regnault, 1906; 20º Niaux (Ariège), Molard and Cartailhac, 1906; 21º Le Portel, Dr. Jeannel and Cartailhac, 1908; 22º Mazoulas (Spain), Alcade del Rio, 1908; 23º La Pasiega (Spain), Obermaier 1911; 24º La Pasiega (Spain), Obermaier 1711, Monographie Breuil, etc., 1913; 25º Tuc d'Audoubert (Ariège), Comte de Bégouen, 1912; 26º Velez Blanco (Almeria), Breuil, etc., 1914; 27º Las Balneras (Salamanca), Carie, Breuil, 1910, 1915; 28º La Pileta (Malaga), Breuil, Obermaier, etc., 1915; 29º Las Grabadas de la Cueva de Penches (Madrid) 1917, etc.

[1] Cf. Abbé A. H. Breuil, *La question Aurignacienne*; *Etude critique de stratigraphie comparée, Revue préhistorique*, 1907, p. 173-219; Id., *Les Gisements presolutréens du type d'Aurignac;* International Congres of Anthropology, Monaco, 1906, I, p. 323-350, 1907; Id., *Essai de stratigraphie des dépôts de l'âge du renne*, First Prehistoric Congress of France, p. 74-80, 1906.

the Charente (La Quina, la Chaise) in the Dordogne (Cro-
Magnon, Gorge d'Enfer); in the Gironde (Pair-non-Pair);
in the Saône-et-Loire (lower level of the Solutré); in the
Yonne (Arcy-sur-Cure), etc.

The Aurignacian question is counted among the most
important of the Paleolithic period. With the Aurignac
level begins sculpture, engraving and painting, that is,

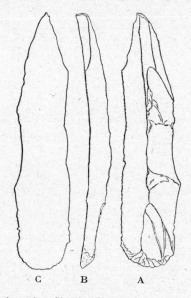

C   B   A

Fig. 131. — Aurignacian flint implements, serving both as scrapers
and gravers.

A. View of chipped and retouched side.— B. Lateral view.— C. Chipped side.

the evolution of Paleolithic art, and with it one of the
finest manifestations of human intelligence.

1. *Industry.* — All the Mousterian implements are found
at this level; but we note also the appearance of new types
that are quite characteristic but long confused with those
of the Magdalenian. They consist of blades with a single
and with a double notch; a kind of instrument intended for
polishing wood, bone or reindeer horn; blades with their
edge beaten down and assuming the form of knife blades

of all sizes called *Gravette blades*. The awls terminate in a more or less sharp point; the tough burin similar to the busk bodkins (fig. 131); some simple chisels ending in a dihedral angle intended for cutting such hard materials as reindeer horn, bone, ivory and stone, preparatory to engraving or carving. If their invention is not recent, their use is new (fig. 115). The articles of bone are numerous. The bone point with a split base is the most characteristic implement at this level. It might have been a brace for an arrow or a javelin.

The coloring minerals : hematite, ochre, etc., are found in a many Aurignacian sites; they probably served for painting and later on for tatooing the body, and in decorating the grottos.

The personal ornaments are represented by shells and perforated teeth, showing the esthetic preoccupation of this remote epoch. It is evident that its arts are another clear proof of human intelligence. [1]

2. *The Aurignacian fauna.* — The almost constant presence of the *ursus spelæus* and of the *hyæna spelæa*, and of the *rhinoceros tichorhinus* is noted. Besides these the *bison priscus*, the *equus cabalus*, the *cervus elaphus*, the reindeer, the ibex and the roc are found.

The lower level at Solutré is of the Aurignacian epoch and contains the remains of more than one hundred thousand horses. This fact and some drawings have led certain authors to hold that the horse was domesticated at this epoch. The hypothesis seems very probable (cf. fig. 123).

3. *The Aurignacian human races.* [2] — The Grimaldi Race. — Two skeletons were discovered, on June 3rd 1901, in one of the grottos at Grimaldi, that of the Infants, at a lower level pertaining to the end of the Mousterian or to the beginning of the Aurignacian, although buried in the

---

[1] Cf. Breuil, *Études de Morphologie paléolithique*, in *Revue d'Anthropologie*, Feb. 1911.

[2] Cf. Boule, *Les hommes fossiles*, p. 274 and 275, section of the grotto of Grimaldi, Paris, Masson.

Mousterian bed which contained ten meters of sediment made from human deposits. These two skeletons were buried at a depth of 8.50 meters. They belong to the *negroid* type and constitute a race truly distinct from that of Neanderthal, and closely related to that of Cro-Magnon which already existed. One of these two skeletons is that of an old woman and the other that of a young man of from

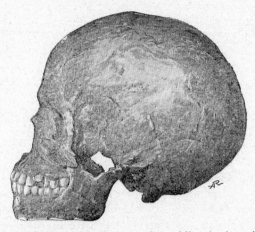

Fig. 132. — Negroid skull from Grimaldi. Aurignacian level.
(Verneau.)

15 to 17 years of age. Their respective heights are 1.56 and 1.60 m., the cranial capacities 1 375 and 1 580 cc. The face is broad but rather low; the skull is *dolichocephalic.* The forehead is well developed, vertical, the orbital ridges not very prominent, the orbits broad, low and acute. The nose very broad, depressed at the base; the upper maxillary has a very pronounced prognathism.

The majority of these cranial and facial characteristics are negroid (fig. 132) but must not be confused with those of the negro race. Boule finds resemblances between them and the South African Buschmen and Hottentots. Verneau sees a relationship between this race and that of Cro-Magnon which immediately followed it in the locality.

In the same grotto, the Canon of Villeneuve had found

at the Upper Aurignacian level two skeletons belonging to the Cro-Magnon race which we shall study later.

2° *Solutrian Epoch.* — The site at Solutré near Mâcon (Saône-et-Loire) is at the foot of a Jurrassic escarpment and covers more than a hectare (2 471 acres) to a depth of from 5 to 7 meters (fig. 133).

The base is Aurignacian, as the implements of the fire-

Fig. 133. — Prehistoric station of Solutré at the base of the lower escarpment.

places and workshops that are found there indicate. It contains a heap of horses that used to serve as food for these hunters; the upper layer contains fire places and graves.

The flint industry seems to attain its maximum perfection in the Solutrian epoch. The Aurignacian flints are retained, but a new process of chipping allows of the formation of what have been called laurel leaves and ash leaves. They are very thin blades and of a large size from which small fragments were methodically detached over the entire surface. They might have served as spear-heads and the smallest as arrow-heads (fig. 134).

The fourteen blades from Volgu (Saône-et-Loire) because of their dimensions 0.25 m. to 0. 35 m., and of the delicacy of the work, are masterpieces of Paleolithic art. The notched arrow-heads characterize the upper level (fig. 135).

At the base pedunculated arrow-heads with the Solutrian retouching scarcely shown are found. This is also noted in such other implements as chisels, awls, etc., (fig. 136).

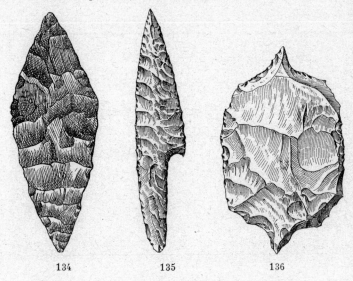

134   135   136

Fig. 134. — Solutrian type. Laurel leaf type of spear-head.
Fig. 135. — Notched Solutrian point, entire and well executed.
Fig. 136. — Flint double awl. Solutrian type.

Among the Solutrian sites we note the grotto of Lacave (Lot) where its explorer Armand Viré came across three stages of Solutrian fireplaces, which with the rubbish separating them attained a height of 7 meters. He found there, at the base, a commander's staff. [1] Some beautiful

[1] Cf. Déchelette, *op. cit.*, p. 146, for the list of Solutrean stations. We may mention Laugerie-Haute. Gorge d'Enfer, Cro-Magnon, Les Eyzies (Dordogne). Le Placard (Charente), Pair-non-Pair (Gironde), Volgu and Solutré (Saône-et-Loire).

bone needles were removed from the second layer. An antilope's head engraven on reindeer horn was found in the third. The Solutrian industry, common in the regions of Dordogne, Charente and Lot, is missing in the north of France, but is found at Predmost in Moravia and Altamira in Spain.

3° *The Magdalenian Epoch.* — This period takes its name

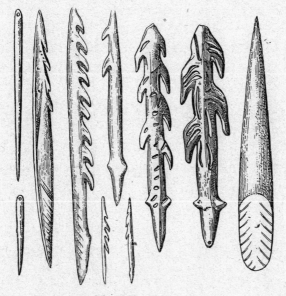

Fig. 137. — Various models of Magdalenian reindeer-horn harpoons, Magdalenian bone needles.

from the grotto of La Madeleine near Eyzies in Dordogne. Early man took refuge in these grottos and rock shelters to protect himself from the cold. He still remained a nomadic hunter and redoubled his activity, in perfecting and multiplying his equipment for hunting and fishing. The flint implements no longer include the fine delicately retouched Solutrian blades, but are made up for the most part, of blades of all shapes and sizes with sharp edges, that were used as knives or carefully retouched to fill many new needs.

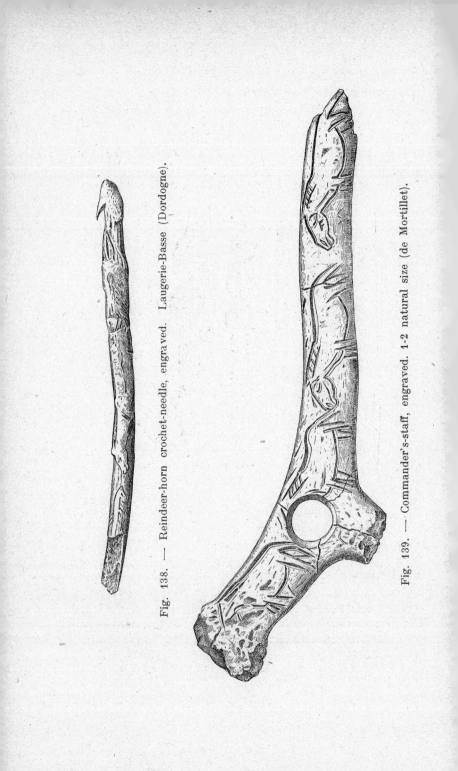

Fig. 138. — Reindeer-horn crochet-needle, engraved. Laugerie-Basse (Dordogne).

Fig. 139. — Commander's-staff, engraved. 1-2 natural size (de Mortillet).

The work in bone was gradually improved from the Aurignacian epoch. From reindeer horn, harpoons with double rows of barbs variously disposed were made (fig. 137). Points of horn, bone and ivory often replace those of flint. The base which was inserted into the staff shows an obliquely bevelled section instead of a slit, as in the Aurignacian. These weapons were intended for the chase and not for war.

Certain articles served either for making or for adorning man's clothing. Bone spatulas were used to cleanse the flesh side of the skins of animals, flayed with flint. Awls made a series of holes in the hides, and fine needles with eyes, drew thread, cut from tendons or from prepared intestines, through these holes. Piette was inclined to see in certain long thin blades of bone or of horn, with surface fantastically toothed, instruments that might serve for weaving. There were also a kind of shuttle and crochet needles (fig. 138).

What was the function of the *commander's staves* ? (fig. 139). Their ornamentation was often very elaborate and in exquisite taste, in fact, real works of art. The hole constantly found in each might, in our opinion, have served for a cord to join them together so as to serve as a halter, for the domestic horses of this period (fig. 123).

The Magdalenian men wore various *ornaments*; pendants, perforated teeth and shells from which they made bracelets or necklaces. Thus, the skeleton of Menton which is in the Paris Museum had the head covered with a net studded with small shells, and a string of perforated stag teeth around the temples.

The place of origin of these shells draws attention to the *commercial relations* of the inhabitants of a particular grotto. Thus, the fossil shells imported to Mas d'Azil (Ariège) came from the marls of Bordeaux and of Dax; the fossil shells found in the grottos of Périgord, on the contrary, came from the marls of Touraine. Shells have been found at Menton coming either from the nummulitic rock of the Manche, or from the Pliocene rocks of Antibes or from the actual beaches on the Atlantic.

Burials in the Upper Paleolithic. — The question of Quaternary burials is no longer doubtful. It is now certain that there existed real funeral customs in the Glyptic epoch. We have a well authenticated burial at Predmost in Moravia, in the Aurignacian beds. The remains of twenty individuals were found under one large stone slab. [1] The Magdalenian beds likewise afford indisputable instances of the same. The abbé Tournier discovered one in 1894 at Hoteaux (Ain). It was under five thicknesses of Magdalenian fireplaces. The inverted femurs show that it was after an artificial removal of the flesh that the bones had been placed on a bed of red ochre, with a commander's staff and various ornaments. [2]

Back to the same epoch go certain burials at Baousse-Rousse near Menton (Alpes-Maritimes). They seem to illustrate different customs. For some are situated on top of the layers, while others are in deep cavities. Many were collective. One of the corpses had been placed in a lighted fireplace and charred; others seem to have been stripped of their flesh before being buried on the thick layer of coloring matter (red hematite). In the left hand was placed, sometimes a flint, sometimes a piece of gypsum. They were covered with their ornaments, necklaces, nets, etc.

The question of prehistoric burials is very significant and merits a few details relative to the Cro-Magnon race.

This race was discovered in 1868 at Cro-Magnon in the commune of Tayac near Eyzies (Dordogne) on the shores of the Vézère. Workmen that were constructing a railroad discovered the remains of five human skeletons in a rock shelter called Cro-Magnon. These remains were above prehistoric fireplaces. Louis Lartet went to the place to study the excavation scientifically. They found that they were in a true burying place as was shown by the position of the skeletons and the funeral trappings. The antiquity

---

[1] *Anthropologie*, Grotto of Predmost, 1901, p. 148.
[2] Abbé Tournier, *Comptes rendus du VIe Cong. scient. internat. des Cath.*, Fribourg.

of the site studied by Lartet himself is unquestioned.   But
G. Mortillet had stated that Quaternary man never buried
his dead.   The facts had to give way to a preconceived
theory.   Prehistorians in spite of the protestations of some

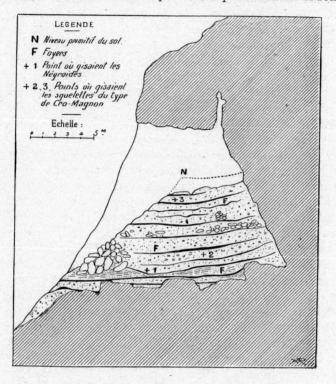

Fig. 140. — Grotto des Enfants (Grimaldi) (*Boule*).

Legend : N. Original level of floor. F. Fireplace. — 1. Location of negroid
skeletons. — 2. Location of Cro-Magnon type skeleton.

scientists of the first rank, like de Quatrefages and Hamy,
gave in.

A new skeleton was discovered in 1872 by Massenat at
Laugerie-Basse opposite Cro-Magnon in strata of the
Paleolithic age along with funeral trappings.   He did not
dare assert that it was a burial, but said that the body had

been crushed by the fall of the block under which it was found. Hamy studied the skeleton and recognized in it the Cro-Magnon race. Some months later, Louis Lartet and Chaplain-Duparc discovered another one of the same epoch, of the same race and intentionally buried in the rock shelter of Duruthy at Sorde (Landes). March 26, 1872, Rivière discovered, in one of the Menton grottos — that of Cavillon — the skeleton so well known under the name of the *Menton Man*, which may be seen in the gallery of Anthropology in the Paris Museum. Here again burial was evident. The tools and ornaments and shell work placed on top of the body gave evidence of it; the body had been sprinkled with red ochre. Rivière was again opposed by de Mortillet, and a number of prehistorians thought they had to give way to his opposing arguments. In 1884, an archeologist Julien excavated the fifth cavern of Grimaldi at Menton. There he discovered the human skeleton, now resting in the Menton Museum. This cavern, called Barma, yielded other skeletons. Its owner, a quarry-man, destroyed it. In 1895, Prince Albert of Monaco decided to explore methodically the other Grimaldi grottos. He charged the Canon Villeneuve with the task of excavating them, for the purpose of solving the problem of the burials, the races and the antiquity of the man of this grotto. The grotto of the Prince was nearly intact. 4 000 cubic meters of material, very interresting from the Paleontological standpoint but devoid of human bones, were removed. The prince decided to complete the excavation of the grotto des Enfants (fig. 140). Rivière had stopped at a depth of 2.70 meters. There remained 8 meters of deposit which might be expected to yield rich results. In fact, four skeletons were discovered at three different levels. Paleontology and stratigraphy facilitated the determination of their geological status.

According to Boule who was present and participated in these labors, these skeletons are certainly Pleistocenic, and go back to an age older than that of the reindeer; i. e. to the Aurignacian. He adds: " The new skeletons exhumed in the grotto des Enfants had been the subjects of true burials under conditions recalling those of the skeletons discovered before; perforated shells, articles of adornment, and red colored bone. The skeletons of the higher levels were of the Cro-Magnon type. They were sent to the Anthropological Museum at Monaco (fig. 141). At the base were

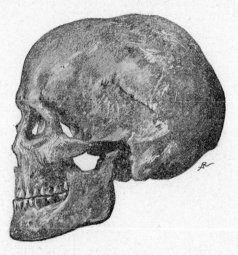

Fig. 141. — Skull from the Grotto des Enfants.
Cro-Magnon race.

found two particularly negroid skeletons, since called Grimaldi race (fig. 132). We must still cite, as belonging to the Cro-Magnon race, the skeleton of Chancelade (1888) that of Brün in Moravia (1891) intentionally buried in the Solutrian age; that of Combe-Capelle (Dordogne) carried away by the antiquarian Kauser and acquired by the Berlin Museum, and of which Klaatsch has mistakenly desired to form a separate race (fig. 142).

In 1914, Verworn found a double Magdalenian burial at Obercassel near Bonn. The list is far from complete. [1]

From this array of facts we can conclude with the abbés Breuil and Bouyssonie that "the hunters of the second race

[1] Boule, *Les hommes fossiles*, p. 262-281.

had respect for the human body. They buried it with care; often with hewn stones at their sides or placed above them, forming a kind of tomb. The body was adorned, colored and surrounded with useful articles, such as tools or weapons of flint. In general, as at Chapelle-aux-Saints the whole was covered with broken bones of animals or

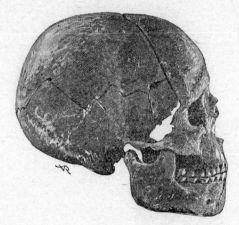

Fig. 142. — Combe-Capelle skull.
Cro-Magnon race.

with flints threwn pell mell as on the floor of a dwelling of savages. The corps was sometimes folded back on itself, recalling the man of Corrèze — and sometimes stretched out at full length" [1] (fig. 143).

Characteristics of the Cro-Magnon race. — The Cro-Magnon race was characterized and so named by de Quatrefages and Hamy. This race occupied a good part of Europe in the Aurignacian epoch, and had its uniform burial rites. The great numbers of entire skeletons, six at Cro-Magnon, ten at the Grimaldi grottos, etc., enabled the anthropologists de Quatrefages, Hamy, Verneau and Boule to make a detailed study of them (figs. 141, 142, 144, 145).

---

[1] Cf. Dict. Apolog., art. *Homme;* Boule, *op. cit.*, p. 283-198; P. Mainage, *Les religions de la préhistoire*, Chap. on Burials.

We shall give a resume of this study according to Boule.[3]

The skull is dolichocephalic and voluminous. Its capacity equals 1590 cc.; the cranial vault is high; the chin is prominent; the superciliary ridges are slightly sallient; the forehead high. The face is relatively low and very broad whereas the skull is narrow and long. "Thus," says de

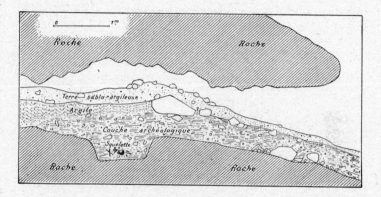

Fig. 143. — Grotto of Chapelle-aux-Saints. (A. J. Bouyssonie and Bardon.)

The skeleton is buried in a ditch above archeological beds.

Quatrefages, "among these savages, contemporaneous with the mammoth, the skull presents in a high degree the characteristics regarded as the indices of a very advanced intellectual development. The bones indicate a very tall stature (1. 82 m.) and an athletic build. The muscular impresses are strong; the tibia flattened into the shape of a sabre-blade. This character, absent in the Neanderthal man appears quite general in the Cro-Magnon race."

"To sum up" concludes Boule (pg. 291) "there is question of a fine race that had played a considerable role in time and space. It did not disappear but continued during the Neolithic. While in our day it may be found in Dordogne, in Spain and among the Kabyles in the Canary Isles."

[1] Cf. Boule, *Les hommes fossiles*, p. 383 sq.

The Chancelade Race. — Dr. Testut of Lyons, who has studied the Magdalenian skeleton of Chancelade, considers it a race related to, but differing from that of Cro-Magnon. He points out some very interesting details.   This skeleton reposed on the left side, the arm was raised, the left hand placed under the head, the right on the left side of the lower maxillary; the lower limbs had been bent back.   A like mode of burial is in vogue among a great number of ancient

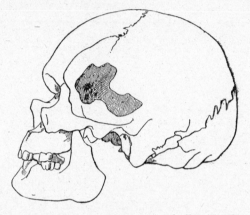

Fig. 144. — Laugerie-Baume skull. (Dordogne)

and modern tribes, for example, among the present Esqui-maux.   The body had been sprinkled with red ochre.   The skeleton was about 1.55 meters long.   The skull, very dolichocephalic (cephalic index = 72), broad and high with a capacity of 1 710 cc. surpassing exceedingly that of the modern Europeans; the profile presents the character-istics of the highest races (fig. 146).   This race with the Cro-Magnon and the Grimaldi races attest both the unity and the variability of the human type during the Paleolithic Epoch.

Dr. Testut found great similarity between the Chancelade skeleton and that of the eastern Esquimaux.   Archeology confirmed these similarities since the implements are the same, the customs the same and the artistic efforts are the same.   Paleolithic tribes might have made their way

gradually to the circumboreal regions by Behring Straits
and the Aleoutian Isles.   Thence, they might have invaded

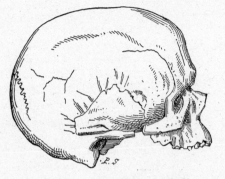

Fig. 145. — Cro-Magnon skull.

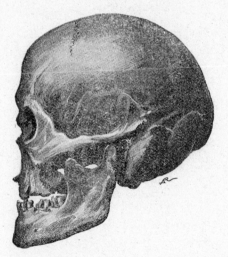

Fig. 146. — Chancelade skull found at the base of Magdelenian
fire-places.

Canada and the American Indians might be their descendants. This theory which gives the path followed by man
as from Asia to Europe, thence to America, is more in

conformity with the reality than the reverse opinion given
by Chamberlain-Boas [1] in America. It is also more in
conformity with tradition.

3. THE NEOLITHIC PERIOD. [2]

1. *Period of Transition (Azilian).* — The great humidity
that prevailed at the end of the Paleo-
lithic Age drove the reindeer and other
steppes fauna from southern Europe.
A mild and uniform temperature began
to extend over all France bringing about
the formation of the peat bogs. The
industry of the inhabitants of Europe
and of the entire Mediterranean basin
shows modifications so profound and
so rapid, that one gets the impression
of a sudden break in the continuity of
habitation, or rather of a sudden invasion of new races with entirely different
customs.

Piette found evidence to make us
conclude otherwise. In 1887, he discovered at Mas d'Azil, on the left bank of
the Arize river in Ariège, a real transition stratum which he called the *Azilian Period.* Along side of Magdalenian
flints were a great number of very small
circular and quadrangular scrapers.
Art had disappeared entirely. There
were no more paintings or drawings, no more carved bones,
no more needles. Crude polishers made from reindeer
horn replaced the thin spatulas. In place of the carefully
rounded longhandled awls, they had very simply fashioned
bone implements. Harpoons still existed. Thousands of

Fig. 147. — Stag-
horn harpoon. La
Tourasse, at St. Mar-
tory (H[te]-Garonne).
1/2 natural size.

---

[1] Cf. Boule, p. 292.
[2] For this period, we refer the reader to Déchelette's *Manuel
d'Archéologie.*

them have been found at Mas d'Azil, but they are very different from those of the preceding stratum. They were made from stag's horn : As the operative part of this horn was reduced to a thin cortical layer, they had to make the shaft flat and broad. The base is ordinarily perforated with a hole made round at first with an awl and then lengthened by cutting (fig. 147).

Two characteristics unite the Azilian industry with more recent strata; the presence of numerous fragments of pottery, and stones made into chisels which are regarded as the oldest polished stones. The most remarkable objects of this Azilian stratum are the ochre-colored pebbles. They are beach pebbles upon which have been painted a great variety of designs, by spreading with a spatula the color prepared in a shell or hollow stone. The paintings are crude and devoid of artistic merit. Some represent parallel bands varying in

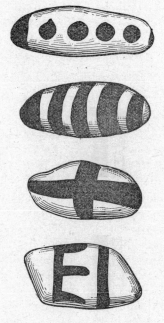

Fig. 148. — Colored pebbles from Mas d'Azil. (Piette.)

number from one to eight, either reaching or not reaching the ends of the pebble. Others represent crosses, either alone or inscribed in a circle, decreasing circles, T shaped, spirals, serpentine bands, zig-zag signs and broken lines... There are also some alphabetical signs as L, E, F, I, M, the Greek eta, gamma, epsilon, iota, mu and sigma; there are also some rather closely resembling the letters of the Phenician and Cypriotic alphabets, etc. Without pushing the bearing of these resemblances too far, we must nevertheless see something other tham mere daubing and scribbling; they are, according to Piette, real graphic signs (fig. 148).

Piette came across two skeletons at Mas d'Azil that had been buried after having been stripped of their flesh, by means of flint, and colored red with ochre. As the bones were not joined together, and as the small bones were lacking, he concluded that the bodies had remained a long time in the open before burial. These two burials show that these people were of the Cro-Magnon race.

Agriculture makes its first appearance, for in the *gravel* beds at Mas d'Azil, Piette came across nut-shells, hazel-nuts, cherry and plum seeds, acorns, perhaps also chestnuts, and a little pile of wheat. The ornamental shells are quite numerous. Few of them are fossils. The recent shells came from the beaches along the ocean and the Mediterranean Sea.

The transition from the Paleolithic to the Neolithic periods did not occur in the same way in all regions. In the north of France, the line of demarcation is indiscernable : perhaps the Neolithic should take its origin from the remains of a retarded Acheulean industry. In the Indies the direct transition from the old Acheulean to the polished axes seems morphologically indisputable. The transitional industry noticed at Mas d'Azil is found, though to a less extent at la Tourasse and at Gourdan (Haute-Garonne) in the grottos at Oban (Scotland) at Lourdes and at Lorthet (Hautes-Pyrénées) at Laugerie-Basse and at the Madeleine (Dordogne) in the grotto of Reilhac (Lot) and at Montfort (Ariège).

2. *The Neolithic epoch.* — Great humidity marks the beginning of the Neolithic epoch. For at this time the grotto of Mas d'Azil shows signs of heavy inundations, and the peat-bogs of the Somme have their bases filled up with uprooted trees.

The fauna was nearly that of today; the beaver, the stag, and the wildboar abounded. There were still some large elk in these regions and the brown bear was not infrequent. A study of the Neolithic epoch is less easy than that of the Paleolithic, for man with rare exceptions, no longer dwelt in caves, thus making the stratigraphic method, elsewhere so fruitful in results, more difficult of application. One is very often obliged to determine dates by comparing the states of the industrial morphology. The latter is a result of the most diverse influences : geographic position, division of work, the skill of the workman and the quality of the material.

Montelius, director of the Stockholm Museum, divides the so called Neolithic epoch into 4 periods, characterized by the mode of burial and by the shape of the polished axes.

First Period. No known burials; the chipped and the polished hatchets are triangular in form and their cross section is pointed.

Second Period : Simple dolmen (or rude stone monument), axes with squared edges, and almost rectangular in shape.

Third Period : Covered graves; thick axes with square edges; beautiful flint knives with tapering type of handle.

Fourth Period : Stone coffins; perforated axes; beautiful flint knives with handles—of the broad blade and narrow handle type. [1]

We shall separate the Neolithic epoch into two chronological divisions—the Old and the Recent. They are otherwise so intimately bound together that they do not show the least break in continuity. They differ only in their extremes.

I. *Old Neolithic.* — *Arisian.* — The Old Neolithic is represented at Mas d'Azil by shell-beds superposed upon those containing the colored pebbles and underlying that which contains the polished axes. In this bed, which Piette calls Arisian, are met numerous shells of an edible snail which frequented moist places, *helix nemoralis,* and which figures considerably in man's diet; fruits such as the acorn, the walnut, hazelnut and plum. The pits of the sloe are so numerous that Piette believes they made a fermented liquor from them.

The flints resemble those of the Azilian bed; the pottery

[1] Cf. Déchelette, *op. cit.,* p. 320.

is quite abundant and delicate; the polished implements are—some fragments used as chisels or scrapers, but never as axes. One burial is of the covered grave type constructed of rows of posts.

Campignian. — The Campignian industry, so called from the Campigny hill near Blangy (Seine-Inférieure) is like that found in the oldest heaps of "kitchen-middens" (kjœkkenmeddings) [1] of Denmark and at the bottom of the peat bogs of the Somme. It was known throughout a great part of northern and western France.

Along with a great number of broad and rounded implements scattered here and there, two very characteristic specimens were found, a paring-knife and a pick. In the former (fig. 150) the single bevelled transversal blade is at the broad extremity of the tool. When this knife takes on a very elongated shape with uniform width, it becomes a chisel; when, instead of terminating in a transversed bevel it is elongated into a more or less blunt point, we have a pick. The use of the pick is very uncertain. Perhaps it served to dig up the ground for the cultivation of cereals, as mill stones for grinding grain were found at Campigny and at Mas d'Azil, showing that the cereals had already been included among the food-stuffs.

Fig. 149. — Chisel from the Kjoek-kenmeddings.

Fig. 150. — Flint paring-knife from Campigny (2/3 natural size).

Elsewhere, as at Fère-en-Tardenois (Aisne) a number

[1] Cf. Déchelette, *op. cit.*, vol. I, p. 322-346.

of small geometrically shaped flints have been found (figs. 151 to 154); they characterize an industrial phase that G. de Mortillet called Tardenoisian.

Pottery is very plentiful at Campigny. It is seldom ornamented, but very well and at times quite beautifully shaped.

The dog was already domesticated and unquestionably also the ox, the sheep and the hog. [1]

II. *Recent Neolithic or Robenhausian.* — On the preceding sites we found no polished axes and even in the Campignian

Figs. 151 to 154. — Flint bits in geometrical shapes.

period polishing was never or at least very seldom resorted to. In neither of the two phases have we noticed any arrow-heads.

The polished axe (fig. 155) becomes the typical implement of the Recent Neolithic Period. [2] The dimensions vary from four to fifty centimeters. The material from which they were made was quite varied. Flint predominated, but we find also the semiprecious stones jadite, fibrolite, chloromelanite, etc.; soft rocks were also used. Many of these axes were only "objets de luxe".

[1] Le Campignien, *Fouille d'un fond de cabane au Campigny*, by d'Ault, Salmon and Capitan.—The station of la Vignette, Capitan, *Revue mens. d'Ec. d'anthrop.*, July, 1897. — Kjœkkenmeddings, Marlat, *Société vaudoise des sciences nat.*, 1859-1860.—*Comptes rendus du Congrès international d'anthrop. préhist. de Copenhague*, 1869 p. 135-160.

[2] Two Neolithic regions may show profound differences. Thus at Mas d'Azil along with the polished a es are found many articles made from bone, and almost no chipped flints; in the north, on the contrary, the bone articles are rare and the flints innumerable.

To make a flint axe they began by rough-hewing and
cutting away two faces of a flint nodule; then a finer
finish gave it definite shape.   Thus prepared, the axe was
ground on a flint rock or very hard sandstone.   To facilitate the operation, wet sand was placed between the axe
and the polishing stone.   The friction produced grooves of

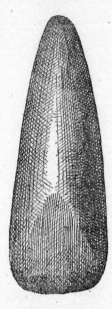

Fig.   155. —   Polished
axe. Triangular Neoli-
thic type.

Fig. 156. — Axe fastened
into stag-horn handle.
(Concise palafitte.)

varying depths in the polishing stone.   Ordinarily the
polishers were portable but some were fixed in the ground
and were several cubic meters in size.

The stone axe was fitted to different kinds of handles.
The heel was often fastened into a sheath or socket of
deer-horn (fig. 156) fitted into a wooden handle.   Towards
the end of the Neolithic period, there were hatchets with a
perforation into which the handle was fastened.   These
circular holes were made with wet sand, set in motion by a

rapidly revolving reed. Tomahawks, annular disks and annular bracelets were made in the same way.

There is in the Guimet Museum a whole collection of Neolithic vases made of hard stone, displaying marvellous handicraft and a perfect artistic sense. They come from Egypt.

The polish was given also to very straight and elongated chisels and to gouges with concave blades (figs. 157 to 162). The other tools were only occasionally polished. Such were the different picks, burins, awls and scrapers, knives, spear-heads, daggers, etc. The working of flint in the Neolithic period attained a degree of perfection difficult to surpass. The above drawings (figs. 161 to 165) give us some idea of this. Towards the end of the Neolithic period, the spear-heads and daggers were truly wonderful, especially in Denmark (figs. 166 to 168).

The arrow-heads frequently assume the Solutrian shapes; but ordinarily they are of small chip type, often with a peduncle and two pinions or lateral barbs. The arrows were shot by means of bows of yew-wood, many examples of which are found in the palafittes. Another arrow-head, frequent at the end of the Neolithic period, has the appearance of a small Campignian knife with which they fastened the small chisels into the handles (figs. 169 to 187).

The bone and stag-horn implements are less varied. Besides axehandles there are bodkins, polishers, chisels, picks, fish-hooks and harpoons (fig. 188). The workmanship displayed by the Neolithic man, in fashioning hard stone especially flint, is really remarkable.

At Mur-de-Barrez at Aveyron, veritable shafts were sunk to a depth of 12 meters into the lime stone to get at the flint shelves. The large blocks of flint, previously quarried, supplied numerous fine laminae of flint up to 40 centimeters in length, which were then exported and traded. Thus we find the flint laminae of Grand-Presigny (Indre-et-Loire) all over France, and even in Switzerland as for instance at Robenhausen. The nodules, known to peasants under the name of butter-stones "livres de

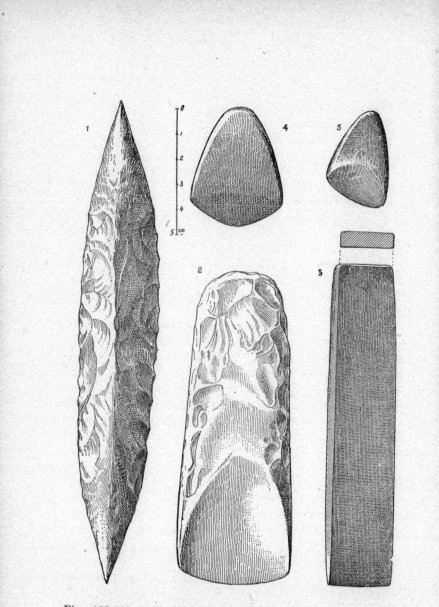

Figs. 157-161. — Neolithic flint tools : 1. Double-pointed poignard slightly polished; 2. Concave gouge of polished flint; 3. Quadrangular polished stone graver; 4. and 5. Small triangular axes polished to the shape of concave gouges.

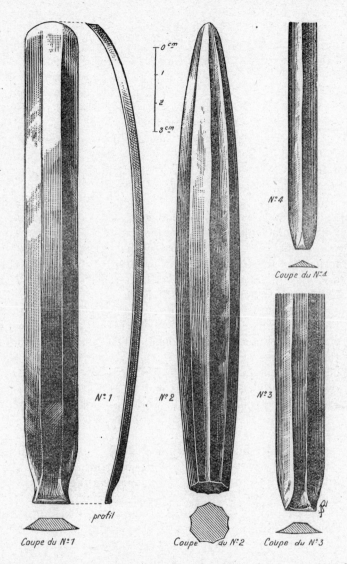

Figs. 162-165. — 1, 3, 4, Observe lateral *(profil)* and cross-sectional *(coupe)* view of blades. 2. Nucleus from which a series of uniform blades were detached.

beurre" were thrown away or were shaped and polished into axes or other implements.

Hand made pottery, [1] at times very beautiful, was extensively used. The vases, often of large dimension, are decorated with rather artistic geometrical designs. Although mediocre artists, the Neolithic men did not scorn the use of necklaces and breast-plates. For this purpose they used the teeth of animals and shells of the period either entire or cut into pieces, and such semiprecious stones as the callaïs (a kind of turquoise) jadéite, serpentine, jet and alabaster. They dyed their linen and hemp clothing and also made fish lines. *Stock-raising and agriculture* was their principle occupation. The dog, the ox, the sheep, the hog and the goat were domesticated; wheat, millet, various oliagenous plants, apples, nuts, raspberries, etc., were cultivated. It is probable that they also made a fermented drink from the raspberries, for in the palafittes are found great accumulations of their seeds, as if the fruit had been crushed to obtain the juice.

On becoming an agriculturist man of necessity had to have a *fixed* dwelling, and to defend his possessions against the encroachments of other men. This is why the men of the Neolithic period showed warlike habits, united into clan-like organizations and sought to render access to their dwellings difficult. To this end as at Catenay (Oise) at Peu-Richard (Ch.-Inf.), in the Jura, in the Franche-Comté, they built intrenched camps on high places whose area varied from 1 to 20 hectares.

There was sometimes an outer ditch 7 meters wide by 3.9 in depth, crossed by a 9 to 10 meter bridge. A second ditch served as additional protection. On the shores of the lakes at Geneva, Annecy, Clairvaux, Chalain, Bourget and the greater part of the Swiss lakes, the dwellings were raised on piles and are called palafittes (fig. 189). Very ingenious were the expedients resorted to in constructing their dwellings over the water. They sank a certain number of piles vertically into the mud assuring their

[1] Déchelette, *Manuel d'Archéol. préhist.*, vol. i, p. 545-564.

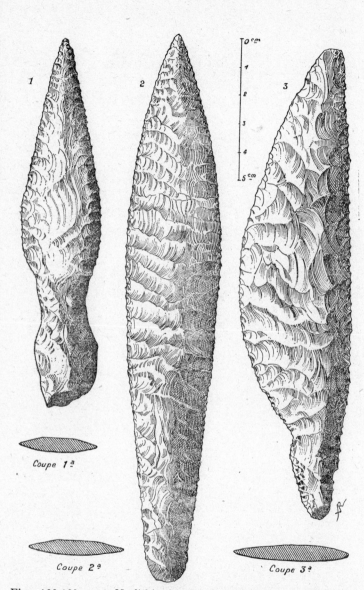

Figs. 166-168. — 1. Neolithic chipped flint poignard; 2. Spear head fashioned with marvellous exactness, symmetry and dexterity. 3. Flint implement of the same make, called Danish saw. *(Issy Seminary Collection Coupe; section.)*

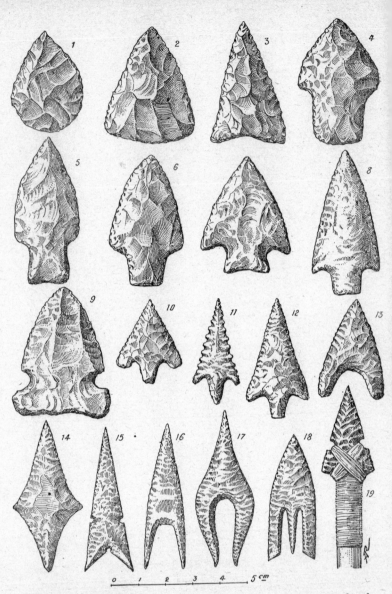

Figs. 169-187. - Different types of Neolithic and more recent arrowheads.

1, 2, 3, Ovoid, triangular; 4, 5, 6, pedunculated arrow-heads; 7, 8, pinnioned arrow-heads; 9, double notched arrow-heads; 10, 12, Pedunculated and pinnioned arrow-head; 11, Barbed arrow-head from the dolmen of Aveyron; 12-13, Egyptien arrow-head; 14, Arrow-head from the dolmen of Argenteuil; 15, 16, 17, 18, The four most beautiful specimens of arrowheads of which we know; 19, Arrow-heads used by the California Indians. *(Issy Seminary Collection, except 14, 17, 18, 19.)*

stability by heaping up stones about the base of each.   They
then laid others horizontally, supporting them from beneath
by large stones.   Between these, other piles were fixed vertically.   Above all they built a floor covered over with a roof,
and established communication with the shore either by
means of a narrow foot-bridge
or a light boat.   At the Robenhausen Neolithic site a canoe carved out of the trunk of a tree was
found that was 3.60 meters long
and 0.75 m. wide.   Other similar
pirogues were found in the palaf-
fittes; that from Lake Chablain
measured 9.35×0.75 meters.   The
Neolithic Scandinavians sailed
the high seas as far as the British
Isles, as is apparent from the
various articles found on the
Scandinavian sites.   "There is
not the shadow of a doubt that
in the polished stone period constant intercourse, due especially
to the development of coastwise
navigation, brought the peoples
of the various regions of Europe
together, and facilitated the propagation of industrial discoveries
and gradually modified customs.

"In the interior, commercial
routes were opened up also and ma-

Fig. 188. — Stag-horn
harpoon from a Swiss
palafitte.

nufactured articles were exchanged or crude materials transported from one place to another.   One is convinced of this
especially in studying the distribution of articles whose raw
material had to come exclusively from certain regions." [1]

We may cite as instances of this, amber, callais, nephritic
rocks, obsidian and the various flints, etc., dispersed to
numerous Neolithic sites.

[1] Déchelette, *op. cit.*, p. 619.

The extended migrations of Paleolithic populations had prepared the traderoutes for the more sedentary agricultural peoples. These relations of tribes with tribes keep on developing with the industries and agricultural pursuits, so that prehistoric man is everywhere its precursor.

Neolithic burials. — Neolithic man had great respect for his dead. The manner of burial varied in the different places. It is difficult to make a classification. Déche-

Fig. 189. — Ancient palafittes (lake-dwellings) of the Swiss lakes, reconstructed from modern palafittes of New Guinea.

lette [1] gives five categories joined together by intermediates : 1. Burials in the bare earth without any protective covering; 2. Burials in caverns or shelters; 3. Burials under dolmens or covered graves; 4. Burials in artificial grottos; 5. Burials in stone coffins. In all these modes there is manifested the belief of survival after death, if we may judge from the articles these graves contained. These consist of tools of chipped or polished stone, vases, millstones, ochre, hematite, beads from necklaces, precious stones, weapons and characters representing the divinity, and round helmets.

The burials were often collective. Hence in handling

[1] Déchelette, *op. cit.*, p. 449-474.

the remains in the Neolithic sepulchers there resulted very great confusion.

Megalithic Monuments. — Among the most important works of the Neolithic period we may mention the dolmens, the menhirs, colonnades of menhirs, the cromlechs, artificial grottos, intrenched camps, Neolithic villages and lake cities.

The dolmens and menhirs arouse a great deal of curiosity, because of the great size of the blocks set up. The

Fig. 190. — Dolmen

dolmens are real graves. Their form varies with the material used in their construction. In the granitic regions, in Brittany, they are built of enormous granite blocks placed on three or four pillars. In the limestone countries, large natural slabs were used. All that was necessary was to place four of them vertically and cover them with a fifth to form a sort of roof. The latter was $4 \times 3 \times 0.50$ m. in dimension (fig. 190).

The dolmen was often closed with a perforated slab which permitted the living to place in the tomb of the deceased various objects, probably funeral repasts. These tombs are very numerous in France, but they have been found especially on a line running from Armorica to the mouth of the Rhône to the width of two departments. They are found especially in Ardèche, Aveyron, Gard, Lot, Morbihan, and this zone continues through Palestine as far as India.

The dolmens were often covered with earth or heaps of

stones forming a tumulus.   This was the case also with the covered corridors which were only large sized dolmens.   On the tumulus at Saint-Michel in Brittany, there is an accumulation of 35 000 cubic meters of material.   These works remind one of the *pyramids* whose construction is a little

Fig. 191. — Type of menhir.   Standing rock at Croisic. (Loire-Infér.).

more recent.   Both give evidence of the same respect for the dead.

The *menhirs* (fig. 191) or upright stones, abound on French soil, especially in the Armorican peninsula.   They most frequently assume the form of a cone, cylinder or irregular prism.   De Mortillet counted some 6192 including the colonnades and cromlechs.   Morbihan alone has 3450.   The highest is that of Locmariaquer (20.5) which was broken off by lightning.   Its weight was 347 000 kilograms.   It might be compared with the Egyptian obelisks.

The exact purpose of these menhirs is still unknown.   We might consider them as religious symbols like the betyles of the ancient Semitic nations, or even idols.   It is certain they were the center of some pagan cult the traces of which still remain. The colonnade of Cornac may have been a sort of temple of the Sun. [1] The cupulae, winding bands, navicular signs, concentric curves, fantastical scrolls, axes with and without handles, large images of women [2] at times adorn the stones of the dolmens, and the menhirs and also the walls of the sepulchral grottos. Particularly the grottos of the Petit-Morin Valley (Marne).

Neolithic races. — The modifications undergone in the industrial, social and religious conditions of the European peoples were due to the invasion of a new brachycephalic race (the short head). It allied itself with the aboriginal dolichocephalic races and formed a numerous mixed race. In the grotto of L'Homme-Mort (Lozère), of 19 skulls, 17 were dolichocephalic, and only 2 were mesaticephalic and show the influence of the new race. The long bones show this also. The tibias and the fibulas are not entirely flat as in the Magdalenian races. The femurs and the humeri have not always the muscular impressions so well marked.

The burials of Beaumes-Chaudes (Lozère) which are quite at the end of the Neolithic period and which already contain some metallic articles show us 397 dolichocephalic, 146 brachycephalic and 145 intermediates out of 688 skulls measured. The forehead is not very high, the sutures are less complex, but the cranial capacity is great. These men were 1.6 m in height.

The sepulchral caverns of Petit-Morin (Marne) which date from the end of the Neolithic period furnish us 15 dolicocephalic, 12 brachicephalic and 17 intermediates out of 44 skulls measured. The average cranial capacity is 1 535 cc. for the skulls of the men. The characteristics of the Magdalenian race are not very noticeable now.

America, all Europe, northern Africa (Algeria, Egypt),

---

[1] Déchelette, *op. cit.*, p. 438.
[2] In Spain and in the valley of the Danube and in the Balkans, are to be found curious statuettes of stone or terra cotta which are extremely crude.

Palestine, Asia Minor, the Indies, Indo-China, Japan, China, etc., all have known the Neolithic civilization. (This or a similar civilization still exists in the majority of the islands of Oceanica and in the center of Indo-China.)

Extension of the Paleolithic and Neolithic Periods outside of Europe. — Outside of France and the neighboring countries human paleontology is lamentably meagre. We find, it is true, some prehistoric documents all over the world, but scattered and isolated and little studied from the stratigraphic standpoint. In certain countries, as Australia, America and Japan, the Stone Age continued nearly to our own day, while in others it is undoubtedly as old as in Europe. We mention here some of the more promising fields. In Asia, around the Mediterranian researches similar to those in Europe have been made and are still going on. Hundreds of prehistoric sites have already been located in Palestine, in all Syria, in all Southern Asia, [1] where Chellean, Acheulean, Mousterian, Aurignacian, Magdalenian, Azylian and Neolithic implements have been found. The Neolithic bed generally occupies the base of all these. Moreover all lead to the belief that the ancient civilizations of Chaldea and of Egypt are more recent than our Paleolithic. The Tell or ruins at Susa are 35 meters in height. At the base is found bronze, mixed with Neolithic flints. We find in the lœss, the Chellean or Mousterian period as far as Siberia. The most important site is that of Aphontava near Krasnoï-arsk to the north of Mount Altaï. [2]

Savenkov has found upon the rocks of Western Siberia curious engravings and paintings recalling the Paleolithic art of France. We might mention also the neighborhood of Tomsk Irkoustsk and the shores of Lake Baïkal. We find only the Neolithic in Mongolia, Manchuria, Corea, Japan and China.

---

[1] Cf. Vincent, *Canaan*, Paris, Gabalda.
[2] Cf. Boule, *op. cit.*, p. 356.

4. Age of the metals, copper, br nze and iron. [1]

It is impossible to make a sharp distinction between the Neolithic period and the Age of the Metals. It was not in fact, by a sudden transition that copper and bronze replaced stone; but these substances as well as gold and lead, and sometimes iron in the form of small beads, are already found in many of the Neolithic strata and burial places. Everywhere the exclusive use of copper preceded that of bronze; the flat axes of the period resemble very much those made from stone. At first, man used copper, gold and silver whose brightness must have very early caught his eye, as he found them in the natural state. Soon, by some stroke of good fortune, he mixed tin with copper and obtained in this way a more fusible and much harder alloy. This discovery marked a great advance in industry. Thus bronze gave its name to this period of two thousand years which unites the Neolithic period with the Iron Age. The date of the appearance of bronze varies with the locality. It was known very early in the Orient. In Chaldea it is found at the base of Susa at a depth of 35 meters. It is difficult to give a precise date, since the opinion of writers ranges from 5 000 to 3 000 years before Christ. In Europe the bronze age seems to extend from 2 500 to 900 years before Christ. Around 900 B. C. the iron age begins and is divided into two epochs; that of Halstatt extending from 900 to 500, and that of the Tène from 500 B. C.

The Bronze Age forms the period designated as the proto-historic, since it gives us some dates and some names as the result of discoveries made in Chaldea, in Egypt, in Crete and in Cyprus. The name Myceno-Aegean has been applied to its civilization, since its center of diffusion was found

---

[1] On an epoch that already penetrates into the historical period we shall be satisfied with giving very summary details and refer the reader to the work of Déchelette, *Manuel d'Archéologie*, vol. ii, iii and iv

in the Aegean Sea. It spread rapidly into Europe by land and by sea. By way of the Mediterranian it entered Southern Italy, Sicily, Sardinia and Spain. It seems to have passed downwards and then upwards again to Armorica and to Great Britain. It could also have extended by land and gradually invaded Northern Italy and Gaul, as far as Armorica and then passed thence into Great Britain. Copper was imported into the south-east from Gaul

through commercial routes. A second route passed by way of the Danube and the Balkans through Central Europe, the Scandinavian countries and farther to the west, through Switzerland, the Jura Mountains and La Franche-Comté.

The Aegeo-Mycenian civilization was brought to light by the explorations of the hill at Hissarlik, the site of ancient Troy, where from 1871 to 1890, Schliemann discovered 9 cities superposed one above the other, by the excavations made at Mycène, the ancient capital of the Achaean kings, and by those which Evans undertook in Crete and at Cnossos, in 1900, in the ruins of the labyrinthian palace of king Minos. These discoveries enable us to distinguish three periods in the Bronze Age in this region. A Premycenian period from 3000 to 2000 starting with the Copper Age; a First Mycenian period from 2000 to 1500; and a Second Mycenian period from 1500 to 1100 B. C.

Fig. 192. — Copper axe. Primitive form.

In Western Europe we can distinguish four periods : a) from 2500 to 1900; b) from 1900 to 1600; c) from 1600 to 1300; d) from 1300 to 900. [1]

Each region underwent a special evolution and everywhere we see the bronze industry, [2] dependent upon

---

[1] Cf. Déchelette, *Manuel d'Archéologie préhist.*, vol. II.

[2] Montélius places the beginning of the Bronze Age in 2000 years B. C.

geographical position or upon maritime or river travel. Although bronze already abounded in Armorica and in Scandinavia, it is very rare in the Paris basin, while other articles belonging to the first part of this epoch, such as flat axes with straight edges (fig. 192), are extremely few in number. Gironde, on the contrary, has yielded many of this type. It is only towards the middle of this epoch

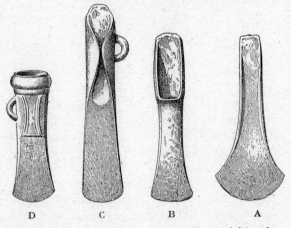

Figs. 193-196. — Bronze axes : A, straight edges; B, with heel; C, with pinions; D, with socket.

(that of the heel-axe) that bronze becomes more common in the north of France; it is almost universal at the end of the period (with the pinioned axes, later with pinions and sockets).

The succession that holds for Picardy is not found the same in Brittany, in England or in Gironde where the pinioned and socketed axes are readily associated (fig. 193 to 196). Whereas all northern France was still in the Bronze Age the south-east, the center and the east were already in possession of their first iron weapons [1] and the

---

[1] According to Montélius, the Iron Age in Egypt goes back to sometime before 1500 B. C., and appeared in Italy with the arrival of the Etruscans. It gradually spread towards the North.

Hallstattian [1] civilization with its cemeteries and tumuli overspread the districts of the Rhine, the Rhône, and the Danube.   This civilization places us at the dawn of European history.   Another civilization succeeds it, whose customs are different.   A civilization that had commercial relations with the Mediterranian, that adorned with coral its sculptured bronzes and that placed in its graves vases imported from Greece as far back as 400 B. C.   This is the epoch of the great limestone tombs of Champagne.

Burial Rites in the Bronze Age.

The graves which date from the Bronze Age are numerous and interesting, because they contain funeral furnishings whose significance can readily be determined.   During the Premycenian period, the tombs were constructed of stone slabs and contained one or more *folded skeletons*.   Small statuettes, rudely carved from stone, are found which are termed amorgian idols.

To the First Mycenian period belongs the exacavated tombs of the Acropolis at Mycene.   These are circular enclosures of stone slabs, six in number, and containing eleven skeletons with their bronze weapons and golden ornaments.

The Second Mycenian period has spherically vaulted tombs, and tombs with compartments in which collective burials were made.   In Syria the skeletons are folded, and placed in terra cotta jars with some articles in bronze. [2] Mesopotamia has many tombs of this period.   We may say the same for Egypt.   In western Europe, burials with the same rites are the general rule.   At first weapons, ornaments and tools are placed above the body in the *Cist* tumuli and dolmens.   Later cremation was the rule.   This undoubtedly signified the more rapid liberation of the soul

[1] The Hallstatian takes its name from the salt mines at Halstatt in Austria.   It extends from 900 to 500 B. C.   The civilisation of the Thene is distinct; it uses numerous enamels; its habitat, more extended than that of Halstatt had Champagne for its center.

[2] Cf. Vincent, *Canaan*, Paris, Gabalda.

of the deceased. In this epoch funeral urns of small size are found in the tumuli. History proper had long since begun in the Orient, then in Italy and later on in France. But all over Germany and Scythia, parallel civilizations continued their progressive evolution and, after an interval of four centuries, emerge to subdue the Roman World and to establish, on the plains of Gallo-Roman France, the Merovingian France.

§ VI. — Identity of the human type throughout the ages.

As regards man's organism we may expect to find that it has undergone some modification throughout the ages. We know that the human species has existed for a very long time. Just as the various animals have been affected by the vicissitudes of external conditions, so man should have been as plastic under these same influences. The environment in which he lived has varied, both chronologically and geographically. Chronologically, the physical conditions have changed many times even in the same locality, since the beginning of the Quaternary period down to the present day. Geographically, for man has spread from a single center over the whole earth, and has had to accommodate himself to the many different climates in which he has lived. The human species, today, presents many very distinct races. The modifications that we note at any given period might well have come into existence gradually, by way of evolution of the primitive type, through the course of the ages. In dealing with the organic identity of man, we need not take the term in its absolute sense, for there is a relative identity which excludes fundamental modifications but admits of accidental. What rule shall we follow in determining the purely accidental changes from those that constitute essential alterations of the human type ? It is not by any organic characteristics, but by his spiritual faculties, by his soul that man is essentially distinguished from the other animals.

Hence, at first sight, it may seem that no particular

physical character is really essentially human. Still the
spiritual faculties which reveal the soul, though properly
not the action of the brain, are intimately dependent upon
it.   Without the brain, which presents and coordinates the
images, a thought cannot be formed in the mind.   A very
considerable quantity of cerebral matter even, is indispensable.   It is generally admitted that a brain weighing less

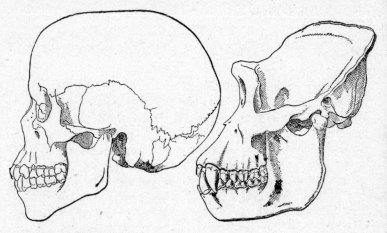

Fig. 197. — Papouan-Negrito skull-   Fig. 198. — Skull of an aged
   from the interior of Borneo.   gorilla.

than 1 000 grammes would infallibly be that of an idiot.
Hence the cerebral development ought to be regarded as a
specific characteristic of man.   All the other organic traits
are of minor importance and their variation may be regarded as purely accidental.   Yet even from the morphological
standpoint alone, there exists a profound difference between the animal and man (figs. 197 and 198). Men have
long sought to bridge this chasm.   It was thought that the
intermediate stage had been found in the Pithecanthropus
of Java.   This discovery by Dubois has been spoken of so
many times and so much importance attached to it, that
we must treat of it in detail. [1]

1. Cf. Boule, *Les hommes fossiles*, p. 93-110.

In 1894, Dubois, a Dutch army physician, discovered at Trinil on the Bengawan, a stream on the island of Java, various widely dispersed bones, which had been cemented in the volcanic tufa by the river. As they were found in an undisturbed stratum with numerous remains of an extinct fauna, they have been regarded as going back to the Up-
per Tertiary or the beginning
of the Quaternary period. It
is impossible to say whether
they belong to the same individual, or even to the same
type. All in all they include
three teeth, a fragment of
the lower jaw, a femur and the upper half of a skull.

Fig. 199. — Molars of the Java pithecanthropus.

The teeth, two rear molars (fig. 199) and one premolar which has never been represented by cut attest a decidedly simian dentition. The rear molars of man have longer and less divergent roots and less developed crowns.

The femur (fig. 200) is of a walking biped. It supposes a height of 1.60 meter. An osseous excrescense is of pathological origin.

The upper part of the skull (fig. 201), evidently the prin-

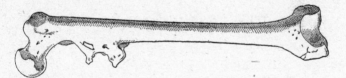

Fig. 200. — Femur of Java pithecanthropus.

cipal part, has been the object of the minutest study. In length and in width it has the dimensions of a normal human skull that is very elongated from front to rear. The forehead is depressed and narrow like that of Neanderthal, and the curve which extends from the base of the nose to the rear is more elliptical than any known human skull. Behind the orbits, the temples sink in so deep that the anterior lobes of the brain could not have been greatly developed (fig. 202). The cranial capacity in as far as one may approximately determine from the upper part of the skull alone, was not more than 800 cc. In this the Java skull ranks below the Neanderthal race, and all the higher

Fig. 201. — Skull-cap cranium of Pithecanthropus, side view.

races whose average cerebral capacity is from 1 400 to 1 600 cc. in certain instances. But, still it is considerably above that of the simian races whose greatest cranial capacity rarely reaches 500 cc. The special formation of the skull presents some characteristics which are also simian. Thus, the frontal lobes, although double those of the apes, are evidently those of an ape having the occipital ridge continuous with the subauricular ridge. Because of these uncertain traits, the type represented by these bones was from the start called *Pithecanthropus erectus*.

The Java discovery must certainly be taken into account for it is a document deserving classification, but with Boule we believe that we must see here only a giant form of gibbon. We wish to cite his testimony which cannot be suspected of being inspired by antievolutionistic bias. " As regards the most important

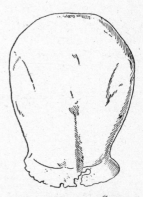

Fig. 202. — Same, viewed from above.

document, the upper half of the skull, it cannot indeed be denied that it occupies a position exactly, I might say ideally, between that of a large ape, like the chimpanzee, and that of a man with archaic characteristics such as the Neanderthal man.

"But we must be exact and so repeat again in this place that resemblance does not always imply descent. From the fact that the pithecanthropus from some known, though otherwise minor characteristics on the whole truly realizes a morphological intermediate stage between the larger apes and man, it does not necessarily follow that it must be considered as a genealogical intermediate. And this distinction is not, as some have pretended, a mere question of words. To pronounce on its real genealogical relation, with full knowledge of the cause it would be necessary to possess at least the complete skull and the lower jawbone of the pithecanthropus, for the more or less anthropomorphic reconstructions made by various men can be of little service in the solution of the problem. In the present state of knowledge, I do not believe we can any longer hold that there is a direct filiation between the pithecanthropus and man as the genealogical tree constructed by Dubois indicates.

"It would certainly be preferable to admit that the evolutionary branch to which the celebrated Java fossil belongs, is different from the human branch... According to Dubois, several naturalists have insisted on the resemblance of the remains of the pithecanthropus to the same parts of the skeleton of a gibbon. Why not suppose, then, that the pithecanthropus represents a giant form of ape allied with the group of gibbons ? The morphology of the parts is favorable to this. The latest geological studies tending to reduce the age of the strata, supports this opinion. A new argument which I believe can be adduced in its favor is that we know of different instances of analogous phenomena. There had been in every country during the Pliocene and the Quaternary periods, giant forms of animals whose present day representatives are very diminutive. Hence we may hold that the pithecanthropus, discovered in the zoological domain of the actual gibbon itself, could have been a large species either of the genus gibbon, or rather of a closely allied genus belonging to the same group. This form would have been larger than its congeners, not only in height, but also in other morphological traits,

notably in brain capacity, a characteristic of the very
first order by which the pithecanthropus approaches

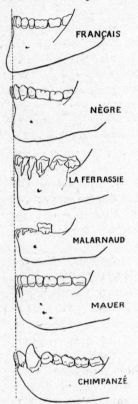

the anthropoids. It would thus
represent an offshoot of the gibbon
branch more highly developed and
more specialized than the closely
allied offshoots, and which might
have disappeared very early,
perhaps on account of this
very specialization. The pithecanthropus might not have belonged to the ancestral line of the
genus homo." [1]

Forced by the evidence to renounce the Java document evolutionists turned their attention
again to the prehistoric races, particularly to that of Neanderthal.
All in all the ancient remains of
man clearly show a structure
identical in the main with that of
actual man. They do not establish an intermediate state between the human and the simian
types. We may nevertheless
grant that the differences noted
between the actual races are less
striking than those existing between prehistoric man and contemporary man. But De Quatrefages, whose authority has great
weight in this matter has very
explicitly said : "Whenever his
remains have permitted us to
judge, we have found in him

Fig. 203. — Profiles of
different low type jaw-
bones compared with
that of a white man.*
Frenchman. — Negro. — La
Ferrassie. — Malardnaud. —
Mauer. — Chimpanze.

(prehistoric man) the feet and the hands which characterize

---

[1] Boule, *Les hommes fossiles*, p. 106.

* These drawings merely show the variability of certain details
of the human organism. It would be a mistake to attribute great

our species; the spinal column has shown the double curve to which Lawrence attached so much importance, and which Serres made the distinctive mark of the human kingdom such as he intended it. The more we investigate the surer we are that each bone of the skeleton, from the largest to the very smallest, bears with it, in its shape and in its proportions, a certificate of origin impossible to misunderstand". [1]

If we admit that the organic type of the contemporary white race is the form most advantageous to humanity, a fact which cannot be demonstrated, it will be evident that the Mousterian race is the lowest in the order of perfection. The cranium has a mean capacity of 1 400 cc. Its walls are thick; the forehead low and receding, the superciliary arches very pronounced; the jaws powerful and protruding, the chin absent, etc. But what does this signify ? The Mousterian race is none the less decidedly human; it cannot be considered an intermediate between the human and the simian type. Indeed, the cranial capacity of 1 400 cc. is more than sufficient for intellectual operations. Some of the most highly cultured men of the white race have fallen below this figure. Among the blacks, who are men in the strictest sense of the word, the average is not as high, being 1 300 cc. The excessive development that the muscles and the bones show can readily be explained by the entirely material labor to which the first men applied themselves. Even, today, between the individual devoted to manual labor and the one that performs inside work are not differences of like kind produced ? The shape of the head, or of the forehead, or of jaw has no more significance. Even today, we come across dolichocephalic and brachycephalic individuals with high or low foreheads, with protruding or receding chins, without there being the least doubt about the identity of the nature of these different types (fig. 203).

importance to them; these jaw-bones remain different from those of animals. Even were there greater resemblances, it would prove nothing. Resemblance does not mean descent.

[1] De Quatrefages, *L'espèce humaine*, chap. xxv.

It is true that a continuous progress seems to have been noted in the past. This progress, even though real, would not be at all surprising. It is natural for the physical type to become refined as habits are tempered, and as the faculties are cultivated. This is a well known fact of the reciprocal influences of mind and body. — But this progress is not as evident as we are led to believe.

This can be seen from the following list of skulls :

Gibraltar ....   1 300 ce
La Quina ....   1 360—
Neanderthal ....   1 408—
Chapelle-aux-Saints ....   1 600—
Chancelade ....   1 700—

Here this constant progress stops and we fall back to :

Neolithic..   1 535—
Modern ....   1 500—

This comparison shows that in the course of the ages, as at the present time, the average cranial capacity has always been both variable and quite constant — quite variable, since it changes from 1 300 to 1 700 cc., without raising the least question about the perfect integrity of the human nature; very constant, since it always oscillates about a mean capacity of 1 500 cc., and since it always remains far removed from the maximum cranial capacity of the apes which is only 500 cc.

The Mousterian race was then perfectly human. Boule believes that it became extinct without leaving any survivors to the present day. It does not seem to be the most primitive race, since it was contemporaneous with other more normal races.

The most recent discoveries contribute still less to bridge the chasm which separates man from the beast, and we shall insist especially on that which has made the greatest stir during the year 1909, that is the Mousterian skeleton found at Chapelle-aux-Saints (Corrèze).

In the month of August 1908, the abbés A. and J. Bouyssonie and L. Bardon, while excavating in a prehistoric bed of the Mousterian period in a grotto in the commune of Chapelle-aux-Saints, discovered in a ditch a human skeleton whose parts were carefully reconstructed by the eminent paleontologist Boule. The skull was almost complete though in fragments. The rest of the body was less well preserved (figs. 204 and 205).

We quote from the abbé Breuil the description he has

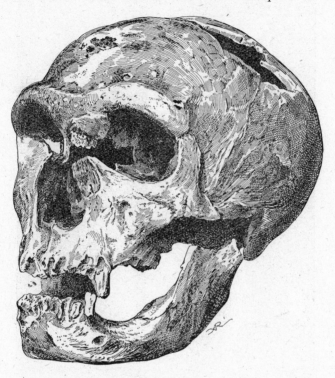

Fig. 204. — Chapelle-aux-Saints skull.

given of it in the *Revue de Fribourg*. [1] "The head is very large, with a cranial capacity certainly much greater than the present average. The upper part faithfully reproduces

[1] *Revue de Fribourg*, Jan. 1909. Cf. Abbé Breuil, *Les plus anciennes races humaines connues*, in *Revue des sciences philosophiques et théologiques*, vol. III (1909); A. Bouyssonie, in *Bulletin de littérature ecclésiastique*, March 1909.

the characteristics found in the skull at Spy, Neanderthal,
Marcilly, Bréchamp, perhaps even more accentuated.   The

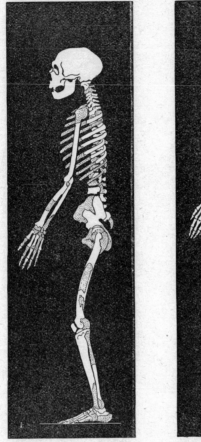

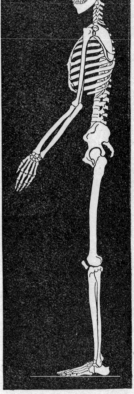

Fig. 205. — Skeleton of a fossil
man from Chapelle-aux-Saints.
reconstructed by Boule.

Fig. 206. — Skeleton of
an Australian native.
(Boule.)

superciliary ridges converge in enormous prominences towards the eyes.   Behind them begins a narrow receding forehead whose curve continues to the very prominent occipital

and projects out in the back.   The very elongated dolichocephalic skull, as the scientists call it, is much depressed
vertically.   Compared with its horizontal proportions its
height is inconsiderable.   The occipital foramen magnum
which in humans rests on the spinal column, is placed
noticeably farther back than in the more recent races.
This calls for a powerful development of the posterior
muscles of the neck.   A condition rendered all the more
urgent by the size of the facial bones and the weight
of the jaw which tended to pull the head forward.   The
eyes of the Chapelle-aux-Saints man are sunk in circular orbits under the formidable ridges which dominate
them.   The nose had to be large and flat, for the yawning
opening of the nasal cavities exceeds by more than a
third that of a European and by a fourth that of an
Australian.   Under the cheekbones, there are no canine
sockets, the bony surface continuing from a single plane
to the edge of the upper jaw, projects strongly foreward
like a muzzle.   This unhead of detail implies, in the
visage of our man, the absence of the two symmetrical
depressions that run from the nostrils to the corner of the
mouth and give the human physiognomy its mobility of
expression...   The lower jaw is powerfully articulated by
means of enormous condyles with the rest of the head, and
presents a receding chin, as in the already known fragments
of the same race.   As to the teeth, apart from some
stumps, we find only the sockets, showing that our man
was aged and had already lost them.   The canines were
small, entirely human; the molars large and strong.   The
Chapelle-aux-Saints man finds his place lower than even
the lowest of all known races.   As to the bones of the limbs,
let us merely remark that they denote a stature less than
1.60 meters, and that the shape of the heads of the femur
and of the tibia, specially the very accentuated curvature
of the former, shows that when in the upright posture, the
lower limbs are slightly bent and the knees projecting
foreward.   We have already remarked these peculiarities
in previously known bones " (figs. 205 and 206).

In spite of this not very flattering picture, Breuil con-

cludes that the Chapelle-aux-Saints skeleton belongs to a
' well characterized fossilized human race, in many respects
similar to the uncivilized men of Australia, but very much
lower" (fig. 207).

The abbé A. Bouyssonie, the discoverer, says the same. [1]

Fig. 207. — Actual Australian belonging to the Aruntas tribe showing
some of the characters of the Neanderthal race. *(Boule.)*

"It was a man. The anatomy, the burial, the industry
prove this. First the anatomy. In the description
which I have given of the skeleton, I have insisted on that

[1] A. Bouyssonie, in *Dict. d'Apologétique*, art. Homme; *Revue du
Clergé*, April 1, 1913, p. 18-72; *Revue pratique d'Apologétique*, April
1, 1921, p. 49 sq.; *Bulletin de littérature ecclésiastique*, March 1902.
Cf. Boule, *Les hommes fossiles*, Paris, Masson.

in which it differs from present man and on that in which it approaches the apes. But beyond these details, the rest — and that is the main part — is very much nearer to us and with greater reason much nearer the savages, as for instance the Australians, than to the most highly develop-.ed ape extinct or existing. Even a summary examination of the skeleton leaves no doubt in this matter. Secondly it was intentionally buried, and this supposes that we are dealing with a man, the apes not having the habit of burying their kind. Finally the industry which accompanies the skeleton was indeed too remarkable to be the work of a mere animal. To fashion the scrapers and points from flint or from quartz, human intelligence was necessary. " The same conclusion is drawn from the discovery made in the same year 1908 at Moustier Dordogne, by a Swiss merchant named Hausen. There was question again of a skeleton having the same race traits buried under similar conditions and surrounded by chipped implements of the Mousterian period. [1]

The skeleton discovered at la Ferrassie (Dordogne) in the month of September 1909 by Peyrony and Capitan, presents, according to Breuil, all the traits of a perfectly characterized Neanderthal man. [2] That of Quina (Charente) discovered in 1911 belongs to the same race (figs. 113 and 114).

§ VII. — Intelligence of Primitive Man.

It is note-worthy that the human organism save for some slight variations, has remained identically the same from prehistoric times. Still it is important to determine how the human mind in the beginning corresponded with what it is today. Man indeed, is characterized by his mind, and we know that man has always been identically the same if he has always had the same mind. Let no one mistake our meaning. In speaking of the intelligence or

---

[1] Abbé Breuil, *Les plus anciennes races humaines connues*, in *Revue des sciences philosophiques et théologiques*, 1909, vol. III.
[2] *Ibid.*

mind of the first men, we do not wish to say that they had as much knowledge as we, or that they had the facilities for study possessed by the cultured races. We do not wish to deny the real progress of the human species, this constant movement towards the acquisition of greater knowledge that is evident in the history of civilized nations. What we do intend to show is that the first men were really endowed with intelligence as we, hence as far removed from the animal kingdom as are we.

Beyond this, the problem of the intelligence of primitive man is the same as any relating to uncultured or uncivilized men of modern times. That which tends to show the existence of a human mind in an ignorant savage, must serve also to prove the existence of the same mind in the Quaternary races whose miserable remains recall an uncivilized condition. Now by what means can we recognize human intelligence in the savage ? We may enter into relations with him, and we may learn his language; we may educate him and find him susceptible of an intellectual development comparable with our own, since he is able to acquire our ideas and our knowledge; we may consider his actions, his industry, his works of art, and find in his efforts evidence of abstraction, of reasoning, even the power of invention. All this appears so unlike what we find in the keenest animals, so similar to what we observe in civilized men, that we conclude without hesitation that the savages thrown entirely on the resources of their nature alone, show themselves to be as completely men as we, and separated from the brute beast by the same barrier.

When there is question of prehistoric man, we have, it is true, fewer data upon which to base our arguments, but what we have are of such a nature as to lead us logically to the same conclusion. We cannot interrogate them to establish whether they have intelligence, but we can interrogate their works.

They have left us their weapons, their tools of stone and of bone, their works of art, their pottery, their funeral monuments, etc., etc. In all these objects, as in so many books, they have written in very legible characters what was their nature and even the power of their mind. In fact, the remains of their industry show us that they were at least as advanced as the modern savages. For what more have the Fuegians, the Australians, the Minco-pians, the Negritos, etc., than stone implements, axes, arrow-heads and harpoons similar to those which we have found at Saint-Acheul, Chelles, Moustier, Solutré and la Madeleine ? There was then at least as much intelligence in our Quaternary ancestors as in the races which have still their stone industry. Furthermore, the Quaternary wea-pons and tools are in fact always ascribed by anthro-pologists to men like ourselves. Or rather whenever a fragment of flint does not bear evident trace of an intelli-gent action it is attributed to the mechanical forces of nature; whenever signs of intentional chipping, beaten surface, conchoidal percussion marks, retouching, or sym-metry are found, the action of an intelligent man is recog-nized. Does not the investigation of these facts, prior to all discussion, demonstrate that anthropologists start from the principle that man has at all times been characterized by the intelligence that is manifested in his works ?

Finally we need but examine the most ancient implements to discover in his work signs of intelligence, of a faculty capable of making abstraction, of reasoning, of fore-seeing, of combining and looking even beyond the immediate necessity.

That an ape when attacked should defend itself with its fists, or even by picking up a stone to throw at its aggressor, is a phenomenon reducible to sense reaction due to a simple association of images. But when a living creature takes this rock, which it has chipped off with the intention of making an implement of a determined shape, that which no animal has ever done, it means that man had intelligence in prehistoric times. He could do this only because he was possessed of an intelligence capable of abstraction and even of creating. For even to make the Chellean axe which is the first and most elementary of implements used by man, a number of intellectual acts were necessary. Man had to think that a pointed shape given to an ordinary stone rendered it more advantageous; he had to create the image of the axe before realizing it; he had to determine the points of least resistance, regulate the direction and the force of the blow, etc.   There was in all this an art which had to be invented and taught.   Is not the fact that one generation of men knew how to derive profit from the progress realized by a preceding generation, itself one of the characteristic signs of intelligence ?   We may analyse all the work of the first man, and we shall find in all the same evidence of a mind.

It has been rightly remarked that these prehistoric men had to have great intellectual power, for they have known how to create and invent their implements.   In geometry Euclid did not go very far, but by creating the fundamental theorems, he gave evidence of genius.   Similarly, he who invented the lever, the wheel, etc., possessed the intellect of a genius greater than he who combined the elements into a locomotive.   We must say as much for those who invented the flint axe and the art of pounding a flint nodule to obtain knives; who have produced the first tools and the first arrows.   Now it was Quaternary man, who was the real creator of the first elements of our modern industry. Why then refuse him a mind similar to our own ?

It should be enough to enumerate the principal inventions of *prehistoric* man to demonstrate his intelligence. We mention only the fashioning of the flint to make of it tools capable of supplying his needs, and weapons with which to overcome the most formidable animals; the working in wood, horn, bone, ivory and stone, to adapt them to his needs and to his fancy; fire, its production, its utilization, its conservation, i. e. the most widely distributed and the most necessary form of energy; hunting and fishing; the subduing of animals to serve him; agriculture with its principal products; dyeing, pottery manufacture, sculpture, engraving, painting, navigation, architecture, the metallurgy of gold, copper, bronze. iron, etc. Each one of these inventions is sufficient to demonstrate the intelligence of the inventor.   Of course they do not all date from the Chellean period, but at this epoch they are numerous enough to let us see that their authors had intelligence.

If man, in the beginning is *homo faber*, he is primarily *homo sapiens*, an intelligent man who adapted means to an end with a perfection that astonishes us, for most of us might not realize what he has accomplished were we deprived of the means. There is here, undoubtedly question only of Quaternary man, whose remains we possess, and anthropologists deny us the right to attribute what we find in him, to primitive man. Indeed they say the man whose works you show was already far advanced in civilization, but before making the Chellean axe, for how many centuries was he not evolving, employing only natural fragments and ordinary stones for weapons ? He was already man. It is prior to this condition that we must place his evolution and seek for his slow transition from the simian to the human state.

This hypothesis to which evolutionism must perforce attach itself is not only gratuitous, but even contrary to real scientific facts. It seems to us that, if we go back scientifically from the Quaternary man to primitive man, we ought to suppose that the latter was endowed with an intelligence like our own, and as powerful as our own. Indeed, we have not the right to seek primitive man much beyond our Quaternary ancestors. If we should meet with the remains of the human organism long before coming across the traces of his industry, we might have reason to ask whether man did not live long ages before the manufacture of tools and weapons; but the implements of man are just as old as his skeletal remains. The Chellean industry undoubtedly goes back to the beginning of the Third Interglaciary; the first relics of the human body are of the same period. How is it that man living so many centuries even in Europe, had spread so little, that not a single human bone had been preserved before the Chellean period, and that even in the Chellean period itself where we find the first monuments of his industry we still see so few traces of his body ? May we not conclude that during the Interglacial Period, man made his first appearance in France and wandered in groups along the shores of the rivers where he left his tools ? Do not a few centuries suffice for the human family, created in Asia, to multiply and spread as far as Europe ? But finding man intelligent and industrious so close to his origin, have we not the right to conclude that he was such at the time of his creation ?

§ VIII. — RELIGION OF THE FIRST MEN.

Certain philosophers were disposed to conclude from what precedes that the first men had to have religious sentiments and practices. Since he was intelligent, primitive man should have been led from the facts of nature to the idea of causality and to the idea of God; by the consciousness of his intellectual acts and of his free will, to the knowledge of the spirituality and the immortality of his soul. From this summary knowledge of God and of himself, he would conclude the necessity of worshipping the Creator.

This is indeed solid argumentation, but it holds only for those who admit the perfect identity of man throughout the ages. Now it is precisely this important truth that we should like to bring out prominently, by adducing new evidence, so we shall once more have recourse very briefly to the data of positive science to strengthen a merely speculative conclusion.

We must first of all understand what is meant by the word Religion. By taking it in a too restricted sense, some writers have considered entire nations atheistic. We believe that de Quatrefages is right when he says that we must hold every man religious who believes these two things : a) that there exist superior beings capable of influencing his destiny, either for good or for evil; b) that a part of himself survives after death, whatever be the condition that he imagines beyond the grave. We have three ways of discovering these esentials of all Religion in primitive man. Studying the religious status of actually living peoples; discovering in history the most ancient religious facts; and seeking in the prehistoric period itself the first manifestations of worship. [1]

The religious status of the present nations has frequently been discussed. Scientists of note like Livingstone, Baker, Monnat, Dalton, Bradley, Lubbock, Broca et al. have taught that certain tribes of men have absolutely no religious ideas. Monnat says of the Mincopies (Andaman Islands) "They have no ideas of a Supreme Being, no religion, no belief in a future life." Sir Messenger Bradley says of an Australian tribe : "They have no superstions of any sort, and have not the least idea of a future life." According to Broca, "there exist among the inferior races, tribes without worship, without dogmas, without metaphysical ideas, without collective beliefs, and in consequence without Religion. " [2]

De Quatrefages to the very end of his life never ceased to protest against these statements. "I have sought for atheism with the greatest care" says he "but I have no where met with it, except as an erratic condition among some philosophical sects belonging to the oldest civilized nations." [3]

The eminent anthropologist endeavors to show what preoccupations have hindered certain travellers or missionaries from recognizing the Religion of uncivilized tribes; then he shows to what results a more attentive study has lead. The Mincopies, for example, reputed to have no Religion, have in reality quite exalted beliefs. They regard man as animated with two principles : *the mind and the soul*. Both survive at death, but separate at this moment, and dwell in distinct regions till the moment of future resurrection. The mind betakes itself to a vast jungle, situated under the earth where it finds all its earthly acquaintances. The soul alone is judged by Pûluga, the

---

[1] We leave the task of treating this fundamental question to specialists. It has become the object of a special science at the present time : The History of Religions. Cf. De la Baullaye, *L'étude comparée des religions.* Paris, Colin.

[2] Cf. Joly, *L'homme avant les métaux,* p. 302 sq.

[3] De Quatrefages, *Introduction à l'étude des races humaines,* p. 254.

Supreme God of these tribes and, according to its merits, is admitted either into the place of delights or is precipitated into a frozen inferno. [1] Such are the savages of whom Monnat says they have neither religion, nor belief in a future life.

Without quoting other examples that one may find in the works of de Quatrefages, we believe the fact well established that all the tribes of men have at least a rudimentary Religion. According to Emile Burnouf, the grossest fetishism is itself a species of religion, for "to condense all the powers of the earth into a piece of wood or into a stone" or into the image of a man or of an animal "it was necessary that man should have been aware of invisible and sovereign forces in nature."

To these examples we may add some others of more recent date, supplied by missionaries who pass their entire lives in the midst of these peoples and can give a more accurate account of their mentality, their beliefs and their practices than the occasional traveller. Among such missionaries, we may cite especially Mgr. Le Roy. In his work *The Religion of the Primitives*, he has studied the tribes reputed the very lowest, such as the Bantous and the Nigritians who live in the forest by hunting and gathering fruits. He has found among all, side by side with superstitious beliefs, ideas of God, of the soul, of spirits, of morals, of the priesthood, of sacrifice, of prayer, of worship, which surprise us by their purity. In *Christus*, Monsignor Le Roy gives his conclusions : "Everywhere and at all times men show themselves to us grouped in families, and these families appear to us united by a Religion formed from a small number of beliefs, practices, moral obligations and institutions which being at the base of all the rest can reasonably be considered the primary and fundamental elements of Religion."

But this universality of Religion in the present has a

---

[1] De Quatrefages, *Introduction...*, p. 259, 260.

[2] Cf. Huby, *Christus*, Paris, Beauchesne, 1914, p. 18-98; Bricout, *Où en est l'histoire des religions ?*, Paris, Letouzey; Dhorme, *La religion Assyro-Babylonienne*, Paris, Gabalda.

great bearing on the past. For, either these religious beliefs are the fruit of the human mind, or they are the common heritage of a primitive condition. If we admit that among all peoples the human mind has created Religion, it is imperative that its necessity should be quite evident, so as to impose itself in such a way on all peoples. And if the most miserable of savage tribes have discovered it and preserved it, how is it that primitive man who was as good as they, had not found it also? If we hold, that it is a heritage common to all races, it would be necessary to place its origin as far back as the origin of the human race. For the human families dispersed at a very early date, and in the course of time, became greatly isolated without exchanging either commodities or ideas, as do modern nations. The earliest date which can be considered of an historic character, at the very most, is 5 000 years before the Christian era, and at the least, 4 000 years. At this epoch, certain tablets were engraved which show us Our-Nina, king of Chaldea, working with his own hands to build a temple to the divinity. Among all peoples, the oldest monuments appertain to Religion. It is even important to remark that, the higher we ascend in the history of nations, whatsoever they be, the more profound and extensive do we see the religious influence in ordinary life. To be thoroughly convinced of this, it suffices to read the work of Dhorme on *La Religion assyro-babylonienne.* [1]

Thus, far from making us assist at the creation and the progress of Religion, history rather speaks to us of the impediments placed by the civil power in the way of its free exercise. As civilization progresses, man seems to tend towards atheism rather than to have risen from it. Wheresoever the life of a people disappears into the shadows of prehistory, everything inclines us to the belief that at that time the domination of the religious element had to be supreme. May we not then deduce from these observations that in the beginning man was religious and not atheistic?

[1] Paris, Gabalda.

Finally does prehistory itself furnish us data on the religious thought of the first men ? Before giving an answer, two observations are necessary.—A people can have sentiments and practices of Religion without leaving any evidence to posterity. When in the future anthropologists will have made excavations on the island of Andaman, they will find some skulls and some implements, but no sign that will show them that the Mincopies had had lofty religious ideas. It is the same for several other tribes. This fact shows us with what rashness a scientist concludes the atheism of primitive races from the fact that no sensible evidence reveals their Religion.—The marks of Religion capable of surviving through the ages are extremely few in number. Such are the burials and the attendant circumstances, such as the stone or bone articles similar to the amulets and the fetiches of the modern savage.

Were the Neolithic peoples of western Europe religious ? Everything seems to point that way. Moreover, no one doubts it. These peoples were in part composed of families coming from the Orient whence they had brought the custom of polishing stone and of domesticating animals. Now the Neolithic age of Europe should correspond to the time when Egypt and Chaldea were at the height of their civilization, and when the worship of the divinity was held in highest esteem. It would be incredible that the religious sentiment which was common in Asia, had not spread with civilization over all Europe.—Moreover "the belief in another life is manifested among the Neolithic tribes by the care given their graves". These tombs are either natural caverns or artificial grottos, or at times large dolmens, but in all of them are found mortuary offerings "of tools, vases, ornaments, weapons which were to serve the deceased in their new existence." [1]

The latest discoveries confirm the fact that graves were in use ever since the Paleolithic period, as we have already shown. The recent discoveries at Chapelle-aux-Saints, at Quina, at Ferrassie, at Grimaldi, etc., have

[1] De Quatrefages, *Introduction à l'études des races humaines*, p. 281.

revealed indisputable facts concerning Mousterian graves.
Thus we lack evidence only for the Chellean phases. But
the progress of discovery is so rapid that we have the right
to hope that some day graves will be found in the oldest
beds. Moreover, even if we should find none, the conclusion does not of necessity follow that the men of Chelles
and of Saint-Acheul were devoid of religious practices.
For the absence of religious indications is easily explained.
The absence of all Religion in the first men however would
be inexplicable. [1]

This short summary is enough to convince us that
whether we can reckon historically, prehistorically or by
legitimate induction, it is but natural to admit that primitive
man had some Religion. At least it would be absolutely
illogical to suppose the contrary.

§ IX. — The Origin of uncivilized Men.

In the theory of evolution, the question of uncivilized
men holds an important place. They are represented as
undeveloped, or backward members of the human family,
i. e. deprived of reason, of religion and of morals. What
they are today, all men were at one time. In the intermediate phase between the brute condition and the civilized
state, man resembled the contemporary savage. We find
his remains among the prehistoric documents. When the
races, more favored by organism or by environment, grew
and overcame the civilization of the less favored races, they
remained backward and survived as faithful evidence of
the sad condition through which all races have passed.

This theory supposes the following two facts demonstrated : 1. that the first men were as uncivilized and as low as
the lowest of modern savages; 2. that the present uncivilized races are actually backward and not degraded. Now

[1] Cf. Joly, *L'homme avant les métaux*, l. II, c. VII, *La Religion*. Cf.
Mainage, *Les religions de la préhistoire*, p. 372. Déchelette, *Manuel
d'Archéologie*, vol. I, II; R. P. Lemonnyer, *La révélation primitive*,
Paris, Gabalda, 1914, p. 167 sq.

these two facts, if they are not entirely false are very debatable, and cannot be admitted in the absolute way they are proposed. Of the prehistoric races we know only those of Europe. To show that they were uncivilized, the fact of their having left stone tools similar to the implements in use among the present uncivilized peoples is invoked. Their roaming life of hunters and of fishermen without fixed abode, without any trace of burials in the beginning is adduced as evidence.—There is no need to exaggerate this uncivilized condition of the first men of western Europe. There is no doubt that they were already highly civilized in the Neolithic age, although they had not yet the use of metals. In the Paleolithic period, the Madeleine man is a good, artistic and ingenious workman. At best one might say that the Saint-Acheul man spent his whole wandering and uncivilized life along the rivers. But he was also a skilful artisan and hunter.

Whatever the appearance of an uncivilized life, their condition must be clearly distinguished from that of contemporary uncivilized races. In fact, the man of Chelles, of Saint-Acheul, of Moustier is simple, possesses an elementary industry, but he makes progress, he acquires new knowledge, he gradually increases his conquests of nature. The modern savage, on the contrary, is a degraded being, in process of retrogression, who unconsciously and uselessly preserves the traces of a more advanced ancient civilization. Without being *a priori* condemned to complete extinction he inevitably will become so. It is not true then to say that the modern savage is a faithful image of the Quaternary man. He is not backward in his development. He has descended the incline of decadence. To determine what the contemporary savage is will serve the cause of Quaternary man.

The contemporary savage is degraded and not backward. — To establish the truth of this proposition it is not necessary to show that the savages count, among their ancestors, men as cultured and as civilized as modern Europeans or Americans. It is sufficient to prove by retracing the course of their history and by studying the traces which they have preserved of their past, that their ancestors were more educated, more civilized, more favorably situated than they themselves are. We shall not take up all the uncivilized tribes of modern times, but shall cite the principal ones only, remarking that we may say as much for all the others. [1]

The Australian native appears to be placed on the lowest rung of the human ladder. Some writers have gone so far as to deny him the same origin as the rest of humanity, and regard him as a sort of intermediate between the ape and man. His features are not flattering; his stature is small, his head broad, his forehead narrow and receding, the eyes black and deepset, the nose flat, the jawbones very prognathous and the bones of the skull very thick; his color varies from dark-brown to dull-red; and the glossy hair approaches that of the white races. His implements are very primitive. He possesses the stone axe, the spear, the sagaie and the boomerang. He has neither bow nor arrows. (Dr. Jousset, *Évolution*, p. 188.)

This miserable people exhibits unequivocal traces of a more favorable former condition. Thus, the children, taken at an early age, show excellent intellectual dispositions, learning the foreign languages with ease. Up to the age of puberty, they, like the negroes of the United States, show themselves, in the schools, superior to some of their white comrades.—According to the Canadian scientist Hale, all the Australian dialects have an astonishing perfection. The grammar includes seven declensions, each declension having ten or twelve cases, more logically determined than in the Aryan languages. The verbs have conjugations, moods and numerous tenses; the derivation of words is well ordered; the prefixes and suffixes have an infinite variety of shades of expression. This richness of language, undeniable testimony of a well developed intelligence,

[1] We refer our readers to the works of de Quatrefages, in which this scientist has in a sort of way made a geological history of all the peoples. Cf. *L'espèce humaine; Hommes fossiles et hommes sauvages*, Paris, Alcan.

surpasses both the power and the needs of the present
Australians. Their language therefore bears witness to a
more fortunate condition from which they have so miserably fallen. [1] We may cite many other mementoes of a
better state; paintings and carvings among which we note
heads surrounded by a luminous nimbus, a personage
attired in a red robe, an extensive astronomical knowledge
that enables them to determine the hours with great
exactness, and circumcision formerly practised by a great
number of peoples of Asiatic origin.

The evident decadence which the Australians have
undergone has for its cause the unfavorable circumstances
under which they are compelled to live, always struggling,
always in quest of food, in a tropical climate. Hale asks
kimself whether an Aryan race in similar circumstances
would not have descended to the same level as the Australians.

The *Tinneh* or Dené-Djindjié are not far behind the
Australians in decadence. Relegated to an unhealthy
district of North America, between the Hudson Bay and
the Alaskan Peninsula, they have great difficulty in obtaining their sustenance. Constant cold arrests nearly all
vegetation. When this savage cannot obtain the flesh of
animals to eat, he is obliged to subsist on the mosses and
lichens that he gathers from the rocks. Ordinarily without
fixed abode and without social organization, he builds a
hut only when absolutely forced to do so by the cold. [2]
"Egotistic, gluttonous, hard on the aged, the women and
the sick who are so many idle mouths to feed—he is for
all that, sober, not over vindictive, kind, even generous
towards those from whom he expects some service" (de
Nadaillac).

In spite of the brutalizing influences of his surroundings, the Tinneh possesses a true human intelligence, is
susceptible of being educated and elevated, and is capable
of progress. His language is remarkable "for the variety

---

[1] Cf. De Nadaillac, *Le problème de la vie*, chap. VII.
[2] De Nadaillac, *Correspondant*, 1892, p. 229.

of expressions, the richness of inflections, the multiplicity of auxiliary verbs; all characteristics testifying to a highly developed language." De Nadaillac applies to the language of the Tinneh what Max. Muller said of that of the Iroquois. "The people that has built up such a language was composed of men with a powerful reasoning faculty". At present, incapable of such mental power, the Tinneh are then, like the Australians, the descendents of a race more highly developed than they.

We must say the same for the Morioris, unfortunate savages of the Chatham islands in Polynesia. At the beginning of the fifteenth century they left the Hawaian Islands, where they had enjoyed a certain amount of civilization. After two centuries of semi-isolation and misery, they have fallen to the lowest condition of savagery; giving up the cultivation of the soil, held in so high esteem by their ancestors, they now gain a livelihood by hunting and fishing exclusively. [1]

The miserable condition of the Fuegians of Tierra del Fuego of the South American coast is equally due to decadence. Darwin placed them in the lowest stage of humanity, nearly as low as the higher animals. Exclusively hunters and fishermen, the Fuegians possess the bow, and their arrows are equipped with chipped stone points. Have they fallen again below the polished stone stage, or are they merely backward in the chipped stone phase ? Their language and history answer this question. Their language, according, to Bove, is so rich that it can only be the relic of an ancient civilization; the Jagan, one of their dialects is a very pure and grammatically very complete language, with more than 30 000 words [2].

Father Gusinde, Vice-director of the Ethnological Museum of Santiago, Chili, and Father Koppers visited the Fuegian tribe of Vagans in 1921-22, lived among them more

---

[1] Cf. Jousset, *Évolution*, p. 18; De Quatrefages, *Hommes fossiles et hommes sauvages*.

[2] Cf. Jousset, *Ibid.*; Vigouroux, *Les Livres saints*, vol. IV.

than three months, and were able to study their customs and beliefs. They are a very primitive tribe and live by fishing, hunting, gathering fruits and plants. Their weapons are the spear, the harpoon and the sling. They are classed among the pygmies. They admit the existence of God Whom they recognize as the Eternal, Almighty Master of all things, the Supreme and Invisible Spirit Who is feared, but invoked and very often thanked. They admit a certain immortality and spirituality of the soul. Darwin was mistaken then, when he represented them as being without God and without Religion. [1]

The Buschmen may be cited as the most degraded men in Africa; they are degenerate Hottentots. The latter in turn according to ethnologists of note might only be Egyptian emigrants debased and deformed by misery.

It is useless to prolong this enumeration. Take any tribe, even the most uncivilized and you come to the same conclusion : the savages have been overcome by the misery of their surroundings inducing degeneracy. Moreover, we may instance striking examples taken from the midst of even civilized nations. Do we not see, under the twofold influence of vice and privation, real savages being formed and walking the streets of our large cities ? Let it be enough to remark here how far removed all this is from the theory of anthropologists who consider the savage as an undeveloped type of the human family, as a faithful witness of a primitive stage through which all races have passed.

How civilized man became uncivilized.—No human race is by its nature condemned to decadence. All men, under favorable conditions, can make progress in civilization. However all races do not react with equal energy against the real factors of the savage state. The black race is the weakest, the white race the strongest. But is not this actual weakness of the black race a sad effect of long continued decadence ?—Isolation, what ever may have been said of it, is no longer a true cause of decline. If a family, driven by war or famine migrates to a place near

---

[1] *Études*, Oct. 1922, p. 152.

the desert, it will be able to settle there and develop a
civilized tribe, provided the environment is favorable, and
the tribe has not previously lost all power of reaction to the
environment. — The difficulties of material existence are
the real factors producing savagery. Isolated from civilized centers, thrown upon an ungrateful soil, perpetually
struggling against climatic extremes, ever in the clutches
of famine, solely absorbed by material needs, the most
civilized man quickly becomes debased under the weight
of excessive fatigues and continual privations. Where the
soil is fertile, as in the Soudan, the negroes are agriculturists
and shepherds, with fixed abode. Their life is simple, but
not savage. On the contrary, where the environment is
poor, men are hunters, without fixed domicile, without
political organization, without a religion other than a gross
and often cruel fetishism, reduced to the rudimentary
industries of chipped or polished stone. We easily understand what intellectual degradation results under such
conditions. Without losing intelligence nor the aptitude
for instruction, the savages become children—lazy,
filled with horror for all effort, deprived of that ingenuity
which characterizes the civilized races. We may, perhaps,
not so readily understand how decadence affects and disfig-
ures the physical appearance itself. Yet it is so. The
soul and body are in too close dependence, for the decadence
of one not to effect the decline of the other. Mortality
increases. Longevity among savages would be surprizing.
Irregularity of regime, unclean habits, lack of care in time
of sickness, powerlessnes in the face of epidemics; these
are the things which are everlastingly decimating the
inferior races. Without being able to formulate an absolutely general law, it is nevertheless a rather ordinary fact
that the savage state brings about diminution of the skull
thickening, of its walls exaggeration of the facial bones, so
that prognathism and dolichocephaly gradually come into
evidence. By a strange reversal of influences, it is the
lack of culture which produces deformation of the head, and
this deformation in turn renders culture all the more difficult. This is what we meet with in the savage in

a state of inferiorit y which is accentuated day by day.

To what the uncivilized man is reduced.—From all that has been said, it is asey to foresee what kind of man the degenerate will be. As long as he will remain under the influence of the trying conditions which crush him, he will continue to decline, to become physically and intellectually enfeebled, a prey to his enemies and a victim to the difficulties of his environment, and his race will end in extinction. But if he succeeds in extricating himself from these restraints and this misery, if by his own efforts or through the compassion of another he should be placed in more advantageous circumstances, he will reascend the slope, he will be able to educate himself, to become civilized. It is the fear of being stigmatized as decadent that keeps humanity unimpaired and ever capable of more astonishing reactions.—Of the two hypotheses which will be oftener realized ? Assuredly the former, for how will an enfeebled savage be able to take possession of a land where men stronger than he are in power ? Would not other less degraded individuals, if conquered by him on his own ungrateful soil in time, come to dispute with him his miserable sustenance ? Can we hope that civilized nations, that only too patently seek to dispossess them, will ever open their arms to these unfortunate barbarians ? This is beyond the limit of philanthropy. Are all the facts in agreement with these statements? A search into history will reveal the fall and disappearance of entire nations. Not to go beyond our present subject, we may mention truly uncivilized tribes that have disappeared, or that are in the way of disappearing. The Tasmanians lost their last representative in 1877. A frightful mortality, a too low birthrate, the difficulty of conditions as well as the cruelty of the colonists, all have concurred in their extinction. There remains but a small remnant of the Iroquois and the Esquimaux. The Indians of the United States are diminishing each day. Foreseeing their early extinction and desirous of preserving what is left of their dialects, their vocal sounds are being collected for future linguistic study. The Australians, on the decrease since the introduction of alcohol and European licentuousness, will survive the invasion of foreigners, but a few years more. We may also foresee the extinction of the Buschmen and many of the African races, if the Europeans in taking possession of Africa supplant and do not elevate the natives.

That the savages are still capable of advancing towards a better condition, history leaves no doubt. Certainly we do not see how the barbarous tribes, remaining by themselves, would ever become civilized. But having removed from their native environment or artificially transported to better surroundings, they have been able to make progress. In the Philippines the Spaniards have raised the level of the Negritos. On the coast of New Zealand the Benedictines have shown of what education the Australians were capable. [1] Who does not know the marvels wrought by the efforts of the Marists on Wallis Island in Oceanica, where the well conducted education has made the savages worthy of being raised to the Catholic priesthood ? Moreover, no one any longer holds that the savage cannot be civilized. Since they have descended very low, perhaps a foreign influence was necessary, not only to create a proper environment, but even to overcome their natural apathy.

The example of the Tinneh, which we take from de Nadaillac, [2] shows to what degree a change of conditions may arouse the savages to advance towards progress. Thus some branches of the Tinneh migrated into South America. Their traces are found all through British Columbia, Oregon and California. In California, under the name of Hupa (Hopis), they constituted a fine strong race remarkable for the domination which they exercised over the tribes previously established in the country. From the Hupa (Hopis) sprang the Navajos who removed to Arizona and to New Mexico. There, in the year 1542, the Spaniards ound them cultivating the soil, living in commodious houses, manufacturing objects of beaten silver. The religious chants and the legends of the Navajos testify to their intelligence, their respect for women and their high morality.

[1] Dr. Jousse' *Évolution*, p. 201.
De Nadaillac, *roblème de la vie*, p. 278.

Conclusions.

If we take into account only the data of Science and of Reason, we are to a certain extent able to sketch in broad lines the history of the human species.

1. At a very remote period, whose date Science cannot determine, but which may be more than 15 000 years, there appeared on the earth the first human pair, formed and determined in their nature by a superior, intelligent and personal Power Whom we call God.

2. The first man, whose physical portrait we can outline only in a very general way, was endowed with a truly spiritual intelligence, and with a free will. Capable of arriving at the knowledge of his own soul and of the Author of his being, he had by that fact to know his duties towards himself and towards God, and to have a sense of his moral responsibility.

3. We do not wish to say that his knowledge was highly developed, that he knew the secrets of nature, that he was from the very beginning capable of utilizing all forms of physical energy that the world presented to him. Created in a simple state, he was destined for progress. And it is precisely by its incessant progress in all branches of knowledge and of industry that the human race stands in contrast with the animal species which are established in perpetual uniformity. Thus man has not evolved from the condition of the brute to the status of a being animated with a mind. But, endowed with a mind at his creation, he went forward, he evolved, if you wish, towards an ever higher state of civilization.

4. This civilization was simple at first. Placed in a fàvorable environment whose geographical position cannot be determined, man lived without effort on the spontaneous fruits of the earth. As the human species multiplied, it became necessary to force the earth through cultivation, to yield a portion of its riches, or to hunt wild animals more assiduously. For these purposes, man was compelled to make for himself tools and weapons. At first, he used the

native materials as the stone which lay about him; later, he fashioned them into a more useful shape. We cannot say at this distance at what time the knowledge of the metals and their malleability were discovered.

5. As men increased in number at the primitive center and developed their civilization with great activity, struggles could not fail to arise, due to the inevitable jealousies and especially by the necessities of material existence. The population becoming too dense, it had to divide. Certain branches of the human family went forth to seek food and peace further away. Bearing with them the recollections of family and of the art of making implements, they began to populate the globe. While civilization at the center continued to progress, the caravans wandering in the uncultivated wastes became subject to all the baneful effects of climate, and to all the consequences of a badly protected existence. Among these wanderers, some found an environment rich in natural resources and were able to make progress, others were thrown upon an ungrateful soil, where they became the victims of a slow decadence.

This picture, so conformed to the facts of history and of the prehistoric sciences, seems to harmonize perfectly two facts too often given as contradictory: the identity of the human nature throughout the ages and man's incessant movement in the direction of progress.

Here the office of the theologian comes in. To the facts of Science and Reason he adds those of Revelation. On the many points where purely human Science hesitates, Theology gives sure solutions. In that which touches on the gravest interests of humanity, it gives us knowledge that our limited intelligence could never have discovered. But it does not enter into the plan of this work. Let us therefore conclude, and this will be our final word, that primitive man, such as real Science presents him to the eyes of Faith, is fit to receive all the communications of the supernatural order, truth or grace, with which the Divine Bounty enriches him.

REFERENCES

Annales de philosophie chrétienne :
   Mgr. d'Hulst, Le positivisme et la science expérimentale, Oct. 1891.
   Farges, L'évolution et les évolutions, Déc. 1897.
Année biologique :
   Dastre, 1895.
   Ed. Perrier, 1895, p. 531-533.
Anthropologie :
   Boule, Les grottes d'Oban, vii, p. 319 et *passim*.
   Breuil, 1910, p. 385.
   Cartailhac, vii, p. 309.
   Commont, vi, p. 286; viii, p. 595; ix, p. 134; Les industries de l'ancien Saint-Acheul, 1908, p. 517-572; Grotte de Predmost, p. 148, 1901.
   D'Arras, 1892, p. 724.
   De Bave, 1889, p. 72.
   Fisher, H., vii, p. 635.
   Harle, v, p. 402.
   Mission Pavie, vii, p. 556.
   Moulier, Abbé, vii, 571.
   Parat, Abbé, 1901, p. 125.
   Patroni, viii, p. 129.
   Piette, Notes pour servir à l'art primitif, April 1894. Mas-d'Azil, vi, 3; viii, 1. — Spirales paléolithiques, vii, p. 690. — Classification des harpons, vi, p. 283. — vii, p. 64, 125, 345, 635, 730.
   Paléolithique de Somaliland, vi, p. 389; vii, p. 341, 567.
   Reinach, viii, 53; Taubach (Weimar), viii; Egypt, viii, p. 327.
   Das Schweizerbild; viii, p. 346.
   Verneau, iii, 1892; vi, p. 36.

Zumoffen, L'âge de pierre en Phénicie, VIII, 41, VIII, p. 272;
Amérique du Nord, IV, p. 26; VII, p. 726; VIII, p. 212, 489.
Congrès international d'anthropologie, 1900, XII, p. 111 sq.
Boule, 1895, p. 497, Station du lac Karar (Algeria) 1900,
p. 1.

Annuaire du Bureau des Longitudes :
1898, 1921, A, 20; 375, 384.

Assoc. franc. pour l'avenir des sciences :
Catalogue préhistorique du dip. d'Orban, par Pallary,
1891, 1893, 1896.
Piette, Phases successives de la civilisation pendant l'âge
du renne, Sept. 20th, 1892.

Astrophysical Journal :
The Evolution of Solars, M. Schuster, 1903, p. 165-200.

Comptes rendus de l'Académie des Sciences :
Balard, 1865, IX, 384.
Belot, 1905, 1922, *passim*, 1920, p. 658, 1563.
Bernard, Claude, 1862, IV, p. 977.
Dastre, 1894, p. 298, Nov. 26th, 1906.
Hardy, Abri sous roche de Raymunden près Chancelade,
Dec. 17th, 1888.
Lapique, L, May 2th, June 6nd, 1922.
Mavet, I, Dec. 12th, 1921, p. 1245.
Pasteur, 1879, LXXV. p. 781 973, 982, 1171, 1219; March
14th, 1910, p. 384; XLVII, p. 80, Oct. 1914, p. 442, Articles
on Pasteur, Fermentation and Spontaneous Generation,
1859-1877.
Portier, Paul and Duval, Marcel; May 22nd 1922, p. 1366,
1493-1495.
Pouchet, L., p. 303, 532.
Trecul, 1872, LXXV, p. 1161; 1860, L, p. 532.
Veronnet, June 28th, 1918, p. 328, 642, 812; June 28th,
1920; May 27th, 1922, p. 1366, 1403-1405.

Le Correspondant :
Briot, Le carrier et des travaux de Pasteur, Dec. 10th 1922.
D'Hulst, Mgr. L'Évolutionisme religieux, April 10th, 1897.
De Nadailhac, Instinct et Intelligence 1891, Dec. 1892,
Jan. 15th. — Les dates préhistoriques, Nov. 10th, and
25th, 1893. — Le problème de la vie, 1892, p. 229.
Dastre, 1907, LVI, p. 32-33, March 21st, 1891, Article on
Tyndall, XLII, p. 57; XLIV, p. 39, 118.

Dublin Review :
  Clifford's Articles, 1881. 1883.

Études, Paris :
  Carrel, April 1913.
  De Sinety; Les preuves et les limites du transformisme,
    1911, ii, p. 660-690
  Teilhard de Chardin, June 1921, p. 526-538; Oct. 1922,
    p. 152.

Nature :
  Boule, 1021, p. 384.
  Dastre, lxix (1907), p. 33.
  Moulier, Abbé, July 25th, 1897, lxxix, p. 33.

Précis de biochimie :
  Atwater, 498, 505, 512.
  Lambling, 34 et sq.

Science et Vie :
  Belot, Sept. 1920.

The Nineteenth Century :
  Mivart, Feb. 1898.

Revue anthropologique :
  Breuil, H. Études morphologiques du paléolithique. Feb.
    1911. — Études morphologiques du paléolithique supé-
    rieur. Feb. 1912, p. 129; 1918. Nos. 11 and 12; 1914,
    Grotte at dessins aurignaciens.

Revue apologétique :
  Le Dantec, Les théories évolutionistes, x.
  P. M. Perier, June 15th, 1922, p. 350, July 1922.

Revue biblique :
  P. Germer, Durand sur la Palestine.
  Lagrange, L'Hexameron, July 1896. Les sources du Pen-
    tateuque, Jan. 1898.

Revue des Deux Mondes :
  De Kirwan, Oct. 1897.
  Dr. Roux, L'œuvre scientifique de Pasteur, Dec. 15th, 1922.
  Fouillée, Origine de l'instinct, Oct. 1886.

Revue de Fribourg :
  Breuil, Jan. 1909.

Revue de Génétique, par l'abbé Vieulles.

Revue des fac. cath. d'Angers :
L'abbé Hy, Les plantes fossiles, April 1895, p. 558.

Revue de philosophie et de théologie :
Vial, 1921-1922

Revue de Philosophie :
Duhem, i, p. 457.
De Sinety, 1910, p. 338-356.
Hertwig, Sept. and Oct. 1910, p. 215-441.
Vignon, M. P., 1904-1905.
Wassmann, 1910, p. 314 sq.
Teilhard de Chardin, April 1923, p. 144-174; 1919, p. 52, 152, 338, 479.

Revue des Jeunes, Paris.

Revue des questions scientifiques :
Arcelin, Quelques problèmes relatifs à l'antiquité préhis-torique, Jan. 1896.
De Quatrefages, xxxv, 563 sq.
De Foville, Études sur Göttler, Schæfer et Clifford, vii, viii, xii.
De Sinety, Un demi-siècle de Darwinisme, Jan. 1910, 1-38, 480-512.
Dierckw, July, 1894.
Galton, 1914, p. 358, 363.
Gregoire, Oct. 1905, Les recherches de Mendel et les mende-listes sur l'hérédité, 1912, lxv, p. 353-390; lxxi, p. 576-629.
Maréchal, S. J., xxviii, p. 519; xxix, p. 31.
Salée, Achille, July, 1920, p. 124, 135 sq.
Sabatier et Senderens, 1922, ii, p. 205.
Termier, 1920, i, p. 68, 71-77, 1877-1881; Oct. 1914, p. 420, 442, 521, 583; Oct. 1920, p. 379; 1921, p. 113, 158; July 20th, 1922, p. 179, 181, 208; Oct. 1922, p. 315-342, 442; Oct. 1923, p. 475.

Revue de questions scientifiques, Bruxelles :
De Kirwan (Jean d'Estienne), i, ii.

Revue des sciences philosophiques et théologiques, Paris :
Breuil, Abbé, Les plus anciennes races humaines con-nues, iii, p. 728 (1909).

Revue du Clergé :
Bouyssonie, Nov. 15th, 1910; April, 1913, p. 48-72; 1912, p. 230, 683.

Revue du Monde catholique :
De Kirwan, Oct. 1897.

Revue générale des sciences :
Belot, 1910, p. 642.
Bosler, 1919, p. 530.
De la Vaulx, 1922, p. 336.
Deperet, 1923, p. 130 sq.
Richard, 1922, p. 677.
Senderens, Les colloïdes et la vie, June 30th, 1922, p. 358.
Puiseux, June 15th, 1917, p. 345.
Veronnet, 1923, p. 165-171.

Revue mens. Éc. d'anthropologie de Paris :
Bardon et Bouyssonie, La Coumbo del Bouitou (Corrèze), 1907, p. 120. — La grotte de Lacoste près Brive, 1900.
Breuil, H., Études de morphologie paléolithiques : 1, La transition du Moustérien vers l'Aurignacien à l'abri Aubry et au Moustier, 1909, p. 320.
Capitan, Nov. 15th, 1895; Nov. 15th, 1896, Station de la Vignette, July 1897.
D'Ault du Mesnil, Sept. 15th, 1896.
Le Campignien, Fouille d'un fonds de cabane au Campigny par d'Ault, Salmon et Capitan.
De Mortillet, A. Prépulseurs à crochet modernes et préhistoriques, 1891, p. 241.
Boissons fermentées, Sept. 15th, 1897.
Hamy, 1878, p. 112, IIIe série.
Mitour, Station magdalenienne a Saint-Mihiel (Meuse), 1897, III.

Revue philosophique :
Le Dantec, Théories néo-lamarckiennes, Nov. and Dec. 1897.

Revue pratique d'Apologétique, Paris, Beauchesne :
Colin, Les théories évolutionnistes, x.
Lemonner, Y., I, p. 1-20; 470; v, p. 601 sq., 722 sq.
Leduc, Stéphane, III, p. 477-483.
Baudrillart Mgr. L'apologétique de Mgr d'Hulst, III, p. 13 sq., 1906-1907.
Guibert, Feb. 1st, 1908, p. 600-620, April, 1921.

Revue préhistorique :
Breuil, H. La question aurignacienne, 1907, Nos. 6 and 7.
Étude critique de stratigraphie comparée, 1907, p. 173-

219. *Idem*, Les gisements présolutriéens du type d'Aurignac.

Revue de synthèse historique :
L'archéologie celtique, August, 1901.

Revue scientifique :
De Quatrefages : Origine de l'homme, August 23rd, 1890.
La théorie de R. Wallace, *Idem*, p. 231. — Les théories transformistes, July 20th, 1898.
Giard, Les facteurs de l'évolution, Nov. 23rd, 1889.

Bulletin de littérature ecclésiastique :
Bouyssonie, A., March 1909.

Bulletin de la Société anthrop. de Paris :
Piette, La Grotte de Gourdon, April 18th, 1873, 1894.

Matériaux pour servir à l'histoire de l'homme :
Cartailhac, Squelette de Langerie, IIe série, VII, p. 224. — Grotte de Altamira, 1881.

Comptes rendus du IIIe Congrès scientifique des catholiques à Bruxelles :
Section d'anthropologie, p. 298 (1894).
Congrès catholique de 1891. L'époque glaciaire.

BIBLIOGRAPHY.

General Works.

Book of Popular Science (*The*. The Grolier Society, N. Y. (15 vols).
Catholic Encyclopedia The. Encyclopedia Press.
Collection Sciences et Religion. Bloud, Paris.
Collection Sciences et Foi. Gabalda, Paris.
Dictionnaire d'Apologétique. Beauchesne, Paris.
Dictionnaire de la Bible. Letouzey et Ané, Paris.
Dictionnaire de Théologie catholique. Letouzey et Ané, Paris.
Dictionnaire des Sciences anthropologiques.
Guide to the Babylonian and Assyrian Antiquities. British Museum. London, 1908.
Guide to the British Museum.
Guide to the Egyptian Collection in the British Museum.
Standard text-books of Chemistry, Philosophy, Psychology and Physics.

Apologetics.

Aveling, Rev. Fr., *Science and Faith*. Herder.

Arduin, *La religion en face de la science*. Lyon.

Brennan, Rev. M. S., *What Catholics have done for Science*. Herder.

Brownson, F., *Faith and Science*.

Caro, *Le matérialisme et la science*. Hachette, Paris.

De Broglie, *Le positivisme et la science expérimentale*. Palmé, Paris. — *Religion et critique*. Palmé, Paris.

De Cyon, E., *Dieu et science*. Alcan, Paris.

De Lapparent, *La Providence créatrice*. Bloud, Paris. — *Science et apologétique*. Bloud, Paris. — *Science et philosophie*. · Bloud, Paris.

Donat, Rev. Jos., S. J., *The Freedom of Science*. Jos. F. Wagner, N. Y.

Duilhe de Saint-Projet, *Apologie scientifique de la foi chrétienne*. Edition Senderens. Poussielgue, Paris.

Fonsegrive, G., *L'attitude du catholique devant la science*. Paris.

Friedel, J., *Le matérialisme contemporain*.

Eymieu, *Le naturalisme devant la science*. Perrin, Paris. — *La part des croyants dans les progrès de la science au XIXᵉ siècle*. Perrin, Paris.

Gerard, Rev. Jno., S. J., *Church versus Science*. — *Science and Romance*. C. T. S. — *Modern Science and Ancient Faith*. C. T. S.

Gmeiner, *Modern scientific Views and christian Doctrine compared*.

Grasset, *Les limites de la biologie*. Alcan, Paris.

Grégoire, *Le matérialisme contemporain*.

Guibert, *Les croyances religieuses et les sciences de la nature*. Beauchesne, Paris.

Hettinger, *Apologie des Christentums*. Herder. — *Evidences of Christianity*. Benziger.

Hand, R. J. E., *Ideals of Science and Faith*.

Kane, Robt., *God or Chaos*.

Kneller, K. A., S. J., *Christianity and the Leaders of modern Science*. Herder.

Koch, F. G., *A Manual of Apologetics*. Jos. F. Wagner.

Le Conte, *Religion and Science*.

Madden, R. W. J., *Reaction from agnostic Science*. Herder.

Mainage, P., *Les mouvements de la jeunesse catholique au XIXᵉ siècle*. Bloud, Paris.

Moulard et Vincent, *Apologétique chrétienne*. Bloud, Paris.

Murat, D., *L'idée de Dieu dans les sciences contemporaines*. Tequi, Paris.

Pettigrew, J-B., *Design in Nature*. Longmans, Green and Co.

Ronayne, Rev. Maurice, *Religion and Science*. P. Collier, N. Y.

Picard, *Chrétien ou agnostique*.

Saulze, J.-B., *Le monisme matérialiste en France*. Bauchesne, Paris.

Sheehan, *Apologetics and catholic Doctrine*.

Scott, Martin, S. J., *Christ or Chaos*. G. J. Kenedy, N. Y.

Smith, *Genesis and Science*.

Vaughan, Most Rev. B. R., *Science and Religion*.

Walsh, Jas. J. M. D. Ph. D., *The Popes and Science*. The Dolphin Press, Phila.—*Catholic Churchmen and Science*. The Dolphin Press, Phila.

Windle, Bertram C. Sc. D.. *The catholic Church and its reactions with Science*. The Macmillan Co.—*The Church and Science*. Herder.

Wiseman, Card. Nicholas, *Lectures on Church and Science*. Burns and Oates, London.

Zahm, Rev. J. C. S. C. *The catholic Church and modern Science*. Ave Maria.—*Catholic Science and catholic Scientists*. Kilmer.

Cosmology, Geology and Stratigraphy.

Agassiz, *Geological Sketches*. Houghton.

Arrhenius, S., *Destinies of the Stars*. Putnam.—*Life of the Universe, as conceived by Man*. Harper.—*Worlds in the Making*. Harper.

Belot, *Essai de cosmogonie tourbillonnaire*. Gauthier-Villars, Paris.

Berget's, *Appearance of Life on Worlds and the Hypothesis of Arrhénius*.—Smithsonian Inst. Report '13.

Bigourdan, *Astronomie*. Flammarion, Paris.

Bosler, J., *Modern Theories of the Sun*. Smithson. Inst. Rpt. '14.

Chamberlin, Thos. C., *On glacial Drift*. Univ. of Chicago Press. —*The Origin of the Earth*. Univ. of Chicago Press.

Chamberlin and Salisbury, *Geology*. Holt.

Clerke, Agnes M., *Popular History of Astronomy during the XIXth Century*. Macmillan. Co.—*System of Stars*. MacMillan.—*Modern Cosmogonies*. Macmillan Co.

Darwin Sir Geo. H., *Scientific Papers*. Putnam.—*Tides and kindred Phenomena in the Solar System*. Houghton.

De Lapparent, *Traité de géologie*. Bloud, Paris.

D'Estienne, J. (de Kirwan), *Comment s'est formé l'univers*. Paris.

Descartes, *Complete works*. Vol. IV. *The World*, c. v. Putnam.

Duhem, P., *Système du monde*. Hermann, Paris.

Duhem, *La théorie physique*. Chevalier, Paris.

De Margerie, *La face de la terre*. Colin, Paris

Du Ligondès Lt. Col., *Formation mécanique du système du monde*. Gauthier-Villars, Paris.

Faye, *Sur l'origine du monde*. Gauthier-Villars.

Geikie, Sir Archibald, *Climate and Time.—Modern Denudation. Text Book of Geology*. Macmillan.

Geikie, Jas., *Earth Sculptures, or The Origin of Land Forms*. Putnam.—*Mountains. Their Origin, Growth and Decay*. Van Nostrand.—*Prehistoric Europe*. Van Nostrand.—*The great Ice Age and its Relation to the Antiquity of Man*.

Graubau, *Principles of Stratigraphy*. D. C. Heath and Co. — *Text-book of Geology*.

Hale, *Beyond the milky way*. Scribner.

Haug, *Traité de géologie*. Vol. I, Colin, Paris.

Hutten, Jas., *The theory of the Earth*.

Heer, *Ur-Welt der Schweiz*.

Jeans, J. H., *Problems of Cosmogony and Stellar Dynamics*. Putnam.

Joly Jno., *Radio-activity and Geology*. Van Nostrand.

Kant, *Theory of the Heavens.—Allgemeine Naturgeschichte und Theorie des Himmels*. (Ostwalds Klassiker). Leipzig.

Kelvin Lord (Willian Thomson), *Second Law of Thermo-dynamics*. Am. Bk. Co.—*Popular Lectures and Addresses*. Macmillan. —*Treatise in Natural Philosophy*. Putnam.

Kavser, *Lehrbuch der Geologie : Formations-Kunde*. Stuttgart.

La Place, *Mécanique céleste*. Trans. by Bowditch. Boston.— *Exposition du système du monde*. Œuvres, VI, Paris.— *Introduction à la théorie analytique des probabilités*, LXI. —*Philosophical Essays on Probabilities*. Wiley.

Le Conte Jos. H., *The Elements of Geology*. Appletom.—*Critical Periods in the History of the Earth*. Univ. of California.

Lockyer Sir Norman, *Inorganic Evolution.* MacMillan.—*The Spectroscope and its Application.*—*The Chemistry of the Sun.*—*The meteoric Hypothesis.* MacMillan.

Lucretius, *De natura rerum.*

Lvell, Sir Charles, *Principles of Geology*, Am. Bk. Co.

Moullard L., *Les cosmogonies anciennes*, Paris.

Moreux, *Le problème solaire.* Bertaux, Paris.—*Astronomy today.* Dutton.—*Origines et formation des mondes.* Doin, Paris.

Neumayr, *Erdgeschichte.*

Newcomb Simon, *Astronomy for Everybody.* Doubleday.

O'Neill Rev. Jno., *Cosmology.*

Perrier, E., *Earth before History.* Knopf.

Poincaré, H., *Leçons sur les hypothèses cosmogoniques.* Hermann, Paris.

Powell, Jno. W., *Canyons of the Colorado.* Smiths. Inst. Rpt.

Richard, *L'océanographie.*

Schuster M., *The Evolution of the solar Stars.*

See J., *Researches on the Evolution of the stellar Systems.* Nicholas and Son. Lynn. Mass.—*The capture Theory of cosmical Evolution.*

Termier, *A la gloire de la terre.* Paris, Nouvelle librairie nationale.

Verronet, *Les hypothèses cosmogoniques.* Hermann, Paris.

Wolf, *Les hypothèses cosmogoniques*, Paris.

Woodruff, *The Evolution of the Earth.*

Biblical Cosmology.

Augustine Saint, *De Genesi ad litteras.*

Brucker, *Questions naturelles d'Écriture sainte.* Paris.

Castelein, *La première page de Moïse.* Louvain.

Corluy, *Spicilegium dogmatico-biblicum.*

Cornelius a Lapide, *Cosmogonie naturelle comparée avec la Genèse.* Rome.

D'envieu Fabre, *Les origines de la terre et de l'homme d'après la Bible et d'après la science.* Paris.

De Lestrade Lavaud, *Accord de la science avec le premier chapitre de la Genèse.* Paris.

Gaul Rev. Cyril, O. S. B., *Rome and the Study of Scripture.* Abbey Press, St. Meinrad. Indiana.

Gigot, *Special Introduction to the Old Testament.* Benziger Bros.

Güttler, *Les sciences naturelles et la Bible dans leurs rapports avec la création*. Fribourg-en-Brisgau.

Hautcœur, *La Bible et la science de la nature*. Paris.

Hummelauer, *In Genesim*.

James, Constantine, *Moïse et Darwin, ou l'homme de la Genèse comparé à l'homme-singe*.

Lagrange, *Historical Criticism and the Old Testament*. Herder.

Lenormant, *Origines de l'histoire d'après la Bible et les traditions des peuples orientaux*. Paris.

Meignan, *Le Monde et l'homme primitif selon la Bible*, Paris.

Molloy, Rev. Geo., *Geology and Revelation*. Longmans, Green and Co.

Pelt, *Histoire de l'Ancien Testament*. Paris.

Pianciani, *Commentaire sur le récit mosaïque de la création; cosmogonie naturelle comparée avec la Genèse*, from Cornelius a Lapide.

Pozzy, *La terre et le récit biblique de la création*. Paris.

Schaeffer, *La Bible et la science*. Munster, trans. from the German.

Reusch, *Nature and the Bible*. Scribner.

Raingeard, *Notions de géologie : accord de la cosmogonie scientifique avec le cosmogonie sacrée*. Rodez.

Vigouroux, *Les Livres saints et la critique rationaliste*. Paris.— *Mélanges bibliques. Le cosmogonie d'après les Pères de l'Église*. Paris. — *Manuel biblique*. Paris.

Zahm, *Bible, Science and Faith*. Murphy.

CHEMISTRY, PHYSICS (ENERGY).

Andrade, E. N., *The Structure of the Atom*. Harcourt.

Atwater, *Respiration calorimeter* (Atwater and Gano) *Experiments on Metabolism of Matter and Energy in the human Body*. Exp. Station Bul. 69, 136, Supt. of Documents.

Atwater and Chas. Ford Langworthy, *Digest of metabolism. Experiments in which the Balance of Income and Outgo was determined*. Rev. Ed. Exp. Sta. Bu .

Berthaud, *New Theories of Matter and the Atom*. MacMillan.

Bohr, H. N. D., *Theory of Spectra and atomic Constitution*. MacMillan.

Brunhes, *La dégradation de l'énergie*.

Comstock, D. F. and Troland L. T., *The Nature of Matter and Electricity*.

Cox, J., *Beyond the Atom*.

Duhem, P., *La théorie physique*. Chevalier, Paris.

Duclaux, *La chimie organique.*

Gibson, A. H., *Natural Sources of Energy.* Putnam.

Harrow Benj, *The Romance of the Atom.* Boni and Liveright.

Houllevigne, *La matière.*

Lambling, *Précis de biochimie.* Masson, Paris.

Le Bon, Gustave, *Evolution of Forces.* Appleton.—*Evolution of Matter.* Scritbner.

Le Dantec, *Théorie nouvelle de la vie,* Paris.

Lodge, Sir O., *Atoms and Rays,* Doran.

Loeb, *Dynamics of Living Matter.* Lemke. Many other works in Biochemistry.

Millikan, Robt., *The Electron,* etc. Univ. of Chicago Press.

Mills, John, *Within the Atom.* Van Nostrand.

Pesch, *Philosophia naturalis.*

Perrin, J. B., *Atoms.* Van Nostrand.

Planck, M. K., *Origin and Development of the Quantum Theory,* Oxford.

Poincare, H., *Connection betw. the Ether and Matter.* Smithsonian Inst. B.

Poincaré, L., *New Physics and its Application.* Appleton.

Richardson, O. W., *The Electron theory of Matter.* Putnam.

Russell. Bertrand, *The A. B. C. of the Atoms.* Dalton.

Rutherford, E., *Radioactive substances and their Reactions.* Putnam.

Senderens, *Les colloïdes et la vie.*

Soddy Frederick, *Matter and Energy.* Holt.—*Chemistry of the Radio-elements.* Longmans.—*The Interpretation of Radium and the Structure of the Atom.* Putnam.

Tillieux, *Physique.*—*Essai d'un traité élémentaire de physique selon les théories modernes.*

Ward, James, *On the Conservation of Energy.*

BIOLOGY, EMBRYOLOGY, HEREDITY, SPONTANEOUS GENERATION
MENDELISM, PHYSIOLOGY.

Arthus, *Précis de Physiologie.* Masson, Paris.

Asmuth, J. and Hull, *Haeckel's Frauds and Forgeries.*

Bastian, Charlton, *Nature and Origin of Living Matter.* Lippincott.—*Origin of Life.* Putnam.—*Evolution of Life.* Dutton.

Bateson, Wm., *Heredity.* Smithsonian Rept. 1915.—*Mendel's Principles of Genetics.* Putnam.—*Problems of Genetics.* Yale Univ. Press.—*Methods and Scope of Genetics.* Putnam.

Bernard, Claude, *Introduction à l'étude de la médecine expéri-mentale*, annotée par le Père Sertillanges.

Blanchard, *La vie et les êtres organisés.*

Bonnier, *Le monde végétal.*

Brass, *Ernst Haeckel als Biologe und die Wahrheit.—Die Zelle, das Element des Organischen Welts.*

Brass and Gemelli, *L'origine dell' Homo e la falsificazioni de F. Haeckel.*

Brooks, *Laws of Heredity.*

Brunet, *Microbes et toxines.* Flammarion, Paris.

Brunhes, *Outlines of comparative Physiology and Morphology of Animals.* Appleton.

Burbank, Luther, *Complete Works.* L. Burbank Soc. Santa Rosa. Calif.—*How Nature makes Plants to our Order.* Monograph.—*Luther Burbank. His Methods and Discoveries. —Plant Breeding. Comments on Experiments of De Vries.* Open Ct.

Cochin, *L'évolution de la vie.* Masson, Paris.

Dalbis, *Anatomie et physiologie animale.* De Gigord, Paris.

Dastre, Jules, *Life and Death.* Scribner.

Delage, *La structure du protoplasme et les théories de l'hérédité.* Paris.

Delbœuf, *La matière brute et la matière vivante.*

De Nadailhac, *Le problème de la vie.* Masson, Paris.

Descours, L. *Pasteur and his Work.* Stokes.

De Vries, *Die Mutations-Theorie.* Leipzig.—*Intracellular Pan-genesis and a Paper on Fertilization and Hybridization. —Species and Varieties. Their Origin by Mutation.*

Driesch, *History and Theory of Vitalism.* MacMillan.

Duclaux, E. *Pasteur. The History of a Mind.* Saunders.

Duhem, *Histoire d'un esprit.*

Elrington, Fr. P. O., *Life of Gregor Mendel.* C. T. S.

Gemelli, *L'enigma della vita.* Florence.

Gerard, Rev. Jno., S. J., *The Origin of Life.* C. T. S.

Grasset, *Limites de la biologie.* Gabalda, Paris.

Haeckel, *History of Creation* and other works. Appleton.

Hertwig, *Algemeine Biologie.*

Huxley, *Discourses biological and geological.* Appleton.

Kreidel, Rev. G. A., *Notes of a catholic Biologist.* Herder.

Leclerc du Sablon, *Mutants ou hybrides.* Flammarion, Paris.

Le Dantec, *The Nature and Origin of Life.* Barnes.

Littré, *Génération spontanée et transformisme.*

Manquat, *Les tropismes.* Vagner, Nancy.

Mendel, Gregor. J., *Experiments in Plant Hybridization.*

Milne-Edwards, *Rapports sur le progrès des sciences.* Zoologie. Paris.

Maumus, *La cellule.* Bonne Presse, Paris.

McKeough, Michael, O. Praem., *The rationales seminales in St. Augustin.* Doctor's thesis. Cath. University of America, Washington, D. C.

Parker G. H., *Biology and social Problems.*

Pouchet, *Histoire d'un savant par un ignorant.* Hetzel, Paris.

Punnett, *Mendelism.* MacMillan.

Spallanzani, *Expériences sur les reproductions animalcules.—Essai sur les animalcules infusoires.—Expériences microscopiques.*

Reinke, *Einleitung in die theoretische Biologie.*

Thomas, Saint, *On spontaneous generation. Summa Theol.,* I^a, art. 1, ad 1um.

Tyndall, *Fragments of Science.* Appleton.

Vallery-Radot, *The Life of Pasteur.* Doubleday Page and Co.

Vallet, *La vie et l'hérédité. Praelectiones,* II.

Weismann, *Essays on Heredity.* Oxford.—*Germ-plasm Theory of Heredity.* Scribner.—*Germinal Selection as Sources of definite variation.* Open Ct.

Wallace, *The World of Life.* Moffat.

Wassmann, *Modern Biology.* Herder.

Wilson, *The Cell in Development and Inheritance.*

Windle, Bertram C., *The Secret of the Cell.* Herder.—*Vitalism and Scholasticism.* Herder.—*What is Life.* Herder.

PHILOSOPHY, PSYCHOLOGY, (INSTINCT, INTELLIGENCE, SOUL).

Acloque, A., *Les nouvelles de la vie végétale.* Bonne Presse, Paris. —*Les merveilles de la vie animale.* Bonne Presse, Paris.

Baudin, *Psychologie,* de Gigord, Paris.

Beruis, *Spiritualité et immortalité.* Poussielgue, Paris.

Blanchard, *La vie des êtres animés.* Masson, Paris.

Bossuet, *La connaissance de Dieu et de soi-même.* Bonne Presse.

De Bonniot, *La bête comparée à l'homme.* Retaux, Paris.

De Lapparent, *Science et philosophie.* Bloud, Paris.

Driesch, H., *Science and Philosophy of the Organism,* MacMillan.

Delbœuf, *Mélanges philosophiques.—La matière brute et la matière vivante.*

Fabre, *Souvenirs entomologiques. Life and Love of the Insects.*
MacMillan.*The mason Bee.* Dodd, Meade and Co., N. Y.
—*The ramble Bee.* Dodd, Meade and Co., N. Y.—*The hunting
Wasps.* Meade and Co., N. Y. — *The wonders of Instinct.*
Century.—*Social Life in the Insect World.* Century. Other
works.

Farges, *Le cerveau, l'âme et ses facultés.* Berche et Tralin.—
La vie et l'évolution.—Matière et forme.

Ferrière, F., *La vie et l'âme.*

Flourens, *L'instinct et l'intelligence.*

Gruenden, H. S. J., *Experimental Psychology.* Herder.—*Psychology without a Soul.* Herder.

Huxley, *Man's Place in Nature.* Appleton.

Joly, H., *L'homme et l'animal,* Hachette, Paris.—*L'instinct.*
Fontemoing, Paris.

Maher, *Psychology,* Longmans, Green and Co., N. Y.

Mende, Efw. J., *The Beginnings of Science biologically and psy-
chologically considered.* B. G. Badger, Boston.

Mercier, Card., *A Manual of modern scholastic Philosophy.* Herder.—*Origins of contemporary Psychology.* F. J. Kenedy,

Mivart, St. George, *The Origin of Human Reason,* Benziger.

Piat, *La personne humaine.* Alcan, Paris.

Poincaré, H., *Science and Hypothesis.* Scribner.—*The Value of
Science.* Teachers College.

Regnon, *La métaphysique des causes.* Tequi, Paris.

Richet, *L'homme et l'intelligence.*

Romanes, G. J., *Animal Intelligence.* Appleton.

Stonyhurst, Series of text-books of philosophy.

Wasmann, Rev. E. S. J., *Comparative Studies in the Psychology
of Ants and higher Animals.* Herder.—*Instinct and Intelligence in the animal Kingdom.* Herder.

Evolution, Darwinism and Origin of Species.

Agassiz, *Structure of animal Life.* Scribner.—*An Essay on classification.—De l'espèce et de la classification en zoologie.*

Bateson, Wm., *Darwin and modern Science.*

Burmueller, *Mensch oder Affe?*

Caustier, *Histoire naturelle.*

Cope, Edw. D., *The Origin of the Fittest.—The primary Factors
of organic Evolution.* Open Court.—*Syllabus of Lectures on
the Vertabrata.* Appleton.—Other works.

Cuvier, *Influences du monde ambiant sur les formes animales.* — *The animal Kingdom.*

Darwin Chas., *Descent of Man.* Appleton.—*Origin of Species.* Appleton.—*Variation of Animals and Plants under Domestication.* Appleton.

Darwin, Erasmus, *Zoonomia.*

Darwin, Francis, *Life and Letters of Charles Darwin.*

Darwin, Leonard, *Organic Evolution. Outstanding difficulties and possible Explanations.* MacMillan.

Daumont, *Les preuves, les principes, les limites de l'évolution.* Gabalda.—*Les théories évolutionnistes.*

Dawson, J. W., *Modern Ideas of Evolution.* Revell.—*Chain of Life.*

Delage, Yves M. and Marie Goldsmith, *Theories of Evolution.* Huebsch.

Deperet. Chas., *Transformations of the Animal Kingdom.* Appleton.

De Quatrefages, *Darwin et ses précurseurs français.* Alcan, Paris. —*Les émules de Darwin.* Alcan, Paris.

De Sinety, *Un demi-siècle de darwinisme.* Louvain.

De Vries, *Darwin and modern Science.*

Dorlodot, Canon. D. D., *Darwinism and catholic Thought.* Benziger Bros.

Dubois, *Pithecanthropus erectus.*

Duhem, *Histoire d'un esprit.*

Duval, *Le darwinisme.*

Faivre, *La variabilité des espèces et ses limites.* Alcan, Paris.

Frank, Karl, *The Theory of Evolution in the Light of the Facts.* Herder.

Gaudry, *Les enchaînements du monde animal dans les temps géologiques.* Paris.—*Les ancêtres de nos animaux dans les temps géologiques.* Paris.

Gerard, Rev. John., S. J., *Bergson.* Herder.—*The old Riddle and the newest Answer.* Longmans.

Haeckel, Ernst., *Evolution of Man.* Truth-seeker.—*Last Words on Evolution.* Truth-seeker.—*The last Link.* MacMillan.— *Riddle of the Universe.* Putnam.—*Wonders of Life.* Harpers.

Hartmann Van, *Darwinismus.*—*Wahrheit und Irrtum in Darwinismus.*

Hauber, U. A, Ph. D., *A catholic Opinion on the Evolution Controversy.* St. Ambrose College, Davenport. Iowa.

Henderson, *Fitness of the Environment.* MacMillan.

Hertwig, *Comparative and experimental Evolution of Vertebrates.*—*Manual of Zoology.* Holt.